TIDE TABLES 20

CU00925824

Summer time figures are enclosed within a shaded box. See title to each table for necessary adjustments.

○ Full Moon
● New Moon
☾/☽ Half moon – first or last quarter

Please see www.theca.org.uk for corrections and supplements

PLYMOUTH (DEVONPORT)

LAT 50°22′N
LONG 4°11′W

TIMES AND HEIGHTS OF HIGH AND LOW WATER (Heights in Metres)

TIME ZONE UT
For Summer Time (area enclosed in shaded box) add 1 hour

2024

JANUARY

Date	Day	Time	m	Time	m	Time	m	Time	m	Moon
1	M	0235	1.7	0838	5.1	1501	1.7	2103	4.7	
2	TU	0306	1.9	0915	4.9	1533	1.9	2142	4.5	
3	W	0340	2.0	0954	4.8	1609	2.0	2225	4.4	
4	TH	0421	2.2	1039	4.6	1655	2.2	2315	4.3	☾
5	F	0517	2.3	1133	4.5	1758	2.2			
6	SA	0016	4.3	0631	2.4	1237	4.5	1912	2.2	
7	SU	0127	4.4	0747	2.3	1352	4.5	2020	2.1	
8	M	0237	4.6	0853	2.0	1503	4.7	2122	1.8	
9	TU	0339	4.8	0953	1.7	1605	4.8	2218	1.6	
10	W	0432	5.1	1048	1.4	1700	5.0	2311	1.3	
11	TH	0522	5.3	1141	1.1	1751	5.2			●
12	F	0002	1.1	0611	5.5	1231	0.9	1840	5.3	
13	SA	0050	1.0	0658	5.6	1319	0.8	1929	5.3	
14	SU	0137	0.9	0745	5.7	1405	0.7	2016	5.3	
15	M	0221	0.9	0832	5.6	1450	0.8	2101	5.3	
16	TU	0305	1.0	0918	5.5	1533	0.9	2146	5.1	
17	W	0347	1.2	1003	5.3	1617	1.2	2231	4.9	
18	TH	0432	1.5	1051	5.1	1704	1.5	2321	4.7	☽
19	F	0524	1.8	1147	4.8	1800	1.8			
20	SA	0022	4.5	0629	2.0	1255	4.6	1910	2.1	
21	SU	0134	4.5	0752	2.1	1410	4.5	2032	2.1	
22	M	0245	4.6	0914	2.0	1520	4.5	2144	1.9	
23	TU	0348	4.8	1018	1.8	1619	4.7	2240	1.7	
24	W	0440	5.0	1110	1.5	1709	4.8	2328	1.5	
25	TH	0525	5.2	1155	1.3	1752	5.0			○
26	F	0010	1.3	0605	5.3	1235	1.2	1830	5.0	
27	SA	0047	1.2	0641	5.3	1312	1.1	1905	5.0	
28	SU	0120	1.2	0716	5.3	1343	1.2	1938	5.0	
29	M	0149	1.3	0749	5.3	1411	1.2	2010	5.0	
30	TU	0215	1.4	0821	5.2	1435	1.4	2041	4.9	
31	W	0239	1.5	0851	5.0	1458	1.5	[illegible]	[illegible]	

FEBRUARY

Date	Day	Time	m	Time	m	Time	m	Time	m	Moon
1	TH	0303	1.6	0920	4.9	1523	1.7	2140	4.6	
2	F	0333	1.8	0951	4.7	1556	1.9	2215	4.5	☾
3	SA	0413	2.0	1034	4.5	1642	2.1	2307	4.3	
4	SU	0511	2.2	1136	4.3	1752	2.3			
5	M	0020	4.3	0646	2.4	1257	4.3	1932	2.3	
6	TU	0147	4.4	0818	2.2	1429	4.4	2053	2.0	
7	W	0308	4.7	0932	1.8	1546	4.7	2201	1.7	
8	TH	0412	5.0	1035	1.4	1646	4.9	2301	1.3	
9	F	0506	5.3	1131	1.0	1739	5.2	2353	0.9	●
10	SA	0557	5.6	1222	0.6	1829	5.4			
11	SU	0041	0.6	0646	5.8	1308	0.4	1916	5.5	
12	M	0126	0.4	0733	5.8	1352	0.3	2001	5.5	
13	TU	0208	0.4	0817	5.8	1433	0.4	2042	5.5	
14	W	0247	0.6	0859	5.7	1511	0.6	2120	5.3	
15	TH	0324	0.8	0938	5.4	1548	1.0	2157	5.0	
16	F	0402	1.2	1017	5.0	1627	1.5	2234	4.7	☽
17	SA	0445	1.7	1101	4.6	1713	1.9	2325	4.4	
18	SU	0541	2.1	1211	4.2	1816	2.3			
19	M	0053	4.2	0707	2.4	1349	4.1	1959	2.4	
20	TU	0223	4.3	0906	2.2	1507	4.2	2136	2.2	
21	W	0331	4.5	1012	1.9	1608	4.5	2232	1.8	
22	TH	0424	4.8	1100	1.5	1655	4.7	2316	1.4	
23	F	0508	5.1	1142	1.2	1735	4.9	2356	1.2	
24	SA	0546	5.2	1219	1.0	1810	5.0			○
25	SU	0031	1.0	0622	5.3	1252	0.9	1844	5.1	
26	M	0101	1.0	0655	5.3	1321	0.9	1916	5.1	
27	TU	0127	1.0	0727	5.3	1345	1.0	1946	5.1	
28	W	0149	1.1	0757	5.2	1405	1.1	2013	5.0	
29	TH	0210	1.2	0824	5.1	1425	1.3	2038	4.9	

MARCH

Date	Day	Time	m	Time	m	Time	m	Time	m	Moon
1	F	0233	1.3	0848	4.9	1448	1.4	2059	4.8	
2	SA	0300	1.5	0912	4.7	1518	1.7	2126	4.6	
3	SU	0336	1.8	0951	4.5	1559	1.9	2218	4.4	☾
4	M	0427	2.1	1059	4.3	1659	2.3	2337	4.3	
5	TU	0558	2.3	1226	4.1	1854	2.4			
6	W	0111	4.3	0755	2.2	1409	4.3	2034	2.1	
7	TH	0246	4.6	0917	1.7	1532	4.6	2148	1.6	
8	F	0354	5.0	1022	1.2	1632	5.0	2247	1.1	
9	SA	0449	5.4	1116	0.7	1723	5.3	2338	0.7	
10	SU	0539	5.7	1205	0.3	1810	5.5			●
11	M	0024	0.3	0627	5.8	1249	0.1	1855	5.6	
12	TU	0106	0.2	0712	5.9	1330	0.1	1937	5.7	
13	W	0146	0.2	0754	5.8	1409	0.2	2015	5.6	
14	TH	0223	0.4	0833	5.6	1444	0.5	2049	5.4	
15	F	0259	0.7	0909	5.3	1519	1.0	2119	5.1	
16	SA	0334	1.2	0941	4.8	1554	1.5	2148	4.7	
17	SU	0414	1.7	1016	4.4	1637	2.0	2229	4.4	☽
18	M	0509	2.2	1119	4.0	1740	2.4			
19	TU	0000	4.1	0633	2.5	1332	3.9	1922	2.6	
20	W	0201	4.2	0855	2.3	1449	4.1	2118	2.2	
21	TH	0309	4.4	0953	1.8	1546	4.4	2210	1.8	
22	F	0400	4.8	1037	1.4	1630	4.7	2252	1.4	
23	SA	0441	5.0	1116	1.1	1707	4.9	2329	1.1	
24	SU	0519	5.2	1151	0.9	1742	5.1			
25	M	0003	1.0	0554	5.3	1222	0.9	1816	5.2	○
26	TU	0032	0.9	0628	5.3	1250	0.9	1848	5.2	
27	W	0058	0.9	0701	5.3	1313	0.9	1918	5.2	
28	TH	0121	1.0	0731	5.2	1335	1.1	1944	5.1	
29	F	0143	1.1	0757	5.1	1357	1.2	2008	5.0	
30	SA	0208	1.2	0823	4.9	1421	1.4	2032	4.9	
31	SU	0236	1.4	0852	4.7	1453	1.6	2103	4.7	

APRIL

Date	Day	Time	m	Time	m	Time	m	Time	m	Moon
1	M	0313	1.7	0936	4.5	1534	1.9	2158	4.5	
2	TU	0407	2.0	1044	4.2	1638	2.3	2314	4.3	☾
3	W	0544	2.2	1211	4.1	1835	2.4			
4	TH	0049	4.4	0738	2.1	1356	4.3	2016	2.0	
5	F	0225	4.7	0858	1.6	1514	4.7	2128	1.5	
6	SA	0332	5.1	1000	1.1	1610	5.0	2225	1.0	
7	SU	0426	5.4	1053	0.6	1659	5.3	2314	0.6	
8	M	0515	5.7	1140	0.3	1744	5.5			●
9	TU	0000	0.3	0602	5.8	1224	0.1	1828	5.6	
10	W	0042	0.2	0647	5.8	1304	0.2	1908	5.6	
11	TH	0122	0.3	0729	5.7	1342	0.4	1945	5.5	
12	F	0159	0.5	0807	5.4	1418	0.7	2018	5.3	
13	SA	0235	0.9	0841	5.1	1452	1.2	2046	5.1	
14	SU	0311	1.3	0911	4.7	1528	1.7	2115	4.8	
15	M	0353	1.8	0946	4.3	1613	2.1	2156	4.4	☽
16	TU	0448	2.2	1049	4.0	1715	2.5	2307	4.2	
17	W	0606	2.4	1305	3.9	1840	2.6			
18	TH	0125	4.2	0808	2.3	1416	4.1	2031	2.3	
19	F	0232	4.4	0913	1.9	1509	4.4	2129	1.9	
20	SA	0322	4.7	0958	1.5	1553	4.7	2212	1.5	
21	SU	0405	4.9	1037	1.3	1631	4.9	2251	1.3	
22	M	0444	5.1	1112	1.1	1707	5.0	2326	1.1	
23	TU	0521	5.2	1144	1.0	1743	5.1	2357	1.0	○
24	W	0558	5.2	1214	1.0	1817	5.2			
25	TH	0026	1.0	0633	5.2	1241	1.0	1849	5.2	
26	F	0054	1.0	0706	5.1	1308	1.1	1918	5.2	
27	SA	0122	1.1	0736	5.0	1335	1.2	1946	5.1	
28	SU	0151	1.2	0808	4.9	1405	1.4	2018	5.0	
29	M	0225	1.4	0845	4.7	1442	1.6	2058	4.8	
30	TU	0309	1.7	0934	4.5	1530	1.9	2152	4.7	

MAY

Date	Day	Time	m	Time	m	Time	m	Time	m	Moon
1	W	0410	1.9	1039	4.3	1641	2.2	2303	4.5	☾
2	TH	0541	2.0	1201	4.2	1820	2.2			
3	F	0029	4.5	0715	1.8	1333	4.4	1949	1.9	
4	SA	0157	4.8	0830	1.5	1444	4.7	2058	1.5	
5	SU	0303	5.1	0931	1.1	1540	5.0	2156	1.1	
6	M	0358	5.3	1024	0.7	1629	5.3	2247	0.8	
7	TU	0449	5.5	1112	0.5	1716	5.5	2334	0.5	
8	W	0537	5.6	1157	0.4	1800	5.5			●
9	TH	0017	0.5	0623	5.5	1239	0.5	1841	5.5	
10	F	0058	0.5	0705	5.4	1318	0.7	1919	5.4	
11	SA	0138	0.8	0745	5.2	1355	1.0	1952	5.3	
12	SU	0216	1.1	0820	4.9	1432	1.3	2023	5.1	
13	M	0255	1.4	0854	4.6	1511	1.7	2056	4.8	
14	TU	0337	1.8	0934	4.3	1555	2.1	2139	4.6	
15	W	0429	2.1	1032	4.1	1650	2.3	2238	4.3	☽
16	TH	0532	2.2	1207	4.0	1757	2.4			
17	F	0014	4.3	0646	2.2	1321	4.1	1911	2.3	
18	SA	0135	4.4	0759	2.0	1417	4.3	2020	2.1	
19	SU	0231	4.5	0856	1.8	1504	4.6	2115	1.8	
20	M	0319	4.7	0942	1.5	1548	4.8	2201	1.6	
21	TU	0404	4.9	1023	1.4	1629	4.9	2242	1.4	
22	W	0446	5.0	1102	1.2	1709	5.1	2320	1.2	
23	TH	0528	5.0	1138	1.2	1747	5.2	2357	1.1	○
24	F	0607	5.1	1214	1.1	1823	5.2			
25	SA	0032	1.1	0646	5.1	1249	1.2	1859	5.2	
26	SU	0109	1.1	0723	5.0	1325	1.3	1934	5.2	
27	M	0147	1.2	0802	4.9	1403	1.4	2013	5.1	
28	TU	0229	1.3	0846	4.8	1447	1.5	2058	5.0	
29	W	0318	1.5	0937	4.6	1539	1.7	2150	4.9	
30	TH	0417	1.6	1036	4.5	1642	1.9	2253	4.8	☾
31	F	0527	1.7	1146	4.5	1756	1.9			

JUNE

Date	Day	Time	m	Time	m	Time	m	Time	m	Moon
1	SA	0006	4.8	0642	1.6	1300	4.6	1913	1.8	
2	SU	0122	4.8	0753	1.5	1407	4.7	2022	1.6	
3	M	0229	5.0	0857	1.3	1506	4.9	2124	1.3	
4	TU	0329	5.1	0954	1.1	1559	5.1	2219	1.1	
5	W	0423	5.2	1046	1.0	1649	5.3	2310	0.9	
6	TH	0514	5.2	1134	0.9	1735	5.3	2357	0.9	●
7	F	0602	5.2	1218	0.9	1818	5.4			
8	SA	0041	0.9	0647	5.1	1300	1.0	1859	5.3	
9	SU	0123	1.0	0729	5.0	1340	1.2	1935	5.2	
10	M	0203	1.2	0808	4.8	1418	1.4	2009	5.1	
11	TU	0242	1.4	0844	4.7	1456	1.6	2045	4.9	
12	W	0322	1.6	0923	4.5	1535	1.8	2124	4.8	
13	TH	0404	1.8	1007	4.3	1619	2.0	2210	4.6	
14	F	0450	2.0	1100	4.3	1709	2.2	2305	4.5	☽
15	SA	0544	2.1	1201	4.2	1807	2.2			
16	SU	0009	4.4	0644	2.1	1305	4.3	1910	2.2	
17	M	0119	4.4	0745	2.0	1404	4.4	2011	2.0	
18	TU	0222	4.5	0842	1.8	1459	4.6	2108	1.8	
19	W	0320	4.6	0934	1.7	1549	4.8	2159	1.6	
20	TH	0412	4.8	1023	1.5	1636	5.0	2247	1.4	
21	F	0500	4.9	1109	1.3	1720	5.1	2333	1.2	
22	SA	0546	5.0	1154	1.2	1803	5.2			○
23	SU	0018	1.1	0631	5.0	1238	1.2	1845	5.3	
24	M	0103	1.0	0716	5.1	1322	1.1	1928	5.3	
25	TU	0148	1.0	0801	5.0	1406	1.2	2012	5.3	
26	W	0233	1.0	0847	5.0	1451	1.2	2057	5.3	
27	TH	0320	1.1	0935	4.9	1538	1.3	2146	5.2	
28	F	0409	1.2	1025	4.8	1628	1.5	2238	5.0	☾
29	SA	0502	1.4	1121	4.7	1725	1.6	2338	4.9	
30	SU	0603	1.6	1223	4.6	1830	1.8			

SUNRISE AND SUNSET TIMES

PLYMOUTH
At 50°22′N 4°11′W

Month	Day	Sunrise	Sunset
UT			
Jan	01	0817	1623
	15	0811	1641
Feb	01	0752	1709
	15	0729	1733
Mar	01	0700	1759
	15	0630	1822
BST (UT+1)			
Apr	01	0653	1949
	15	0623	2012
May	01	0552	2037
	15	0529	2058
Jun	01	0511	2119
	15	0505	2130
Jul	01	0510	2131
	15	0523	2122
Aug	01	0545	2100
	15	0606	2035
Sep	01	0632	2001
	15	0653	1930
Oct	01	0717	1854
	15	0740	1824
UT			
Nov	01	0708	1652
	15	0731	1631
Dec	01	0755	1616
	15	0811	1613

PLYMOUTH (DEVONPORT)
LAT 50°22′N
LONG 4°11′W

TIMES AND HEIGHTS OF HIGH AND LOW WATER (Heights in Metres)

TIME ZONE UT
For Summer Time (area enclosed in shaded box) add 1 hour

2024

JULY

Day	Time	m	Day	Time	m
1	0045	4.8	16	0001	4.3
	0711	1.6		0637	2.2
M	1328	4.6	TU	1256	4.3
	1943	1.8		1914	2.2
2	0157	4.7	17	0115	4.3
	0822	1.6		0749	2.1
TU	1434	4.7	W	1407	4.4
	2054	1.7		2023	2.1
3	0304	4.7	18	0235	4.4
	0927	1.6		0854	1.9
W	1534	4.9	TH	1512	4.6
	2158	1.5		2126	1.8
4	0405	4.8	19	0342	4.6
	1026	1.4		0953	1.7
TH	1629	5.0	F	1608	4.9
	2255	1.3		2224	1.5
5	0459	4.9	20	0438	4.8
	1119	1.3		1049	1.4
F	1718	5.2	SA	1659	5.1
●	2345	1.2		2318	1.2
6	0549	5.0	21	0530	5.0
	1206	1.2		1141	1.2
SA	1803	5.2	SU	1746	5.3
			○		
7	0031	1.1	22	0008	1.0
	0634	5.0		0619	5.1
SU	1249	1.2	M	1230	1.0
	1844	5.3		1833	5.5
8	0113	1.1	23	0056	0.8
	0715	5.0		0707	5.2
M	1329	1.2	TU	1316	0.9
	1921	5.2		1919	5.6
9	0152	1.1	24	0142	0.7
	0753	4.9		0753	5.3
TU	1405	1.3	W	1400	0.8
	1956	5.2		2005	5.6
10	0227	1.2	25	0226	0.6
	0827	4.8		0838	5.3
W	1437	1.4	TH	1442	0.8
	2029	5.1		2049	5.5
11	0259	1.4	26	0307	0.7
	0900	4.7		0920	5.2
TH	1508	1.6	F	1523	1.0
	2103	4.9		2132	5.4
12	0329	1.6	27	0349	1.0
	0935	4.6		1003	5.0
F	1539	1.8	SA	1605	1.2
	2139	4.8		2216	5.1
13	0400	1.8	28	0432	1.3
	1014	4.5		1049	4.8
SA	1613	1.9	SU	1651	1.5
☽	2218	4.6	☾	2305	4.8
14	0437	1.9	29	0522	1.6
	1058	4.4		1144	4.6
SU	1657	2.1	M	1749	1.9
	2303	4.5			
15	0528	2.1	30	0008	4.6
	1151	4.3		0627	1.9
M	1759	2.3	TU	1253	4.5
				1905	2.1
			31	0131	4.4
				0750	2.1
			W	1410	4.5
				2036	2.1

AUGUST

Day	Time	m	Day	Time	m
1	0250	4.4	16	0158	4.3
	0914	[illegible]		0825	2.2
TH	1519	4.6	F	1442	4.6
	2152	[illegible]		2104	1.9
2	0356	4.6	17	0322	4.5
	1019	1.7		0934	1.8
F	1617	4.9	SA	1547	4.9
	2250	1.5		2208	1.5
3	0451	4.7	18	0422	4.8
	1111	1.4		1034	1.4
SA	1706	5.7	SU	1640	5.2
	2338	1.2		2304	1.1
4	0537	4.9	19	0514	5.1
	1157	1.2		1128	1.1
SU	1748	5.2	M	1729	5.5
●			○	2355	0.7
5	0021	1.7	20	0602	5.3
	0619	5.[illegible]		1217	0.7
M	1237	1.7	TU	1817	5.7
	1827	5.3			
6	0100	1.0	21	0042	0.5
	0655	5.0		0650	5.4
TU	1313	1.7	W	1301	0.5
	1902	5.3		1903	5.8
7	0134	1.0	22	0126	0.3
	0729	5.0		0734	5.5
W	1344	1.7	TH	1343	0.5
	1934	5.3		1948	5.8
8	0203	1.7	23	0207	0.4
	0800	5.0		0816	5.5
TH	1411	1.2	F	1423	0.5
	2006	5.2		2029	5.7
9	0228	1.2	24	0245	0.6
	0830	4.9		0856	5.4
F	1435	1.4	SA	1501	0.8
	2036	5.1		2109	5.5
10	0249	1.4	25	0322	0.9
	0900	4.8		0934	5.2
SA	1456	1.6	SU	1538	1.1
	2105	4.9		2148	5.1
11	0310	1.6	26	0400	1.4
	0930	4.7		1013	4.9
SU	1520	1.8	M	1620	1.6
	2134	4.7	☾	2229	4.7
12	0336	1.8	27	0445	1.8
	1004	4.5		1102	4.5
M	1553	2.0	TU	1714	2.1
☽	2211	4.5		2332	4.3
13	0414	2.0	28	0547	2.3
	1049	4.3		1223	4.3
TU	1642	2.2	W	1836	2.4
	2305	4.3			
14	0514	2.3	29	0119	4.1
	1155	4.3		0730	2.4
W	1812	2.4	TH	1356	4.3
				2038	2.3
15	0021	4.2	30	0245	4.2
	0701	2.4		0913	2.2
TH	1318	4.3	F	1509	4.6
	1950	2.3		2149	1.9
			31	0350	4.5
				1012	1.8
			SA	1605	4.9
				2239	1.5

SEPTEMBER

Day	Time	m	Day	Time	m
1	0439	4.8	16	0405	4.9
	1058	1.4		1017	1.3
SU	1649	5.1	M	1620	5.4
	2322	1.2		2246	0.9
2	0519	5.0	17	0454	5.3
	1139	1.2		1109	0.9
M	1728	5.3	TU	1708	5.7
				2334	0.5
3	0001	1.0	18	0540	5.5
	0555	5.1		1156	0.6
TU	1215	1.0	W	1755	5.8
●	1803	5.4	○		
4	0036	0.9	19	0019	0.3
	0628	5.2		0626	5.6
W	1248	0.9	TH	1239	0.4
	1836	5.4		1841	5.9
5	0106	0.9	20	0102	0.2
	0659	5.2		0709	5.7
TH	1316	1.0	F	1320	0.3
	1907	5.4		1925	5.9
6	0131	1.0	21	0141	0.3
	0729	5.2		0749	5.6
F	1339	1.1	SA	1359	0.5
	1938	5.3		2005	5.7
7	0151	1.2	22	0219	0.6
	0758	5.1		0827	5.5
SA	1359	1.3	SU	1436	0.8
	2006	5.1		2043	5.4
8	0209	1.3	23	0254	1.0
	0825	5.0		0902	5.2
SU	1418	1.5	M	1513	1.3
	2031	5.0		2119	5.0
9	0229	1.5	24	0331	1.6
	0850	4.8		0937	4.9
M	1441	1.7	TU	1554	1.8
	2056	4.8	☾	2156	4.5
10	0255	1.7	25	0415	2.1
	0918	4.6		1021	4.5
TU	1512	1.9	W	1650	2.3
	2130	4.5		2259	4.1
11	0330	2.0	26	0519	2.5
	1003	4.4		1157	4.2
W	1557	2.2	TH	1818	2.6
☽	2230	4.3			
12	0423	2.3	27	0112	4.0
	1113	4.3		0721	2.7
TH	1718	2.5	F	1341	4.3
	2350	4.1		2031	2.3
13	0620	2.5	28	0233	4.2
	1241	4.3		0858	2.3
F	1927	2.4	SA	1451	4.6
				2130	1.9
14	0134	4.2	29	0331	4.5
	0806	2.3		0949	1.9
SA	1418	4.6	SU	1542	4.9
	2047	1.9		2215	1.5
15	0307	4.6	30	0415	4.8
	0918	1.8		1032	1.5
SU	1527	5.0	M	1624	5.1
	2151	1.4		2254	1.2

OCTOBER

Day	Time	m	Day	Time	m
1	0451	5.1	16	0429	5.4
	1110	1.2		1043	0.9
TU	1700	5.3	W	1644	5.7
	2331	1.0		2308	0.6
2	0524	5.2	17	0514	5.6
	1145	1.0		1130	0.6
W	1734	5.4	TH	1731	5.9
●			○	2354	0.4
3	0003	0.9	18	0558	5.7
	0557	5.3		1214	0.4
TH	1216	1.0	F	1817	5.9
	1807	5.4			
4	0032	1.0	19	0035	0.4
	0628	5.3		0641	5.8
F	1243	1.0	SA	1256	0.5
	1839	5.4		1901	5.8
5	0056	1.1	20	0115	0.5
	0658	5.3		0722	5.7
SA	1306	1.2	SU	1335	0.6
	1910	5.3		1942	5.6
6	0116	1.2	21	0153	0.9
	0727	5.2		0759	5.5
SU	1327	1.3	M	1414	1.0
	1938	5.2		2020	5.2
7	0136	1.4	22	0230	1.3
	0753	5.1		0834	5.2
M	1349	1.4	TU	1453	1.4
	2004	5.0		2057	4.9
8	0158	1.5	23	0308	1.8
	0818	5.0		0909	4.9
TU	1414	1.6	W	1536	1.9
	2031	4.8		2136	4.5
9	0226	1.8	24	0354	2.2
	0849	4.8		0953	4.6
W	1447	1.9	TH	1633	2.3
	2111	4.6	☾	2244	4.1
10	0303	2.1	25	0457	2.6
	0939	4.6		1120	4.3
TH	1534	2.2	F	1754	2.5
☽	2212	4.3			
11	0358	2.4	26	0045	4.0
	1048	4.4		0634	2.7
F	1701	2.5	SA	1308	4.4
	2332	4.2		1949	2.4
12	0555	2.6	27	0159	4.2
	1213	4.4		0815	2.4
SA	1905	2.3	SU	1415	4.6
				2051	2.0
13	0114	4.3	28	0254	4.5
	0744	2.3		0910	2.0
SU	1350	4.7	M	1506	4.8
	2025	1.9		2137	1.7
14	0243	4.7	29	0337	4.8
	0855	1.8		0954	1.7
M	1501	5.1	TU	1548	5.0
	2127	1.3		2216	1.4
15	0340	5.0	30	0415	5.0
	0953	1.3		1033	1.4
TU	1555	5.4	W	1626	5.2
	2220	0.9		2252	1.2
			31	0450	5.2
				1108	1.2
			TH	1702	5.3
				2325	1.2

NOVEMBER

Day	Time	m	Day	Time	m
1	0524	5.3	16	0533	5.7
	1140	1.2		1151	0.7
F	1737	5.3	SA	1755	5.7
●	2355	1.2			
2	0558	5.4	17	0012	0.7
	1210	1.2		0618	5.7
SA	1812	5.3	SU	1235	0.7
				1841	5.6
3	0022	1.2	18	0054	0.9
	0631	5.3		0700	5.6
SU	1237	1.3	M	1317	0.9
	1845	5.2		1924	5.4
4	0047	1.3	19	0134	1.1
	0701	5.3		0739	5.5
M	1304	1.3	TU	1358	1.2
	1916	5.1		2006	5.1
5	0113	1.4	20	0213	1.4
	0730	5.2		0817	5.3
TU	1331	1.5	W	1440	1.5
	1946	5.0		2046	4.8
6	0141	1.6	21	0254	1.8
	0800	5.1		0855	5.0
W	1403	1.6	TH	1525	1.8
	2021	4.8		2128	4.5
7	0214	1.8	22	0339	2.1
	0838	4.9		0939	4.8
TH	1442	1.9	F	1615	2.1
	2105	4.6		2223	4.3
8	0256	2.0	23	0432	2.4
	0928	4.8		1038	4.6
F	1535	2.1	SA	1716	2.3
	2204	4.4	☾	2345	4.2
9	0357	2.3	24	0538	2.5
	1032	4.6		1201	4.5
SA	1657	2.3	SU	1828	2.4
☽	2317	4.3			
10	0533	2.4	25	0059	4.3
	1149	4.6		0655	2.5
SU	1834	2.1	M	1315	4.5
				1942	2.2
11	0044	4.4	26	0158	4.4
	0710	2.2		0805	2.3
M	1314	4.8	TU	1412	4.6
	1953	1.8		2039	2.0
12	0206	4.7	27	0247	4.6
	0823	1.8		0900	2.0
TU	1427	5.1	W	1501	4.8
	2056	1.4		2126	1.8
13	0307	5.0	28	0331	4.9
	0923	1.4		0946	1.8
W	1525	5.4	TH	1546	5.0
	2151	1.1		2207	1.6
14	0359	5.3	29	0413	5.1
	1016	1.1		1027	1.6
TH	1618	5.6	F	1629	5.1
	2241	0.8		2245	1.5
15	0447	5.5	30	0453	5.2
	1105	0.8		1105	1.5
F	1707	5.7	SA	1710	5.1
○	2328	0.7		2320	1.4

DECEMBER

Day	Time	m	Day	Time	m
1	0531	5.3	16	0600	5.5
	1141	1.4		1222	1.0
SU	1749	5.2	M	1828	5.3
●	2355	1.4			
2	0608	5.3	17	0040	1.1
	1216	1.3		0645	5.5
M	1827	5.2	TU	1307	1.0
				1914	5.2
3	0028	1.4	18	0123	1.2
	0643	5.3		0727	5.5
TU	1251	1.4	W	1350	1.2
	1903	5.1		1956	5.1
4	0103	1.4	19	0203	1.4
	0718	5.3		0806	5.3
W	1327	1.4	TH	1431	1.3
	1940	5.0		2036	4.9
5	0139	1.5	20	0242	1.6
	0754	5.2		0844	5.2
TH	1406	1.5	F	1511	1.6
	2019	4.9		2113	4.7
6	0218	1.7	21	0320	1.8
	0835	5.1		0921	5.0
F	1450	1.6	SA	1550	1.8
	2105	4.8		2152	4.6
7	0304	1.8	22	0400	2.0
	0923	5.0		1002	4.8
SA	1541	1.8	SU	1632	2.0
	2157	4.7	☾	2236	4.4
8	0359	2.0	23	0445	2.2
	1019	4.9		1050	4.6
SU	1643	1.9	M	1720	2.2
☽	2258	4.6		2330	4.3
9	0506	2.1	24	0540	2.3
	1123	4.9		1147	4.5
M	1754	1.9	TU	1817	2.3
10	0008	4.6	25	0032	4.3
	0624	2.1		0644	2.4
TU	1235	4.9	W	1252	4.5
	1910	1.8		1920	2.2
11	0121	4.7	26	0138	4.4
	0742	1.9		0751	2.3
W	1348	5.0	TH	1400	4.5
	2019	1.6		2022	2.1
12	0229	4.9	27	0240	4.6
	0850	1.7		0852	2.1
TH	1454	5.1	F	1502	4.6
	2121	1.4		2117	1.9
13	0329	5.1	28	0335	4.8
	0950	1.4		0945	1.9
F	1554	5.2	SA	1557	4.8
	2216	1.3		2207	1.8
14	0423	5.3	29	0424	5.0
	1044	1.2		1034	1.7
SA	1649	5.3	SU	1646	4.9
	2308	1.1		2253	1.6
15	0513	5.4	30	0508	5.2
	1135	1.1		1119	1.5
SU	1740	5.3	M	1731	5.0
○	2356	1.1	●	2336	1.4
			31	0550	5.3
				1203	1.3
			TU	1814	5.1

PORTLAND
LAT 50°34'N
LONG 2°26'W

TIMES AND HEIGHTS OF HIGH AND LOW WATER (Heights in Metres)

TIME ZONE UT
For Summer Time (area enclosed in shaded box) add 1 hour

Double low waters occur at Portland. The predictions are for the first low water. The second low water occurs from 3 to 4 hours later and, at springs, may be lower that the first

2024

JANUARY

Date	Day	Time	m
1	M	0210 0937 1443 2204	0.6 1.8 0.6 1.6
2	TU	0237 1010 1511 2237	0.7 1.7 0.6 1.5
3	W	0308 1042 1544 2313	0.7 1.6 0.6 1.4
4	TH ☾	0349 1119 1628	0.8 1.5 0.6
5	F	0000 0446 1210 1724	1.4 0.8 1.4 0.6
6	SA	0110 0554 1320 1830	1.4 0.9 1.4 0.7
7	SU	0231 0709 1440 1941	1.5 0.8 1.5 0.6
8	M	0337 0825 1552 2051	1.6 0.8 1.5 0.6
9	TU	0436 0931 1659 2153	1.8 0.7 1.7 0.6
10	W	0529 1031 1757 2250	2.0 0.6 1.8 0.5
11	TH ●	0618 1126 1849 2342	2.1 0.5 1.9 0.4
12	F	0705 1215 1940	2.2 0.3 2.0
13	SA	0028 0753 1301 2031	0.3 2.3 0.2 2.0
14	SU	0113 0842 1346 2117	0.3 2.3 0.2 2.0
15	M	0156 0928 1430 2158	0.3 2.2 0.2 2.0
16	TU	0240 1011 1516 2237	0.3 2.1 0.2 1.8
17	W	0323 1053 1601 2320	0.4 2.0 0.3 1.7
18	TH ☽	0407 1139 1649	0.6 1.8 0.5
19	F	0011 0456 1238 1744	1.6 0.7 1.6 0.6
20	SA	0120 0558 1355 1851	1.5 0.8 1.4 0.7
21	SU	0236 0724 1512 2009	1.5 0.9 1.4 0.8
22	M	0344 0911 1622 2115	1.5 0.9 1.4 0.7
23	TU	0444 1010 1724 2210	1.7 0.8 1.6 0.7
24	W	0536 1057 1815 2258	1.8 0.6 1.7 0.6
25	TH O	0622 1137 1900 2341	2.0 0.5 1.8 0.5
26	F	0704 1214 1941	2.0 0.4 1.8
27	SA	0019 0743 1249 2018	0.4 2.1 0.3 1.9
28	SU	0055 0818 1323 2048	0.3 2.0 0.3 1.8
29	M	0128 0851 1354 2115	0.3 2.0 0.3 1.8
30	TU	0156 0921 1419 2140	0.4 1.9 0.4 1.7
31	W	0221 0945 1442	0.4 1.8 0.4

FEBRUARY

Date	Day	Time	m
1	TH	0247 1006 1509 2224	0.5 1.7 0.4 1.5
2	F ☾	0317 1035 1544 2259	0.5 1.6 0.4 1.5
3	SA	0357 1117 1632 2350	0.6 1.5 0.5 1.4
4	SU	0459 1215 1735	0.7 1.4 0.6
5	M	0102 0615 1338 1848	1.4 0.8 1.3 0.7
6	TU	0247 0745 1521 2021	1.5 0.8 1.4 0.7
7	W	0404 0930 1639 2146	1.6 0.7 1.5 0.6
8	TH	0508 1029 1746 2243	1.8 0.5 1.7 0.5
9	F ●	0603 1121 1844 2333	2.0 0.3 1.9 0.3
10	SA	0656 1206 1941	2.2 0.2 2.0
11	SU	0018 0749 1249 2032	0.2 2.3 0.0 2.1
12	M	0101 0839 1330 2111	0.1 2.4 0.0 2.2
13	TU	0141 0921 1411 2144	0.1 2.4 0.0 2.1
14	W	0220 0957 1451 2214	0.1 2.2 0.1 2.0
15	TH	0257 1030 1529 2243	0.3 2.0 0.2 1.8
16	F ☽	0331 1104 1607 2316	0.4 1.7 0.4 1.6
17	SA	0407 1145 1649	0.6 1.5 0.6
18	SU	0000 0453 1311 1756	1.4 0.8 1.2 0.8
19	M	0157 0710 1457 1943	1.3 0.9 1.2 0.9
20	TU	0326 0900 1614 2052	1.4 0.9 1.3 0.8
21	W	0431 0947 1713 2148	1.5 0.7 1.5 0.7
22	TH	0522 1031 1800 2237	1.7 0.6 1.6 0.5
23	F	0607 1113 1843 2322	1.9 0.4 1.8 0.4
24	SA O	0649 1153 1924	2.0 0.3 1.9
25	SU	0001 0729 1230 2001	0.3 2.1 0.2 1.9
26	M	0037 0804 1302 2031	0.2 2.1 0.2 1.9
27	TU	0108 0834 1328 2055	0.2 2.0 0.2 1.9
28	W	0134 0859 1350 2114	0.2 1.9 0.2 1.8
29	TH	0157 0916 1412 2126	0.3 1.8 0.3 1.7

MARCH

Date	Day	Time	m
1	F	0221 0932 1436 2145	0.3 1.7 0.3 1.6
2	SA	0245 1001 1504 2219	0.4 1.6 0.3 1.6
3	SU ☾	0315 1043 1541 2306	0.5 1.5 0.4 1.5
4	M	0405 1139 1645	0.6 1.3 0.6
5	TU	0012 0536 1303 1812	1.4 0.7 1.2 0.7
6	W	0215 1011 1511 2033	1.4 0.7 1.3 0.7
7	TH	0345 0937 1628 2138	1.5 0.6 1.5 0.6
8	F	0450 1021 1733 2230	1.8 0.4 1.7 0.4
9	SA	0548 1106 1831 2318	2.0 0.2 1.9 0.2
10	SU ●	0642 1149 1924	2.2 0.0 2.1
11	M	0001 0734 1229 2010	0.1 2.4 -0.1 2.2
12	TU	0042 0822 1308 2048	0.0 2.4 -0.1 2.3
13	W	0120 0903 1346 2120	0.0 2.4 -0.1 2.2
14	TH	0155 0935 1420 2145	0.1 2.2 0.1 2.0
15	F	0227 1002 1453 2208	0.2 2.0 0.3 1.8
16	SA	0258 1031 1524 2237	0.4 1.7 0.5 1.6
17	SU ☽	0330 1107 1555 2314	0.6 1.4 0.7 1.4
18	M	0407 1203 1629	0.8 1.1 0.9
19	TU	0011 0700 1452 1914	1.2 0.9 1.1 0.9
20	W	0313 0816 1606 2020	1.3 0.8 1.3 0.8
21	TH	0414 0908 1654 2116	1.5 0.7 1.5 0.7
22	F	0501 0955 1736 2206	1.7 0.5 1.6 0.5
23	SA	0544 1040 1817 2253	1.8 0.3 1.8 0.3
24	SU	0624 1123 1856 2336	2.0 0.2 1.9 0.2
25	M O	0703 1201 1932	2.0 0.1 2.0
26	TU	0012 0738 1232 2004	0.2 2.1 0.1 2.0
27	W	0041 0809 1256 2029	0.2 2.0 0.2 2.0
28	TH	0106 0831 1319 2045	0.2 1.9 0.2 1.9
29	F	0131 0844 1342 2054	0.2 1.8 0.2 1.8
30	SA	0156 0904 1408 2116	0.3 1.7 0.3 1.7
31	SU	0221 0937 1434 [illegible]	0.3 1.6 0.4 [illegible]

APRIL

Date	Day	Time	m
1	M	0251 1023 1507 2242	0.4 1.5 0.5 1.5
2	TU ☾	0341 1124 1608 2352	0.6 1.3 0.6 1.4
3	W	0523 1307 1758	0.7 1.2 0.8
4	TH	0200 0937 1502 2021	1.4 0.6 1.3 0.7
5	F	0327 0925 1612 2119	1.5 0.4 1.5 0.5
6	SA	0430 1001 1711 2209	1.8 0.3 1.8 0.4
7	SU	0527 1043 1805 2255	2.0 0.1 2.0 0.2
8	M ●	0620 1126 1854 2339	2.2 0.0 2.2 0.1
9	TU	0710 1205 1939	2.3 -0.1 2.3
10	W	0018 0757 1242 2018	0.0 2.4 -0.1 2.3
11	TH	0054 0836 1316 2050	0.0 2.3 0.0 2.2
12	F	0127 0908 1349 2114	0.1 2.1 0.2 2.0
13	SA	0159 0935 1421 2140	0.3 1.9 0.4 1.8
14	SU	0233 1008 1452 2214	0.5 1.6 0.6 1.6
15	M ☽	0308 1048 1522 2255	0.7 1.3 0.8 1.4
16	TU	0357 1144 1552 2350	0.8 1.1 0.9 1.3
17	W	0624 1440 1837	0.9 1.1 1.0
18	TH	0240 0729 1540 1942	1.3 0.8 1.3 0.9
19	F	0341 0825 1622 2038	1.4 0.6 1.5 0.7
20	SA	0426 0914 1703 2129	1.6 0.5 1.6 0.5
21	SU	0508 1002 1742 2218	1.7 0.3 1.8 0.4
22	M	0549 1046 1820 2302	1.9 0.3 1.9 0.3
23	TU O	0629 1125 1857 2340	2.0 0.2 2.0 0.3
24	W	0706 1157 1931	2.0 0.2 2.0
25	TH	0010 0738 1222 2000	0.2 2.0 0.2 2.0
26	F	0038 0800 1249 2016	0.2 1.9 0.2 2.0
27	SA	0107 0819 1318 2033	0.3 1.8 0.3 1.9
28	SU	0138 0848 1350 2103	0.3 1.7 0.3 1.8
29	M	0211 0929 1423 2146	0.4 1.6 0.4 1.7
30	TU	0253 1022 1504 2241	0.5 1.4 0.6 1.5

MAY

Date	Day	Time	m
1	W ☾	0400 1129 1623 2354	0.6 1.3 0.7 1.4
2	TH	0529 1311 1754	0.6 1.2 0.8
3	F	0139 0927 1443 1938	1.4 0.5 1.4 0.7
4	SA	0301 0900 1546 2048	1.6 0.4 1.6 0.6
5	SU	0402 0934 1641 2141	1.8 0.3 1.8 0.4
6	M	0459 1015 1734 2229	2.0 0.2 2.0 0.3
7	TU	0553 1057 1822 2312	2.1 0.1 2.1 0.2
8	W ●	0642 1137 1906 2353	2.2 0.1 2.2 0.2
9	TH	0728 1214 1946	2.2 0.1 2.2
10	F	0029 0809 1248 2020	0.2 2.1 0.2 2.1
11	SA	0104 0844 1323 2051	0.3 1.9 0.3 2.0
12	SU	0141 0917 1358 2125	0.4 1.8 0.5 1.8
13	M	0220 0954 1434 2202	0.5 1.6 0.6 1.7
14	TU	0305 1036 1511 2244	0.7 1.4 0.8 1.5
15	W ☽	0418 1126 1606 2333	0.8 1.2 0.9 1.4
16	TH	0543 1243 1752	0.8 1.2 0.9
17	F	0041 0646 1450 1900	1.3 0.7 1.2 0.9
18	SA	0220 0743 1536 1958	1.4 0.6 1.4 0.8
19	SU	0326 0834 1617 2051	1.5 0.5 1.6 0.6
20	M	0417 0921 1659 2139	1.6 0.4 1.7 0.5
21	TU	0505 1005 1741 2224	1.7 0.4 1.9 0.5
22	W	0550 1045 1821 2304	1.8 0.3 2.0 0.4
23	TH O	0631 1119 1858 2340	1.9 0.3 2.0 0.4
24	F	0706 1152 1931	1.9 0.3 2.1
25	SA	0015 0736 1227 1957	0.3 1.9 0.3 2.0
26	SU	0052 0807 1305 2027	0.3 1.8 0.3 2.0
27	M	0132 0847 1345 2107	0.3 1.7 0.4 1.9
28	TU	0216 0934 1430 2154	0.4 1.6 0.5 1.8
29	W	0308 1028 1523 2247	0.4 1.5 0.6 1.7
30	TH ☾	0409 1129 1625 2350	0.5 1.4 0.6 1.6
31	F	0515 1249 1732	0.5 1.4 0.7

JUNE

Date	Day	Time	m
1	SA	0108 0628 1410 1845	1.6 0.5 1.5 0.7
2	SU	0224 0757 1512 2000	1.6 0.5 1.6 0.6
3	M	0327 0856 1607 2106	1.7 0.4 1.7 0.6
4	TU	0427 0943 1701 2200	1.8 0.3 1.9 0.5
5	W	0525 1028 1752 2250	1.9 0.3 2.0 0.4
6	TH ●	0619 1111 1838 2334	1.9 0.3 2.1 0.4
7	F	0707 1151 1921	2.0 0.3 2.1
8	SA	0014 0751 1229 2001	0.4 1.9 0.3 2.1
9	SU	0054 0831 1308 2038	0.4 1.8 0.4 2.0
10	M	0134 0907 1346 2115	0.4 1.7 0.5 1.9
11	TU	0216 0943 1425 2152	0.5 1.6 0.6 1.8
12	W	0301 1020 1503 2229	0.6 1.5 0.7 1.6
13	TH	0349 1101 1541 2309	0.6 1.4 0.8 1.5
14	F ☽	0444 1148 1627 2354	0.7 1.3 0.8 1.4
15	SA	0550 1250 1736	0.7 1.3 0.8
16	SU	0051 0655 1407 1907	1.4 0.6 1.3 0.8
17	M	0202 0749 1512 2006	1.4 0.6 1.5 0.7
18	TU	0309 0836 1606 2057	1.5 0.5 1.6 0.7
19	W	0410 0919 1656 2145	1.6 0.5 1.8 0.6
20	TH	0507 1002 1744 2232	1.7 0.5 1.9 0.5
21	F	0557 1048 1827 2320	1.8 0.4 2.0 0.5
22	SA O	0643 1133 1908	1.8 0.4 2.1
23	SU	0005 0725 1217 1949	0.4 1.9 0.3 2.1
24	M	0049 0808 1301 2030	0.3 1.9 0.3 2.1
25	TU	0133 0853 1346 2113	0.3 1.8 0.3 2.1
26	W	0219 0939 1431 2157	0.3 1.8 0.4 2.0
27	TH	0307 1026 1519 2243	0.3 1.7 0.4 1.9
28	F ☾	0357 1117 1609 2333	0.3 1.6 0.5 1.8
29	SA	0449 1216 1703	0.4 1.5 0.6
30	SU	0033 0547 1326 1804	1.6 0.5 1.5 0.7

SUNRISE AND SUNSET TIMES

PORTLAND

AT 50°34′N 2°26′ W

UT		Sunrise	Sunset
Jan	01	0811	1616
	15	0805	1634
Feb	01	0745	1702
	15	0721	1727
Mar	01	0654	1751
	15	0623	1815
BST (UT+1)			
Apr	01	0646	1942
	15	0616	2005
May	01	0544	2030
	15	0522	2051
Jun	01	0503	2113
	15	0457	2124
Jul	01	0502	2125
	15	0515	2116
Aug	01	0537	2054
	15	0558	2029
Sep	01	0624	1954
	15	0645	1923
Oct	01	0710	1848
	15	0732	1818
UT			
Nov	01	0701	1645
	15	0725	1624
Dec	01	0749	1608
	15	0804	1605

JULY

	Time	m		Time	m
1 M	0144 0652 1433 1914	1.5 0.5 1.5 0.7	16 TU	0041 0554 1349 1835	1.4 0.6 1.4 0.8
2 TU	0254 0806 1535 2033	1.5 0.6 1.6 0.7	17 W	0153 0703 1506 1959	1.4 0.6 1.5 0.8
3 W	0402 0912 1635 2151	1.6 0.5 1.7 0.7	18 TH	0316 0821 1613 2118	1.4 0.6 1.7 0.7
4 TH	0507 1007 1730 2251	1.6 0.5 1.9 0.6	19 F	0431 0933 1711 2219	1.5 0.5 1.8 0.6
5 F ●	0605 1055 1820 2335	1.7 0.5 2.0 0.5	20 SA	0535 1032 1803 2313	1.7 0.5 2.0 0.5
6 SA	0656 1139 1905	1.8 0.4 2.1	21 SU ○	0629 1124 1852	1.8 0.4 2.1
7 SU	0013 0742 1219 1948	0.4 1.8 0.4 2.1	22 M	0001 0721 1211 1941	0.3 1.9 0.3 2.2
8 M	0050 0824 1257 2027	0.4 1.8 0.4 2.0	23 TU	0044 0813 1255 2029	0.2 2.0 0.2 2.3
9 TU	0128 0858 1334 2103	0.3 1.8 0.4 2.0	24 W	0127 0900 1338 2113	0.1 2.0 0.2 2.2
10 W	0205 0929 1410 2136	0.4 1.7 0.4 1.9	25 TH	0209 0939 1420 2152	0.1 2.0 0.2 2.2
11 TH	0241 0959 1442 2207	0.4 1.6 0.5 1.8	26 F	0252 1015 1502 2230	0.1 1.9 0.3 2.0
12 F	0311 1030 1510 2237	0.5 1.5 0.6 1.6	27 SA	0335 1054 1544 2310	0.2 1.8 0.4 1.8
13 SA ☽	0336 1102 1542 2309	0.5 1.4 0.6 1.5	28 SU ☾	0419 1138 1629 2358	0.3 1.6 0.6 1.6
14 SU	0408 1141 1626 2348	0.5 1.4 0.7 1.5	29 M	0508 1239 1723	0.5 1.5 0.7
15 M	0455 1234 1725	0.6 1.3 0.8	30 TU	0108 0609 1400 1840	1.4 0.7 1.4 0.9
			31 W	0235 0735 1515 2052	1.3 0.8 1.5 0.9

AUGUST

	Time	m		Time	m
1 TH	0352 0856 1620 2156	1.4 0.7 1.6 0.8	16 F	0247 0745 1542 2121	1.3 0.7 1.6 0.7
2 F	0500 0953 1717 2243	1.5 0.7 1.8 0.6	17 SA	0414 0926 1647 2214	1.5 0.6 1.8 0.5
3 SA	0556 1042 1806 2324	1.6 0.5 1.9 0.5	18 SU	0521 1022 1744 2303	1.6 0.5 2.0 0.4
4 SU ●	0643 1126 1851	1.8 0.4 2.1	19 M ○	0618 1112 1836 2348	1.8 0.3 2.2 0.2
5 M	0002 0728 1205 1934	0.4 1.9 0.3 2.1	20 TU	0712 1158 1926	2.0 0.2 2.3
6 TU	0038 0808 1242 2012	0.3 1.9 0.3 2.1	21 W	0029 0805 1240 2017	0.1 2.1 0.1 2.4
7 W	0112 0842 1317 2045	0.2 1.9 0.3 2.1	22 TH	0110 0849 1321 2101	0.0 2.2 0.1 2.4
8 TH	0144 0907 1349 2114	0.2 1.8 0.3 1.9	23 F	0149 0923 1400 2137	0.0 2.1 0.1 2.3
9 F	0212 0931 1415 2139	0.3 1.7 0.4 1.8	24 SA	0228 0953 1437 2209	0.1 2.0 0.2 2.1
10 SA	0233 0953 1439 2200	0.3 1.6 0.5 1.7	25 SU	0305 1022 1513 2242	0.2 1.9 0.4 1.8
11 SU	0254 1015 1505 2223	0.4 1.5 0.5 1.6	26 M ☾	0342 1056 1550 2322	0.4 1.7 0.6 1.6
12 M ☽	0322 1043 1540 2256	0.4 1.5 0.6 1.5	27 TU	0422 1141 1639	0.6 1.5 0.8
13 TU	0403 1127 1635 2347	0.5 1.4 0.7 1.4	28 W	0035 0523 1333 1848	1.3 0.8 1.3 0.9
14 W	0502 1231 1747	0.6 1.4 0.8	29 TH	0232 0722 1505 2040	1.2 0.9 1.4 0.9
15 TH	0058 0614 1414 1916	1.3 0.7 1.4 0.8	30 F	0354 0835 1611 2130	1.3 0.9 1.6 0.8
			31 SA	0454 0930 1703 2214	1.5 0.7 1.8 0.6

SEPTEMBER

	Time	m		Time	m
1 SU	0540 1019 1749 2257	1.7 0.6 1.9 0.4	16 M	0506 1004 1724 2243	1.7 0.5 2.0 0.3
2 M	0622 1104 1831 2337	1.8 0.4 2.1 0.3	17 TU	0600 1052 1816 2326	1.9 0.3 2.2 0.1
3 TU ●	0704 1144 1912	2.0 0.3 2.1	18 W ○	0650 1137 1905	2.1 0.2 2.4
4 W	0014 0742 1221 1949	0.2 2.0 0.2 2.1	19 TH	0007 0737 1219 1953	0.0 2.3 0.1 2.5
5 TH	0048 0814 1254 2019	0.1 2.0 0.2 2.1	20 F	0046 0819 1258 2037	0.0 2.3 0.1 2.4
6 F	0116 0838 1322 2045	0.2 2.0 0.2 2.0	21 SA	0123 0853 1334 2113	0.0 2.3 0.1 2.3
7 SA	0137 0858 1345 2106	0.3 1.9 0.3 1.9	22 SU	0158 0920 1408 2143	0.2 2.1 0.3 2.1
8 SU	0156 0913 1407 2120	0.3 1.8 0.4 1.7	23 M	0230 0946 1441 2214	0.4 1.9 0.5 1.8
9 M	0215 0927 1429 2141	0.4 1.7 0.5 1.6	24 TU ☾	0302 1019 1518 2255	0.6 1.7 0.7 1.5
10 TU	0238 0956 1453 2218	0.4 1.6 0.6 1.5	25 W	0336 1102 1610	0.8 1.5 0.9
11 W ☽	0306 1040 1534 2311	0.5 1.5 0.7 1.4	26 TH	0015 0427 1218 1844	1.2 1.0 1.3 1.0
12 TH	0357 1143 1712	0.7 1.4 0.8	27 F	0238 0655 1457 1955	1.2 1.1 1.4 0.9
13 F	0029 0539 1338 2039	1.2 0.8 1.4 0.8	28 SA	0357 0801 1556 2049	1.4 1.0 1.6 0.7
14 SA	0243 0816 1523 2115	1.3 0.8 1.5 0.6	29 SU	0436 0857 1642 2136	1.6 0.8 1.8 0.6
15 SU	0403 0914 1627 2159	1.5 0.7 1.8 0.4	30 M	0515 0946 1725 2220	1.8 0.6 1.9 0.4

OCTOBER

	Time	m		Time	m
1 TU	0555 1033 1805 2303	1.9 0.4 2.0 0.3	16 W	0533 1027 1750 2258	2.0 0.4 2.2 0.1
2 W ●	0633 1116 1843 2342	2.1 0.3 2.1 0.2	17 TH ○	0620 1112 1839 2339	2.2 0.3 2.3 0.1
3 TH	0709 1154 1918	2.1 0.3 2.1	18 F	0703 1153 1925	2.3 0.2 2.4
4 F	0015 0739 1225 1949	0.2 2.1 0.3 2.1	19 SA	0017 0743 1231 2007	0.1 2.4 0.2 2.3
5 SA	0040 0804 1252 2014	0.3 2.1 0.3 2.0	20 SU	0053 0817 1307 2044	0.2 2.3 0.3 2.2
6 SU	0101 0822 1315 2031	0.3 2.0 0.4 1.9	21 M	0127 0846 1342 2118	0.3 2.2 0.4 2.0
7 M	0121 0833 1338 2045	0.4 1.9 0.4 1.8	22 TU	0200 0919 1419 2156	0.5 2.0 0.6 1.7
8 TU	0143 0851 1401 2112	0.4 1.8 0.5 1.6	23 W	0233 0957 1502 2241	0.7 1.8 0.8 1.5
9 W	0205 0923 1426 2153	0.5 1.7 0.6 1.5	24 TH ☾	0307 1044 1629 2352	0.9 1.6 0.9 1.3
10 TH ☽	0229 1008 1504 2254	0.6 1.6 0.7 1.3	25 F	0420 1148 1804	1.1 1.4 0.9
11 F	0306 1119 1656	0.8 1.4 0.8	26 SA	0227 0616 1427 1906	1.3 1.1 1.4 0.9
12 SA	0024 0519 1317 2029	1.2 0.9 1.4 0.7	27 SU	0327 0720 1525 2002	1.4 1.0 1.5 0.7
13 SU	0236 0756 1501 2057	1.3 0.9 1.6 0.6	28 M	0405 0817 1609 2052	1.6 0.9 1.7 0.6
14 M	0347 0851 1604 2134	1.6 0.7 1.8 0.4	29 TU	0444 0908 1651 2138	1.8 0.7 1.8 0.5
15 TU	0443 0940 1659 2216	1.8 0.5 2.0 0.2	30 W	0522 0955 1731 2222	1.9 0.6 1.9 0.4
			31 TH	0558 1040 1809 2304	2.1 0.5 2.0 0.3

NOVEMBER

	Time	m		Time	m
1 F ●	0633 1120 1845 2338	2.1 0.4 2.1 0.3	16 SA	0631 1127 1859 2350	2.3 0.4 2.2 0.3
2 SA	0704 1154 1917	2.2 0.4 2.0	17 SU	0711 1208 1943	2.3 0.4 2.2
3 SU	0004 0732 1221 1944	0.4 2.1 0.4 2.0	18 M	0027 0750 1247 2025	0.3 2.3 0.4 2.1
4 M	0028 0751 1248 2004	0.4 2.1 0.4 1.9	19 TU	0104 0827 1326 2106	0.4 2.2 0.5 1.9
5 TU	0055 0809 1318 2029	0.4 2.0 0.5 1.8	20 W	0141 0906 1409 2146	0.6 2.0 0.6 1.7
6 W	0124 0835 1350 2104	0.5 1.9 0.5 1.7	21 TH	0220 0948 1500 2230	0.7 1.8 0.7 1.5
7 TH	0153 0913 1428 2152	0.6 1.8 0.6 1.5	22 F	0301 1032 1611 2319	0.9 1.7 0.8 1.4
8 F	0223 1005 1528 2255	0.7 1.6 0.7 1.4	23 SA ☾	0402 1123 1720	1.0 1.5 0.8
9 SA ☽	0312 1116 1654	0.8 1.5 0.7	24 SU	0045 0528 1230 1821	1.3 1.1 1.4 0.8
10 SU	0020 0510 1250 2020	1.3 0.9 1.5 0.7	25 M	0232 0636 1410 1917	1.4 1.0 1.4 0.7
11 M	0210 0644 1428 2033	1.4 0.9 1.6 0.6	26 TU	0320 0735 1512 2009	1.5 0.9 1.5 0.6
12 TU	0317 0811 1531 2101	1.6 0.8 1.8 0.4	27 W	0400 0829 1601 2057	1.7 0.8 1.6 0.6
13 W	0411 0908 1627 2144	1.8 0.6 1.9 0.3	28 TH	0440 0917 1648 2142	1.8 0.7 1.7 0.5
14 TH	0501 0956 1721 2227	2.0 0.5 2.1 0.3	29 F	0518 1004 1732 2224	2.0 0.6 1.8 0.5
15 F ○	0548 1043 1812 2309	2.2 0.4 2.2 0.2	30 SA	0557 1046 1813 2300	2.1 0.6 1.9 0.5

DECEMBER

	Time	m		Time	m
1 SU ●	0633 1124 1850 2333	2.1 0.5 1.9 0.5	16 M	0653 1158 1934	2.2 0.5 2.0
2 M	0705 1159 1923	2.1 0.5 1.9	17 TU	0013 0737 1240 2020	0.4 2.2 0.5 2.0
3 TU	0007 0734 1234 1954	0.5 2.1 0.5 1.9	18 W	0053 0819 1322 2100	0.5 2.2 0.5 1.9
4 W	0043 0803 1312 2028	0.5 2.1 0.5 1.8	19 TH	0132 0900 1404 2137	0.5 2.1 0.5 1.8
5 TH	0121 0839 1354 2109	0.5 2.0 0.5 1.7	20 F	0211 0938 1449 2212	0.6 1.9 0.6 1.6
6 F	0202 0922 1442 2157	0.6 1.9 0.5 1.6	21 SA	0250 1016 1536 2248	0.7 1.8 0.6 1.5
7 SA	0247 1012 1537 2251	0.6 1.8 0.5 1.5	22 SU ☾	0327 1054 1626 2328	0.8 1.7 0.7 1.4
8 SU ☽	0343 1109 1637 2357	0.7 1.7 0.6 1.4	23 M	0403 1135 1720	0.9 1.5 0.7
9 M	0449 1219 1743	0.8 1.6 0.6	24 TU	0018 0454 1226 1824	1.4 0.9 1.4 0.7
10 TU	0121 0559 1340 1853	1.5 0.8 1.6 0.6	25 W	0130 0639 1335 1923	1.4 1.0 1.4 0.7
11 W	0233 0713 1450 2007	1.6 0.8 1.7 0.5	26 TH	0244 0747 1448 2015	1.5 0.9 1.4 0.7
12 TH	0332 0826 1552 2107	1.7 0.8 1.8 0.5	27 F	0343 0841 1554 2101	1.6 0.8 1.5 0.6
13 F	0427 0927 1653 2158	1.9 0.7 1.8 0.5	28 SA	0435 0930 1653 2146	1.8 0.7 1.6 0.6
14 SA	0519 1022 1752 2246	2.0 0.6 1.9 0.4	29 SU	0522 1019 1745 2232	1.9 0.7 1.7 0.6
15 SU ○	0608 1113 1845 2332	2.2 0.5 2.0 0.4	30 M ●	0606 1107 1832 2316	2.0 0.6 1.8 0.5
			31 TU	0647 1151 1914	2.1 0.5 1.9

POOLE HARBOUR
LAT 50°42′N
LONG 1°59′W

TIMES AND HEIGHTS OF HIGH AND LOW WATER (Heights in Metres)

TIME ZONE UT
For Summer Time (area enclosed in shaded box) add 1 hour

Sea level is above mean tide level from 2 hours after LW to 2 hours before the next LW. HW will occur between 5 hours after LW and 3 hours before the next LW. Predictions are for the first identified HW occuring between these times (but lower or higher HWs may occur earlier or later than this).

2024

JANUARY

Date	Day	Time	m	Time	m	Time	m	Time	m
1	M	0015	1.8	0720	1.1	1043	1.9	1935	0.8
2	TU	0121	1.7	0758	1.2	1108	1.8	2014	0.9
3	W	0000	1.6	0841	1.2	1143	1.7	2059	1.0
4	TH ☾	0017	1.6	0931	1.2	1223	1.7	2152	1.1
5	F	0113	1.6	1028	1.3	1317	1.6	2252	1.1
6	SA	0754	1.9	1131	1.2	1433	1.6	2355	1.1
7	SU	0631	1.8	1235	1.2	1617	1.6		
8	M	0056	1.1	0643	1.8	1333	1.0	1736	1.7
9	TU	0153	1.0	0605	1.9	1427	0.8	1947	1.8
10	W	0247	0.9	0702	2.1	1517	0.7	2035	1.9
11	TH ●	0338	0.8	0836	2.2	1606	0.5	2123	2.1
12	F	0427	0.7	0928	2.3	1652	0.4	2208	2.1
13	SA	0514	0.6	1016	2.3	1737	0.3	2252	2.2
14	SU	0601	0.6	1059	2.4	1823	0.3	2334	2.1
15	M	0648	0.7	1141	2.3	1909	0.4		
16	TU	0016	2.0	0736	0.8	1219	2.2	1957	0.5
17	W	0057	1.9	0827	0.9	1256	2.0	2048	0.7
18	TH ☽	0138	1.8	0924	1.0	1331	1.8	2147	0.9
19	F	0219	1.7	1030	1.1	1415	1.7	2257	1.0
20	SA	0309	1.6	1141	1.2	1514	1.6		
21	SU	0008	1.1	0848	1.9	1249	1.1	1859	1.7
22	M	0113	1.1	0729	1.8	1350	1.0	1942	1.7
23	TU	0212	1.0	0801	1.9	1443	0.8	2023	1.8
24	W	0303	1.0	0832	1.9	1530	0.7	2059	1.8
25	TH ○	0350	0.9	0856	2.0	1613	0.6	2128	1.9
26	F	0432	0.9	0914	2.1	1653	0.6	2154	2.0
27	SA	0511	0.8	0947	2.1	1729	0.6	2224	2.0
28	SU	0546	0.8	1025	2.1	1801	0.6	2300	2.0
29	M	0618	0.9	1100	2.1	1831	0.6	2337	1.9
30	TU	0649	0.9	1125	1.9	1902	0.7	2359	1.8
31	W	0723	0.9	1048	1.9	1938	0.7		

FEBRUARY

Date	Day	Time	m	Time	m	Time	m	Time	m
1	TH	0801	1.0	1107	1.8	2018	0.9	2325	1.7
2	F ☾	0845	1.0	1138	1.8	2106	1.0		
3	SA	0000	1.7	0937	1.1	1219	1.7	2203	1.1
4	SU	0051	1.6	1040	1.2	1316	1.6	2309	1.2
5	M	0237	1.6	1150	1.2	1519	1.5		
6	TU	0018	1.2	0445	1.7	1301	1.1	1911	1.6
7	W	0129	1.1	0657	1.8	1407	0.9	1951	1.8
8	TH	0232	0.9	0747	2.0	1504	0.6	2035	1.9
9	F ●	0327	0.7	0838	2.2	1553	0.4	2117	2.1
10	SA	0415	0.6	0924	2.3	1638	0.2	2158	2.2
11	SU	0500	0.4	1007	2.4	1721	0.1	2237	2.3
12	M	0544	0.4	1047	2.5	1804	0.1	2315	2.2
13	TU	0627	0.4	1125	2.4	1846	0.2	2352	2.1
14	W	0710	0.6	1201	2.2	1930	0.4		
15	TH	0026	2.0	0756	0.8	1231	2.0	2016	0.7
16	F ☽	0052	1.8	0847	1.0	1252	1.8	2109	1.0
17	SA	0110	1.7	0950	1.1	1326	1.6	2222	1.2
18	SU	0202	1.6	1114	1.2	1437	1.5	2353	1.3
19	M	0325	1.5	1235	1.1	2116	1.8		
20	TU	0109	1.2	0928	1.8	1340	1.0	1953	1.7
21	W	0207	1.1	0756	1.8	1431	0.9	2022	1.7
22	TH	0254	1.0	0826	1.8	1515	0.7	2052	1.8
23	F	0337	0.9	0845	1.9	1556	0.6	2113	1.9
24	SA ○	0416	0.8	0850	2.0	1633	0.5	2127	2.0
25	SU	0451	0.7	0924	2.1	1706	0.5	2155	2.1
26	M	0522	0.7	1001	2.2	1735	0.5	2229	2.1
27	TU	0550	0.7	1037	2.1	1802	0.6	2303	2.0
28	W	0618	0.7	1108	2.0	1831	0.6	2332	1.9
29	TH	0649	0.7	1039	1.9	1904	0.7	2235	1.8

MARCH

Date	Day	Time	m	Time	m	Time	m	Time	m
1	F	0724	0.8	1033	1.9	1941	0.8	2244	1.8
2	SA	0804	0.9	1102	1.8	2024	1.0	2320	1.8
3	SU ☾	0850	1.0	1144	1.7	2115	1.1		
4	M	0006	1.7	0951	1.1	1235	1.6	2227	1.3
5	TU	0107	1.6	1112	1.2	1403	1.5	2352	1.3
6	W	0615	1.7	1239	1.1	2056	1.7		
7	TH	0117	1.2	0649	1.8	1352	0.8	1950	1.8
8	F	0221	0.9	0739	2.0	1447	0.5	2024	2.0
9	SA	0312	0.7	0826	2.2	1534	0.3	2101	2.2
10	SU ●	0358	0.5	0909	2.4	1618	0.1	2138	2.3
11	M	0440	0.3	0949	2.5	1659	0.0	2215	2.4
12	TU	0522	0.3	1028	2.5	1740	0.1	2251	2.3
13	W	0603	0.3	1105	2.4	1821	0.2	2326	2.2
14	TH	0644	0.5	1140	2.2	1903	0.5	2355	2.0
15	F	0728	0.7	1210	2.0	1947	0.8	2358	1.8
16	SA	0816	0.9	1216	1.8	2038	1.1		
17	SU ☽	0005	1.7	0916	1.1	1239	1.6	2156	1.3
18	M	0046	1.6	1048	1.2	1930	1.8	2342	1.4
19	TU	0739	1.7	1214	1.2	2103	1.9		
20	W	0055	1.3	0655	1.7	1316	1.0	1934	1.7
21	TH	0147	1.2	0727	1.7	1406	0.9	1959	1.8
22	F	0232	1.0	0605	1.7	1450	0.7	2024	1.8
23	SA	0313	0.9	0706	1.8	1530	0.6	2035	1.9
24	SU	0351	0.8	0809	2.0	1606	0.6	2047	2.1
25	M ○	0424	0.7	0853	2.1	1638	0.5	2120	2.2
26	TU	0453	0.6	0934	2.2	1705	0.6	2155	2.2
27	W	0521	0.6	1010	2.2	1732	0.6	2229	2.1
28	TH	0549	0.6	1042	2.1	1801	0.7	2255	2.0
29	F	0619	0.7	1058	1.9	1833	0.8	2212	1.9
30	SA	0653	0.7	1007	1.9	1909	0.9	2216	1.9
31	SU	0731	0.8	1037	1.8	1951	1.0	[illegible]	[illegible]

APRIL

Date	Day	Time	m	Time	m	Time	m	Time	m
1	M	0815	1.0	1121	1.7	2041	1.2	2341	1.8
2	TU ☾	0913	1.1	1216	1.6	2157	1.3		
3	W	0045	1.7	1047	1.1	1935	1.8	2342	1.3
4	TH	0546	1.7	1220	1.0	2006	1.8		
5	F	0102	1.2	0626	1.8	1328	0.8	1927	1.9
6	SA	0201	0.9	0717	2.0	1422	0.5	2000	2.1
7	SU	0249	0.7	0804	2.2	1509	0.3	2037	2.2
8	M ●	0334	0.5	0846	2.3	1553	0.2	2113	2.3
9	TU	0417	0.3	0927	2.4	1634	0.1	2149	2.4
10	W	0457	0.3	1006	2.4	1715	0.2	2225	2.4
11	TH	0538	0.3	1044	2.3	1756	0.4	2258	2.2
12	F	0620	0.5	1121	2.1	1839	0.7	2325	2.0
13	SA	0704	0.7	1155	1.9	1925	1.0	2310	1.9
14	SU	0752	0.9	1147	1.7	2020	1.2	2332	1.8
15	M ☽	0851	1.1	1209	1.6	2140	1.4		
16	TU	0010	1.6	1016	1.2	1917	1.9	2312	1.4
17	W	0543	1.7	1136	1.1	2035	1.9		
18	TH	0018	1.3	0613	1.6	1238	1.1	1901	1.8
19	F	0112	1.2	0644	1.6	1330	1.0	1924	1.8
20	SA	0159	1.1	0542	1.7	1415	0.9	1939	1.8
21	SU	0240	1.0	0635	1.8	1456	0.8	1935	2.0
22	M	0318	0.8	0734	1.9	1532	0.7	2005	2.1
23	TU ○	0351	0.7	0822	2.0	1604	0.7	2043	2.2
24	W	0422	0.7	0904	2.1	1634	0.7	2119	2.2
25	TH	0451	0.6	0942	2.1	1703	0.7	2152	2.2
26	F	0522	0.6	1016	2.1	1736	0.8	2218	2.1
27	SA	0555	0.7	1045	2.0	1811	0.9	2223	2.0
28	SU	0631	0.7	1003	1.9	1850	1.0	2204	2.0
29	M	0711	0.8	1029	1.8	1935	1.2	2244	1.9
30	TU	0800	0.9	1117	1.7	2033	1.3	2339	1.8

MAY

Date	Day	Time	m	Time	m	Time	m	Time	m
1	W ☽	0905	1.0	1231	1.6	2200	1.3		
2	TH	0238	1.7	1034	1.0	1926	1.9	2326	1.3
3	F	0354	1.7	1152	0.9	2026	1.9		
4	SA	0034	1.1	0555	1.8	1256	0.8	1858	1.9
5	SU	0131	0.9	0651	2.0	1350	0.6	1933	2.1
6	M	0221	0.7	0739	2.1	1439	0.4	2011	2.2
7	TU	0307	0.5	0824	2.2	1525	0.4	2048	2.3
8	W ●	0352	0.4	0905	2.3	1609	0.4	2124	2.3
9	TH	0434	0.4	0946	2.3	1652	0.5	2200	2.3
10	F	0516	0.5	1025	2.2	1735	0.7	2234	2.2
11	SA	0600	0.6	1105	2.1	1821	0.9	2302	2.1
12	SU	0646	0.7	1147	1.9	1910	1.1	2246	1.9
13	M	0735	0.9	1247	1.7	2006	1.3	2311	1.8
14	TU	0829	1.0	1150	1.6	2112	1.4	2348	1.7
15	W ☾	0931	1.1	1237	1.5	2225	1.4		
16	TH	0035	1.6	1043	1.1	1952	2.0	2331	1.4
17	F	0140	1.6	1149	1.1	2052	1.9		
18	SA	0028	1.3	0600	1.6	1245	1.1	1857	1.8
19	SU	0117	1.2	0528	1.7	1333	1.0	1849	1.9
20	M	0200	1.1	0613	1.7	1414	1.0	1858	2.0
21	TU	0238	1.0	0704	1.8	1451	0.9	1926	2.1
22	W	0314	0.9	0751	1.9	1527	0.8	2000	2.2
23	TH ○	0348	0.8	0834	2.0	1602	0.8	2036	2.2
24	F	0424	0.7	0916	2.1	1639	0.8	2113	2.2
25	SA	0501	0.7	0957	2.1	1717	0.9	2151	2.2
26	SU	0539	0.7	1038	2.0	1759	1.0	2227	2.1
27	M	0621	0.7	1123	1.9	1844	1.1	2258	2.0
28	TU	0707	0.8	1216	1.8	1937	1.2	2320	1.9
29	W	0801	0.8	1319	1.8	2039	1.2		
30	TH ☽	0102	1.9	0904	0.9	1824	2.0	2149	1.2
31	F	0210	1.8	1012	0.9	1918	2.0	2258	1.2

JUNE

Date	Day	Time	m	Time	m	Time	m	Time	m
1	SA	0310	1.8	1120	0.9	2014	2.0		
2	SU	0001	1.1	0413	1.8	1222	0.8	1836	1.9
3	M	0059	1.0	0631	1.9	1319	0.7	1912	2.0
4	TU	0153	0.8	0721	2.0	1411	0.7	1949	2.1
5	W	0242	0.7	0806	2.1	1501	0.7	2027	2.2
6	TH ●	0330	0.6	0849	2.1	1549	0.7	2103	2.2
7	F	0416	0.6	0930	2.1	1635	0.8	2139	2.2
8	SA	0500	0.6	1012	2.1	1721	0.9	2215	2.2
9	SU	0545	0.6	1052	2.0	1808	1.0	2250	2.1
10	M	0630	0.7	1135	1.9	1855	1.1	2318	2.0
11	TU	0715	0.8	1224	1.8	1943	1.2	2259	1.9
12	W	0800	0.9	1338	1.7	2032	1.3	2328	1.8
13	TH	0844	1.0	1208	1.6	2121	1.3		
14	F ☾	0007	1.7	0931	1.1	1252	1.6	2215	1.3
15	SA	0054	1.7	1024	1.1	1937	1.9	2314	1.3
16	SU	0152	1.6	1124	1.2	2035	1.9		
17	M	0013	1.3	0312	1.6	1225	1.2	1830	1.8
18	TU	0104	1.2	0435	1.7	1318	1.1	1838	1.9
19	W	0151	1.1	0539	1.7	1406	1.1	1819	2.0
20	TH	0235	1.0	0723	1.8	1451	1.0	1858	2.1
21	F	0319	0.8	0814	1.9	1537	0.9	1948	2.2
22	SA ○	0403	0.7	0904	2.0	1622	0.9	2052	2.2
23	SU	0446	0.6	0953	2.1	1706	0.9	2150	2.2
24	M	0530	0.6	1038	2.1	1753	0.9	2240	2.2
25	TU	0615	0.6	1124	2.1	1840	0.9	2327	2.2
26	W	0702	0.6	1209	2.0	1931	1.0		
27	TH	0011	2.1	0752	0.7	1255	1.9	2025	1.0
28	F ☽	0056	2.0	0845	0.7	1342	1.8	2123	1.1
29	SA	0141	1.9	0943	0.8	1432	1.8	2225	1.1
30	SU	0230	1.9	1047	0.9	1949	2.0	2330	1.1

SUNRISE AND SUNSET TIMES

POOLE
At 50°42'N 1°59' W

		Sunrise	Sunset
UT			
Jan	01	0810	1614
	15	0803	1632
Feb	01	0744	1700
	15	0720	1725
Mar	01	0652	1749
	15	0622	1813
BST (UT+1)			
Apr	01	0644	1941
	15	0614	2003
May	01	0542	2029
	15	0519	2050
Jun	01	0500	2112
	15	0455	2122
Jul	01	0459	2124
	15	0512	2115
Aug	01	0535	2053
	15	0556	2028
Sep	01	0622	1953
	15	0643	1922
Oct	01	0708	1846
	15	0731	1816
UT			
Nov	01	0659	1643
	15	0723	1621
Dec	01	0748	1606
	15	0803	1603

JULY

Date	Day	Time	m	Time	m	Time	m	Time	m
1	M	0325	1.8	1151	0.9	1832	1.9		
2	TU	0031	1.0	0625	1.8	1253	1.0	1902	2.0
3	W	0130	1.0	0715	1.9	1351	0.9	1939	2.0
4	TH	0225	0.8	0801	1.9	1446	0.9	2016	2.1
5	F ●	0316	0.7	0844	2.0	1537	0.9	2052	2.1
6	SA	0405	0.7	0924	2.0	1626	0.9	2125	2.2
7	SU	0449	0.6	1002	2.1	1711	0.9	2159	2.2
8	M	0532	0.6	1037	2.1	1754	0.9	2234	2.2
9	TU	0613	0.6	1113	2.0	1835	1.0	2309	2.1
10	W	0651	0.7	1151	2.0	1913	1.1	2337	2.0
11	TH	0726	0.8	1232	1.8	1950	1.1	2311	1.9
12	F	0802	0.9	1144	1.7	2028	1.2	2337	1.8
13	SA ☾	0842	1.0	1209	1.7	2112	1.2		
14	SU	0013	1.7	0928	1.1	1249	1.7	2204	1.3
15	M	0058	1.7	1022	1.2	1346	1.7	2302	1.3
16	TU	0156	1.6	1122	1.2	1516	1.7		
17	W	0003	1.2	0321	1.6	1225	1.2	1639	1.8
18	TH	0105	1.2	0451	1.7	1327	1.2	1732	1.9
19	F	0204	1.0	0606	1.7	1426	1.1	1826	2.0
20	SA	0257	0.8	0818	1.9	1519	1.0	1951	2.1
21	SU ○	0347	0.7	0906	2.0	1609	0.9	2104	2.3
22	M	0433	0.5	0950	2.1	1656	0.8	2154	2.4
23	TU	0518	0.4	1032	2.2	1741	0.7	2238	2.4
24	W	0602	0.4	1112	2.2	1826	0.7	2319	2.4
25	TH	0646	0.4	1152	2.2	1911	0.8		
26	F	0000	2.3	0730	0.5	1231	2.1	1958	0.9
27	SA	0038	2.2	0818	0.6	1309	1.9	2051	1.0
28	SU ☽	0115	2.0	0911	0.8	1346	1.8	2152	1.1
29	M	0155	1.8	1014	1.0	1430	1.8	2302	1.2
30	TU	0249	1.7	1127	1.1	1535	1.7		
31	W	0013	1.1	0639	1.8	1239	1.2	2108	2.0

AUGUST

Date	Day	Time	m	Time	m	Time	m	Time	m
1	TH	0119	1.1	0725	1.8	1345	1.2	1940	2.0
2	F	0218	0.9	0808	1.8	1442	1.1	2014	2.0
3	SA	0309	0.8	0846	1.9	1531	1.0	2046	2.1
4	SU ●	0355	0.6	0919	2.0	1616	0.9	2110	2.2
5	M	0436	0.6	0947	2.1	1656	0.9	2137	2.2
6	TU	0514	0.5	1013	2.1	1734	0.9	2210	2.3
7	W	0550	0.6	1043	2.1	1808	0.9	2245	2.2
8	TH	0621	0.6	1117	2.1	1838	0.9	2318	2.1
9	F	0650	0.7	1151	2.0	1909	1.0	2310	2.0
10	SA	0722	0.8	1129	.9	1945	.0	2304	.9
11	SU	0759	0.9	1127	.8	2026	.1	2328	.8
12	M ☾	0843	.1	1152	.8	2116	.2		
13	TU	0002	.7	0936	.2	1232	.8	2215	.3
14	W	0050	.7	1039	.3	1336	.7	2322	.3
15	TH	0213	.6	1149	.3	1604	.7		
16	F	0033	1.2	0945	1.8	1302	1.3	1839	1.9
17	SA	0143	1.0	0740	1.8	1411	1.2	1917	2.0
18	SU	0242	0.8	0819	1.9	1506	1.0	2012	2.2
19	M ○	0332	0.6	0859	2.1	1555	0.8	2059	2.4
20	TU	0417	0.3	0938	2.3	1639	0.6	2143	2.5
21	W	0459	0.2	1016	2.4	1721	0.5	2224	2.6
22	TH	0541	0.2	1053	2.4	1803	0.5	2303	2.6
23	F	0622	0.3	1130	2.3	1845	0.6	2341	2.4
24	SA	0704	0.4	1206	2.2	1930	0.8		
25	SU	0018	2.2	0748	0.7	1238	2.0	2019	1.0
26	M ☽	0052	2.0	0839	1.0	1303	1.9	2121	1.1
27	TU	0128	1.8	0946	1.2	1343	1.7	2242	1.2
28	W	0236	1.6	1117	1.3	1937	2.0		
29	TH	0004	1.2	0839	1.9	1238	1.3	2043	1.9
30	F	0112	1.1	1008	2.0	1341	1.2	1927	1.9
31	SA	0206	0.9	0800	1.9	1432	1.1	1959	2.0

SEPTEMBER

Date	Day	Time	m	Time	m	Time	m	Time	m
1	SU	0253	0.8	0832	1.9	1516	1.0	2026	2.0
2	M	0336	0.6	0859	2.0	1557	0.9	2038	2.1
3	TU ●	0415	0.5	0917	2.1	1634	0.8	2104	2.3
4	W	0450	0.5	0938	2.2	1708	0.8	2141	2.3
5	TH	0522	0.6	1009	2.2	1737	0.8	2218	2.3
6	F	0549	0.6	1043	2.2	1804	0.8	2252	2.2
7	SA	0615	0.7	1114	2.1	1832	0.9	2312	2.0
8	SU	0645	0.8	1110	1.9	1905	0.9	2227	1.9
9	M	0720	1.0	1038	1.9	1943	1.0	2241	1.9
10	TU	0759	1.1	1100	1.9	2028	1.2	2317	1.8
11	W ☾	0848	1.3	1140	1.8	2128	1.3		
12	TH	0003	1.7	0957	1.4	1233	1.8	2248	1.3
13	F	0115	1.5	1123	1.4	1806	1.8		
14	SA	0012	1.2	0852	1.8	1250	1.3	1829	1.9
15	SU	0126	1.0	0729	1.9	1357	1.1	1910	2.0
16	M	0222	0.7	0801	2.0	1448	0.9	1958	2.2
17	TU	0309	0.5	0839	2.2	1533	0.7	2043	2.4
18	W ○	0353	0.2	0915	2.4	1616	0.5	2124	2.6
19	TH	0435	0.1	0953	2.5	1657	0.4	2204	2.6
20	F	0515	0.2	1030	2.5	1738	0.4	2244	2.6
21	SA	0556	0.3	1106	2.4	1819	0.5	2322	2.4
22	SU	0637	0.5	1140	2.2	1902	0.7		
23	M	0000	2.2	0722	0.8	1206	2.0	1951	1.0
24	TU ☽	0036	1.9	0814	1.1	1211	1.9	2054	1.2
25	W	0131	1.7	0930	1.4	1250	1.7	2227	1.2
26	TH	0701	2.0	1112	1.4	1909	1.9	2348	1.2
27	F	0837	2.0	1225	1.4	1820	1.9		
28	SA	0049	1.1	0659	1.9	1320	1.3	1854	1.9
29	SU	0140	0.9	0730	1.9	1408	1.1	1926	1.9
30	M	0226	0.8	0800	1.9	1450	1.0	1941	2.0

OCTOBER

Date	Day	Time	m	Time	m	Time	m	Time	m
1	TU	0308	0.7	0820	2.0	1530	0.9	1945	2.1
2	W ●	0346	0.6	0827	2.1	1606	0.8	2029	2.2
3	TH	0421	0.6	0856	2.2	1638	0.8	2110	2.3
4	F	0450	0.7	0933	2.3	1705	0.8	2149	2.3
5	SA	0516	0.7	1008	2.3	1731	0.8	2224	2.2
6	SU	0543	0.8	1036	2.2	1800	0.8	2249	2.0
7	M	0613	0.9	1035	2.0	1832	0.9	2151	1.9
8	TU	0647	1.0	0958	2.0	1908	1.0	2210	1.9
9	W	0726	1.2	1027	1.9	1951	1.1	2249	1.8
10	TH ☾	0813	1.3	1111	1.9	2047	1.2	2339	1.6
11	F	0922	1.5	1207	1.8	2221	1.2		
12	SA	0707	1.9	1111	1.5	1739	1.8	2351	1.1
13	SU	0805	1.9	1234	1.3	1806	1.9		
14	M	0059	0.9	0701	2.0	1332	1.1	1849	2.0
15	TU	0153	0.7	0734	2.1	1422	0.8	1936	2.2
16	W	0241	0.4	0812	2.3	1507	0.6	2020	2.4
17	TH ○	0326	0.3	0849	2.4	1550	0.4	2102	2.5
18	F	0408	0.2	0927	2.5	1632	0.4	2143	2.6
19	SA	0449	0.3	1005	2.5	1713	0.4	2224	2.5
20	SU	0531	0.4	1041	2.4	1755	0.5	2304	2.3
21	M	0615	0.7	1114	2.2	1840	0.7	2345	2.1
22	TU	0702	1.0	1130	2.0	1930	0.9		
23	W	0034	1.9	0758	1.2	1129	1.9	2034	1.1
24	TH ☽	0541	2.0	0918	1.4	1208	1.8	2158	1.2
25	F	0652	2.0	1045	1.5	1318	1.7	2313	1.1
26	SA	0811	2.0	1151	1.4	1744	1.8		
27	SU	0013	1.1	0627	1.9	1246	1.3	1819	1.8
28	M	0105	1.0	0657	1.9	1335	1.2	1847	1.8
29	TU	0152	0.9	0722	1.9	1419	1.0	1823	1.9
30	W	0234	0.8	0723	2.0	1458	0.9	1911	2.0
31	TH	0313	0.8	0739	2.1	1534	0.8	1958	2.1

NOVEMBER

Date	Day	Time	m	Time	m	Time	m	Time	m
1	F ●	0347	0.8	0816	2.2	1605	0.8	2040	2.2
2	SA	0417	0.8	0854	2.3	1634	0.8	2120	2.2
3	SU	0446	0.8	0928	2.3	1703	0.8	2157	2.1
4	M	0517	0.9	0955	2.2	1735	0.8	2227	2.0
5	TU	0551	1.0	1007	2.1	1810	0.8	2153	1.9
6	W	0628	1.1	0946	2.0	1849	0.9	2158	1.8
7	TH	0711	1.2	1016	2.0	1935	1.0	2240	1.7
8	F	0803	1.3	1104	1.9	2034	1.1	2338	1.6
9	SA ☾	0918	1.4	1211	1.8	2159	1.1		
10	SU	0658	2.0	1049	1.4	1701	1.8	2320	1.0
11	M	0800	1.9	1202	1.2	1739	1.9		
12	TU	0025	0.8	0635	2.0	1300	1.0	1826	2.0
13	W	0120	0.7	0709	2.1	1352	0.8	1914	2.1
14	TH	0210	0.5	0746	2.2	1439	0.6	1959	2.3
15	F ○	0257	0.4	0825	2.3	1525	0.5	2043	2.4
16	SA	0343	0.4	0903	2.4	1609	0.4	2125	2.4
17	SU	0427	0.5	0942	2.4	1652	0.5	2207	2.3
18	M	0512	0.6	1019	2.3	1737	0.5	2250	2.2
19	TU	0558	0.8	1055	2.2	1824	0.7	2334	2.0
20	W	0648	1.0	1119	2.1	1914	0.8		
21	TH	0028	1.8	0744	1.2	1106	1.9	2010	1.0
22	F	0530	2.1	0848	1.4	1140	1.8	2114	1.1
23	SA ☽	0627	2.0	0959	1.4	1225	1.7	2223	1.1
24	SU	0727	2.0	1106	1.4	1334	1.6	2328	1.1
25	M	0828	2.0	1205	1.3	1802	1.7		
26	TU	0024	1.1	0639	1.9	1257	1.2	1831	1.7
27	W	0113	1.0	0656	1.9	1342	1.1	1827	1.7
28	TH	0157	1.0	0653	2.0	1423	1.0	1851	1.8
29	F	0236	1.0	0704	2.0	1459	0.9	1931	1.9
30	SA	0312	0.9	0732	2.1	1534	0.8	2013	2.0

DECEMBER

Date	Day	Time	m	Time	m	Time	m	Time	m
1	SU ●	0347	0.9	0807	2.2	1608	0.8	2055	2.0
2	M	0422	0.9	0844	2.2	1644	0.7	2137	2.0
3	TU	0500	0.9	0922	2.2	1721	0.7	2220	2.0
4	W	0539	1.0	0959	2.1	1801	0.7	2305	1.9
5	TH	0622	1.1	1031	2.1	1844	0.8	2357	1.8
6	F	0709	1.1	1042	2.0	1932	0.8		
7	SA	0057	1.7	0802	1.2	1121	1.9	2028	0.9
8	SU ☾	0555	2.0	0905	1.2	1337	1.8	2132	0.9
9	M	0647	2.0	1015	1.2	1441	1.8	2242	0.9
10	TU	0741	2.0	1125	1.2	1547	1.8	2348	0.8
11	W	0619	1.9	1228	1.0	1809	1.9		
12	TH	0048	0.8	0651	2.0	1324	0.9	1859	2.0
13	F	0143	0.7	0729	2.1	1416	0.7	1945	2.1
14	SA	0234	0.7	0808	2.2	1505	0.6	2030	2.1
15	SU ○	0324	0.7	0847	2.2	1553	0.5	2113	2.2
16	M	0412	0.7	0926	2.3	1639	0.5	2156	2.1
17	TU	0459	0.8	1005	2.3	1724	0.5	2238	2.1
18	W	0546	0.9	1041	2.2	1810	0.6	2320	2.0
19	TH	0634	1.0	1115	2.1	1856	0.7		
20	F	0003	1.9	0722	1.1	1134	2.0	1941	0.8
21	SA	0053	1.8	0809	1.2	1120	1.9	2026	0.9
22	SU ☽	0548	2.0	0857	1.3	1151	1.8	2112	1.0
23	M	0630	1.9	0948	1.3	1231	1.7	2204	1.1
24	TU	0712	1.9	1052	1.4	1322	1.6	2309	1.2
25	W	0806	1.9	1201	1.3	1437	1.5		
26	TH	0016	1.2	0917	1.9	1256	1.2	2157	1.7
27	F	0109	1.2	0648	1.8	1342	1.1	1857	1.7
28	SA	0155	1.1	0644	1.9	1425	1.0	1920	1.7
29	SU	0239	1.1	0638	2.0	1506	0.9	1959	1.8
30	M ●	0323	1.0	0722	2.1	1548	0.8	2047	1.9
31	TU	0406	0.9	0818	2.1	1630	0.7	2134	2.0

SOUTHAMPTON
LAT 50°54′N
LONG 1°24′W

TIMES AND HEIGHTS OF HIGH AND LOW WATER (Heights in Metres)

TIME ZONE UT
For Summer Time (area enclosed in shaded box) add 1 hour

High Waters - important note.
Double High Waters occur at Southampton.
The predictions are for the first High Water.

2024

JANUARY

Date	Day	Time	m	Time	m	Time	m	Time	m
1	M	0131	4.1	0738	1.6	1338	4.0	1952	1.4
2	TU	0208	4.0	0811	1.7	1415	3.9	2026	1.6
3	W	0249	4.0	0850	1.9	1456	3.7	2110	1.7
4	TH ☾	0331	3.9	0939	2.0	1544	3.6	2205	1.9
5	F	0420	3.8	1040	2.1	1634	3.5	2310	2.0
6	SA	0515	3.7	1146	2.0	1735	3.5		
7	SU	0015	2.0	0616	3.7	1249	1.9	1846	3.6
8	M	0116	1.8	0726	3.9	1348	1.7	2000	3.8
9	TU	0213	1.6	0830	4.1	1443	1.4	2104	4.1
10	W	0306	1.4	0922	4.3	1534	1.1	2154	4.3
11	TH ●	0357	1.2	1013	4.5	1623	0.8	2240	4.4
12	F	0445	1.0	1058	4.6	1710	0.6	2351	4.6
13	SA	0532	0.8	1145	4.6	1756	0.5		
14	SU	0034	4.6	0618	0.8	1249	4.7	1841	0.5
15	M	0120	4.6	0703	0.8	1336	4.6	1926	0.6
16	TU	0211	4.5	0749	0.9	1427	4.4	2012	0.8
17	W	0311	4.4	0838	1.2	1526	4.3	2101	1.1
18	TH ☽	0333	4.2	0932	1.4	1552	4.0	2159	1.4
19	F	0434	4.1	1036	1.7	1653	3.8	2307	1.7
20	SA	0535	4.0	1154	1.8	1803	3.7		
21	SU	0024	1.8	0635	3.9	1310	1.8	1909	3.7
22	M	0134	1.8	0740	3.9	1411	1.6	2012	3.8
23	TU	0232	1.7	0840	4.0	1502	1.4	2219	4.0
24	W	0322	1.5	0929	4.1	1549	1.2	2304	4.2
25	TH ○	0409	1.3	1016	4.2	1632	1.0	2246	4.1
26	F	0451	1.2	1057	4.2	1713	0.9	2323	4.2
27	SA	0533	1.1	1136	4.2	1752	0.9		
28	SU	0001	4.2	0610	1.1	1210	4.2	1827	0.9
29	M	0117	4.3	0642	1.2	1242	4.2	1855	1.0
30	TU	0143	4.3	0708	1.3	1313	4.1	1919	1.1
31	W	0135	4.1	0733	1.3	1345	4.0	1946	1.2

FEBRUARY

Date	Day	Time	m	Time	m	Time	m	Time	m
1	TH	0212	4.1	0805	1.4	1423	4.0	2022	1.3
2	F ☾	0252	4.0	0846	1.5	1507	3.9	2106	1.5
3	SA	0334	3.9	0936	1.7	1554	3.7	2201	1.8
4	SU	0423	3.7	1042	1.9	1651	3.5	2315	2.0
5	M	0618	3.7	1201	2.0	1754	3.4		
6	TU	0038	2.0	0631	3.6	1322	1.8	1923	3.6
7	W	0157	1.8	0805	3.9	1432	1.5	2052	4.0
8	TH	0259	1.5	0910	4.2	1527	1.1	2146	4.3
9	F ●	0351	1.1	0959	4.4	1615	0.6	2227	4.5
10	SA	0437	0.7	1047	4.6	1700	0.3	2335	4.7
11	SU	0521	0.5	1147	4.8	1742	0.2		
12	M	0016	4.7	0603	0.4	1230	4.8	1824	0.1
13	TU	0100	4.7	0645	0.4	1315	4.7	1905	0.3
14	W	0147	4.6	0726	0.6	1403	4.5	1947	0.6
15	TH	0243	4.5	0809	0.9	1500	4.3	2031	0.9
16	F ☽	0302	4.2	0857	1.2	1518	4.0	2122	1.4
17	SA	0355	3.9	0955	1.6	1621	3.7	2228	1.8
18	SU	0459	3.8	1117	1.9	1734	3.6		
19	M	0003	2.1	0607	3.6	1257	2.0	1848	3.5
20	TU	0129	2.0	0716	3.6	1402	1.8	1955	3.6
21	W	0226	1.9	0947	3.9	1451	1.5	2057	3.8
22	TH	0311	1.6	1009	4.0	1533	1.2	2143	4.0
23	F	0354	1.3	1035	4.1	1613	0.9	2313	4.2
24	SA ○	0433	1.0	1037	4.1	1652	0.8	2302	4.2
25	SU	0511	0.9	1111	4.2	1729	0.7	2338	4.2
26	M	0547	0.9	1144	4.2	1802	0.8		
27	TU	0006	4.2	0615	1.0	1218	4.2	1827	0.9
28	W	0105	4.3	0636	1.0	1311	4.3	1847	0.9
29	TH	0130	4.3	0659	1.0	1341	4.3	1913	1.0

MARCH

Date	Day	Time	m	Time	m	Time	m	Time	m
1	F	0202	4.3	0731	1.0	1354	4.2	1947	1.1
2	SA	0216	4.2	0809	1.1	1436	4.0	2028	1.3
3	SU ☾	0257	4.0	0854	1.4	1521	3.8	2117	1.7
4	M	0346	3.7	0951	1.8	1653	3.7	2224	2.0
5	TU	0439	3.5	1123	2.0	1716	3.3		
6	W	0021	2.2	0549	3.4	1319	1.9	1907	3.5
7	TH	0202	1.9	0751	3.8	1427	1.4	2038	4.0
8	F	0253	1.4	0856	4.1	1515	0.9	2127	4.3
9	SA	0338	0.9	0944	4.4	1559	0.5	2213	4.6
10	SU ●	0421	0.5	1026	4.6	1641	0.2	2314	4.8
11	M	0502	0.2	1126	4.8	1722	0.0	2354	4.8
12	TU	0542	0.1	1208	4.8	1801	0.0		
13	W	0036	4.8	0622	0.2	1252	4.7	1841	0.2
14	TH	0122	4.6	0701	0.4	1340	4.5	1920	0.5
15	F	0215	4.5	0742	0.8	1440	4.3	2002	1.0
16	SA	0222	4.1	0826	1.2	1448	3.9	2051	1.5
17	SU ☽	0312	3.8	0920	1.6	1546	3.6	2158	2.0
18	M	0417	3.5	1045	2.0	1710	3.5	2344	2.2
19	TU	0534	3.4	1228	2.0	1819	3.4		
20	W	0107	2.1	0642	3.4	1335	1.9	1929	3.5
21	TH	0204	1.9	0745	3.5	1424	1.6	2026	3.7
22	F	0248	1.6	0845	3.7	1506	1.3	2114	3.9
23	SA	0328	1.2	1011	4.0	1546	1.0	2249	4.2
24	SU	0407	1.0	1010	4.1	1624	0.8	2233	4.2
25	M ○	0443	0.8	1044	4.2	1659	0.7	2309	4.3
26	TU	0516	0.8	1116	4.2	1731	0.8	2336	4.3
27	W	0543	0.9	1149	4.2	1755	0.9		
28	TH	0031	4.4	0604	0.9	1242	4.3	1816	0.9
29	F	0058	4.4	0630	0.8	1314	4.4	1845	0.9
30	SA	0111	4.3	0703	0.9	1351	4.3	1920	1.0
31	SU	0145	4.2	0741	1.0	1410	4.1	2001	1.3

APRIL

Date	Day	Time	m	Time	m	Time	m	Time	m
1	M	0226	4.0	0825	1.3	1457	3.9	2049	1.7
2	TU ☾	0313	3.7	0920	1.7	1636	3.7	2159	2.1
3	W	0406	3.4	1110	2.0	1657	3.4		
4	TH	0035	2.1	0534	3.4	1307	1.8	1855	3.7
5	F	0146	1.8	0727	3.8	1405	1.3	2015	4.1
6	SA	0233	1.3	0832	4.1	1452	0.9	2105	4.4
7	SU	0316	0.8	0916	4.4	1535	0.5	2145	4.6
8	M ●	0358	0.5	1003	4.6	1617	0.2	2251	4.8
9	TU	0438	0.2	1104	4.7	1657	0.1	2331	4.8
10	W	0518	0.2	1146	4.7	1736	0.2		
11	TH	0012	4.7	0557	0.3	1231	4.6	1816	0.4
12	F	0057	4.6	0637	0.5	1321	4.4	1856	0.7
13	SA	0148	4.4	0717	0.8	1333	4.1	1939	1.2
14	SU	0154	4.0	0801	1.2	1423	3.9	2029	1.6
15	M ☽	0236	3.7	0856	1.6	1525	3.7	2138	2.0
16	TU	0336	3.4	1015	1.9	1638	3.5	2306	2.2
17	W	0454	3.3	1138	2.0	1837	3.6		
18	TH	0021	2.2	0648	3.4	1247	1.9	1845	3.5
19	F	0124	2.0	0705	3.4	1343	1.7	1947	3.7
20	SA	0213	1.7	0807	3.6	1430	1.4	2038	3.9
21	SU	0256	1.4	0939	3.9	1512	1.1	2207	4.2
22	M	0334	1.1	0934	4.0	1549	1.0	2157	4.2
23	TU ○	0410	1.0	1014	4.1	1624	0.9	2234	4.3
24	W	0441	0.9	1048	4.2	1655	0.9	2304	4.3
25	TH	0509	0.9	1148	4.3	1723	0.9		
26	F	0001	4.4	0536	0.8	1218	4.4	1750	1.0
27	SA	0032	4.4	0606	0.8	1253	4.4	1823	1.0
28	SU	0043	4.3	0642	0.9	1333	4.3	1902	1.2
29	M	0124	4.2	0723	1.1	1421	4.2	1945	1.4
30	TU	0209	4.0	0810	1.4	1520	4.0	2039	1.8

MAY

Date	Day	Time	m	Time	m	Time	m	Time	m
1	W ☽	0256	3.7	0915	1.7	1641	3.8	2209	2.0
2	TH	0405	3.6	1100	1.8	1700	3.7	2353	2.0
3	F	0529	3.6	1226	1.6	1830	3.9		
4	SA	0107	1.7	0654	3.8	1329	1.3	1940	4.2
5	SU	0201	1.3	0800	4.1	1420	1.0	2035	4.4
6	M	0247	0.9	0851	4.3	1506	0.7	2116	4.6
7	TU	0331	0.6	0936	4.5	1549	0.5	2228	4.7
8	W ●	0413	0.5	1042	4.6	1631	0.5	2308	4.7
9	TH	0454	0.4	1128	4.5	1712	0.5	2351	4.6
10	F	0535	0.5	1217	4.4	1754	0.7		
11	SA	0036	4.5	0616	0.7	1232	4.2	1837	1.0
12	SU	0126	4.3	0659	1.0	1316	4.1	1923	1.3
13	M	0127	4.0	0745	1.3	1407	3.9	2014	1.6
14	TU	0218	3.8	0838	1.5	1504	3.8	2115	1.9
15	W ☾	0313	3.6	0942	1.8	1605	3.7	2223	2.1
16	TH	0416	3.4	1048	1.9	1701	3.6	2330	2.1
17	F	0603	3.5	1152	1.9	1800	3.6		
18	SA	0033	2.0	0707	3.5	1252	1.8	1859	3.7
19	SU	0129	1.8	0811	3.7	1345	1.6	1950	3.9
20	M	0215	1.6	0858	3.9	1429	1.4	2041	4.1
21	TU	0254	1.4	0859	3.9	1509	1.3	2123	4.2
22	W	0330	1.2	0942	4.1	1546	1.2	2159	4.3
23	TH ○	0404	1.0	1019	4.2	1621	1.1	2232	4.3
24	F	0438	0.9	1127	4.3	1656	1.1	2308	4.3
25	SA	0514	0.9	1201	4.4	1732	1.1	2348	4.4
26	SU	0552	0.9	1240	4.4	1812	1.1		
27	M	0028	4.3	0633	0.9	1324	4.3	1856	1.2
28	TU	0114	4.2	0719	1.1	1416	4.2	1946	1.4
29	W	0202	4.1	0812	1.3	1517	4.1	2045	1.6
30	TH ☽	0258	3.9	0917	1.4	1636	4.1	2157	1.7
31	F	0359	3.8	1030	1.5	1648	4.0	2311	1.7

JUNE

Date	Day	Time	m	Time	m	Time	m	Time	m
1	SA	0512	3.8	1141	1.5	1755	4.0		
2	SU	0020	1.6	0622	3.9	1246	1.4	1904	4.2
3	M	0123	1.4	0727	4.0	1344	1.2	1959	4.3
4	TU	0217	1.1	0821	4.2	1436	1.0	2051	4.4
5	W	0305	0.9	0910	4.2	1523	0.9	2136	4.4
6	TH ●	0350	0.8	1033	4.3	1609	0.9	2254	4.5
7	F	0436	0.8	1123	4.3	1655	0.9	2338	4.4
8	SA	0519	0.8	1131	4.2	1740	1.0		
9	SU	0023	4.3	0604	0.9	1218	4.2	1826	1.2
10	M	0027	4.1	0647	1.0	1302	4.1	1911	1.3
11	TU	0113	4.0	0731	1.2	1348	4.0	1956	1.5
12	W	0156	3.9	0816	1.4	1434	3.9	2044	1.7
13	TH	0242	3.7	0904	1.6	1522	3.9	2135	1.9
14	F ☾	0331	3.6	0956	1.7	1616	3.8	2229	2.0
15	SA	0422	3.5	1052	1.9	1707	3.8	2326	2.0
16	SU	0522	3.4	1149	1.9	1758	3.7		
17	M	0024	2.0	0626	3.5	1245	1.8	1900	3.8
18	TU	0117	1.8	0726	3.6	1337	1.7	1956	3.9
19	W	0205	1.6	0824	3.8	1425	1.6	2046	4.1
20	TH	0250	1.4	0908	4.0	1510	1.4	2126	4.2
21	F	0334	1.2	0952	4.1	1555	1.3	2212	4.3
22	SA ○	0417	1.0	1036	4.2	1639	1.2	2253	4.3
23	SU	0501	0.9	1151	4.4	1724	1.1	2336	4.4
24	M	0546	0.8	1231	4.4	1809	1.1		
25	TU	0018	4.4	0631	0.8	1315	4.4	1855	1.1
26	W	0103	4.3	0717	0.8	1404	4.4	1943	1.1
27	TH	0218	4.3	0805	1.0	1500	4.4	2034	1.3
28	F ☽	0314	4.2	0858	1.1	1608	4.3	2130	1.4
29	SA	0343	4.0	0957	1.3	1625	4.1	2233	1.5
30	SU	0444	3.9	1101	1.4	1726	4.1	2341	1.6

SUNRISE AND SUNSET TIMES

SOUTHAMPTON
At 50°54'N 1°24'W

UT		Sunrise	Sunset
Jan	01	0808	1610
	15	0802	1629
Feb	01	0742	1657
	15	0718	1722
Mar	01	0650	1747
	15	0619	1810
BST (UT+1)			
Apr	01	0641	1938
	15	0611	2001
May	01	0539	2027
	15	0516	2049
Jun	01	0457	2110
	15	0451	2121
Jul	01	0456	2123
	15	0509	2113
Aug	01	0532	2051
	15	0553	2026
Sep	01	0619	1951
	15	0641	1920
Oct	01	0706	1843
	15	0729	1813
UT			
Nov	01	0658	1640
	15	0722	1618
Dec	01	0746	1603
	15	0802	1600

JULY

Date	Day	Time	m	Time	m	Time	m	Time	m
1	M	0551	3.9	1208	1.5	1827	4.1		
2	TU	0050	1.6	0657	3.9	1314	1.5	1930	4.1
3	W	0153	1.4	0757	3.9	1414	1.5	2028	4.2
4	TH	0248	1.3	0855	4.0	1509	1.4	2119	4.2
5	F ●	0338	1.1	1037	4.2	1559	1.3	2207	4.2
6	SA	0425	1.0	1130	4.3	1646	1.2	2249	4.2
7	SU	0510	0.9	1126	4.2	1731	1.1	2333	4.2
8	M	0553	0.9	1205	4.2	1814	1.1		
9	TU	0011	4.1	0634	0.9	1248	4.2	1855	1.2
10	W	0054	4.1	0712	1.1	1325	4.1	1933	1.4
11	TH	0129	4.0	0747	1.2	1403	4.1	2007	1.5
12	F	0206	3.9	0821	1.4	1438	4.0	2043	1.7
13	SA ☾	0247	3.8	0859	1.6	1517	3.9	2124	1.8
14	SU	0326	3.6	0945	1.8	1559	3.8	2216	1.9
15	M	0416	3.5	1042	1.9	1647	3.7	2316	2.0
16	TU	0506	3.4	1145	2.0	1742	3.6		
17	W	0018	1.9	0612	3.4	1247	2.0	1848	3.7
18	TH	0121	1.8	0731	3.6	1349	1.8	2002	3.9
19	F	0221	1.6	0846	3.9	1447	1.6	2103	4.1
20	SA	0316	1.3	0941	4.1	1540	1.4	2157	4.3
21	SU ○	0406	1.0	1024	4.3	1629	1.1	2242	4.4
22	M	0453	0.7	1107	4.4	1715	0.9	2321	4.5
23	TU	0538	0.6	1216	4.6	1759	0.8		
24	W	0026	4.6	0621	0.5	1258	4.6	1843	0.7
25	TH	0110	4.6	0704	0.5	1344	4.6	1926	0.8
26	F	0158	4.5	0747	0.6	1436	4.5	2012	1.0
27	SA	0250	4.4	0833	0.9	1540	4.4	2100	1.2
28	SU ☽	0318	4.1	0924	1.2	1555	4.2	2158	1.5
29	M	0414	3.9	1025	1.5	1654	4.0	2308	1.7
30	TU	0522	3.8	1138	1.8	1802	3.9		
31	W	0029	1.8	0635	3.7	1258	1.9	1909	3.9

AUGUST

Date	Day	Time	m	Time	m	Time	m	Time	m
1	TH	0144	1.7	0745	3.7	1408	1.8	2013	3.9
2	F	0242	1.5	0952	4.0	1504	1.6	2110	4.0
3	SA	0331	1.3	1037	4.2	1551	1.4	2154	4.1
4	SU ●	0415	1.0	1116	4.3	1635	1.2	2311	4.3
5	M	0457	0.8	1154	4.3	1717	1.0	2316	4.2
6	TU	0536	0.8	1232	4.3	1756	1.0	2351	4.1
7	W	0614	0.8	1305	4.3	1832	1.1		
8	TH	0026	4.1	0647	1.0	1334	4.3	1903	1.2
9	F	0059	4.1	0714	1.1	1401	4.3	1927	1.4
10	SA	0131	4.0	0737	1.3	1355	4.1	1953	1.4
11	SU	0207	4.0	0806	1.4	1430	4.1	2028	1.5
12	M ☾	0248	3.9	0845	1.6	1513	3.9	2113	1.7
13	TU	0332	3.7	0935	1.9	1559	3.8	2214	2.0
14	W	0419	3.5	1046	2.1	1648	3.6	2333	2.1
15	TH	0518	3.4	1211	2.2	1749	3.5		
16	F	0053	2.0	0634	3.4	1332	2.1	1927	3.7
17	SA	0209	1.7	0839	3.9	1440	1.7	2052	4.1
18	SU	0307	1.3	0927	4.2	1532	1.3	2138	4.3
19	M ○	0355	0.9	1009	4.4	1617	0.9	2222	4.5
20	TU	0439	0.5	1052	4.6	1700	0.6	2305	4.7
21	W	0521	0.3	1154	4.8	1742	0.5		
22	TH	0005	4.8	0602	0.2	1235	4.8	1823	0.4
23	F	0048	4.8	0642	0.3	1320	4.7	1904	0.6
24	SA	0134	4.6	0723	0.5	1409	4.6	1945	0.8
25	SU	0226	4.4	0805	0.9	1516	4.4	2030	1.2
26	M ☽	0249	4.1	0853	1.3	1521	4.1	2126	1.6
27	TU	0345	3.8	0955	1.8	1625	3.9	2243	1.9
28	W	0504	3.7	1125	2.1	1740	3.7		
29	TH	0023	2.0	0617	3.6	1255	2.1	1848	3.7
30	F	0135	1.9	0731	3.6	1401	2.0	1954	3.8
31	SA	0229	1.6	0836	3.8	1450	1.7	2200	4.0

SEPTEMBER

Date	Day	Time	m	Time	m	Time	m	Time	m
1	SU	0313	1.3	0927	4.1	1533	1.4	2218	4.2
2	M	0354	1.0	1102	4.3	1615	1.1	2248	4.3
3	TU ●	0433	0.8	1127	4.4	1654	1.0	2252	4.2
4	W	0511	0.7	1119	4.3	1731	0.9	2325	4.2
5	TH	0547	0.8	1153	4.3	1804	1.0		
6	F	0001	4.2	0617	1.0	1253	4.4	1829	1.2
7	SA	0055	4.3	0637	1.1	1317	4.4	1846	1.2
8	SU	0124	4.3	0657	1.2	1345	4.4	1913	1.3
9	M	0158	4.2	0727	1.3	1356	4.2	1947	1.4
10	TU	0214	4.1	0805	1.5	1433	4.0	2029	1.6
11	W ☾	0257	3.8	0850	1.8	1520	3.8	2121	1.9
12	TH	0426	3.7	0952	2.2	1609	3.6	2255	2.2
13	F	0444	3.4	1155	2.4	1712	3.4		
14	SA	0049	2.1	0612	3.4	1334	2.1	1911	3.7
15	SU	0201	1.7	0817	4.0	1429	1.7	2030	4.1
16	M	0251	1.2	0909	4.4	1515	1.2	2120	4.4
17	TU	0335	0.7	0950	4.6	1557	0.8	2159	4.6
18	W ○	0417	0.4	1027	4.8	1638	0.5	2242	4.8
19	TH	0458	0.2	1130	4.9	1718	0.3	2342	4.9
20	F	0537	0.2	1211	4.9	1758	0.4		
21	SA	0025	4.8	0617	0.3	1254	4.8	1838	0.5
22	SU	0111	4.7	0656	0.6	1343	4.6	1918	0.8
23	M	0203	4.5	0738	1.0	1356	4.3	2002	1.3
24	TU ☽	0220	4.1	0827	1.5	1445	4.0	2058	1.7
25	W	0320	3.8	0934	2.0	1558	3.7	2227	2.1
26	TH	0448	3.7	1115	2.3	1711	3.6		
27	F	0000	2.1	0554	3.5	1232	2.3	1900	3.6
28	SA	0106	2.0	0703	3.6	1334	2.1	1920	3.6
29	SU	0200	1.7	0805	3.8	1423	1.8	2021	3.8
30	M	0244	1.4	0856	4.0	1506	1.4	2105	4.0

OCTOBER

Date	Day	Time	m	Time	m	Time	m	Time	m
1	TU	0325	1.1	0939	4.2	1547	1.1	2223	4.2
2	W ●	0404	0.9	1014	4.3	1625	1.0	2224	4.3
3	TH	0441	0.9	1049	4.4	1700	1.0	2258	4.3
4	F	0515	0.9	1118	4.4	1731	1.0	2328	4.3
5	SA	0542	1.1	1148	4.4	1752	1.1		
6	SU	0025	4.4	0601	1.2	1242	4.5	1813	1.2
7	M	0054	4.4	0625	1.2	1312	4.4	1841	1.2
8	TU	0129	4.4	0658	1.3	1323	4.3	1917	1.3
9	W	0146	4.2	0736	1.5	1402	4.1	1958	1.6
10	TH ☾	0231	3.9	0821	1.9	1445	3.8	2049	1.9
11	F	0405	3.8	0923	2.3	1537	3.6	2237	2.2
12	SA	0424	3.5	1155	2.4	1655	3.5		
13	SU	0034	2.0	0602	3.6	1313	2.0	1847	3.8
14	M	0135	1.6	0744	4.1	1404	1.6	1959	4.1
15	TU	0224	1.2	0839	4.5	1448	1.2	2053	4.5
16	W	0308	0.8	0923	4.7	1531	0.8	2133	4.7
17	TH ○	0350	0.5	1001	4.8	1612	0.5	2237	4.9
18	F	0431	0.3	1104	5.0	1653	0.4	2319	4.9
19	SA	0511	0.4	1146	4.9	1732	0.4		
20	SU	0003	4.8	0551	0.5	1229	4.8	1813	0.6
21	M	0050	4.6	0632	0.8	1318	4.6	1855	0.9
22	TU	0149	4.4	0716	1.2	1331	4.2	1940	1.3
23	W	0201	4.1	0807	1.7	1417	3.9	2038	1.7
24	TH ☽	0303	3.8	0918	2.1	1524	3.7	2200	2.0
25	F	0419	3.7	1043	2.3	1635	3.5	2318	2.1
26	SA	0620	3.8	1152	2.2	1826	3.6		
27	SU	0021	2.0	0622	3.7	1254	2.1	1840	3.5
28	M	0118	1.8	0723	3.8	1347	1.8	1938	3.7
29	TU	0206	1.6	0815	4.0	1432	1.5	2033	3.9
30	W	0250	1.4	0859	4.2	1514	1.3	2156	4.2
31	TH	0330	1.2	1022	4.4	1552	1.1	2152	4.2

NOVEMBER

Date	Day	Time	m	Time	m	Time	m	Time	m
1	F ●	0407	1.1	1015	4.4	1626	1.1	2228	4.3
2	SA	0440	1.1	1047	4.4	1655	1.1	2304	4.3
3	SU	0507	1.2	1119	4.4	1720	1.1		
4	M	0002	4.4	0533	1.2	1216	4.5	1747	1.1
5	TU	0034	4.4	0603	1.3	1223	4.4	1821	1.2
6	W	0111	4.4	0639	1.4	1302	4.3	1859	1.3
7	TH	0156	4.3	0721	1.6	1343	4.1	1943	1.5
8	F	0249	4.1	0810	1.9	1430	3.9	2039	1.8
9	SA ☾	0358	4.0	0923	2.2	1527	3.7	2217	2.0
10	SU	0420	3.8	1113	2.2	1647	3.7	2349	1.9
11	M	0543	3.9	1230	1.9	1809	3.8		
12	TU	0055	1.6	0659	4.2	1328	1.6	1922	4.1
13	W	0149	1.3	0801	4.4	1417	1.2	2021	4.4
14	TH	0236	1.0	0852	4.7	1502	0.9	2105	4.5
15	F ○	0321	0.8	0933	4.8	1546	0.7	2216	4.7
16	SA	0405	0.7	1042	4.8	1628	0.6	2301	4.7
17	SU	0447	0.7	1125	4.8	1711	0.6	2349	4.6
18	M	0530	0.8	1211	4.7	1754	0.8		
19	TU	0041	4.5	0615	1.1	1300	4.5	1839	1.0
20	W	0058	4.3	0702	1.4	1311	4.2	1926	1.3
21	TH	0146	4.1	0754	1.7	1358	3.9	2019	1.6
22	F	0242	3.9	0853	1.9	1454	3.7	2122	1.8
23	SA ☽	0346	3.9	1000	2.1	1557	3.6	2229	2.0
24	SU	0438	3.8	1107	2.2	1657	3.5	2332	2.0
25	M	0538	3.8	1210	2.1	1844	3.7		
26	TU	0031	1.9	0633	3.8	1306	2.0	1858	3.6
27	W	0124	1.8	0730	4.0	1355	1.7	1951	3.8
28	TH	0211	1.6	0819	4.1	1437	1.5	2130	4.1
29	F	0252	1.5	0901	4.2	1515	1.4	2210	4.2
30	SA	0331	1.4	0944	4.3	1551	1.3	2204	4.2

DECEMBER

Date	Day	Time	m	Time	m	Time	m	Time	m
1	SU ●	0406	1.3	1020	4.4	1624	1.2	2324	4.4
2	M	0441	1.3	1055	4.4	1659	1.1	2352	4.4
3	TU	0515	1.3	1131	4.4	1734	1.1		
4	W	0024	4.4	0553	1.3	1211	4.4	1813	1.1
5	TH	0103	4.4	0634	1.4	1251	4.3	1855	1.2
6	F	0148	4.4	0719	1.5	1333	4.2	1942	1.3
7	SA	0240	4.3	0810	1.7	1427	4.1	2037	1.5
8	SU ☾	0341	4.2	0913	1.8	1524	3.9	2145	1.6
9	M	0408	4.0	1027	1.9	1627	3.9	2259	1.7
10	TU	0513	4.1	1141	1.8	1736	3.9		
11	W	0009	1.6	0621	4.2	1248	1.6	1844	4.0
12	TH	0112	1.4	0726	4.3	1347	1.4	1950	4.2
13	F	0207	1.3	0823	4.5	1438	1.1	2046	4.3
14	SA	0257	1.1	0908	4.5	1526	1.0	2208	4.5
15	SU ○	0346	1.0	0956	4.5	1613	0.8	2257	4.5
16	M	0433	1.0	1116	4.6	1659	0.8	2349	4.5
17	TU	0519	1.0	1201	4.5	1744	0.8		
18	W	0043	4.4	0605	1.1	1245	4.4	1828	0.9
19	TH	0046	4.3	0651	1.3	1330	4.3	1912	1.1
20	F	0128	4.2	0736	1.5	1338	4.0	1957	1.3
21	SA	0215	4.1	0822	1.7	1424	3.9	2043	1.5
22	SU ☽	0303	4.0	0911	1.9	1514	3.7	2134	1.8
23	M	0354	3.9	1006	2.0	1606	3.6	2230	1.9
24	TU	0441	3.8	1107	2.1	1700	3.5	2331	2.0
25	W	0539	3.8	1210	2.1	1803	3.5		
26	TH	0031	2.0	0633	3.8	1308	2.0	1906	3.6
27	F	0126	2.0	0736	3.9	1356	1.8	2005	3.8
28	SA	0214	1.8	0829	4.0	1440	1.6	2059	3.9
29	SU	0259	1.7	0919	4.2	1523	1.4	2146	4.1
30	M ●	0342	1.5	1001	4.3	1605	1.2	2225	4.2
31	TU	0425	1.3	1038	4.3	1647	1.0	2308	4.3

PORTSMOUTH
LAT 50°48′N
LONG 1°07′W

TIMES AND HEIGHTS OF HIGH AND LOW WATER (Heights in Metres)

TIME ZONE UT
For Summer Time (area enclosed in shaded box) add 1 hour

2024

JANUARY

	Time	m		Time	m
1 M	0239 0744 1437 1959	4.3 1.6 4.2 1.4	**16** TU	0257 0758 1501 2021	4.7 1.0 4.5 0.9
2 TU	0316 0819 1516 2036	4.3 1.7 4.0 1.6	**17** W	0353 0850 1600 2114	4.6 1.2 4.4 1.1
3 W	0354 0900 1600 2119	4.2 1.8 3.9 1.7	**18** TH ☽	0446 0949 1659 2217	4.5 1.5 4.2 1.4
4 TH ☾	0438 0950 1650 2213	4.1 1.9 3.8 1.8	**19** F	0540 1059 1801 2329	4.4 1.6 4.0 1.6
5 F	0529 1053 1749 2320	4.0 2.0 3.7 1.9	**20** SA	0638 1213 1905	4.2 1.7 3.9
6 SA	0628 1204 1858	3.9 2.0 3.7	**21** SU	0038 0742 1319 2014	1.7 4.1 1.7 3.9
7 SU	0029 0734 1305 2013	1.9 4.0 1.8 3.8	**22** M	0142 0845 1418 2124	1.8 4.1 1.6 4.0
8 M	0128 0842 1400 2119	1.8 4.1 1.6 4.0	**23** TU	0240 0942 1511 2224	1.7 4.2 1.4 4.1
9 TU	0222 0937 1452 2210	1.6 4.3 1.4 4.2	**24** W	0332 1028 1558 2307	1.5 4.3 1.2 4.3
10 W	0314 1022 1543 2254	1.4 4.5 1.1 4.4	**25** TH ○	0419 1109 1642 2344	1.4 4.4 1.1 4.4
11 TH ●	0405 1105 1631 2337	1.2 4.6 0.9 4.6	**26** F	0501 1148 1722	1.2 4.4 1.0
12 F	0453 1146 1718	1.0 4.7 0.7	**27** SA	0021 0541 1226 1759	4.4 1.2 4.4 0.9
13 SA	0021 0540 1229 1804	4.7 0.9 4.7 0.6	**28** SU	0059 0616 1304 1832	4.5 1.2 4.4 1.0
14 SU	0108 0626 1314 1848	4.8 0.9 4.7 0.6	**29** M	0136 0647 1339 1901	4.4 1.2 4.3 1.1
15 M	0200 0711 1405 1934	4.8 0.9 4.6 0.7	**30** TU	0210 0714 1410 1928	4.4 1.3 4.2 1.1
			31 W	0240 0742 1441 [illegible]	4.3 1.3 4.2 [illegible]

FEBRUARY

	Time	m		Time	m
1 TH	0312 0816 1518 2033	4.3 1.4 4.1 1.3	**16** F ☽	0413 0912 1629 2137	4.5 1.3 4.2 1.4
2 F ☾	0350 0856 1601 2115	4.2 1.5 3.9 1.5	**17** SA	0503 1018 1730 2254	4.2 1.6 4.0 1.8
3 SA	0436 0945 1654 2209	4.0 1.7 3.8 1.7	**18** SU	0602 1143 1840	4.0 1.8 3.7
4 SU	0531 1050 1800 2322	3.9 1.9 3.6 1.9	**19** M	0016 0714 1300 1959	2.0 3.8 1.9 3.7
5 M	0639 1215 1925	3.8 1.9 3.7	**20** TU	0131 0827 1406 2120	2.0 3.8 1.7 3.8
6 TU	0053 0806 1336 2100	1.9 3.8 1.7 3.9	**21** W	0234 0929 1459 2225	1.8 3.9 1.5 4.1
7 W	0206 0918 1440 2155	1.8 4.1 1.4 4.2	**22** TH	0323 1014 1543 2252	1.6 4.1 1.2 4.2
8 TH	0306 1006 1534 2240	1.5 4.3 1.1 4.4	**23** F	0405 1051 1624 2323	1.3 4.2 1.0 4.4
9 F ●	0358 1049 1622 2322	1.1 4.5 0.7 4.6	**24** SA ○	0443 1128 1701 2358	1.1 4.3 0.9 4.4
10 SA	0444 1130 1706	0.8 4.7 0.5	**25** SU	0519 1206 1735	1.0 4.4 0.8
11 SU	0005 0528 1212 1750	4.8 0.6 4.8 0.3	**26** M	0034 0552 1241 1806	4.5 1.0 4.4 0.8
12 M	0050 0611 1257 1832	4.9 0.5 4.8 0.3	**27** TU	0107 0620 1313 1832	4.5 1.0 4.4 0.9
13 TU	0139 0653 1345 1913	4.9 0.6 4.8 0.4	**28** W	0137 0644 1341 1857	4.4 1.0 4.3 1.0
14 W	0232 0736 1437 1956	4.8 0.7 4.6 0.7	**29** TH	0204 0710 1408 1924	4.4 1.0 4.3 1.0
15 TH	0324 0821 1533 2042	4.7 1.0 4.5 1.0			

MARCH

	Time	m		Time	m
1 F	0232 0741 1441 1957	4.3 1.1 4.2 1.1	**16** SA	0335 0839 1601 2103	4.4 1.3 4.2 1.5
2 SA	0305 0817 1521 2036	4.2 1.2 4.1 1.3	**17** SU ☽	0423 0940 1702 2226	4.1 1.7 3.9 1.9
3 SU ☾	0348 0902 1613 2125	4.0 1.5 3.8 1.6	**18** M	0524 1116 1817 2356	3.8 1.9 3.7 2.1
4 M	0445 1000 1722 2232	3.8 1.8 3.6 2.0	**19** TU	0645 1235 1942	3.6 2.0 3.6
5 TU	0600 1134 1903	3.6 2.0 3.6	**20** W	0111 0808 1342 2134	2.1 3.6 1.8 3.8
6 W	0044 0746 1329 2041	2.1 3.7 1.8 3.8	**21** TH	0215 0922 1435 2226	1.9 3.8 1.6 4.1
7 TH	0204 0858 1431 2135	1.8 4.0 1.4 4.2	**22** F	0301 0957 1518 2231	1.6 4.0 1.3 4.2
8 F	0259 0946 1520 2219	1.4 4.3 1.0 4.5	**23** SA	0341 1030 1557 2257	1.3 4.2 1.1 4.4
9 SA	0345 1028 1605 2301	1.0 4.6 0.6 4.7	**24** SU	0417 1105 1632 2331	1.1 4.3 0.9 4.5
10 SU ●	0428 1110 1647 2343	0.6 4.7 0.3 4.9	**25** M ○	0451 1141 1705	1.0 4.4 0.9
11 M	0509 1152 1729	0.4 4.8 0.2	**26** TU	0004 0522 1215 1735	4.5 0.9 4.4 0.9
12 TU	0026 0550 1235 1809	4.9 0.3 4.9 0.2	**27** W	0035 0549 1246 1802	4.5 0.9 4.4 0.9
13 W	0112 0630 1322 1849	4.9 0.4 4.8 0.4	**28** TH	0103 0614 1313 1828	4.5 0.9 4.4 0.9
14 TH	0200 0711 1412 1930	4.8 0.6 4.7 0.7	**29** F	0129 0641 1341 1856	4.4 0.9 4.4 1.0
15 F	0248 0752 1506 2013	4.7 0.9 4.5 1.1	**30** SA	0156 0712 1414 1929	4.4 1.0 4.3 1.1
			31 SU	0230 0748 1456 2009	4.2 1.1 4.1 1.4

APRIL

	Time	m		Time	m
1 M	0315 0833 1551 2100	4.0 1.4 3.9 1.7	**16** TU	0445 1045 1748 2325	3.7 1.9 3.7 2.2
2 TU ☾	0416 0933 1708 2212	3.8 1.7 3.7 2.0	**17** W	0607 1158 1912	3.5 2.0 3.7
3 W	0540 1133 1853	3.6 1.9 3.7	**18** TH	0036 0735 1303 2045	2.1 3.5 1.9 3.9
4 TH	0045 0725 1313 2016	2.0 3.7 1.7 4.0	**19** F	0140 0848 1358 2131	1.9 3.7 1.7 4.1
5 F	0149 0833 1409 2110	1.7 4.0 1.3 4.3	**20** SA	0228 0927 1443 2154	1.7 3.9 1.4 4.3
6 SA	0239 0921 1457 2154	1.3 4.3 0.9 4.6	**21** SU	0308 1002 1521 2225	1.4 4.1 1.2 4.4
7 SU	0323 1003 1541 2236	0.9 4.6 0.6 4.8	**22** M	0343 1038 1556 2259	1.2 4.2 1.1 4.5
8 M ●	0405 1045 1623 2317	0.6 4.7 0.4 4.9	**23** TU ○	0416 1114 1629 2332	1.1 4.3 1.0 4.5
9 TU	0446 1128 1704	0.4 4.8 0.3	**24** W	0447 1148 1701	1.0 4.4 1.0
10 W	0000 0526 1213 1744	4.9 0.4 4.8 0.4	**25** TH	0003 0517 1219 1732	4.5 1.0 4.4 1.0
11 TH	0043 0606 1300 1825	4.9 0.5 4.8 0.6	**26** F	0032 0547 1249 1803	4.5 0.9 4.4 1.0
12 F	0127 0646 1351 1905	4.8 0.7 4.6 0.9	**27** SA	0100 0618 1322 1835	4.5 0.9 4.4 1.1
13 SA	0213 0728 1445 1949	4.6 1.0 4.5 1.2	**28** SU	0132 0653 1401 1912	4.4 1.0 4.3 1.3
14 SU	0259 0813 1539 2041	4.3 1.3 4.2 1.7	**29** M	0211 0733 1450 1957	4.3 1.2 4.2 1.5
15 M ☽	0347 0914 1637 2203	4.0 1.7 3.9 2.0	**30** TU	0301 0822 1552 2053	4.1 1.4 4.0 1.8

MAY

	Time	m		Time	m
1 W ☽	0407 0928 1709 2222	3.9 1.7 3.9 2.0	**16** TH	0519 1113 1821 2349	3.6 1.9 3.8 2.1
2 TH	0530 1124 1833	3.8 1.7 4.0	**17** F	0641 1214 1932	3.6 1.9 3.9
3 F	0016 0656 1241 1946	1.9 3.9 1.5 4.2	**18** SA	0050 0750 1309 2027	2.0 3.7 1.8 4.0
4 SA	0118 0801 1338 2040	1.6 4.1 1.3 4.5	**19** SU	0143 0843 1355 2109	1.8 3.9 1.6 4.2
5 SU	0209 0851 1427 2125	1.3 4.3 1.0 4.7	**20** M	0224 0927 1436 2148	1.6 4.0 1.5 4.3
6 M	0255 0936 1512 2208	1.0 4.5 0.8 4.8	**21** TU	0301 1007 1514 2225	1.4 4.2 1.3 4.4
7 TU	0338 1021 1556 2250	0.7 4.7 0.7 4.8	**22** W	0336 1046 1551 2300	1.2 4.3 1.2 4.5
8 W ●	0420 1106 1638 2333	0.6 4.7 0.6 4.8	**23** TH ○	0412 1122 1629 2333	1.1 4.4 1.2 4.5
9 TH	0502 1154 1720	0.6 4.7 0.7	**24** F	0448 1157 1706	1.0 4.4 1.1
10 F	0017 0544 1243 1803	4.8 0.7 4.7 0.9	**25** SA	0006 0525 1232 1744	4.5 1.0 4.5 1.1
11 SA	0101 0626 1337 1846	4.7 0.8 4.6 1.1	**26** SU	0040 0603 1312 1823	4.5 1.0 4.5 1.2
12 SU	0146 0709 1431 1932	4.5 1.1 4.4 1.4	**27** M	0119 0644 1359 1907	4.4 1.0 4.4 1.3
13 M	0232 0756 1521 2025	4.3 1.3 4.3 1.7	**28** TU	0203 0729 1453 1956	4.3 1.1 4.3 1.5
14 TU	0320 0852 1612 2133	4.1 1.6 4.1 1.9	**29** W	0258 0822 1555 2055	4.2 1.3 4.3 1.6
15 W ☾	0413 1005 1710 2244	3.8 1.8 3.9 2.1	**30** TH ☽	0403 0927 1659 2211	4.1 1.4 4.2 1.7
			31 F	0513 1047 1805 2332	4.0 1.5 4.3 1.7

JUNE

	Time	m		Time	m
1 SA	0623 1200 1908	4.0 1.4 4.4	**16** SU	0642 1209 1919	3.7 1.9 4.0
2 SU	0038 0726 1300 2005	1.5 4.2 1.3 4.5	**17** M	0042 0750 1300 2017	1.9 3.8 1.8 4.1
3 M	0134 0820 1354 2054	1.3 4.3 1.2 4.6	**18** TU	0131 0847 1348 2107	1.8 3.9 1.7 4.2
4 TU	0224 0911 1443 2141	1.2 4.4 1.1 4.7	**19** W	0215 0937 1434 2152	1.6 4.0 1.6 4.3
5 W	0312 1001 1531 2228	1.0 4.5 1.0 4.7	**20** TH	0259 1022 1519 2232	1.4 4.2 1.4 4.4
6 TH ●	0358 1053 1617 2314	0.9 4.5 1.0 4.7	**21** F	0343 1103 1604 2309	1.2 4.3 1.3 4.5
7 F	0443 1145 1703 2359	0.9 4.5 1.1 4.6	**22** SA ○	0427 1142 1648 2347	1.1 4.4 1.2 4.5
8 SA	0528 1237 1748	0.9 4.5 1.1	**23** SU	0511 1222 1732	1.0 4.5 1.1
9 SU	0043 0612 1328 1834	4.5 1.0 4.5 1.3	**24** M	0026 0555 1305 1817	4.5 0.9 4.6 1.1
10 M	0127 0656 1416 1918	4.4 1.1 4.4 1.4	**25** TU	0108 0639 1353 1903	4.5 0.9 4.6 1.1
11 TU	0211 0740 1500 2005	4.3 1.3 4.3 1.6	**26** W	0155 0725 1447 1951	4.5 0.9 4.6 1.2
12 W	0256 0826 1544 2055	4.1 1.5 4.2 1.8	**27** TH	0248 0814 1543 2043	4.4 1.0 4.5 1.3
13 TH	0343 0916 1629 2150	3.9 1.6 4.1 1.9	**28** F ☽	0348 0909 1639 2143	4.3 1.2 4.5 1.4
14 F ☾	0434 1013 1718 2249	3.8 1.8 4.0 2.0	**29** SA	0450 1011 1735 2250	4.2 1.3 4.4 1.5
15 SA	0533 1112 1816 2348	3.7 1.9 3.9 2.0	**30** SU	0552 1119 1832 2358	4.2 1.4 4.4 1.5

SUNRISE AND SUNSET TIMES

PORTSMOUTH
At 50°48′N 1°07′ W

UT		Sunrise	Sunset
Jan	01	0807	1610
	15	0800	1628
Feb	01	0740	1656
	15	0717	1721
Mar	01	0649	1746
	15	0618	1809
BST (UT+1)			
Apr	01	0640	1937
	15	0610	2000
May	01	0538	2026
	15	0515	2047
Jun	01	0457	2109
	15	0451	2120
Jul	01	0455	2121
	15	0508	2112
Aug	01	0531	2050
	15	0552	2025
Sep	01	0618	1950
	15	0640	1918
Oct	01	0705	1842
	15	0628	1812
UT			
Nov	01	0656	1639
	15	0720	1618
Dec	01	0745	1602
	15	0800	1559

PORTSMOUTH
LAT 50°48′N
LONG 1°07′W

TIMES AND HEIGHTS OF HIGH AND LOW WATER (Heights in Metres)

TIME ZONE UT
For Summer Time (area enclosed in shaded box) add 1 hour

2024

JULY

Date	Time	m	Date	Time	m
1 M	0654 1225 1931	4.1 1.5 4.4	16 TU	0627 1159 1859	3.7 1.9 3.9
2 TU	0101 0755 1325 2029	1.5 4.1 1.5 4.4	17 W	0034 0752 1303 2018	1.9 3.7 1.9 4.0
3 W	0200 0856 1422 2124	1.4 4.2 1.4 4.4	18 TH	0135 0912 1402 2124	1.8 3.9 1.8 4.1
4 TH	0254 0956 1516 2215	1.3 4.3 1.4 4.4	19 F	0232 1004 1457 2211	1.6 4.1 1.6 4.3
5 F ●	0345 1052 1607 2302	1.2 4.4 1.3 4.5	20 SA	0325 1046 1549 2251	1.3 4.3 1.4 4.4
6 SA	0433 1142 1654 2345	1.1 4.4 1.2 4.5	21 SU ○	0414 1126 1638 2330	1.0 4.5 1.2 4.6
7 SU	0518 1227 1739	1.0 4.5 1.2	22 M	0500 1206 1723	0.8 4.6 1.0
8 M	0027 0601 1309 1821	4.4 1.0 4.5 1.2	23 TU	0010 0544 1249 1807	4.6 0.6 4.7 0.9
9 TU	0109 0641 1352 1901	4.4 1.0 4.4 1.3	24 W	0052 0627 1336 1850	4.7 0.6 4.8 0.8
10 W	0150 0718 1433 1938	4.3 1.1 4.4 1.4	25 TH	0138 0710 1428 1934	4.6 0.6 4.7 0.9
11 TH	0231 0753 1511 2014	4.2 1.3 4.3 1.5	26 F	0229 0755 1521 2021	4.6 0.7 4.7 1.0
12 F	0310 0828 1546 2050	4.1 1.4 4.2 1.7	27 SA	0326 0843 1613 2113	4.5 1.0 4.6 1.2
13 SA ☾	0349 0906 1623 2132	4.0 1.6 4.1 1.8	28 SU ☽	0424 0938 1704 2214	4.3 1.2 4.5 1.5
14 SU	0433 0953 1706 2225	3.9 1.7 4.0 1.9	29 M	0524 1045 1801 2327	4.2 1.5 4.3 1.7
15 M	0524 1051 1757 2328	3.7 1.9 3.9 1.9	30 TU	0629 1159 1904	4.0 1.7 4.1
			31 W	0040 0741 1309 2012	1.7 3.9 1.8 4.1

AUGUST

Date	Time	m	Date	Time	m
1 TH	0147 0854 1414 2115	1.7 4.0 1.3 4.2	16 F	0112 0851 1348 2103	1.9 3.8 2.0 4.0
2 F	0247 1001 1511 2206	1.5 4.2 1.3 4.3	17 SA	0219 0944 1449 2150	1.6 4.1 1.7 4.2
3 SA	0338 1051 1600 2249	1.3 4.3 1.4 4.3	18 SU	0313 1025 1539 2230	1.3 4.4 1.3 4.5
4 SU ●	0423 1129 1644 2329	1.1 4.4 1.2 4.4	19 M ○	0401 1104 1624 2309	0.9 4.6 1.0 4.7
5 M	0504 1206 1724	1.0 4.5 1.1	20 TU	0445 1144 1707 2349	0.6 4.8 0.7 4.8
6 TU	0008 0544 1245 1803	4.4 0.9 4.5 1.1	21 W	0527 1226 1749	0.4 4.9 0.6
7 W	0047 0619 1324 1837	4.4 0.9 4.5 1.1	22 TH	0031 0608 1311 1830	4.8 0.3 4.9 0.6
8 TH	0125 0651 1400 1907	4.3 1.0 4.5 1.2	23 F	0115 0649 1400 1911	4.8 0.4 4.9 0.7
9 F	0200 0718 1432 1934	4.3 1.2 4.4 1.3	24 SA	0204 0730 1452 1955	4.7 0.6 4.8 0.9
10 SA	0231 0746 1502 2003	4.2 1.3 4.3 1.4	25 SU	0259 0814 1543 2043	4.6 1.0 4.6 1.2
11 SU	0305 0817 1535 2039	4.1 1.4 4.2 1.5	26 M ☽	0358 0906 1634 2143	4.4 1.4 4.4 1.6
12 M ☾	0345 0856 1615 2124	4.0 1.6 4.1 1.7	27 TU	0500 1019 1731 2307	4.1 1.8 4.1 1.8
13 TU	0433 0946 1705 2224	3.8 1.8 3.9 1.9	28 W	0611 1146 1842	3.9 2.0 3.9
14 W	0534 1055 1806 2345	3.7 2.1 3.8 2.0	29 TH	0026 0733 1301 2000	1.9 3.8 2.1 3.9
15 TH	0656 1231 1934	3.6 2.1 3.8	30 F	0137 0906 1408 2110	1.8 3.9 1.9 4.0
			31 SA	0235 1026 1501 2158	1.6 4.2 1.7 4.2

SEPTEMBER

Date	Time	m	Date	Time	m
1 SU	0322 1106 1544 2233	1.3 4.4 1.4 4.3	16 M	0255 1000 1521 2206	1.2 4.5 1.2 4.6
2 M	0404 1111 1624 2309	1.1 4.5 1.2 4.4	17 TU	0340 1039 1604 2245	0.8 4.8 0.8 4.8
3 TU ●	0443 1142 1702 2346	0.9 4.5 1.1 4.4	18 W ○	0422 1118 1645 2325	0.5 5.0 0.6 4.9
4 W	0519 1217 1737	0.9 4.6 1.0	19 TH	0503 1159 1725	0.3 5.0 0.5
5 TH	0023 0552 1252 1808	4.4 0.9 4.6 1.1	20 F	0006 0544 1242 1806	5.0 0.3 5.0 0.5
6 F	0058 0619 1324 1833	4.4 1.0 4.5 1.1	21 SA	0051 0624 1327 1846	4.9 0.5 5.0 0.6
7 SA	0127 0644 1351 1857	4.4 1.1 4.5 1.2	22 SU	0139 0704 1416 1928	4.8 0.7 4.8 0.9
8 SU	0154 0709 1418 1924	4.3 1.2 4.4 1.3	23 M	0233 0747 1507 2015	4.6 1.1 4.6 1.3
9 M	0224 0738 1449 1957	4.3 1.3 4.3 1.4	24 TU ☾	0335 0838 1600 2116	4.4 1.6 4.3 1.7
10 TU	0303 0813 1529 2038	4.1 1.5 4.1 1.6	25 W	0440 1003 1702 2251	4.1 2.0 4.0 2.0
11 W ☽	0353 0859 1621 2133	3.9 1.8 3.9 1.9	26 TH	0554 1132 1820	3.8 2.2 3.7
12 TH	0457 1004 1729 2306	3.7 2.2 3.7 2.1	27 F	0006 0723 1243 1948	2.0 3.8 2.2 3.7
13 F	0631 1231 1910	3.6 2.3 3.7	28 SA	0113 0927 1347 2147	1.9 4.0 2.0 4.0
14 SA	0106 0826 1343 2038	2.0 3.9 2.0 4.0	29 SU	0210 1018 1437 2230	1.7 4.3 1.7 4.2
15 SU	0206 0919 1436 2126	1.6 4.2 1.6 4.3	30 M	0256 1053 1519 2216	1.4 4.4 1.5 4.3

OCTOBER

Date	Time	m	Date	Time	m
1 TU	0336 1049 1558 2247	1.2 4.5 1.2 4.4	16 W	0313 1010 1538 2218	0.8 4.9 0.8 4.8
2 W ●	0413 1115 1633 2322	1.0 4.6 1.1 4.5	17 TH ○	0355 1050 1619 2300	0.6 5.0 0.6 5.0
3 TH	0448 1147 1706 2357	1.0 4.6 1.0 4.5	18 F	0437 1131 1700 2343	0.5 5.1 0.5 5.0
4 F	0518 1220 1735	1.0 4.6 1.1	19 SA	0518 1213 1741	0.5 5.1 0.6
5 SA	0029 0546 1249 1800	4.5 1.1 4.6 1.1	20 SU	0028 0559 1257 1823	4.9 0.7 5.0 0.7
6 SU	0057 0612 1314 1825	4.5 1.2 4.5 1.2	21 M	0118 0641 1344 1905	4.8 1.0 4.8 1.0
7 M	0123 0638 1340 1853	4.4 1.3 4.5 1.2	22 TU	0214 0726 1435 1953	4.6 1.3 4.5 1.4
8 TU	0154 0708 1411 1926	4.4 1.4 4.3 1.4	23 W	0317 0819 1529 2055	4.4 1.7 4.2 1.8
9 W	0234 0744 1452 2007	4.2 1.6 4.1 1.6	24 TH ☾	0421 0945 1630 2225	4.1 2.1 3.9 2.0
10 TH ☽	0327 0831 1548 2102	4.0 1.9 3.9 1.9	25 F	0530 1105 1747 2335	3.9 2.2 3.7 2.1
11 F	0439 0938 1705 2251	3.8 2.3 3.7 2.1	26 SA	0656 1212 1915	3.9 2.2 3.7
12 SA	0616 1225 1846	3.8 2.2 3.7	27 SU	0038 0851 1313 2118	2.0 4.1 2.1 3.9
13 SU	0046 0753 1323 2007	1.9 4.0 1.9 4.0	28 M	0134 0939 1405 2156	1.8 4.3 1.8 4.1
14 M	0141 0849 1412 2056	1.5 4.4 1.5 4.4	29 TU	0221 1006 1447 2149	1.6 4.4 1.6 4.2
15 TU	0229 0931 1456 2138	1.2 4.7 1.1 4.6	30 W	0301 1015 1525 2221	1.4 4.5 1.4 4.4
			31 TH	0338 1044 1559 2257	1.3 4.6 1.2 4.5

NOVEMBER

Date	Time	m	Date	Time	m
1 F ●	0412 1117 1632 2332	1.2 4.6 1.2 4.5	16 SA	0411 1106 1636 2325	0.8 5.0 0.7 4.9
2 SA	0444 1149 1702	1.2 4.6 1.1	17 SU	0455 1150 1720	0.8 4.9 0.7
3 SU	0004 0515 1218 1731	4.5 1.2 4.6 1.2	18 M	0014 0539 1235 1804	4.8 0.9 4.8 0.9
4 M	0034 0545 1245 1801	4.5 1.3 4.6 1.2	19 TU	0107 0624 1322 1849	4.7 1.2 4.7 1.1
5 TU	0104 0616 1314 1833	4.5 1.4 4.5 1.2	20 W	0204 0711 1411 1937	4.6 1.4 4.5 1.4
6 W	0139 0650 1349 1910	4.4 1.5 4.4 1.4	21 TH	0303 0804 1503 2034	4.4 1.7 4.2 1.6
7 TH	0223 0731 1433 1954	4.3 1.7 4.2 1.6	22 F	0358 0911 1559 2144	4.2 2.0 4.0 1.9
8 F	0321 0822 1533 2053	4.1 1.9 4.0 1.8	23 SA ☾	0455 1024 1703 2252	4.1 2.1 3.8 2.0
9 SA ☽	0433 0935 1649 2230	4.0 2.1 3.9 1.9	24 SU	0600 1130 1816 2353	4.0 2.2 3.7 2.0
10 SU	0553 1148 1814	4.0 2.1 3.9	25 M	0711 1231 1927	4.0 2.1 3.8
11 M	0009 0712 1249 1927	1.8 4.2 1.8 4.1	26 TU	0049 0811 1324 2024	1.9 4.1 1.9 3.9
12 TU	0107 0811 1339 2021	1.5 4.5 1.5 4.4	27 W	0138 0855 1409 2111	1.8 4.3 1.7 4.1
13 W	0156 0858 1425 2108	1.2 4.7 1.2 4.6	28 TH	0220 0935 1447 2154	1.6 4.4 1.6 4.2
14 TH	0242 0940 1510 2152	1.0 4.9 0.9 4.8	29 F	0259 1013 1523 2235	1.5 4.5 1.4 4.3
15 F ○	0327 1023 1553 2238	0.8 5.0 0.8 4.8	30 SA	0336 1050 1558 2314	1.4 4.5 1.3 4.4

DECEMBER

Date	Time	m	Date	Time	m
1 SU ●	0413 1124 1634 2348	1.4 4.6 1.2 4.5	16 M	0440 1137 1707	1.1 4.7 0.9
2 M	0450 1156 1710	1.3 4.6 1.2	17 TU	0011 0528 1222 1753	4.6 1.1 4.7 0.9
3 TU	0020 0527 1227 1747	4.5 1.3 4.6 1.1	18 W	0103 0614 1307 1838	4.6 1.2 4.6 1.0
4 W	0055 0604 1301 1825	4.5 1.4 4.5 1.2	19 TH	0154 0659 1353 1922	4.6 1.4 4.4 1.2
5 TH	0135 0644 1340 1906	4.5 1.4 4.4 1.2	20 F	0242 0745 1440 2007	4.5 1.5 4.3 1.4
6 F	0222 0728 1426 1952	4.4 1.5 4.3 1.3	21 SA	0328 0833 1528 2055	4.3 1.7 4.1 1.6
7 SA	0318 0820 1523 2047	4.3 1.7 4.2 1.5	22 SU ☾	0413 0926 1618 2149	4.2 1.9 3.9 1.8
8 SU ☽	0420 0923 1630 2155	4.3 1.8 4.1 1.6	23 M	0500 1028 1713 2251	4.1 2.0 3.8 1.9
9 M	0525 1045 1741 2316	4.3 1.8 4.1 1.6	24 TU	0553 1133 1817 2352	4.0 2.1 3.7 2.0
10 TU	0629 1202 1847	4.3 1.7 4.1	25 W	0655 1232 1927	4.0 2.0 3.7
11 W	0025 0729 1303 1947	1.5 4.4 1.5 4.3	26 TH	0046 0759 1323 2032	2.0 4.0 1.9 3.8
12 TH	0122 0824 1355 2041	1.4 4.6 1.3 4.4	27 F	0136 0856 1408 2128	1.9 4.1 1.8 4.0
13 F	0214 0914 1445 2134	1.3 4.7 1.2 4.5	28 SA	0222 0945 1450 2217	1.8 4.2 1.6 4.2
14 SA	0304 1003 1533 2227	1.2 4.7 1.0 4.6	29 SU	0307 1028 1533 2259	1.6 4.4 1.4 4.3
15 SU ○	0352 1051 1621 2320	1.1 4.8 0.9 4.6	30 M ●	0351 1105 1615 2335	1.5 4.5 1.2 4.4
			31 TU	0434 1139 1657	1.4 4.5 1.1

SHOREHAM
LAT 50°50′N
LONG 0°15′W

TIMES AND HEIGHTS OF HIGH AND LOW WATER (Heights in Metres)

TIME ZONE UT
For Summer Time (area enclosed in shaded box) add 1 hour

2024

JANUARY

Date	Day	Time	m	Time	m	Time	m	Time	m
1	M	0211	5.7	0816	1.5	1415	5.4	2037	1.4
2	TU	0245	5.5	0857	1.6	1451	5.2	2117	1.6
3	W	0322	5.3	0941	1.8	1533	5.0	2202	1.8
4	TH ☽	0406	5.1	1032	2.0	1626	4.8	2253	2.0
5	F	0505	5.0	1130	2.1	1736	4.7	2354	2.1
6	SA	0614	4.9	1234	2.1	1848	4.8		
7	SU	0101	2.1	0720	5.0	1340	1.9	1952	5.0
8	M	0207	1.9	0819	5.3	1441	1.7	2049	5.3
9	TU	0306	1.7	0912	5.6	1534	1.4	2142	5.6
10	W	0357	1.4	1001	5.9	1622	1.1	2231	5.9
11	TH ●	0444	1.2	1048	6.1	1708	0.9	2319	6.1
12	F	0530	1.0	1135	6.2	1755	0.7		
13	SA	0006	6.3	0617	0.8	1221	6.3	1842	0.6
14	SU	0054	6.4	0704	0.8	1308	6.3	1930	0.6
15	M	0141	6.4	0752	0.8	1355	6.2	2018	0.6
16	TU	0228	6.3	0842	0.9	1443	6.1	2108	0.8
17	W	0315	6.1	0934	1.0	1534	5.8	2159	1.0
18	TH ☾	0406	5.9	1029	1.2	1628	5.5	2255	1.3
19	F	0501	5.6	1131	1.5	1730	5.2	2359	1.6
20	SA	0605	5.3	1240	1.7	1842	5.0		
21	SU	0110	1.8	0720	5.1	1350	1.7	2005	5.0
22	M	0220	1.8	0834	5.2	1454	1.6	2114	5.2
23	TU	0320	1.6	0936	5.4	1549	1.4	2210	5.4
24	W	0411	1.4	1026	5.6	1636	1.2	2256	5.7
25	TH O	0455	1.3	1109	5.8	1717	1.0	2337	5.9
26	F	0535	1.1	1147	5.9	1755	0.9		
27	SA	0014	5.9	0611	1.1	1221	5.9	1831	0.9
28	SU	0047	6.0	0646	1.1	1252	5.8	1904	0.9
29	M	0117	5.9	0718	1.1	1319	5.7	1937	1.0
30	TU	0142	5.8	0751	1.2	1346	5.7	2009	1.1
31	W	0207	5.7	0823	1.3	1414	5.5	2038	1.3

FEBRUARY

Date	Day	Time	m	Time	m	Time	m	Time	m
1	TH	0235	5.6	0855	1.4	1447	5.4	2108	1.5
2	F ☽	0310	5.4	0930	1.6	1526	5.2	2146	1.7
3	SA	0353	5.2	1018	1.9	1616	4.9	2239	2.0
4	SU	0451	4.9	1124	2.1	1729	4.6	2355	2.2
5	M	0620	4.8	1248	2.1	1912	4.7		
6	TU	0126	2.1	0748	4.9	1410	1.8	2026	5.0
7	W	0244	1.8	0853	5.3	1516	1.4	2127	5.5
8	TH	0343	1.4	0948	5.7	1609	1.0	2221	5.9
9	F ●	0432	1.0	1038	6.1	1656	0.7	2310	6.2
10	SA	0518	0.7	1126	6.4	1742	0.4	2357	6.5
11	SU	0604	0.5	1213	6.5	1827	0.3		
12	M	0042	6.6	0650	0.4	1257	6.6	1913	0.2
13	TU	0126	6.7	0735	0.4	1341	6.5	1958	0.3
14	W	0208	6.6	0820	0.5	1423	6.3	2042	0.5
15	TH	0249	6.3	0905	0.7	1507	6.0	2126	0.8
16	F ☾	0332	5.9	0952	1.1	1554	5.5	2214	1.3
17	SA	0421	5.5	1046	1.5	1650	5.1	2314	1.8
18	SU	0522	5.0	1202	1.9	1804	4.7		
19	M	0042	2.1	0642	4.7	1331	2.0	1947	4.6
20	TU	0205	2.1	0822	4.7	1441	1.8	2109	4.9
21	W	0309	1.8	0930	5.1	1537	1.5	2202	5.3
22	TH	0359	1.5	1018	5.4	1621	1.2	2244	5.6
23	F	0440	1.2	1058	5.7	1700	1.0	2322	5.9
24	SA O	0516	1.1	1133	5.8	1734	0.9	2356	6.0
25	SU	0550	1.0	1205	5.9	1807	0.8		
26	M	0025	6.0	0622	0.9	1231	5.9	1840	0.8
27	TU	0050	6.0	0653	0.9	1253	5.9	1910	0.9
28	W	0110	5.9	0723	1.0	1317	5.8	1937	0.9
29	TH	0133	5.9	0749	1.0	1344	5.8	2000	1.1

MARCH

Date	Day	Time	m	Time	m	Time	m	Time	m
1	F	0200	5.8	0814	1.2	1414	5.6	2028	1.3
2	SA	0232	5.6	0847	1.4	1450	5.4	2105	1.5
3	SU ☽	0311	5.3	0931	1.7	1535	5.0	2156	1.9
4	M	0403	4.9	1034	2.0	1640	4.6	2311	2.2
5	TU	0526	4.6	1206	2.1	1844	4.5		
6	W	0059	2.2	0726	4.7	1349	1.9	2010	4.9
7	TH	0230	1.8	0838	5.2	1500	1.4	2114	5.5
8	F	0328	1.3	0935	5.7	1552	0.9	2207	6.0
9	SA	0415	0.8	1025	6.1	1638	0.5	2255	6.4
10	SU ●	0500	0.5	1112	6.5	1722	0.2	2340	6.7
11	M	0544	0.3	1157	6.6	1806	0.1		
12	TU	0022	6.8	0628	0.2	1240	6.7	1850	0.1
13	W	0104	6.8	0712	0.2	1321	6.6	1933	0.2
14	TH	0143	6.6	0754	0.4	1401	6.4	2014	0.5
15	F	0221	6.3	0835	0.7	1441	6.0	2054	0.9
16	SA	0300	5.8	0917	1.1	1525	5.5	2138	1.4
17	SU ☾	0346	5.3	1005	1.6	1621	4.9	2234	1.9
18	M	0447	4.7	1119	2.0	1735	4.5		
19	TU	0016	2.3	0610	4.4	1310	2.2	1927	4.5
20	W	0148	2.2	0808	4.5	1421	1.9	2052	4.8
21	TH	0251	1.9	0913	4.9	1515	1.6	2141	5.3
22	F	0338	1.5	0958	5.3	1557	1.2	2220	5.6
23	SA	0416	1.2	1035	5.6	1633	1.0	2255	5.9
24	SU	0450	1.0	1108	5.8	1706	0.9	2327	6.0
25	M O	0523	0.9	1137	5.8	1738	0.8	2355	6.0
26	TU	0554	0.8	1202	5.9	1810	0.8		
27	W	0016	6.0	0625	0.8	1225	5.9	1841	0.8
28	TH	0038	6.0	0653	0.9	1250	5.9	1906	0.9
29	F	0103	6.0	0718	0.9	1318	5.9	1931	1.0
30	SA	0132	5.9	0746	1.0	1349	5.7	2001	1.2
31	SU	0204	5.7	0821	1.2	1425	5.5	2041	1.5

APRIL

Date	Day	Time	m	Time	m	Time	m	Time	m
1	M	0244	5.3	0908	1.5	1512	5.1	2136	1.9
2	TU ☽	0337	4.9	1013	1.9	1622	4.7	2255	2.2
3	W	0505	4.6	1144	2.0	1827	4.6		
4	TH	0043	2.1	0706	4.7	1328	1.8	1951	5.0
5	F	0209	1.7	0819	5.2	1437	1.3	2054	5.6
6	SA	0306	1.1	0915	5.7	1528	0.8	2146	6.1
7	SU	0352	0.7	1005	6.2	1613	0.4	2232	6.5
8	M ●	0436	0.4	1051	6.4	1657	0.2	2316	6.7
9	TU	0520	0.2	1135	6.6	1741	0.2	2358	6.8
10	W	0603	0.2	1218	6.6	1824	0.2		
11	TH	0038	6.7	0647	0.3	1259	6.5	1906	0.4
12	F	0116	6.5	0728	0.5	1339	6.3	1947	0.7
13	SA	0154	6.1	0809	0.8	1419	5.9	2028	1.1
14	SU	0233	5.7	0850	1.2	1504	5.4	2111	1.5
15	M ☾	0319	5.2	0937	1.6	1559	5.0	2206	2.0
16	TU	0420	4.7	1043	2.0	1709	4.6	2339	2.3
17	W	0537	4.4	1235	2.2	1840	4.5		
18	TH	0118	2.2	0725	4.4	1347	2.0	2012	4.8
19	F	0219	1.9	0837	4.8	1440	1.6	2103	5.2
20	SA	0305	1.6	0923	5.1	1522	1.3	2143	5.5
21	SU	0343	1.3	1000	5.4	1558	1.1	2218	5.7
22	M	0418	1.1	1032	5.6	1633	1.0	2249	5.9
23	TU O	0451	0.9	1100	5.7	1706	0.9	2316	5.9
24	W	0524	0.9	1128	5.8	1740	0.9	2342	6.0
25	TH	0556	0.9	1157	5.9	1811	0.9		
26	F	0009	6.0	0626	0.9	1227	5.9	1841	1.0
27	SA	0038	5.9	0656	0.9	1259	5.9	1911	1.1
28	SU	0111	5.8	0730	1.0	1334	5.7	1948	1.2
29	M	0148	5.6	0810	1.2	1415	5.5	2033	1.5
30	TU	0232	5.3	0901	1.5	1509	5.2	2132	1.8

MAY

Date	Day	Time	m	Time	m	Time	m	Time	m
1	W ☾	0331	5.0	1007	1.7	1625	4.9	2251	2.0
2	TH	0502	4.7	1131	1.8	1806	4.9		
3	F	0023	1.9	0640	4.9	1259	1.6	1923	5.3
4	SA	0139	1.5	0751	5.3	1405	1.2	2025	5.7
5	SU	0236	1.1	0848	5.7	1458	0.8	2117	6.1
6	M	0325	0.7	0939	6.0	1546	0.6	2204	6.4
7	TU	0411	0.5	1027	6.3	1631	0.4	2249	6.5
8	W ●	0456	0.4	1113	6.4	1716	0.4	2332	6.5
9	TH	0540	0.4	1157	6.4	1801	0.5		
10	F	0013	6.4	0625	0.5	1239	6.3	1844	0.7
11	SA	0053	6.2	0707	0.7	1321	6.1	1926	0.9
12	SU	0133	5.9	0748	0.9	1403	5.8	2008	1.2
13	M	0213	5.6	0830	1.2	1448	5.5	2052	1.6
14	TU	0300	5.2	0917	1.6	1540	5.1	2144	1.9
15	W ☽	0356	4.8	1013	1.9	1639	4.9	2252	2.1
16	TH	0501	4.5	1127	2.0	1745	4.8		
17	F	0021	2.1	0613	4.5	1249	2.0	1857	4.8
18	SA	0129	2.0	0727	4.6	1349	1.8	2002	5.1
19	SU	0220	1.7	0825	4.9	1436	1.6	2049	5.3
20	M	0302	1.5	0907	5.2	1517	1.4	2127	5.5
21	TU	0340	1.3	0944	5.4	1556	1.2	2202	5.7
22	W	0416	1.1	1021	5.6	1633	1.2	2237	5.8
23	TH O	0453	1.0	1057	5.7	1710	1.1	2311	5.9
24	F	0529	1.0	1133	5.8	1746	1.1	2346	5.9
25	SA	0605	0.9	1210	5.9	1822	1.1		
26	SU	0021	5.9	0642	0.9	1248	5.9	1901	1.1
27	M	0100	5.8	0723	1.0	1330	5.8	1944	1.2
28	TU	0143	5.7	0808	1.1	1417	5.6	2033	1.4
29	W	0233	5.5	0900	1.2	1513	5.5	2132	1.5
30	TH ☾	0333	5.2	1002	1.4	1620	5.3	2242	1.6
31	F	0447	5.1	1114	1.4	1734	5.3	2356	1.5

JUNE

Date	Day	Time	m	Time	m	Time	m	Time	m
1	SA	0604	5.2	1226	1.4	1845	5.5		
2	SU	0104	1.4	0715	5.3	1331	1.2	1949	5.7
3	M	0204	1.1	0817	5.5	1428	1.0	2046	5.9
4	TU	0258	0.9	0913	5.8	1521	0.9	2138	6.1
5	W	0348	0.8	1005	5.9	1610	0.8	2226	6.2
6	TH ●	0436	0.7	1054	6.0	1658	0.8	2312	6.2
7	F	0523	0.7	1141	6.1	1744	0.9	2356	6.1
8	SA	0608	0.8	1226	6.1	1828	1.0		
9	SU	0037	6.0	0652	0.9	1308	6.0	1911	1.1
10	M	0118	5.8	0733	1.0	1350	5.8	1952	1.3
11	TU	0158	5.5	0813	1.2	1432	5.6	2034	1.5
12	W	0240	5.3	0855	1.4	1515	5.4	2119	1.7
13	TH	0327	5.0	0941	1.6	1603	5.2	2209	1.8
14	F ☽	0419	4.8	1033	1.8	1655	5.0	2306	2.0
15	SA	0516	4.7	1130	1.9	1751	4.9		
16	SU	0008	2.0	0616	4.7	1231	1.9	1849	5.0
17	M	0111	1.9	0715	4.8	1333	1.8	1944	5.1
18	TU	0209	1.7	0810	5.0	1429	1.7	2035	5.3
19	W	0258	1.5	0901	5.2	1518	1.5	2122	5.5
20	TH	0343	1.3	0947	5.5	1603	1.4	2205	5.7
21	F	0426	1.2	1032	5.7	1646	1.2	2247	5.8
22	SA O	0507	1.0	1115	5.8	1728	1.1	2329	5.9
23	SU	0549	0.9	1159	5.9	1810	1.0		
24	M	0011	6.0	0633	0.8	1242	6.0	1854	1.0
25	TU	0055	6.0	0718	0.8	1328	6.0	1941	1.0
26	W	0141	5.9	0805	0.8	1415	6.0	2030	1.0
27	TH	0230	5.8	0855	0.9	1506	5.9	2124	1.1
28	F ☾	0323	5.6	0950	1.0	1600	5.8	2222	1.2
29	SA	0422	5.5	1048	1.1	1659	5.6	2325	1.3
30	SU	0525	5.3	1152	1.3	1802	5.5		

SUNRISE AND SUNSET TIMES

SHOREHAM
At 50°50′N 0°15′W

		Sunrise	Sunset
UT			
Jan	01	0803	1606
	15	0757	1624
Feb	01	0737	1653
	15	0713	1718
Mar	01	0645	1742
	15	0615	1806
BST (UT+1)			
Apr	01	0637	1934
	15	0607	1957
May	01	0535	2022
	15	0512	2044
Jun	01	0453	2105
	15	0447	2116
Jul	01	0452	2118
	15	0505	2108
Aug	01	0527	2046
	15	0548	2022
Sep	01	0615	1946
	15	0636	1915
Oct	01	0701	1839
	15	0724	1809
UT			
Nov	01	0653	1636
	15	0717	1614
Dec	01	0741	1558
	15	0757	1555

SHOREHAM
LAT 50°50′N
LONG 0°15′W

TIMES AND HEIGHTS OF HIGH AND LOW WATER (Heights in Metres)

TIME ZONE UT
For Summer Time (area enclosed in shaded box) add 1 hour

2024

JULY

Day	Time	m	Day	Time	m
1 M	0030 0634 1258 1910	1.4 5.2 1.4 5.5	**16** TU	0003 0617 1229 1850	2.0 4.7 2.1 4.9
2 TU	0135 0746 1402 2017	1.4 5.3 1.4 5.5	**17** W	0110 0725 1339 1954	2.0 4.8 2.0 5.0
3 W	0237 0853 1502 2118	1.3 5.4 1.3 5.7	**18** TH	0218 0828 1446 2052	1.8 5.0 1.8 5.3
4 TH	0333 0952 1557 2212	1.1 5.6 1.2 5.8	**19** F	0317 0923 1541 2143	1.5 5.3 1.5 5.6
5 F	0424 1045 1646 ● 2301	1.0 5.8 1.1 5.9	**20** SA	0406 1014 1629 2231	1.2 5.7 1.3 5.8
6 SA	0511 1132 1732 2346	0.9 5.9 1.1 5.9	**21** SU	0451 1102 1713 ○ 2317	1.0 5.9 1.0 6.0
7 SU	0555 1216 1815	0.9 6.0 1.1	**22** M	0536 1149 1758	0.8 6.1 0.9
8 M	0027 0637 1256 1855	5.9 0.9 6.0 1.1	**23** TU	0002 0621 1234 1843	6.2 0.6 6.3 0.8
9 TU	0105 0715 1333 1933	5.8 1.0 5.9 1.2	**24** W	0047 0706 1319 1929	6.2 0.5 6.4 0.7
10 W	0141 0752 1409 2009	5.6 1.1 5.8 1.3	**25** TH	0132 0752 1403 2016	6.2 0.5 6.4 0.7
11 TH	0215 0828 1443 2047	5.5 1.2 5.6 1.4	**26** F	0217 0839 1447 2104	6.1 0.6 6.2 0.8
12 F	0249 0906 1517 2127	5.3 1.4 5.4 1.6	**27** SA	0304 0927 1534 2155	6.0 0.8 6.0 1.0
13 SA	0325 0946 1554 ☽ 2212	5.1 1.6 5.2 1.7	**28** SU	0354 1018 1625 ☾ 2251	5.7 1.1 5.7 1.3
14 SU	0409 1032 1640 2304	4.9 1.8 5.0 1.9	**29** M	0450 1117 1724 2358	5.3 1.4 5.4 1.6
15 M	0506 1125 1741	4.7 1.9 4.9	**30** TU	0558 1229 1835	5.0 1.7 5.1
			31 W	0113 0724 1346 1959	1.7 4.9 1.8 5.1

AUGUST

Day	Time	m	Day	Time	m
1 TH	0225 0846 1453 2112	1.5 5.0 1.7 5.3	**16** F	0147 0805 1425 2032	2.0 4.9 2.0 5.1
2 F	0325 0949 1549 2208	1.4 5.4 1.5 5.5	**17** SA	0259 0907 1525 2128	1.6 5.3 1.6 5.6
3 SA	0416 1040 1637 2255	1.2 5.7 1.3 5.7	**18** SU	0350 1000 1613 2217	1.2 5.8 1.2 5.9
4 SU	0500 1123 1719 ● 2336	1.0 5.9 1.1 5.8	**19** M	0435 1048 1657 ○ 2303	0.8 6.1 0.9 6.2
5 M	0540 1203 1758	0.9 6.0 1.0	**20** TU	0518 1133 1740 2349	0.6 6.4 0.6 6.4
6 TU	0013 0617 1238 1834	5.9 0.9 6.0 1.0	**21** W	0602 1218 1824	0.4 6.6 0.5
7 W	0047 0652 1311 1908	5.8 0.9 6.0 1.1	**22** TH	0032 0646 1300 1909	6.5 0.3 6.7 0.4
8 TH	0116 0724 1339 1940	5.8 1.0 5.9 1.1	**23** F	0115 0730 1342 1954	6.5 0.3 6.6 0.5
9 F	0142 0756 1402 2012	5.7 1.1 5.8 1.2	**24** SA	0157 0814 1423 2038	6.4 0.5 6.4 0.7
10 SA	0207 0827 1426 2044	5.5 1.2 5.5 1.4	**25** SU	0240 0858 1505 2124	6.1 0.8 6.1 1.0
11 SU	0236 0858 1456 2118	5.4 1.4 5.5 1.5	**26** M	0326 0946 1553 ☾ 2217	5.7 1.2 5.6 1.5
12 M	0310 0932 1534 ☽ 2200	5.2 1.7 5.2 1.8	**27** TU	0421 1043 1651 2328	5.2 1.7 5.1 1.9
13 TU	0355 1019 1626 2300	4.9 2.0 4.9 2.1	**28** W	0533 1206 1810	4.8 2.1 4.8
14 W	0502 1129 1750	4.5 2.2 4.7	**29** TH	0100 0715 1337 1955	2.1 4.6 2.1 4.8
15 TH	0020 0648 1259 1924	2.2 4.5 2.3 4.8	**30** F	0217 0846 1446 2110	1.9 4.9 1.9 5.1
			31 SA	0317 0943 1540 2201	1.6 5.4 1.5 5.5

SEPTEMBER

Day	Time	m	Day	Time	m
1 SU	0403 1027 1622 2242	1.3 5.7 1.3 5.7	**16** M	0330 0941 1552 2159	1.1 6.0 1.0 6.1
2 M	0442 1105 1700 2319	1.0 6.0 1.1 5.9	**17** TU	0413 1027 1635 2244	0.7 6.4 0.7 6.4
3 TU	0517 1140 1734 ● 2353	0.9 6.1 1.0 6.0	**18** W	0455 1111 1717 ○ 2328	0.4 6.7 0.4 6.6
4 W	0551 1213 1807	0.9 6.1 0.9	**19** TH	0537 1154 1800	0.3 6.8 0.3
5 TH	0021 0623 1240 1838	6.0 0.9 6.1 1.0	**20** F	0011 0621 1235 1844	6.7 0.3 6.8 0.3
6 F	0045 0654 1302 1908	5.9 0.9 6.0 1.0	**21** SA	0053 0704 1315 1927	6.6 0.4 6.7 0.5
7 SA	0106 0723 1321 1937	5.8 1.0 5.9 1.1	**22** SU	0134 0747 1355 2010	6.5 0.6 6.4 0.8
8 SU	0130 0749 1346 2003	5.8 1.2 5.8 1.3	**23** M	0215 0830 1436 2055	6.1 1.0 6.0 1.2
9 M	0158 0814 1415 2032	5.6 1.4 5.6 1.5	**24** TU	0301 0916 1524 ☾ 2146	5.7 1.4 5.5 1.6
10 TU	0230 0848 1451 2112	5.4 1.7 5.3 1.8	**25** W	0358 1014 1625 2300	5.1 1.9 4.9 2.1
11 W	0312 0936 1538 ☽ 2211	5.1 2.0 4.9 2.1	**26** TH	0514 1149 1750	4.7 2.3 4.6
12 TH	0413 1047 1656 2338	4.7 2.3 4.6 2.3	**27** F	0045 0704 1324 1946	2.2 4.6 2.3 4.6
13 F	0621 1232 1902	4.5 2.4 4.7	**28** SA	0201 0830 1431 2054	2.0 5.0 1.9 5.0
14 SA	0125 0746 1408 2014	2.1 4.9 2.0 5.1	**29** SU	0257 0921 1520 2140	1.7 5.4 1.6 5.4
15 SU	0240 0850 1507 2111	1.6 5.4 1.5 5.6	**30** M	0340 1001 1559 2218	1.3 5.8 1.3 5.7

OCTOBER

Day	Time	m	Day	Time	m
1 TU	0416 1037 1633 2252	1.1 6.0 1.1 5.9	**16** W	0346 1001 1608 2220	0.7 6.5 0.6 6.5
2 W	0449 1110 1705 ● 2323	1.0 6.1 1.0 6.0	**17** TH	0428 1044 1651 ○ 2304	0.5 6.7 0.4 6.7
3 TH	0521 1140 1737 2349	0.9 6.1 0.9 6.0	**18** F	0512 1127 1735 2348	0.4 6.8 0.4 6.7
4 F	0552 1204 1808	0.9 6.1 1.0	**19** SA	0555 1208 1819	0.4 6.8 0.4
5 SA	0011 0623 1224 1838	6.0 1.0 6.0 1.0	**20** SU	0030 0639 1249 1903	6.6 0.5 6.6 0.6
6 SU	0035 0651 1247 1904	6.0 1.1 6.0 1.1	**21** M	0112 0723 1329 1947	6.4 0.8 6.3 0.9
7 M	0101 0716 1314 1931	5.9 1.2 5.9 1.3	**22** TU	0156 0807 1412 2032	6.1 1.2 5.9 1.3
8 TU	0130 0745 1344 2003	5.8 1.4 5.7 1.5	**23** W	0243 0854 1501 2123	5.6 1.6 5.4 1.7
9 W	0203 0822 1421 2046	5.5 1.7 5.4 1.8	**24** TH	0341 0953 1604 ☾ 2232	5.2 2.0 4.9 2.1
10 TH	0246 0913 1510 ☽ 2147	5.2 2.0 4.9 2.1	**25** F	0453 1122 1723	4.8 2.3 4.6
11 F	0350 1027 1630 2312	4.8 2.3 4.6 2.3	**26** SA	0013 0625 1255 1908	2.2 4.7 2.3 4.6
12 SA	0559 1209 1839	4.6 2.3 4.7	**27** SU	0127 0749 1359 2018	2.1 5.0 2.0 4.9
13 SU	0057 0722 1340 1951	2.1 5.0 1.9 5.2	**28** M	0222 0843 1447 2105	1.8 5.4 1.6 5.3
14 M	0211 0825 1439 2047	1.6 5.6 1.4 5.7	**29** TU	0306 0924 1526 2144	1.5 5.7 1.4 5.6
15 TU	0302 0916 1525 2135	1.1 6.1 0.9 6.2	**30** W	0343 1001 1601 2218	1.3 5.9 1.2 5.8
			31 TH	0417 1033 1635 2247	1.1 6.0 1.1 5.9

NOVEMBER

Day	Time	m	Day	Time	m
1 F	0450 1101 1707 ● 2314	1.1 6.1 1.0 6.0	**16** SA	0449 1102 1713 2328	0.6 6.6 0.5 6.5
2 SA	0523 1126 1740 2342	1.1 6.1 1.0 6.0	**17** SU	0535 1145 1759	0.7 6.6 0.6
3 SU	0555 1153 1811	1.1 6.0 1.1	**18** M	0013 0621 1228 1845	6.4 0.8 6.4 0.8
4 M	0010 0625 1221 1841	6.0 1.2 6.0 1.2	**19** TU	0057 0705 1311 1930	6.3 1.0 6.1 1.0
5 TU	0040 0655 1252 1912	5.9 1.3 5.9 1.3	**20** W	0143 0750 1355 2015	6.0 1.3 5.8 1.3
6 W	0113 0728 1326 1949	5.8 1.5 5.7 1.4	**21** TH	0230 0838 1444 2104	5.7 1.6 5.4 1.6
7 TH	0151 0810 1407 2035	5.6 1.7 5.4 1.7	**22** F	0323 0931 1540 2201	5.4 1.9 5.0 1.9
8 F	0239 0904 1500 2135	5.3 1.9 5.1 1.9	**23** SA	0422 1037 1645 ☾ 2312	5.1 2.1 4.7 2.1
9 SA	0345 1015 1619 ☽ 2252	5.0 2.1 4.8 2.0	**24** SU	0527 1159 1755	4.9 2.2 4.7
10 SU	0526 1142 1804	5.0 2.1 4.9	**25** M	0029 0639 1308 1911	2.1 5.0 2.1 4.8
11 M	0019 0648 1302 1917	1.9 5.2 1.8 5.2	**26** TU	0131 0743 1402 2012	2.0 5.2 1.8 5.0
12 TU	0132 0751 1404 2016	1.6 5.6 1.4 5.7	**27** W	0221 0833 1447 2057	1.8 5.4 1.6 5.3
13 W	0228 0844 1455 2107	1.2 6.1 1.0 6.0	**28** TH	0304 0914 1527 2134	1.6 5.6 1.4 5.5
14 TH	0317 0932 1542 2155	0.9 6.4 0.7 6.3	**29** F	0344 0949 1604 2209	1.4 5.8 1.3 5.7
15 F	0403 1017 1627 ○ 2242	0.7 6.6 0.6 6.5	**30** SA	0421 1023 1640 2244	1.3 5.9 1.2 5.8

DECEMBER

Day	Time	m	Day	Time	m
1 SU	0457 1056 1716 ● 2318	1.3 6.0 1.1 5.9	**16** M	0522 1132 1747	0.9 6.3 0.8
2 M	0533 1130 1751 2353	1.3 6.0 1.1 5.9	**17** TU	0003 0609 1216 1833	6.2 1.0 6.2 0.8
3 TU	0607 1204 1826	1.3 6.0 1.1	**18** W	0049 0653 1300 1917	6.2 1.1 6.0 1.0
4 W	0029 0643 1240 1903	5.9 1.3 5.9 1.2	**19** TH	0133 0736 1343 2000	6.0 1.2 5.8 1.1
5 TH	0107 0721 1319 1943	5.9 1.4 5.8 1.3	**20** F	0215 0819 1425 2042	5.9 1.4 5.5 1.4
6 F	0149 0805 1404 2030	5.7 1.5 5.6 1.4	**21** SA	0259 0903 1510 2125	5.6 1.6 5.3 1.6
7 SA	0238 0857 1456 2124	5.6 1.6 5.4 1.5	**22** SU	0344 0950 1559 ☾ 2213	5.4 1.8 5.0 1.8
8 SU	0336 0959 1600 ☽ 2229	5.4 1.7 5.2 1.6	**23** M	0434 1043 1654 2306	5.2 2.0 4.8 2.0
9 M	0446 1110 1716 2341	5.3 1.7 5.2 1.6	**24** TU	0528 1142 1753	5.0 2.1 4.7
10 TU	0600 1222 1831	5.4 1.6 5.3	**25** W	0006 0626 1248 1854	2.1 5.0 2.1 4.7
11 W	0050 0709 1327 1939	1.5 5.6 1.4 5.5	**26** TH	0113 0725 1354 1954	2.1 5.0 1.9 4.9
12 TH	0153 0810 1426 2039	1.4 5.8 1.2 5.7	**27** F	0217 0821 1449 2049	2.0 5.2 1.7 5.1
13 F	0251 0905 1520 2134	1.2 6.0 1.0 5.9	**28** SA	0310 0909 1536 2136	1.8 5.4 1.5 5.4
14 SA	0344 0956 1611 2227	1.0 6.2 0.8 6.1	**29** SU	0356 0953 1618 2220	1.6 5.6 1.3 5.6
15 SU	0434 1045 1700 ○ 2316	0.9 6.3 0.8 6.2	**30** M	0437 1034 1658 ● 2301	1.4 5.8 1.2 5.8
			31 TU	0516 1114 1737 2342	1.3 5.9 1.0 6.0

DOVER

LAT 51°07′N
LONG 1°19′E

TIMES AND HEIGHTS OF HIGH AND LOW WATER (Heights in Metres)

TIME ZONE UT
For Summer Time (area enclosed in shaded box) add 1 hour

2024

JANUARY

Date	Day	Moon	Time	m	Time	m	Time	m	Time	m
1	M		0201	6.2	0906	1.6	1420	5.8	2114	1.8
2	TU		0236	6.0	0942	1.7	1457	5.6	2151	1.9
3	W		0312	5.8	1022	1.9	1540	5.4	2233	2.1
4	TH	☾	0356	5.6	1109	2.0	1634	5.2	2324	2.3
5	F		0454	5.5	1207	2.1	1744	5.2		
6	SA		0029	2.4	0602	5.4	1316	2.1	1852	5.2
7	SU		0147	2.3	0708	5.5	1424	2.0	1950	5.4
8	M		0257	2.1	0806	5.7	1527	1.8	2042	5.7
9	TU		0357	1.8	0859	5.9	1624	1.5	2131	6.0
10	W		0451	1.5	0949	6.2	1717	1.3	2218	6.3
11	TH	●	0542	1.3	1037	6.4	1808	1.2	2304	6.5
12	F		0632	1.1	1124	6.6	1858	1.0	2349	6.7
13	SA		0723	0.9	1211	6.6	1947	1.0		
14	SU		0034	6.8	0813	0.8	1257	6.6	2034	0.9
15	M		0120	6.8	0900	0.8	1345	6.5	2117	1.0
16	TU		0208	6.8	0945	0.8	1435	6.4	2159	1.1
17	W		0257	6.6	1029	1.0	1528	6.1	2242	1.3
18	TH	☽	0350	6.4	1116	1.3	1626	5.9	2332	1.6
19	F		0449	6.0	1210	1.6	1732	5.6		
20	SA		0029	1.9	0557	5.7	1310	1.8	1848	5.4
21	SU		0137	2.1	0714	5.6	1418	1.9	2002	5.4
22	M		0249	2.0	0830	5.6	1532	1.9	2108	5.6
23	TU		0403	1.9	0935	5.8	1645	1.7	2202	5.8
24	W		0506	1.6	1027	6.0	1740	1.6	2245	6.1
25	TH	○	0557	1.4	1109	6.1	1823	1.5	2323	6.3
26	F		0640	1.3	1145	6.2	1859	1.4	2359	6.4
27	SA		0717	1.2	1218	6.2	1930	1.4		
28	SU		0033	6.5	0749	1.2	1249	6.2	1958	1.4
29	M		0104	6.4	0817	1.2	1318	6.1	2024	1.4
30	TU		0132	6.3	0845	1.3	1344	6.0	2052	1.4
31	W		0156	6.2	0915	1.4	1407	5.9	2123	1.5

FEBRUARY

Date	Day	Moon	Time	m	Time	m	Time	m	Time	m
1	TH		0223	6.1	0947	1.5	1436	5.8	2156	1.7
2	F	☾	0257	6.0	1023	1.7	1514	5.6	2234	2.0
3	SA		0341	5.7	1106	2.0	1604	5.4	2323	2.2
4	SU		0441	5.4	1207	2.2	1721	5.1		
5	M		0037	2.4	0614	5.3	1335	2.2	1914	5.1
6	TU		0215	2.3	0741	5.4	1456	2.0	2023	5.4
7	W		0329	2.0	0846	5.7	1602	1.7	2120	5.8
8	TH		0432	1.6	0942	6.1	1702	1.4	2210	6.2
9	F	●	0530	1.2	1033	6.4	1800	1.1	2256	6.6
10	SA		0626	0.9	1119	6.7	1853	0.8	2340	6.9
11	SU		0719	0.6	1203	6.8	1941	0.7		
12	M		0022	7.1	0807	0.4	1245	6.9	2024	0.6
13	TU		0105	7.1	0849	0.4	1327	6.8	2101	0.6
14	W		0148	7.0	0927	0.5	1410	6.6	2137	0.8
15	TH		0232	6.8	1004	0.7	1456	6.3	2214	1.1
16	F	☽	0318	6.5	1044	1.2	1547	5.9	2256	1.5
17	SA		0411	6.0	1131	1.7	1647	5.5	2350	2.0
18	SU		0516	5.5	1232	2.1	1804	5.1		
19	M		0102	2.3	0642	5.2	1347	2.3	1936	5.1
20	TU		0224	2.3	0825	5.2	1512	2.2	2059	5.4
21	W		0352	2.0	0937	5.5	1641	1.9	2154	5.7
22	TH		0502	1.7	1024	5.8	1734	1.6	2234	6.1
23	F		0551	1.4	1101	6.1	1814	1.4	2309	6.3
24	SA	○	0630	1.2	1131	6.2	1847	1.3	2341	6.4
25	SU		0702	1.1	1159	6.3	1913	1.2		
26	M		0011	6.5	0728	1.1	1225	6.3	1936	1.2
27	TU		0038	6.5	0753	1.1	1249	6.2	1959	1.2
28	W		0100	6.4	0818	1.1	1309	6.2	2026	1.2
29	TH		0120	6.4	0846	1.2	1329	6.2	2055	1.3

MARCH

Date	Day	Moon	Time	m	Time	m	Time	m	Time	m
1	F		0145	6.4	0914	1.3	1358	6.2	2124	1.5
2	SA		0218	6.2	0946	1.5	1435	6.0	2158	1.8
3	SU	☾	0259	6.0	1025	1.9	1521	5.6	2243	2.1
4	M		0351	5.5	1118	2.2	1624	5.2	2349	2.4
5	TU		0528	5.1	1247	2.4	1851	5.0		
6	W		0140	2.4	0729	5.3	1431	2.2	2008	5.4
7	TH		0306	2.0	0838	5.7	1544	1.8	2107	5.9
8	F		0414	1.5	0934	6.1	1648	1.3	2157	6.3
9	SA		0516	1.0	1023	6.5	1746	1.0	2242	6.7
10	SU	●	0613	0.6	1106	6.8	1838	0.7	2324	7.0
11	M		0704	0.4	1147	6.9	1922	0.5		
12	TU		0004	7.2	0749	0.2	1225	7.0	2002	0.4
13	W		0044	7.2	0827	0.2	1304	6.9	2037	0.5
14	TH		0124	7.1	0902	0.4	1345	6.7	2111	0.7
15	F		0206	6.8	0936	0.8	1428	6.4	2146	1.1
16	SA		0250	6.4	1012	1.3	1517	6.0	2225	1.6
17	SU	☽	0341	5.9	1056	1.8	1616	5.5	2316	2.1
18	M		0446	5.3	1159	2.4	1729	5.1		
19	TU		0035	2.5	0612	5.0	1324	2.6	1905	5.0
20	W		0206	2.4	0820	5.1	1454	2.4	2040	5.3
21	TH		0339	2.1	0923	5.4	1618	2.0	2132	5.7
22	F		0444	1.6	1004	5.8	1709	1.6	2211	6.1
23	SA		0529	1.3	1037	6.0	1748	1.4	2245	6.3
24	SU		0605	1.1	1105	6.2	1819	1.3	2315	6.4
25	M	○	0633	1.1	1131	6.3	1843	1.2	2343	6.5
26	TU		0657	1.0	1156	6.3	1906	1.1		
27	W		0007	6.4	0723	1.0	1217	6.3	1932	1.1
28	TH		0027	6.4	0750	1.0	1236	6.3	2000	1.1
29	F		0048	6.4	0818	1.1	1259	6.4	2029	1.2
30	SA		0115	6.4	0846	1.3	1330	6.3	2059	1.4
31	SU		0149	6.3	0918	1.5	1408	6.1	2135	1.7

APRIL

Date	Day	Moon	Time	m	Time	m	Time	m	Time	m
1	M		0231	6.0	0959	1.8	1456	5.7	2221	2.0
2	TU	☾	0326	5.5	1053	2.2	1606	5.2	2328	2.3
3	W		0535	5.1	1220	2.4	1830	5.1		
4	TH		0119	2.3	0715	5.3	1410	2.2	1947	5.5
5	F		0245	1.9	0822	5.7	1522	1.7	2046	6.0
6	SA		0352	1.4	0917	6.2	1624	1.3	2135	6.5
7	SU		0455	0.9	1004	6.6	1721	0.9	2220	6.8
8	M	●	0551	0.6	1046	6.8	1811	0.6	2302	7.1
9	TU		0640	0.3	1126	6.9	1855	0.5	2342	7.2
10	W		0723	0.3	1204	6.9	1935	0.5		
11	TH		0022	7.1	0802	0.4	1242	6.8	2011	0.6
12	F		0101	7.0	0837	0.6	1322	6.7	2047	0.8
13	SA		0143	6.7	0910	1.0	1406	6.4	2122	1.2
14	SU		0227	6.3	0945	1.5	1455	6.0	2201	1.7
15	M	☽	0320	5.8	1027	2.0	1552	5.5	2252	2.1
16	TU		0423	5.3	1130	2.4	1659	5.2		
17	W		0013	2.4	0541	5.0	1258	2.6	1821	5.1
18	TH		0141	2.4	0740	5.0	1420	2.4	1956	5.3
19	F		0258	2.0	0846	5.4	1529	2.1	2054	5.7
20	SA		0358	1.7	0927	5.7	1621	1.7	2135	6.0
21	SU		0444	1.4	1000	5.9	1703	1.5	2209	6.2
22	M		0520	1.2	1028	6.1	1737	1.3	2240	6.3
23	TU	○	0551	1.1	1055	6.2	1805	1.2	2307	6.3
24	W		0621	1.1	1122	6.3	1834	1.2	2332	6.4
25	TH		0652	1.1	1146	6.3	1905	1.1	2357	6.4
26	F		0723	1.1	1210	6.4	1937	1.2		
27	SA		0023	6.4	0755	1.2	1238	6.4	2009	1.2
28	SU		0054	6.3	0826	1.3	1314	6.3	2043	1.4
29	M		0133	6.2	0902	1.5	1357	6.1	2123	1.6
30	TU		0220	5.9	0946	1.8	1453	5.7	2214	1.9

MAY

Date	Day	Moon	Time	m	Time	m	Time	m	Time	m
1	W	☽	0328	5.5	1043	2.1	1619	5.4	2325	2.1
2	TH		0527	5.3	1210	2.2	1801	5.4		
3	F		0101	2.0	0652	5.5	1343	2.0	1916	5.7
4	SA		0218	1.6	0757	5.8	1451	1.6	2016	6.1
5	SU		0323	1.2	0851	6.2	1551	1.3	2108	6.5
6	M		0425	0.9	0939	6.4	1648	1.0	2154	6.7
7	TU		0522	0.7	1022	6.6	1740	0.8	2238	6.9
8	W	●	0613	0.6	1103	6.7	1827	0.7	2321	6.9
9	TH		0657	0.6	1143	6.7	1909	0.7		
10	F		0002	6.9	0738	0.7	1223	6.7	1949	0.8
11	SA		0043	6.7	0815	0.9	1305	6.5	2028	1.0
12	SU		0126	6.4	0850	1.3	1349	6.3	2106	1.3
13	M		0212	6.1	0926	1.6	1437	6.0	2146	1.7
14	TU		0303	5.7	1006	2.0	1529	5.7	2235	2.0
15	W	☾	0401	5.4	1101	2.3	1628	5.5	2343	2.2
16	TH		0507	5.1	1217	2.5	1734	5.3		
17	F		0056	2.2	0625	5.1	1329	2.4	1849	5.3
18	SA		0201	2.1	0740	5.3	1430	2.2	1955	5.5
19	SU		0256	1.8	0831	5.5	1523	1.9	2044	5.8
20	M		0343	1.6	0910	5.7	1609	1.7	2122	5.9
21	TU		0427	1.4	0944	5.9	1650	1.5	2156	6.1
22	W		0508	1.3	1017	6.1	1728	1.4	2228	6.2
23	TH	○	0547	1.2	1048	6.2	1806	1.3	2300	6.3
24	F		0626	1.2	1120	6.3	1843	1.2	2333	6.3
25	SA		0703	1.2	1153	6.3	1920	1.2		
26	SU		0008	6.3	0740	1.2	1229	6.3	1959	1.2
27	M		0047	6.3	0817	1.3	1312	6.3	2039	1.3
28	TU		0133	6.1	0858	1.5	1402	6.2	2124	1.5
29	W		0228	5.9	0945	1.6	1501	6.0	2218	1.6
30	TH	☽	0338	5.7	1043	1.8	1610	5.8	2325	1.7
31	F		0500	5.6	1156	1.9	1723	5.8		

JUNE

Date	Day	Moon	Time	m	Time	m	Time	m	Time	m
1	SA		0038	1.6	0618	5.7	1309	1.8	1836	5.9
2	SU		0145	1.5	0723	5.8	1413	1.6	1941	6.1
3	M		0247	1.3	0820	6.0	1514	1.4	2038	6.3
4	TU		0350	1.1	0912	6.2	1614	1.2	2130	6.4
5	W		0452	1.0	1000	6.3	1712	1.1	2219	6.5
6	TH	●	0547	1.0	1045	6.4	1803	1.0	2306	6.6
7	F		0636	1.0	1128	6.5	1850	1.0	2350	6.5
8	SA		0719	1.1	1210	6.5	1933	1.0		
9	SU		0032	6.4	0759	1.2	1252	6.4	2015	1.2
10	M		0114	6.2	0836	1.4	1335	6.3	2055	1.4
11	TU		0158	6.0	0912	1.6	1418	6.2	2134	1.6
12	W		0244	5.8	0946	1.8	1504	6.0	2214	1.8
13	TH		0333	5.5	1025	2.0	1552	5.7	2259	1.9
14	F	☾	0426	5.3	1113	2.2	1644	5.5	2354	2.0
15	SA		0526	5.2	1215	2.3	1743	5.4		
16	SU		0053	2.0	0629	5.2	1320	2.3	1845	5.4
17	M		0152	2.0	0727	5.3	1421	2.1	1941	5.5
18	TU		0248	1.8	0817	5.5	1517	1.9	2029	5.7
19	W		0341	1.6	0901	5.7	1609	1.7	2113	5.9
20	TH		0431	1.5	0942	5.9	1657	1.5	2155	6.0
21	F		0519	1.3	1022	6.1	1742	1.3	2237	6.2
22	SA	○	0605	1.2	1103	6.2	1826	1.2	2319	6.3
23	SU		0649	1.2	1144	6.4	1910	1.1		
24	M		0002	6.3	0733	1.2	1226	6.5	1956	1.1
25	TU		0047	6.3	0817	1.2	1311	6.5	2042	1.1
26	W		0135	6.3	0902	1.2	1400	6.5	2130	1.1
27	TH		0226	6.2	0948	1.3	1452	6.4	2219	1.2
28	F	☽	0322	6.1	1036	1.4	1547	6.3	2311	1.3
29	SA		0424	5.9	1130	1.5	1646	6.1		
30	SU		0007	1.4	0532	5.8	1230	1.7	1753	6.0

SUNRISE AND SUNSET TIMES

DOVER
At 51°07′N 1°19′E

UT		Sunrise	Sunset
Jan	01	0759	1558
	15	0752	1617
Feb	01	0732	1646
	15	0708	1711
Mar	01	0639	1736
	15	0609	1800
BST (UT+1)			
Apr	01	0630	1928
	15	0600	1951
May	01	0528	2017
	15	0504	2039
Jun	01	0445	2101
	15	0439	2112
Jul	01	0444	2113
	15	0457	2104
Aug	01	0520	2041
	15	0541	2016
Sep	01	0608	1940
	15	0630	1909
Oct	01	0655	1832
	15	0718	1802
UT			
Nov	01	0647	1629
	15	0711	1607
Dec	01	0736	1551
	15	0752	1548

DOVER
LAT 51°07′N
LONG 1°19′E

TIMES AND HEIGHTS OF HIGH AND LOW WATER (Heights in Metres)

TIME ZONE UT
For Summer Time (area enclosed in shaded box) add 1 hour

2024

JULY

Date	Day	Time	m	Time	m	Time	m	Time	m
1	M	0108	1.5	0643	5.7	1334	1.7	1903	5.9
2	TU	0211	1.6	0750	5.7	1439	1.7	2011	5.9
3	W	0318	1.5	0850	5.8	1546	1.6	2114	6.0
4	TH	0428	1.5	0946	6.0	1651	1.4	2211	6.1
5	F ●	0530	1.4	1036	6.1	1748	1.3	2301	6.2
6	SA	0623	1.3	1119	6.3	1838	1.2	2344	6.3
7	SU	0708	1.3	1200	6.4	1923	1.2		
8	M	0024	6.2	0748	1.4	1239	6.4	2005	1.2
9	TU	0102	6.2	0823	1.4	1318	6.4	2041	1.3
10	W	0140	6.1	0853	1.5	1355	6.3	2113	1.4
11	TH	0217	5.9	0919	1.6	1432	6.2	2142	1.5
12	F	0254	5.7	0948	1.7	1507	6.0	2215	1.6
13	SA ☾	0333	5.6	1023	1.9	1545	5.8	2253	1.8
14	SU	0418	5.4	1105	2.1	1633	5.5	2343	2.0
15	M	0517	5.2	1201	2.3	1734	5.4		
16	TU	0046	2.1	0627	5.2	1316	2.3	1843	5.3
17	W	0158	2.1	0731	5.3	1432	2.2	1947	5.5
18	TH	0304	1.9	0828	5.5	1536	2.0	2044	5.7
19	F	0403	1.7	0919	5.8	1631	1.7	2136	6.0
20	SA	0457	1.5	1006	6.1	1723	1.4	2224	6.2
21	SU O	0549	1.3	1050	6.3	1813	1.2	2310	6.4
22	M	0639	1.1	1134	6.6	1903	1.0	2355	6.5
23	TU	0728	1.0	1217	6.7	1952	0.8		
24	W	0038	6.6	0814	0.9	1300	6.8	2039	0.7
25	TH	0122	6.6	0856	0.9	1344	6.8	2122	0.7
26	F	0208	6.5	0935	1.0	1431	6.8	2203	0.8
27	SA	0256	6.3	1015	1.1	1520	6.6	2246	1.1
28	SU ☽	0349	6.1	1059	1.4	1613	6.3	2334	1.4
29	M	0450	5.8	1153	1.7	1715	5.9		
30	TU	0032	1.7	0603	5.5	1258	2.0	1830	5.6
31	W	0141	2.0	0725	5.4	1412	2.1	1956	5.6

AUGUST

Date	Day	Time	m	Time	m	Time	m	Time	m
1	TH	0256	[illegible]	0840	5.5	1530	1.9	2114	5.7
2	F	0421	1.8	0942	5.8	1645	1.7	2214	5.9
3	SA	0528	[illegible]	1031	6.1	1745	1.4	2300	6.1
4	SU ●	0618	1.4	1110	6.3	1833	1.2	2338	6.2
5	M	0659	1.4	1147	6.5	1914	1.1		
6	TU	0011	6.3	0734	1.3	1222	6.5	1949	1.1
7	W	0043	6.3	0802	1.4	1256	6.5	2017	1.2
8	TH	0114	6.2	0824	1.4	1327	6.4	2041	1.2
9	F	0141	6.1	0845	1.4	1353	6.3	2106	1.3
10	SA	0205	6.0	0912	1.5	1416	6.2	2134	1.5
11	SU	0228	5.8	0942	1.7	1445	6.0	2206	1.7
12	M ☾	0300	5.7	1018	1.9	1524	5.7	2246	1.9
13	TU	0344	5.4	1101	2.2	1618	5.4	2339	2.2
14	W	0458	5.1	1206	2.5	1753	5.2		
15	TH	0106	2.4	0658	5.1	1351	2.5	1922	5.3
16	F	0235	2.2	0806	5.4	1509	2.2	2028	5.6
17	SA	0341	1.9	0902	5.8	1610	1.7	2124	6.0
18	SU	0439	1.5	0951	6.2	1706	1.3	2213	6.3
19	M O	0534	1.2	1035	6.6	1800	1.0	2257	6.6
20	TU	0626	1.0	1117	6.8	1851	0.8	2339	6.8
21	W	0714	0.8	1159	7.1	1939	0.6		
22	TH	0020	6.9	0757	0.7	1240	7.2	2022	0.5
23	F	0101	6.9	0835	0.7	1322	7.1	2101	0.5
24	SA	0143	6.7	0911	0.8	1405	7.0	2138	0.7
25	SU	0227	6.5	0948	1.0	1451	6.7	2216	1.1
26	M ☽	0317	6.1	1028	1.4	1543	6.2	2301	1.6
27	TU	0417	5.7	1119	1.9	1645	5.7		
28	W	0000	2.1	0531	5.3	1230	2.3	1807	5.3
29	TH	0118	2.4	0705	5.2	1357	2.4	1957	5.3
30	F	0252	2.3	0836	5.4	1532	2.1	2119	5.6
31	SA	0427	2.0	0935	5.8	1647	1.7	2210	5.9

SEPTEMBER

Date	Day	Time	m	Time	m	Time	m	Time	m
1	SU	0521	1.6	1018	6.2	1738	1.4	2248	6.2
2	M	0604	1.4	1053	6.4	1820	1.2	2320	6.3
3	TU ●	0640	1.3	1127	6.6	1854	1.1	2348	6.4
4	W	0708	1.3	1158	6.6	1921	1.1		
5	TH	0015	6.4	0729	1.3	1228	6.6	1943	1.1
6	F	0041	6.3	0748	1.3	1253	6.5	2005	1.2
7	SA	0102	6.2	0811	1.3	1312	6.4	2030	1.3
8	SU	0119	6.2	0838	1.4	1332	6.3	2057	1.4
9	M	0141	6.1	0908	1.6	1400	6.2	2128	1.6
10	TU	0214	6.0	0941	1.9	1437	5.9	2204	2.0
11	W ☾	0256	5.6	1022	2.2	1525	5.5	2252	2.3
12	TH	0355	5.2	1119	2.6	1713	5.1		
13	F	0008	2.6	0633	5.0	1312	2.6	1907	5.2
14	SA	0210	2.4	0745	5.4	1445	2.2	2014	5.6
15	SU	0322	2.0	0842	5.9	1549	1.7	2108	6.1
16	M	0420	1.5	0930	6.4	1646	1.2	2155	6.5
17	TU	0514	1.2	1014	6.8	1740	0.9	2238	6.8
18	W O	0604	0.9	1055	7.1	1830	0.6	2318	7.0
19	TH	0649	0.7	1136	7.3	1916	0.4	2357	7.0
20	F	0730	0.6	1216	7.3	1957	0.4		
21	SA	0035	7.0	0808	0.7	1256	7.2	2034	0.6
22	SU	0116	6.8	0844	0.8	1339	7.0	2110	0.9
23	M	0200	6.5	0921	1.1	1424	6.6	2147	1.3
24	TU ☽	0250	6.1	1001	1.6	1518	6.1	2230	1.9
25	W	0351	5.7	1052	2.1	1624	5.5	2332	2.4
26	TH	0505	5.3	1210	2.5	1748	5.2		
27	F	0103	2.7	0640	5.1	1349	2.5	1957	5.2
28	SA	0250	2.5	0818	5.4	1528	2.1	2105	5.6
29	SU	0406	2.0	0912	5.8	1628	1.6	2148	5.9
30	M	0454	1.7	0952	6.2	1713	1.3	2222	6.2

OCTOBER

Date	Day	Time	m	Time	m	Time	m	Time	m
1	TU	0533	1.4	1026	6.5	1750	1.2	2251	6.4
2	W ●	0606	1.3	1058	6.6	1820	1.1	2317	6.4
3	TH	0631	1.3	1128	6.6	1843	1.2	2343	6.4
4	F	0651	1.3	1155	6.6	1905	1.2		
5	SA	0006	6.4	0714	1.3	1216	6.5	1930	1.2
6	SU	0025	6.4	0741	1.3	1234	6.4	1958	1.3
7	M	0043	6.4	0810	1.4	1257	6.4	2026	1.5
8	TU	0109	6.3	0840	1.6	1327	6.2	2058	1.7
9	W	0144	6.1	0914	1.9	1405	6.0	2135	2.0
10	TH ☾	0229	5.8	0957	2.2	1456	5.5	2224	2.4
11	F	0332	5.3	1056	2.5	1713	5.1	2335	2.6
12	SA	0603	5.2	1241	2.6	1846	5.3		
13	SU	0141	2.5	0717	5.5	1417	2.1	1952	5.7
14	M	0255	2.0	0815	6.0	1522	1.6	2046	6.2
15	TU	0353	1.5	0904	6.5	1619	1.1	2132	6.6
16	W	0445	1.2	0948	6.9	1713	0.8	2213	6.9
17	TH O	0534	0.9	1030	7.1	1803	0.6	2253	7.0
18	F	0620	0.7	1111	7.3	1849	0.5	2332	7.1
19	SA	0702	0.7	1151	7.3	1930	0.6		
20	SU	0011	7.0	0742	0.8	1232	7.1	2008	0.8
21	M	0053	6.8	0821	1.0	1315	6.8	2045	1.1
22	TU	0139	6.5	0900	1.3	1403	6.4	2123	1.6
23	W	0230	6.2	0942	1.7	1459	5.9	2207	2.1
24	TH ☽	0330	5.7	1035	2.2	1604	5.5	2310	2.5
25	F	0437	5.4	1154	2.5	1722	5.1		
26	SA	0040	2.7	0559	5.3	1325	2.4	1918	5.2
27	SU	0209	2.5	0733	5.5	1447	2.1	2027	5.5
28	M	0318	2.2	0832	5.8	1545	1.7	2110	5.8
29	TU	0408	1.8	0915	6.1	1630	1.5	2145	6.1
30	W	0449	1.6	0951	6.3	1706	1.3	2214	6.2
31	TH	0523	1.4	1024	6.4	1736	1.3	2242	6.3

NOVEMBER

Date	Day	Time	m	Time	m	Time	m	Time	m
1	F ●	0551	1.4	1053	6.5	1803	1.2	2309	6.4
2	SA	0617	1.3	1119	6.4	1832	1.2	2334	6.4
3	SU	0646	1.3	1143	6.4	1902	1.3	2356	6.4
4	M	0717	1.3	1207	6.4	1933	1.4		
5	TU	0021	6.4	0749	1.4	1235	6.3	2005	1.5
6	W	0052	6.3	0822	1.6	1309	6.2	2038	1.7
7	TH	0131	6.2	0900	1.8	1352	5.9	2119	2.0
8	F	0221	5.9	0946	2.0	1451	5.6	2209	2.2
9	SA ☾	0334	5.5	1046	2.2	1646	5.3	2318	2.4
10	SU	0521	5.5	1216	2.2	1816	5.5		
11	M	0101	2.3	0640	5.7	1341	1.9	1921	5.8
12	TU	0216	2.0	0741	6.1	1446	1.5	2016	6.1
13	W	0316	1.6	0832	6.4	1545	1.2	2104	6.4
14	TH	0411	1.3	0920	6.7	1642	0.9	2148	6.7
15	F O	0504	1.0	1004	6.9	1735	0.8	2230	6.8
16	SA	0553	0.9	1048	7.0	1823	0.8	2312	6.9
17	SU	0639	0.9	1132	7.0	1907	0.8	2355	6.8
18	M	0722	0.9	1216	6.8	1948	1.0		
19	TU	0038	6.7	0805	1.1	1300	6.6	2028	1.3
20	W	0125	6.5	0848	1.4	1349	6.3	2108	1.7
21	TH	0214	6.2	0932	1.7	1442	5.9	2152	2.0
22	F	0308	5.9	1023	2.0	1541	5.5	2245	2.4
23	SA ☽	0406	5.7	1126	2.2	1647	5.3	2355	2.6
24	SU	0511	5.5	1237	2.3	1804	5.2		
25	M	0108	2.5	0625	5.5	1342	2.2	1920	5.3
26	TU	0213	2.4	0734	5.6	1439	2.0	2015	5.5
27	W	0309	2.1	0826	5.8	1529	1.8	2056	5.8
28	TH	0356	1.9	0908	6.0	1612	1.6	2133	6.0
29	F	0437	1.7	0943	6.1	1651	1.5	2206	6.1
30	SA	0513	1.5	1016	6.2	1728	1.4	2238	6.2

DECEMBER

Date	Day	Time	m	Time	m	Time	m	Time	m
1	SU ●	0549	1.4	1047	6.3	1805	1.3	2308	6.3
2	M	0624	1.4	1119	6.3	1841	1.3	2339	6.4
3	TU	0701	1.3	1152	6.3	1917	1.4		
4	W	0012	6.4	0738	1.4	1227	6.3	1954	1.5
5	TH	0049	6.4	0816	1.5	1308	6.2	2032	1.6
6	F	0133	6.3	0858	1.6	1355	6.0	2114	1.7
7	SA	0224	6.1	0945	1.7	1452	5.8	2203	1.9
8	SU ☾	0325	6.0	1042	1.8	1605	5.7	2304	2.0
9	M	0435	5.9	1150	1.8	1727	5.6		
10	TU	0016	2.0	0550	5.9	1300	1.7	1840	5.7
11	W	0129	1.9	0659	6.0	1405	1.6	1941	5.9
12	TH	0234	1.7	0759	6.2	1508	1.4	2036	6.1
13	F	0336	1.5	0854	6.4	1612	1.2	2127	6.3
14	SA	0437	1.3	0947	6.5	1712	1.1	2216	6.4
15	SU O	0533	1.2	1036	6.6	1806	1.1	2302	6.5
16	M	0624	1.1	1124	6.6	1854	1.1	2347	6.6
17	TU	0712	1.1	1209	6.5	1939	1.2		
18	W	0030	6.6	0758	1.1	1252	6.4	2021	1.4
19	TH	0113	6.5	0842	1.3	1337	6.2	2059	1.6
20	F	0157	6.4	0923	1.5	1422	6.0	2136	1.8
21	SA	0242	6.2	1003	1.7	1510	5.7	2211	2.0
22	SU ☽	0329	5.9	1044	1.9	1602	5.5	2251	2.2
23	M	0420	5.7	1131	2.0	1700	5.3	2343	2.4
24	TU	0518	5.5	1226	2.1	1804	5.2		
25	W	0048	2.4	0622	5.4	1326	2.1	1908	5.2
26	TH	0156	2.4	0724	5.4	1426	2.0	2003	5.4
27	F	0258	2.2	0817	5.6	1522	1.9	2051	5.6
28	SA	0353	1.9	0904	5.8	1614	1.7	2134	5.8
29	SU	0441	1.7	0946	6.0	1701	1.5	2213	6.0
30	M ●	0525	1.5	1026	6.1	1745	1.4	2251	6.2
31	TU	0608	1.3	1106	6.3	1828	1.3	2328	6.4

SHEERNESS
LAT 51°27′N
LONG 0°45′E

TIMES AND HEIGHTS OF HIGH AND LOW WATER (Heights in Metres)

TIME ZONE UT
For Summer Time (area enclosed in shaded box) add 1 hour

2024

JANUARY

Date	Day	Time	m	Time	m	Time	m	Time	m
1	M	0320	5.2	0936	1.0	1553	5.2	2129	1.4
2	TU	0355	5.1	1009	1.1	1631	5.0	2207	1.5
3	W	0433	5.0	1046	1.2	1712	4.9	2249	1.6
4	TH ☽	0517	4.8	1130	1.3	1759	4.7	2338	1.7
5	F	0609	4.7	1223	1.4	1856	4.7		
6	SA	0037	1.8	0715	4.6	1331	1.5	2001	4.7
7	SU	0154	1.8	0827	4.7	1449	1.4	2107	4.8
8	M	0313	1.6	0934	4.8	1555	1.3	2208	5.0
9	TU	0418	1.4	1035	5.1	1651	1.2	2304	5.2
10	W	0515	1.2	1130	5.3	1742	1.0	2355	5.4
11	TH ●	0609	1.0	1220	5.6	1830	0.9		
12	F	0041	5.5	0703	0.8	1308	5.8	1918	0.9
13	SA	0126	5.6	0755	0.6	1355	5.9	2005	0.8
14	SU	0210	5.7	0845	0.4	1442	5.9	2050	0.8
15	M	0254	5.7	0932	0.4	1529	5.9	2133	0.9
16	TU	0339	5.7	1017	0.4	1617	5.7	2215	1.0
17	W	0424	5.6	1101	0.5	1707	5.5	2258	1.1
18	TH ☾	0513	5.5	1146	0.7	1800	5.3	2346	1.3
19	F	0609	5.3	1237	1.0	1900	5.0		
20	SA	0044	1.4	0714	5.1	1339	1.2	2006	4.9
21	SU	0156	1.5	0827	4.9	1451	1.4	2115	4.9
22	M	0313	1.5	0942	5.0	1601	1.4	2222	5.0
23	TU	0429	1.3	1050	5.1	1703	1.3	2320	5.1
24	W	0536	1.1	1146	5.3	1753	1.3		
25	TH O	0008	5.2	0629	0.9	1233	5.4	1834	1.2
26	F	0049	5.3	0712	0.8	1314	5.5	1909	1.2
27	SA	0126	5.4	0748	0.8	1350	5.5	1940	1.1
28	SU	0159	5.4	0821	0.8	1423	5.5	2010	1.1
29	M	0229	5.4	0850	0.8	1455	5.4	2040	1.1
30	TU	0259	5.4	0918	0.8	1526	5.4	2110	1.1
31	W	0329	5.3	0946	0.9	1557	5.2		

FEBRUARY

Date	Day	Time	m	Time	m	Time	m	Time	m
1	TH	0401	5.2	1015	1.0	1631	5.1	2211	1.3
2	F ☽	0435	5.1	1045	1.1	1710	4.9	2246	1.4
3	SA	0516	4.9	1122	1.3	1757	4.8	2333	1.6
4	SU	0611	4.7	1216	1.5	1859	4.6		
5	M	0040	1.7	0727	4.6	1344	1.6	2017	4.6
6	TU	0224	1.7	0853	4.6	1519	1.5	2134	4.8
7	W	0349	1.5	1010	4.9	1627	1.3	2242	5.1
8	TH	0457	1.1	1115	5.3	1725	1.1	2340	5.3
9	F ●	0600	0.8	1210	5.7	1819	0.9		
10	SA	0028	5.6	0657	0.6	1258	5.9	1909	0.8
11	SU	0113	5.8	0748	0.3	1343	6.1	1955	0.6
12	M	0156	5.9	0835	0.1	1428	6.1	2037	0.6
13	TU	0237	6.0	0918	0.1	1511	6.0	2117	0.7
14	W	0318	6.0	0957	0.2	1554	5.9	2153	0.8
15	TH	0400	5.9	1032	0.5	1637	5.6	2229	0.9
16	F ☾	0444	5.6	1106	0.8	1724	5.3	2310	1.1
17	SA	0534	5.3	1147	1.1	1818	4.9		
18	SU	0002	1.4	0638	5.0	1246	1.4	1926	4.7
19	M	0119	1.6	0800	4.7	1413	1.7	2046	4.6
20	TU	0256	1.5	0930	4.7	1540	1.7	2205	4.7
21	W	0427	1.3	1043	5.0	1652	1.5	2307	5.0
22	TH	0532	1.1	1138	5.3	1743	1.3	2355	5.2
23	F	0619	0.9	1221	5.4	1821	1.2		
24	SA O	0034	5.3	0657	0.8	1258	5.5	1853	1.1
25	SU	0107	5.4	0728	0.7	1329	5.5	1922	1.0
26	M	0137	5.5	0757	0.7	1359	5.5	1951	0.9
27	TU	0205	5.5	0826	0.6	1427	5.5	2020	0.9
28	W	0233	5.5	0853	0.7	1455	5.5	2049	0.9
29	TH	0301	5.5	0920	0.8	1524	5.4	2115	1.0

MARCH

Date	Day	Time	m	Time	m	Time	m	Time	m
1	F	0330	5.4	0944	0.9	1555	5.3	2138	1.2
2	SA	0402	5.2	1005	1.1	1630	5.1	2206	1.3
3	SU ☽	0441	5.1	1034	1.3	1713	4.9	2249	1.4
4	M	0532	4.8	1125	1.5	1810	4.6	2355	1.6
5	TU	0645	4.6	1254	1.7	1932	4.5		
6	W	0146	1.7	0822	4.6	1451	1.6	2105	4.6
7	TH	0328	1.4	0952	5.0	1606	1.3	2222	5.0
8	F	0443	1.0	1100	5.4	1708	1.1	2320	5.4
9	SA	0549	0.7	1154	5.8	1803	0.8		
10	SU ●	0008	5.7	0644	0.4	1240	6.0	1852	0.7
11	M	0052	5.9	0731	0.2	1324	6.2	1936	0.5
12	TU	0133	6.1	0814	0.0	1405	6.2	2017	0.5
13	W	0213	6.1	0853	0.1	1446	6.1	2055	0.5
14	TH	0253	6.1	0929	0.3	1526	5.9	2130	0.7
15	F	0334	5.9	1000	0.6	1605	5.6	2203	0.8
16	SA	0416	5.6	1030	0.9	1647	5.2	2241	1.0
17	SU ☾	0505	5.3	1107	1.3	1737	4.8	2331	1.3
18	M	0609	4.8	1205	1.7	1846	4.5		
19	TU	0051	1.6	0738	4.6	1341	1.9	2016	4.4
20	W	0244	1.5	0913	4.6	1518	1.8	2142	4.6
21	TH	0411	1.3	1025	5.0	1630	1.6	2244	4.9
22	F	0511	1.0	1117	5.3	1719	1.3	2330	5.2
23	SA	0553	0.8	1157	5.4	1755	1.2		
24	SU	0007	5.4	0628	0.8	1231	5.5	1827	1.1
25	M O	0039	5.5	0658	0.7	1300	5.5	1857	0.9
26	TU	0108	5.5	0727	0.6	1328	5.6	1927	0.9
27	W	0136	5.6	0756	0.6	1356	5.6	1957	0.8
28	TH	0204	5.6	0825	0.7	1424	5.6	2027	0.9
29	F	0234	5.5	0852	0.8	1454	5.5	2053	1.0
30	SA	0305	5.4	0915	1.0	1525	5.4	2116	1.1
31	SU	0339	5.3	0936	1.1	1600	5.2	2144	1.2

APRIL

Date	Day	Time	m	Time	m	Time	m	Time	m
1	M	0420	5.1	1009	1.3	1643	5.0	2230	1.3
2	TU ☽	0513	4.9	1106	1.6	1741	4.7	2341	1.5
3	W	0627	4.7	1238	1.8	1904	4.5		
4	TH	0132	1.5	0804	4.7	1427	1.6	2040	4.7
5	F	0310	1.2	0932	5.1	1541	1.3	2156	5.0
6	SA	0425	0.8	1038	5.5	1644	1.0	2254	5.4
7	SU	0529	0.5	1131	5.8	1738	0.8	2342	5.7
8	M ●	0621	0.3	1217	6.0	1827	0.7		
9	TU	0025	5.9	0706	0.2	1258	6.1	1911	0.5
10	W	0106	6.1	0747	0.2	1339	6.1	1952	0.5
11	TH	0148	6.1	0824	0.3	1419	6.0	2032	0.5
12	F	0229	6.1	0858	0.5	1458	5.8	2108	0.6
13	SA	0311	5.9	0929	0.8	1536	5.5	2144	0.8
14	SU	0355	5.5	1000	1.1	1617	5.1	2221	1.0
15	M ☾	0445	5.1	1038	1.5	1705	4.8	2310	1.3
16	TU	0548	4.8	1133	1.8	1811	4.5		
17	W	0028	1.5	0710	4.5	1304	2.0	1939	4.4
18	TH	0217	1.5	0838	4.6	1440	1.9	2103	4.5
19	F	0332	1.3	0950	4.9	1547	1.6	2206	4.8
20	SA	0429	1.0	1041	5.2	1638	1.4	2253	5.1
21	SU	0512	0.9	1122	5.3	1718	1.2	2331	5.3
22	M	0548	0.8	1156	5.4	1753	1.1		
23	TU O	0004	5.4	0621	0.8	1226	5.5	1826	1.0
24	W	0035	5.5	0652	0.7	1255	5.6	1900	0.9
25	TH	0106	5.6	0724	0.7	1325	5.6	1933	0.9
26	F	0138	5.6	0756	0.8	1356	5.6	2006	0.9
27	SA	0211	5.5	0827	0.9	1428	5.5	2038	0.9
28	SU	0246	5.5	0855	1.0	1502	5.4	2108	1.0
29	M	0325	5.4	0925	1.2	1541	5.2	2145	1.1
30	TU	0411	5.2	1007	1.4	1628	5.0	2236	1.2

MAY

Date	Day	Time	m	Time	m	Time	m	Time	m
1	W ☾	0508	5.0	1108	1.6	1728	4.8	2348	1.3
2	TH	0622	4.9	1232	1.7	1847	4.7		
3	F	0126	1.2	0748	5.0	1400	1.5	2013	4.8
4	SA	0248	1.0	0906	5.2	1510	1.3	2124	5.1
5	SU	0358	0.7	1010	5.5	1611	1.1	2222	5.4
6	M	0459	0.6	1103	5.7	1706	0.9	2312	5.7
7	TU	0551	0.4	1149	5.9	1757	0.7	2358	5.9
8	W ●	0636	0.4	1233	5.9	1845	0.6		
9	TH	0042	6.0	0717	0.4	1314	5.9	1930	0.5
10	F	0126	6.0	0756	0.6	1354	5.8	2013	0.6
11	SA	0211	5.9	0831	0.8	1434	5.6	2053	0.7
12	SU	0255	5.7	0904	1.0	1514	5.4	2131	0.9
13	M	0341	5.4	0937	1.3	1554	5.1	2209	1.1
14	TU	0430	5.1	1014	1.5	1640	4.8	2254	1.3
15	W ☽	0527	4.8	1104	1.8	1739	4.6	2359	1.4
16	TH	0632	4.6	1213	1.9	1851	4.5		
17	F	0128	1.4	0744	4.6	1341	1.9	2005	4.5
18	SA	0237	1.3	0853	4.7	1451	1.7	2110	4.7
19	SU	0333	1.2	0949	4.9	1546	1.5	2203	5.0
20	M	0420	1.0	1034	5.1	1633	1.3	2247	5.2
21	TU	0502	0.9	1113	5.3	1714	1.2	2327	5.3
22	W	0541	0.9	1149	5.4	1754	1.0		
23	TH O	0004	5.4	0618	0.9	1224	5.5	1833	1.0
24	F	0040	5.5	0655	0.9	1259	5.6	1912	0.9
25	SA	0117	5.5	0731	0.9	1335	5.6	1951	0.9
26	SU	0156	5.5	0808	0.9	1411	5.5	2031	0.9
27	M	0236	5.5	0845	1.0	1450	5.4	2112	0.9
28	TU	0320	5.5	0925	1.1	1533	5.3	2158	0.9
29	W	0410	5.4	1012	1.3	1623	5.1	2251	1.0
30	TH ☾	0508	5.2	1109	1.4	1722	5.0	2356	1.0
31	F	0614	5.1	1216	1.5	1830	5.0		

JUNE

Date	Day	Time	m	Time	m	Time	m	Time	m
1	SA	0109	1.0	0726	5.2	1327	1.4	1942	5.1
2	SU	0219	0.9	0836	5.3	1433	1.3	2050	5.2
3	M	0324	0.8	0938	5.4	1535	1.2	2150	5.4
4	TU	0425	0.7	1034	5.5	1634	1.0	2246	5.5
5	W	0519	0.7	1124	5.6	1731	0.9	2337	5.6
6	TH ●	0607	0.7	1211	5.6	1825	0.8		
7	F	0026	5.7	0651	0.8	1255	5.6	1915	0.7
8	SA	0114	5.7	0732	0.9	1337	5.6	2001	0.7
9	SU	0200	5.7	0810	1.0	1418	5.5	2044	0.7
10	M	0245	5.5	0845	1.2	1458	5.3	2124	0.9
11	TU	0329	5.4	0918	1.3	1538	5.2	2200	1.0
12	W	0413	5.2	0953	1.5	1619	5.0	2237	1.1
13	TH	0459	5.0	1034	1.6	1704	4.8	2321	1.2
14	F ☽	0548	4.8	1123	1.7	1758	4.7		
15	SA	0016	1.3	0643	4.7	1223	1.8	1859	4.6
16	SU	0123	1.4	0742	4.7	1335	1.8	2002	4.7
17	M	0228	1.3	0841	4.8	1445	1.7	2103	4.8
18	TU	0325	1.2	0937	4.9	1544	1.5	2159	4.9
19	W	0416	1.1	1029	5.1	1636	1.3	2250	5.1
20	TH	0503	1.1	1115	5.3	1724	1.2	2337	5.3
21	F	0548	1.0	1159	5.4	1811	1.0		
22	SA O	0021	5.4	0631	1.0	1241	5.5	1857	0.9
23	SU	0104	5.5	0714	1.0	1322	5.5	1943	0.8
24	M	0147	5.6	0757	0.9	1403	5.5	2031	0.7
25	TU	0232	5.7	0840	0.9	1445	5.5	2119	0.6
26	W	0318	5.7	0925	1.0	1529	5.5	2207	0.6
27	TH	0407	5.6	1010	1.1	1616	5.4	2255	0.7
28	F ☾	0459	5.5	1058	1.2	1707	5.4	2345	0.7
29	SA	0555	5.4	1150	1.3	1804	5.3		
30	SU	0040	0.8	0657	5.2	1248	1.4	1908	5.2

SUNRISE AND SUNSET TIMES

SHEERNESS
At 51°27′N 0°45′E

UT		Sunrise	Sunset
Jan	01	0802	1559
	15	0756	1618
Feb	01	0735	1647
	15	0711	1712
Mar	01	0642	1738
	15	0611	1802
BST (UT+1)			
Apr	01	0632	1930
	15	0601	1954
May	01	0529	2020
	15	0505	2042
Jun	01	0446	2105
	15	0440	2116
Jul	01	0445	2117
	15	0458	2107
Aug	01	0521	2045
	15	0543	2020
Sep	01	0610	1943
	15	0632	1911
Oct	01	0658	1835
	15	0721	1804
UT			
Nov	01	0651	1630
	15	0715	1608
Dec	01	0740	1552
	15	0756	1548

SHEERNESS
LAT 51°27′N
LONG 0°45′E

TIMES AND HEIGHTS OF HIGH AND LOW WATER (Heights in Metres)

TIME ZONE UT
For Summer Time (area enclosed in shaded box) add 1 hour

2024

JULY

Date	Day	Time	m	Time	m	Time	m	Time	m
1	M	0142	0.9	0802	5.2	1354	1.4	2016	5.2
2	TU	0247	1.0	0907	5.2	1503	1.3	2124	5.2
3	W	0352	1.1	1009	5.2	1611	1.2	2228	5.3
4	TH	0454	1.1	1106	5.3	1718	1.1	2328	5.4
5	F ●	0548	1.1	1158	5.4	1817	0.9		
6	SA	0021	5.5	0635	1.1	1244	5.5	1909	0.8
7	SU	0109	5.6	0716	1.1	1327	5.5	1955	0.7
8	M	0153	5.6	0754	1.2	1407	5.4	2036	0.7
9	TU	0234	5.5	0828	1.2	1444	5.4	2112	0.8
10	W	0312	5.4	0900	1.3	1518	5.3	2143	0.9
11	TH	0349	5.3	0930	1.3	1552	5.2	2212	1.0
12	F	0425	5.2	1003	1.4	1628	5.1	2244	1.1
13	SA ☽	0502	5.0	1040	1.5	1707	5.0	2321	1.2
14	SU	0545	4.9	1124	1.7	1753	4.8		
15	M	0006	1.3	0635	4.7	1217	1.8	1852	4.7
16	TU	0107	1.5	0735	4.7	1329	1.8	2002	4.6
17	W	0226	1.5	0842	4.7	1453	1.7	2113	4.7
18	TH	0335	1.4	0947	4.9	1601	1.5	2218	4.9
19	F	0432	1.3	1047	5.1	1659	1.3	2316	5.2
20	SA	0524	1.2	1140	5.3	1754	1.0		
21	SU ○	0006	5.4	0614	1.0	1226	5.5	1847	0.8
22	M	0054	5.7	0701	0.9	1311	5.6	1938	0.6
23	TU	0139	5.8	0748	0.9	1353	5.7	2027	0.5
24	W	0223	5.9	0833	0.8	1435	5.8	2114	0.3
25	TH	0308	6.0	0916	0.8	1517	5.8	2157	0.3
26	F	0353	5.9	0956	0.9	1559	5.8	2239	0.5
27	SA	0439	5.7	1036	1.0	1644	5.6	2319	0.7
28	SU ☾	0528	5.4	1119	1.2	1734	5.5		
29	M	0002	0.9	0624	5.2	1210	1.4	1834	5.2
30	TU	0058	1.2	0727	5.0	1317	1.5	1947	5.0
31	W	0212	1.4	0838	4.9	1440	1.5	2107	5.0

AUGUST

Date	Day	Time	m	Time	m	Time	m	Time	m
1	TH	0329	1.4	0951	5.0	1603	1.4	2223	5.1
2	F	0441	1.4	1057	5.1	1719	1.1	2327	5.3
3	SA	0540	1.3	1151	5.3	1817	0.9		
4	SU ●	0018	5.5	0626	1.3	1236	5.4	1903	0.8
5	M	0102	5.6	0704	1.2	1315	5.5	1943	0.7
6	TU	0140	5.6	0737	1.2	1350	5.5	2017	0.7
7	W	0215	5.6	0808	1.[illegible]	1422	5.5	2048	0.7
8	TH	0247	5.5	0837	1.[illegible]	1452	5.5	2115	0.3
9	F	0317	5.5	0905	1.2	1521	5.5	2141	0.9
10	SA	0348	5.4	0934	1.3	1552	5.4	2208	1.0
11	SU	0419	5.2	1003	1.4	1624	5.2	2236	1.2
12	M ☽	0455	5.0	1036	1.5	1702	5.0	2311	1.4
13	TU	0537	4.9	1119	1.7	1752	4.7		
14	W	0000	1.6	0633	4.7	1221	1.8	1901	4.6
15	TH	0120	1.8	0749	4.6	1402	1.9	2029	4.6
16	F	0258	1.7	0910	4.7	1532	1.6	2151	4.9
17	SA	0407	1.5	1022	5.0	1639	1.3	2257	5.3
18	SU	0505	1.2	1120	5.3	1740	1.0	2351	5.6
19	M ○	0558	1.0	1209	5.6	1836	0.7		
20	TU	0038	5.9	0647	0.9	1253	5.8	1926	0.4
21	W	0123	6.1	0733	0.8	1334	6.0	2012	0.3
22	TH	0205	6.2	0816	0.7	1414	6.1	2055	0.2
23	F	0247	6.1	0856	0.7	1454	6.1	2135	0.3
24	SA	0329	6.0	0934	0.8	1534	6.0	2211	0.5
25	SU	0411	5.7	1010	1.0	1617	5.8	2245	0.8
26	M ☾	0456	5.4	1048	1.2	1705	5.5	2322	1.1
27	TU	0547	5.1	1137	1.4	1805	5.1		
28	W	0016	1.5	0652	4.8	1249	1.6	1926	4.8
29	TH	0142	1.7	0813	4.7	1430	1.6	2058	4.8
30	F	0315	1.8	0937	4.8	1605	1.4	2219	5.1
31	SA	0433	1.6	1045	5.1	1715	1.1	2319	5.4

SEPTEMBER

Date	Day	Time	m	Time	m	Time	m	Time	m
1	SU	0529	1.4	1137	5.3	1805	0.9		
2	M	0005	5.6	0610	1.3	1218	5.5	1845	0.8
3	TU ●	0044	5.6	0643	1.2	1253	5.6	1918	0.8
4	W	0117	5.6	0712	1.1	1324	5.6	1947	0.7
5	TH	0147	5.6	0741	1.1	1353	5.7	2015	0.7
6	F	0215	5.6	0810	1.0	1421	5.7	2042	0.8
7	SA	0243	5.6	0838	1.1	1449	5.6	2108	0.9
8	SU	0311	5.5	0905	1.2	1518	5.5	2132	1.0
9	M	0340	5.4	0929	1.3	1549	5.3	2156	1.2
10	TU	0413	5.2	0955	1.4	1625	5.1	2223	1.4
11	W ☽	0452	5.0	1034	1.6	1712	4.8	2309	1.7
12	TH	0545	4.7	1135	1.8	1819	4.6		
13	F	0028	1.9	0701	4.5	1319	1.8	1953	4.6
14	SA	0225	1.9	0836	4.6	1506	1.6	2126	4.9
15	SU	0341	1.5	0956	5.0	1618	1.2	2236	5.4
16	M	0442	1.2	1055	5.4	1721	0.8	2329	5.8
17	TU	0536	1.0	1144	5.7	1816	0.5		
18	W ○	0016	6.0	0625	0.8	1227	6.0	1904	0.3
19	TH	0059	6.2	0709	0.7	1307	6.1	1948	0.2
20	F	0140	6.2	0752	0.7	1347	6.2	2029	0.2
21	SA	0221	6.1	0832	0.7	1428	6.2	2106	0.4
22	SU	0301	6.0	0909	0.8	1509	6.1	2139	0.7
23	M	0341	5.7	0945	0.9	1552	5.8	2210	1.0
24	TU ☾	0424	5.4	1023	1.1	1641	5.4	2248	1.4
25	W	0513	5.0	1113	1.4	1744	5.0	2342	1.8
26	TH	0620	4.7	1231	1.6	1909	4.7		
27	F	0115	2.0	0748	4.5	1424	1.6	2044	4.8
28	SA	0256	1.9	0916	4.7	1551	1.3	2202	5.1
29	SU	0411	1.7	1022	5.1	1653	1.0	2257	5.4
30	M	0503	1.4	1111	5.3	1738	0.9	2340	5.6

OCTOBER

Date	Day	Time	m	Time	m	Time	m	Time	m
1	TU	0540	1.3	1151	5.5	1813	0.8		
2	W ●	0016	5.6	0612	1.2	1223	5.6	1843	0.8
3	TH	0046	5.6	0642	1.1	1253	5.7	1911	0.8
4	F	0114	5.7	0712	1.0	1321	5.7	1939	0.8
5	SA	0141	5.7	0742	1.0	1349	5.7	2007	0.8
6	SU	0208	5.7	0811	1.0	1419	5.6	2035	0.9
7	M	0237	5.6	0839	1.1	1449	5.5	2100	1.1
8	TU	0307	5.4	0903	1.2	1523	5.3	2122	1.3
9	W	0340	5.3	0930	1.4	1601	5.2	2151	1.5
10	TH ☽	0420	5.0	1010	1.5	1650	4.9	2241	1.7
11	F	0513	4.8	1115	1.6	1757	4.7		
12	SA	0003	1.9	0628	4.6	1256	1.7	1927	4.7
13	SU	0152	1.9	0803	4.7	1439	1.4	2058	5.0
14	M	0310	1.5	0923	5.0	1552	1.0	2207	5.5
15	TU	0410	1.2	1023	5.4	1654	0.7	2301	5.8
16	W	0504	1.0	1112	5.8	1748	0.5	2348	6.0
17	TH ○	0554	0.9	1157	6.0	1835	0.4		
18	F	0031	6.1	0641	0.7	1239	6.2	1919	0.4
19	SA	0112	6.1	0725	0.7	1321	6.2	1958	0.4
20	SU	0153	6.0	0807	0.7	1404	6.2	2035	0.6
21	M	0234	5.9	0847	0.7	1448	6.0	2109	0.9
22	TU	0314	5.6	0926	0.9	1534	5.7	2142	1.2
23	W	0357	5.3	1007	1.1	1626	5.3	2220	1.6
24	TH ☾	0446	4.9	1057	1.4	1729	4.9	2314	1.9
25	F	0552	4.6	1215	1.6	1846	4.7		
26	SA	0038	2.1	0715	4.5	1358	1.6	2011	4.7
27	SU	0216	2.0	0837	4.7	1513	1.3	2125	5.0
28	M	0326	1.8	0943	4.9	1611	1.1	2221	5.2
29	TU	0419	1.5	1033	5.2	1655	1.0	2304	5.4
30	W	0500	1.3	1114	5.4	1731	0.9	2340	5.5
31	TH	0535	1.2	1148	5.5	1802	0.9		

NOVEMBER

Date	Day	Time	m	Time	m	Time	m	Time	m
1	F ●	0010	5.6	0609	1.1	1220	5.6	1833	0.9
2	SA	0039	5.6	0642	1.0	1251	5.6	1904	0.9
3	SU	0108	5.6	0715	1.0	1322	5.6	1935	0.9
4	M	0138	5.6	0747	1.0	1355	5.6	2005	1.0
5	TU	0209	5.6	0819	1.1	1429	5.5	2035	1.1
6	W	0242	5.5	0850	1.1	1506	5.4	2105	1.3
7	TH	0319	5.3	0924	1.2	1549	5.2	2142	1.5
8	F	0402	5.1	1009	1.3	1641	5.1	2235	1.6
9	SA ☽	0456	4.9	1113	1.4	1746	4.9	2348	1.8
10	SU	0606	4.8	1240	1.4	1905	4.9		
11	M	0115	1.7	0729	4.8	1407	1.2	2025	5.1
12	TU	0230	1.5	0844	5.1	1517	1.0	2133	5.4
13	W	0332	1.3	0946	5.4	1619	0.8	2229	5.7
14	TH	0428	1.1	1039	5.7	1714	0.6	2319	5.8
15	F ○	0522	0.9	1128	5.9	1803	0.6		
16	SA	0004	5.9	0614	0.8	1214	6.0	1848	0.6
17	SU	0047	5.9	0702	0.7	1301	6.1	1930	0.7
18	M	0130	5.8	0749	0.7	1348	6.0	2009	0.8
19	TU	0212	5.7	0833	0.7	1435	5.8	2045	1.1
20	W	0255	5.5	0916	0.9	1523	5.6	2120	1.3
21	TH	0338	5.2	0958	1.1	1614	5.3	2158	1.6
22	F	0426	5.0	1044	1.3	1709	5.0	2245	1.8
23	SA ☾	0522	4.7	1146	1.4	1811	4.8	2347	2.0
24	SU	0629	4.6	1306	1.5	1919	4.7		
25	M	0110	2.0	0740	4.6	1416	1.4	2027	4.7
26	TU	0224	1.9	0846	4.8	1512	1.3	2127	4.9
27	W	0323	1.7	0942	4.9	1601	1.2	2216	5.1
28	TH	0412	1.5	1029	5.1	1643	1.1	2257	5.3
29	F	0456	1.3	1111	5.3	1721	1.0	2333	5.4
30	SA	0536	1.2	1149	5.4	1758	1.0		

DECEMBER

Date	Day	Time	m	Time	m	Time	m	Time	m
1	SU ●	0008	5.5	0615	1.1	1225	5.5	1834	1.0
2	M	0042	5.5	0652	1.0	1302	5.5	1909	1.0
3	TU	0117	5.5	0730	1.0	1339	5.5	1944	1.0
4	W	0152	5.5	0808	0.9	1417	5.5	2020	1.1
5	TH	0229	5.4	0848	1.0	1459	5.5	2058	1.2
6	F	0309	5.3	0930	1.0	1544	5.4	2141	1.3
7	SA	0353	5.2	1018	1.1	1635	5.3	2230	1.4
8	SU ☽	0445	5.1	1113	1.1	1733	5.2	2328	1.5
9	M	0544	5.0	1217	1.1	1839	5.1		
10	TU	0034	1.6	0652	5.0	1326	1.1	1950	5.1
11	W	0144	1.5	0803	5.1	1435	1.0	2056	5.2
12	TH	0250	1.4	0910	5.3	1540	1.0	2157	5.4
13	F	0354	1.2	1010	5.5	1641	0.9	2252	5.5
14	SA	0456	1.1	1107	5.6	1736	0.9	2343	5.6
15	SU ○	0555	0.9	1200	5.7	1825	0.9		
16	M	0030	5.6	0650	0.8	1251	5.8	1910	0.9
17	TU	0116	5.6	0741	0.7	1340	5.8	1951	1.0
18	W	0200	5.5	0827	0.7	1427	5.7	2029	1.2
19	TH	0242	5.4	0910	0.8	1513	5.5	2104	1.3
20	F	0323	5.3	0949	0.9	1557	5.3	2138	1.4
21	SA	0404	5.1	1026	1.1	1641	5.1	2215	1.6
22	SU ☾	0448	5.0	1104	1.2	1728	4.9	2258	1.7
23	M	0535	4.8	1151	1.3	1818	4.7	2351	1.8
24	TU	0631	4.7	1250	1.4	1914	4.6		
25	W	0057	1.9	0734	4.6	1358	1.5	2014	4.6
26	TH	0214	1.8	0838	4.7	1501	1.4	2114	4.7
27	F	0321	1.7	0939	4.8	1556	1.3	2209	4.9
28	SA	0416	1.5	1034	5.0	1644	1.2	2259	5.1
29	SU	0506	1.3	1123	5.2	1729	1.2	2343	5.3
30	M ●	0552	1.1	1207	5.3	1810	1.1		
31	TU	0024	5.4	0636	1.0	1249	5.5	1851	1.0

LONDON BRIDGE
LAT 51°30′N
LONG 0°05′W

TIMES AND HEIGHTS OF HIGH AND LOW WATER

TIME ZONE UT
For Summer Time (area enclosed in shaded box) add 1 hour

2024

JANUARY

Day	Time	m	Time	m	Time	m	Time	m
1 M	0439	6.3	1115	0.9	1706	6.4	2311	1.4
2 TU	0512	6.2	1145	1.0	1740	6.2	2346	1.5
3 W	0547	6.1	1217	1.1	1817	6.0		
4 TH ☾	0021	1.6	0627	5.9	1251	1.2	1901	5.9
5 F	0102	1.8	0714	5.8	1332	1.3	1956	5.7
6 SA	0151	1.9	0818	5.7	1428	1.5	2110	5.7
7 SU	0256	1.9	0944	5.8	1552	1.5	2221	5.9
8 M	0436	1.8	1053	6.1	1710	1.3	2326	6.1
9 TU	0553	1.4	1153	6.4	1813	1.1		
10 W	0025	6.4	0657	1.1	1248	6.7	1913	1.0
11 TH ●	0118	6.6	0758	0.8	1340	7.0	2012	1.0
12 F	0208	6.7	0856	0.6	1429	7.1	2108	0.9
13 SA	0255	6.8	0950	0.4	1517	7.3	2158	0.8
14 SU	0340	6.9	1038	0.2	1603	7.3	2244	0.7
15 M	0423	7.0	1121	0.1	1649	7.3	2325	0.7
16 TU	0506	7.0	1200	0.1	1736	7.1		
17 W	0005	0.8	0550	6.9	1237	0.2	1826	6.8
18 TH ☽	0046	1.0	0638	6.7	1316	0.5	1920	6.5
19 F	0132	1.2	0733	6.6	1403	0.8	2018	6.3
20 SA	0228	1.4	0836	6.4	1500	1.1	2120	6.1
21 SU	0335	1.5	0944	6.2	1605	1.3	2228	6.0
22 M	0449	1.4	1055	6.2	1718	1.4	2342	6.1
23 TU	0607	1.2	1205	6.3	1833	1.3		
24 W	0043	6.3	0714	0.9	1303	6.5	1930	1.2
25 TH O	0133	6.4	0807	0.7	1351	6.7	2017	1.2
26 F	0215	6.5	0853	0.7	1433	6.8	2057	1.2
27 SA	0252	6.6	0933	0.6	1510	6.7	2132	1.2
28 SU	0324	6.6	1006	0.7	1543	6.7	2202	1.2
29 M	0353	6.6	1034	0.6	1612	6.7	2230	1.1
30 TU	0422	6.6	1059	0.6	1640	6.6	2259	1.2
31 W	0451	6.5	1125	0.7	1710	6.4	2328	1.2

FEBRUARY

Day	Time	m	Time	m	Time	m	Time	m
1 TH	0521	6.4	1149	0.9	1742	6.3	2355	1.4
2 F ☾	0554	6.2	1212	1.0	1818	6.1		
3 SA	0024	1.5	0634	6.1	1243	1.1	1902	5.8
4 SU	0104	1.6	0724	5.9	1327	1.3	2002	5.6
5 M	0201	1.8	0834	5.7	1434	1.6	2133	5.6
6 TU	0332	1.9	1011	5.8	1629	1.6	2254	5.8
7 W	0520	1.5	1127	6.2	1747	1.3		
8 TH	0005	6.2	0637	1.1	1231	6.6	1901	1.1
9 F ●	0104	6.5	0751	0.7	1327	7.0	2009	0.9
10 SA	0155	6.8	0851	0.3	1417	7.3	2105	0.7
11 SU	0241	7.0	0942	0.0	1504	7.4	2153	0.6
12 M	0324	7.2	1027	-0.2	1548	7.5	2236	0.5
13 TU	0405	7.3	1107	-0.2	1631	7.4	2314	0.5
14 W	0446	7.3	1141	-0.1	1714	7.1	2349	0.6
15 TH	0526	7.2	1211	0.2	1758	6.8		
16 F ☽	0022	0.8	0609	7.0	1239	0.6	1844	6.4
17 SA	0059	1.1	0657	6.6	1314	1.0	1935	6.1
18 SU	0145	1.4	0756	6.3	1406	1.4	2037	5.8
19 M	0252	1.6	0910	5.9	1524	1.7	2156	5.6
20 TU	0415	1.6	1035	5.9	1650	1.7	2325	5.7
21 W	0549	1.3	1155	6.1	1817	1.5		
22 TH	0030	6.1	0701	0.9	1253	6.5	1914	1.3
23 F	0119	6.4	0752	0.7	1338	6.7	2000	1.2
24 SA O	0158	6.6	0833	0.6	1417	6.7	2040	1.1
25 SU	0233	6.6	0909	0.6	1451	6.7	2115	1.1
26 M	0303	6.7	0940	0.6	1519	6.7	2146	1.1
27 TU	0330	6.8	1008	0.5	1544	6.7	2214	1.0
28 W	0357	6.8	1034	0.5	1611	6.7	2241	1.0
29 TH	0425	6.7	1057	0.6	1639	6.6	2307	1.1

MARCH

Day	Time	m	Time	m	Time	m	Time	m
1 F	0454	6.6	1117	0.8	1710	6.4	2330	1.3
2 SA	0525	6.4	1138	0.9	1743	6.1	2356	1.3
3 SU ☾	0602	6.2	1207	1.1	1824	5.9		
4 M	0031	1.4	0650	6.0	1247	1.3	1919	5.6
5 TU	0123	1.6	0755	5.7	1350	1.7	2046	5.4
6 W	0247	1.8	0937	5.7	1559	1.8	2225	5.6
7 TH	0455	1.5	1104	6.1	1727	1.4	2344	6.1
8 F	0623	1.0	1213	6.6	1848	1.1		
9 SA	0044	6.5	0739	0.5	1309	7.1	1955	0.8
10 SU ●	0134	6.9	0835	0.1	1358	7.3	2048	0.6
11 M	0219	7.2	0923	-0.2	1443	7.4	2135	0.5
12 TU	0300	7.4	1005	-0.2	1525	7.4	2216	0.4
13 W	0340	7.5	1042	-0.1	1606	7.3	2253	0.4
14 TH	0420	7.5	1113	0.1	1647	7.0	2326	0.6
15 F	0459	7.3	1136	0.5	1726	6.7	2355	0.8
16 SA	0541	7.0	1159	0.8	1807	6.3		
17 SU ☽	0026	1.0	0628	6.5	1230	1.2	1853	5.9
18 M	0106	1.3	0724	6.1	1319	1.7	1952	5.5
19 TU	0212	1.6	0841	5.7	1446	2.0	2120	5.3
20 W	0344	1.7	1012	5.6	1623	2.0	2257	5.5
21 TH	0518	1.4	1134	6.0	1748	1.6		
22 F	0004	5.9	0633	1.0	1231	6.4	1846	1.3
23 SA	0052	6.3	0721	0.7	1314	6.6	1932	1.2
24 SU	0130	6.5	0800	0.6	1350	6.6	2011	1.1
25 M O	0204	6.7	0834	0.6	1421	6.7	2047	1.0
26 TU	0233	6.8	0906	0.6	1447	6.7	2120	1.0
27 W	0300	6.9	0935	0.6	1512	6.7	2150	0.9
28 TH	0328	6.9	1002	0.6	1540	6.7	2219	0.9
29 F	0357	6.8	1025	0.7	1610	6.6	2245	1.0
30 SA	0428	6.7	1047	0.8	1642	6.4	2308	1.1
31 SU	0501	6.5	1111	0.9	1715	6.2	2334	1.2

APRIL

Day	Time	m	Time	m	Time	m	Time	m
1 M	0540	6.3	1142	1.1	1756	5.9		
2 TU ☾	0010	1.2	0630	6.1	1225	1.4	1853	5.6
3 W	0102	1.4	0738	5.8	1330	1.8	2017	5.4
4 TH	0229	1.6	0916	5.8	1537	1.8	2157	5.6
5 F	0431	1.3	1040	6.2	1703	1.4	2315	6.1
6 SA	0600	0.8	1149	6.7	1822	1.1		
7 SU	0016	6.6	0713	0.4	1244	7.0	1928	0.8
8 M ●	0106	7.0	0808	0.1	1333	7.2	2022	0.6
9 TU	0150	7.3	0854	0.0	1416	7.3	2109	0.5
10 W	0231	7.5	0935	0.0	1458	7.3	2151	0.4
11 TH	0312	7.6	1011	0.2	1539	7.2	2228	0.4
12 F	0353	7.5	1038	0.5	1618	6.9	2300	0.6
13 SA	0434	7.3	1058	0.8	1656	6.5	2328	0.8
14 SU	0517	6.8	1124	1.0	1735	6.1	2358	1.0
15 M ☽	0602	6.4	1158	1.4	1817	5.7		
16 TU	0036	1.3	0657	5.9	1245	1.8	1913	5.4
17 W	0136	1.6	0811	5.6	1403	2.1	2037	5.2
18 TH	0309	1.6	0933	5.5	1544	2.0	2206	5.4
19 F	0428	1.4	1051	5.8	1701	1.7	2318	5.8
20 SA	0533	1.1	1152	6.2	1801	1.4		
21 SU	0010	6.2	0627	0.8	1236	6.4	1851	1.2
22 M	0052	6.5	0712	0.7	1313	6.5	1934	1.1
23 TU O	0127	6.7	0751	0.7	1344	6.6	2013	1.0
24 W	0159	6.8	0827	0.7	1413	6.7	2049	1.0
25 TH	0229	6.9	0859	0.7	1442	6.7	2123	0.9
26 F	0300	6.9	0928	0.7	1514	6.7	2155	0.9
27 SA	0332	6.9	0955	0.8	1547	6.6	2224	0.9
28 SU	0407	6.8	1022	0.9	1621	6.4	2252	0.9
29 M	0445	6.6	1054	1.0	1659	6.2	2323	1.0
30 TU	0529	6.4	1132	1.1	1744	6.0		

MAY

Day	Time	m	Time	m	Time	m	Time	m
1 W ☾	0003	1.1	0623	6.2	1220	1.4	1844	5.7
2 TH	0058	1.2	0733	6.0	1333	1.7	2003	5.7
3 F	0233	1.3	0859	6.1	1515	1.6	2130	5.9
4 SA	0406	1.0	1013	6.4	1633	1.3	2242	6.3
5 SU	0522	0.7	1119	6.7	1747	1.1	2343	6.7
6 M	0635	0.5	1217	6.9	1854	0.9		
7 TU	0035	7.0	0733	0.3	1306	7.0	1951	0.7
8 W ●	0121	7.2	0821	0.3	1350	7.1	2041	0.6
9 TH	0205	7.4	0902	0.5	1432	7.0	2125	0.5
10 F	0248	7.4	0938	0.6	1514	6.9	2204	0.5
11 SA	0331	7.3	1005	0.8	1554	6.7	2238	0.6
12 SU	0414	7.1	1027	1.0	1633	6.4	2306	0.8
13 M	0458	6.7	1058	1.2	1711	6.1	2337	1.0
14 TU	0543	6.3	1135	1.5	1751	5.8		
15 W ☽	0015	1.2	0633	5.9	1221	1.7	1840	5.5
16 TH	0108	1.4	0735	5.6	1322	2.0	1950	5.4
17 F	0223	1.4	0846	5.6	1443	2.0	2111	5.5
18 SA	0337	1.3	0952	5.7	1604	1.8	2218	5.7
19 SU	0437	1.1	1053	6.0	1707	1.6	2317	6.1
20 M	0530	0.9	1145	6.2	1801	1.3		
21 TU	0005	6.4	0620	0.9	1229	6.4	1851	1.2
22 W	0047	6.6	0706	0.8	1307	6.5	1937	1.0
23 TH O	0125	6.8	0748	0.8	1343	6.6	2019	0.9
24 F	0201	6.9	0827	0.8	1420	6.7	2100	0.8
25 SA	0238	6.9	0902	0.8	1457	6.6	2138	0.8
26 SU	0317	6.9	0936	0.8	1535	6.6	2215	0.7
27 M	0357	6.8	1012	0.9	1615	6.4	2250	0.7
28 TU	0440	6.7	1052	1.0	1657	6.3	2328	0.7
29 W	0528	6.6	1138	1.1	1745	6.1		
30 TH ☾	0013	0.8	0623	6.4	1231	1.3	1841	6.1
31 F	0112	0.9	0728	6.3	1339	1.4	1949	6.1

JUNE

Day	Time	m	Time	m	Time	m	Time	m
1 SA	0227	0.9	0839	6.3	1452	1.4	2103	6.2
2 SU	0337	0.8	0946	6.4	1604	1.3	2210	6.4
3 M	0443	0.7	1050	6.5	1714	1.2	2312	6.7
4 TU	0552	0.7	1150	6.6	1822	1.0		
5 W	0008	6.9	0656	0.7	1243	6.7	1924	0.8
6 TH ●	0059	7.0	0749	0.7	1330	6.8	2016	0.6
7 F	0146	7.1	0834	0.8	1415	6.8	2104	0.5
8 SA	0232	7.2	0913	0.9	1458	6.7	2148	0.6
9 SU	0318	7.1	0946	1.1	1539	6.6	2226	0.7
10 M	0402	6.9	1014	1.2	1618	6.4	2258	0.8
11 TU	0444	6.6	1046	1.3	1655	6.2	2328	0.9
12 W	0526	6.3	1122	1.4	1732	6.0		
13 TH	0002	1.0	0609	6.1	1202	1.5	1814	5.9
14 F ☽	0043	1.1	0655	5.9	1248	1.7	1904	5.7
15 SA	0132	1.2	0751	5.7	1340	1.8	2012	5.7
16 SU	0231	1.2	0853	5.7	1442	1.8	2121	5.7
17 M	0337	1.2	0953	5.8	1601	1.8	2223	5.9
18 TU	0437	1.2	1050	6.0	1710	1.5	2319	6.2
19 W	0533	1.1	1146	6.2	1808	1.3		
20 TH	0010	6.5	0626	1.0	1236	6.4	1903	1.0
21 F	0057	6.7	0716	0.9	1322	6.6	1955	0.8
22 SA O	0141	6.8	0804	0.9	1406	6.6	2045	0.7
23 SU	0225	6.9	0851	0.9	1450	6.7	2133	0.6
24 M	0309	7.0	0936	0.9	1532	6.7	2219	0.4
25 TU	0353	7.0	1022	0.8	1614	6.7	2304	0.3
26 W	0439	7.0	1106	0.8	1657	6.6	2346	0.3
27 TH	0525	6.9	1150	0.9	1741	6.6		
28 F ☾	0027	0.4	0616	6.7	1236	1.0	1831	6.5
29 SA	0112	0.5	0713	6.6	1327	1.1	1928	6.5
30 SU	0204	0.6	0814	6.4	1426	1.3	2033	6.4

SUNRISE AND SUNSET TIMES

LONDON BRIDGE
At 51°30′N 0°05′W

UT		Sunrise	Sunset
Jan	01	0806	1602
	15	0759	1621
Feb	01	0738	1650
	15	0714	1716
Mar	01	0645	1741
	15	0614	1805
BST (UT+1)			
Apr	01	0636	1934
	15	0605	1957
May	01	0532	2024
	15	0508	2046
Jun	01	0449	2108
	15	0443	2119
Jul	01	0448	2121
	15	0501	2111
Aug	01	0524	2048
	15	0546	2023
Sep	01	0613	1947
	15	0635	1915
Oct	01	0701	1838
	15	0724	1807
UT			
Nov	01	0654	1633
	15	0718	1611
Dec	01	0744	1555
	15	0800	1551

LONDON BRIDGE
LAT 51°30'N
LONG 0°05'W

TIMES AND HEIGHTS OF HIGH AND LOW WATER

TIME ZONE UT
For Summer Time (area enclosed in shaded box) add 1 hour

2024

JULY

Date	Day	Time	m	Time	m	Time	m	Time	m
1	M	0302	0.8	0917	6.3	1532	1.3	2139	6.5
2	TU	0405	0.9	1021	6.3	1642	1.2	2244	6.5
3	W	0512	1.0	1126	6.3	1755	1.1	2348	6.6
4	TH	0624	1.0	1228	6.4	1902	0.8		
5	F ●	0046	6.7	0726	1.0	1321	6.5	2000	0.6
6	SA	0139	6.9	0816	1.0	1408	6.6	2052	0.5
7	SU	0227	6.9	0901	1.1	1451	6.6	2138	0.5
8	M	0311	6.9	0941	1.2	1531	6.6	2219	0.6
9	TU	0352	6.8	1014	1.2	1606	6.5	2252	0.6
10	W	0430	6.7	1042	1.2	1639	6.5	2319	0.7
11	TH	0504	6.5	1112	1.2	1712	6.4	2345	0.7
12	F	0538	6.3	1144	1.3	1745	6.2		
13	SA ☽	0014	0.8	0613	6.1	1217	1.4	1822	6.1
14	SU	0045	1.0	0652	5.9	1254	1.6	1906	5.9
15	M	0122	1.2	0741	5.7	1338	1.7	2006	5.7
16	TU	0210	1.4	0850	5.6	1437	1.8	2126	5.7
17	W	0326	1.5	1001	5.7	1614	1.7	2235	5.9
18	TH	0448	1.4	1108	6.0	1731	1.4	2338	6.3
19	F	0552	1.2	1211	6.3	1835	1.0		
20	SA	0034	6.6	0653	1.1	1305	6.5	1938	0.8
21	SU O	0125	6.8	0753	1.0	1354	6.7	2037	0.5
22	M	0213	7.1	0850	0.9	1439	6.8	2130	0.3
23	TU	0259	7.2	0940	0.8	1522	6.9	2219	0.1
24	W	0344	7.3	1026	0.6	1604	7.0	2302	-0.1
25	TH	0428	7.3	1108	0.6	1644	7.0	2341	0.0
26	F	0512	7.1	1146	0.7	1725	7.0		
27	SA	0016	0.1	0558	6.9	1224	0.8	1809	6.9
28	SU ☾	0050	0.4	0647	6.6	1305	1.0	1858	6.7
29	M	0129	0.7	0742	6.3	1354	1.2	1958	6.5
30	TU	0221	1.0	0844	6.1	1457	1.4	2107	6.3
31	W	0327	1.3	0952	6.0	1612	1.4	2220	6.2

AUGUST

Date	Day	Time	m	Time	m	Time	m	Time	m
1	TH	0442	1.4	1109	6.0	1734	1.2	2336	6.3
2	F	0607	1.4	1220	6.2	1852	0.9		
3	SA	0041	6.6	0713	1.2	1315	6.4	1952	0.6
4	SU ●	0134	6.8	0805	1.1	1401	6.6	2041	0.5
5	M	0219	6.9	0850	1.1	1440	6.7	2124	0.4
6	TU	0259	6.9	0929	1.1	1515	6.7	2201	0.5
7	W	0335	6.8	1002	1.1	1546	6.7	2231	0.5
8	TH	0406	6.8	1029	1.1	1615	6.7	2255	0.5
9	F	0434	6.6	1054	1.1	1644	6.6	2317	0.6
10	SA	0502	6.5	1121	1.2	1713	6.5	2340	0.8
11	SU	0531	6.3	1148	1.3	1744	6.3		
12	M ☽	0003	1.0	0604	6.0	1215	1.5	1820	6.0
13	TU	0029	1.2	0643	5.8	1248	1.6	1906	5.8
14	W	0106	1.4	0737	5.5	1338	1.8	2011	5.6
15	TH	0204	1.7	0906	5.4	1501	1.9	2149	5.6
16	F	0403	1.8	1033	5.6	1659	1.6	2307	6.0
17	SA	0525	1.5	1146	6.1	1813	1.1		
18	SU	0012	6.5	0636	1.2	1245	6.5	1925	0.7
19	M O	0107	6.9	0744	1.0	1335	6.8	2026	0.4
20	TU	0156	7.2	0841	0.8	1420	7.0	2118	0.1
21	W	0241	7.4	0930	0.7	1502	7.2	2204	-0.1
22	TH	0325	7.4	1014	0.5	1542	7.3	2245	-0.2
23	F	0407	7.3	1054	0.5	1621	7.3	2321	-0.1
24	SA	0448	7.1	1130	0.6	1700	7.2	2351	0.2
25	SU	0530	6.8	1203	0.8	1741	7.0		
26	M ☾	0017	0.6	0614	6.4	1238	1.0	1828	6.7
27	TU	0049	1.0	0704	6.1	1320	1.3	1925	6.3
28	W	0135	1.4	0807	5.7	1422	1.5	2039	6.0
29	TH	0252	1.8	0926	5.6	1546	1.6	2204	5.9
30	F	0421	1.8	1055	5.7	1722	1.3	2328	6.1
31	SA	0557	1.6	1208	6.1	1843	0.9		

SEPTEMBER

Date	Day	Time	m	Time	m	Time	m	Time	m
1	SU	0032	6.5	0659	1.3	1300	6.4	1937	0.6
2	M	0121	6.8	0747	1.1	1342	6.6	2020	0.4
3	TU ●	0201	6.9	0828	1.1	1419	6.7	2058	0.5
4	W	0237	6.8	0905	1.1	1450	6.8	2130	0.5
5	TH	0308	6.8	0937	1.1	1518	6.8	2157	0.5
6	F	0334	6.8	1005	1.0	1545	6.9	2221	0.6
7	SA	0359	6.7	1030	1.1	1612	6.8	2243	0.7
8	SU	0425	6.6	1056	1.1	1640	6.6	2304	0.9
9	M	0454	6.4	1119	1.3	1710	6.4	2324	1.1
10	TU	0525	6.1	1141	1.4	1745	6.2	2347	1.2
11	W ☽	0601	5.9	1210	1.5	1828	5.9		
12	TH	0022	1.4	0650	5.6	1255	1.7	1928	5.7
13	F	0116	1.8	0805	5.3	1406	1.9	2103	5.6
14	SA	0316	2.1	0954	5.4	1628	1.6	2236	6.0
15	SU	0458	1.6	1116	5.9	1749	1.1	2346	6.5
16	M	0613	1.2	1217	6.5	1904	0.6		
17	TU	0042	7.0	0723	1.0	1307	6.9	2005	0.3
18	W O	0131	7.3	0819	0.8	1352	7.2	2055	0.0
19	TH	0216	7.4	0908	0.6	1433	7.4	2139	-0.1
20	F	0258	7.4	0952	0.5	1513	7.5	2218	0.0
21	SA	0340	7.3	1032	0.5	1553	7.5	2252	0.2
22	SU	0420	7.1	1106	0.6	1633	7.4	2318	0.6
23	M	0500	6.7	1138	0.8	1715	7.0	2341	0.9
24	TU ☾	0541	6.3	1210	1.0	1802	6.6		
25	W	0010	1.3	0627	5.9	1249	1.3	1859	6.1
26	TH	0056	1.8	0728	5.5	1350	1.6	2016	5.8
27	F	0218	2.1	0857	5.3	1521	1.7	2144	5.7
28	SA	0359	2.1	1030	5.5	1659	1.4	2307	6.1
29	SU	0530	1.7	1142	6.0	1816	0.9		
30	M	0009	6.5	0630	1.3	1233	6.4	1906	0.6

OCTOBER

Date	Day	Time	m	Time	m	Time	m	Time	m
1	TU	0055	6.7	0717	1.2	1313	6.6	1945	0.6
2	W ●	0133	6.8	0757	1.1	1348	6.7	2019	0.6
3	TH	0206	6.8	0833	1.1	1418	6.8	2050	0.6
4	F	0234	6.8	0905	1.0	1445	6.9	2117	0.7
5	SA	0258	6.8	0935	1.0	1512	6.9	2143	0.7
6	SU	0323	6.8	1003	1.0	1540	6.9	2207	0.8
7	M	0352	6.6	1029	1.1	1610	6.7	2228	1.0
8	TU	0422	6.4	1051	1.2	1643	6.5	2251	1.1
9	W	0453	6.2	1114	1.2	1719	6.3	2319	1.2
10	TH ☽	0529	6.0	1146	1.3	1804	6.1	2357	1.5
11	F	0619	5.7	1231	1.5	1904	5.8		
12	SA	0051	1.8	0731	5.4	1338	1.7	2033	5.7
13	SU	0240	2.1	0914	5.5	1555	1.5	2203	6.1
14	M	0425	1.7	1038	6.0	1714	1.0	2313	6.6
15	TU	0538	1.3	1141	6.5	1829	0.6		
16	W	0011	7.0	0649	1.0	1233	6.9	1932	0.3
17	TH O	0101	7.2	0749	0.9	1319	7.3	2023	0.2
18	F	0147	7.3	0840	0.7	1403	7.5	2107	0.2
19	SA	0230	7.3	0925	0.6	1445	7.6	2146	0.4
20	SU	0312	7.2	1006	0.6	1527	7.6	2218	0.6
21	M	0353	6.9	1042	0.6	1610	7.3	2243	0.9
22	TU	0433	6.6	1113	0.8	1654	6.9	2307	1.2
23	W	0513	6.2	1144	1.0	1741	6.5	2341	1.5
24	TH ☾	0557	5.8	1223	1.3	1837	6.0		
25	F	0027	1.9	0652	5.4	1320	1.6	1949	5.7
26	SA	0140	2.2	0816	5.3	1449	1.6	2109	5.7
27	SU	0320	2.2	0943	5.4	1609	1.4	2225	5.9
28	M	0441	1.9	1056	5.8	1716	1.1	2330	6.2
29	TU	0543	1.5	1151	6.2	1810	0.9		
30	W	0018	6.5	0634	1.3	1234	6.5	1854	0.8
31	TH	0056	6.6	0717	1.2	1310	6.7	1932	0.8

NOVEMBER

Date	Day	Time	m	Time	m	Time	m	Time	m
1	F ●	0129	6.7	0755	1.1	1342	6.8	2007	0.8
2	SA	0157	6.7	0831	1.0	1412	6.9	2039	0.8
3	SU	0225	6.7	0905	1.0	1442	6.9	2108	0.9
4	M	0255	6.7	0936	1.0	1514	6.9	2134	1.0
5	TU	0326	6.6	1005	1.0	1548	6.8	2200	1.0
6	W	0359	6.5	1032	1.0	1624	6.6	2230	1.1
7	TH	0434	6.3	1100	1.1	1705	6.5	2306	1.3
8	F	0514	6.1	1136	1.1	1754	6.3	2350	1.5
9	SA ☽	0606	5.8	1223	1.3	1854	6.1		
10	SU	0047	1.7	0713	5.7	1331	1.4	2012	6.0
11	M	0221	1.9	0839	5.8	1521	1.3	2132	6.2
12	TU	0350	1.7	0959	6.1	1635	1.0	2239	6.6
13	W	0502	1.4	1104	6.5	1745	0.7	2339	6.8
14	TH	0612	1.2	1200	6.9	1852	0.6		
15	F O	0032	7.0	0717	0.9	1250	7.2	1948	0.5
16	SA	0121	7.1	0812	0.8	1337	7.4	2035	0.6
17	SU	0206	7.0	0900	0.6	1422	7.4	2116	0.8
18	M	0250	7.0	0944	0.6	1508	7.4	2151	1.0
19	TU	0333	6.8	1024	0.7	1554	7.2	2218	1.2
20	W	0415	6.5	1058	0.8	1640	6.8	2247	1.4
21	TH	0455	6.2	1130	1.0	1726	6.4	2323	1.6
22	F	0536	5.9	1207	1.2	1817	6.1		
23	SA ☾	0007	1.8	0623	5.6	1255	1.4	1916	5.8
24	SU	0102	2.1	0727	5.5	1404	1.5	2023	5.7
25	M	0216	2.1	0846	5.5	1516	1.4	2127	5.8
26	TU	0341	2.0	0954	5.7	1616	1.3	2229	5.9
27	W	0447	1.8	1055	6.0	1710	1.1	2324	6.1
28	TH	0542	1.5	1147	6.3	1800	1.0		
29	F	0011	6.4	0632	1.3	1230	6.5	1847	1.0
30	SA	0051	6.5	0718	1.1	1309	6.7	1929	1.0

DECEMBER

Date	Day	Time	m	Time	m	Time	m	Time	m
1	SU ●	0127	6.6	0800	1.0	1346	6.8	2008	1.0
2	M	0203	6.7	0841	0.9	1421	6.8	2042	1.0
3	TU	0238	6.7	0919	0.9	1458	6.8	2115	1.0
4	W	0314	6.6	0955	0.8	1536	6.8	2149	1.0
5	TH	0352	6.5	1030	0.8	1617	6.8	2228	1.1
6	F	0431	6.4	1104	0.8	1701	6.7	2310	1.2
7	SA	0513	6.3	1144	0.9	1749	6.5	2358	1.3
8	SU ☽	0602	6.2	1231	1.0	1844	6.4		
9	M	0053	1.5	0658	6.1	1332	1.0	1951	6.3
10	TU	0200	1.6	0807	6.1	1446	1.0	2101	6.3
11	W	0315	1.6	0922	6.3	1556	1.0	2207	6.4
12	TH	0428	1.5	1030	6.5	1704	0.9	2310	6.5
13	F	0541	1.3	1132	6.7	1813	0.9		
14	SA	0009	6.6	0650	1.0	1228	6.9	1917	0.9
15	SU O	0103	6.7	0750	0.8	1320	7.1	2010	0.9
16	M	0152	6.8	0843	0.6	1410	7.1	2057	1.0
17	TU	0239	6.7	0931	0.6	1459	7.1	2138	1.1
18	W	0323	6.7	1016	0.6	1545	7.0	2214	1.3
19	TH	0405	6.5	1055	0.7	1630	6.8	2244	1.4
20	F	0444	6.3	1127	0.9	1712	6.5	2315	1.5
21	SA	0521	6.2	1157	1.0	1754	6.2	2351	1.6
22	SU ☾	0559	6.0	1231	1.1	1837	6.0		
23	M	0030	1.7	0643	5.8	1311	1.2	1926	5.8
24	TU	0115	1.9	0740	5.7	1403	1.3	2024	5.7
25	W	0210	2.0	0851	5.7	1509	1.4	2124	5.7
26	TH	0329	2.0	0956	5.8	1615	1.4	2224	5.8
27	F	0448	1.8	1057	6.0	1713	1.3	2324	6.0
28	SA	0549	1.5	1153	6.3	1807	1.2		
29	SU	0018	6.3	0644	1.2	1241	6.5	1859	1.1
30	M ●	0106	6.5	0736	1.0	1326	6.7	1947	1.1
31	TU	0150	6.6	0825	0.9	1408	6.8	2032	1.1

WALTON-ON-THE-NAZE

LAT 51°51'N
LONG 1°17'E

TIMES AND HEIGHTS OF HIGH AND LOW WATER (Heights in Metres)

TIME ZONE UT
For Summer Time (area enclosed in shaded box) add 1 hour

2024

JANUARY

Date	Day	Time	m	Time	m	Time	m	Time	m
1	M	0230	3.9	0847	0.6	1456	3.8	2040	1.1
2	TU	0306	3.8	0923	0.6	1535	3.6	2118	1.2
3	W	0346	3.7	1003	0.7	1618	3.5	2202	1.3
4	TH ☾	0431	3.6	1050	0.8	1707	3.4	2254	1.4
5	F	0525	3.5	1148	0.9	1806	3.4		
6	SA	0003	1.5	0629	3.4	1257	1.0	1909	3.4
7	SU	0130	1.4	0735	3.5	1402	1.0	2013	3.5
8	M	0237	1.2	0839	3.6	1459	0.9	2115	3.6
9	TU	0334	1.0	0937	3.7	1552	0.9	2211	3.8
10	W	0426	0.8	1031	3.9	1640	0.8	2303	3.9
11	TH ●	0516	0.6	1121	4.1	1727	0.8	2352	4.1
12	F	0605	0.5	1210	4.3	1812	0.7		
13	SA	0038	4.2	0654	0.3	1257	4.4	1858	0.7
14	SU	0124	4.2	0743	0.2	1345	4.4	1944	0.7
15	M	0210	4.3	0830	0.2	1433	4.3	2030	0.8
16	TU	0255	4.2	0918	0.2	1522	4.2	2118	0.9
17	W	0341	4.2	1007	0.3	1614	4.0	2208	1.0
18	TH ☽	0429	4.0	1059	0.4	1708	3.8	2304	1.1
19	F	0523	3.9	1155	0.6	1809	3.7		
20	SA	0007	1.1	0628	3.7	1256	0.7	1918	3.5
21	SU	0117	1.1	0743	3.6	1402	0.9	2031	3.5
22	M	0232	1.1	0854	3.7	1514	1.0	2137	3.6
23	TU	0346	0.9	0956	3.8	1615	1.0	2231	3.8
24	W	0447	0.7	1048	3.9	1702	1.0	2317	3.9
25	TH ○	0534	0.6	1132	3.9	1741	1.0	2357	3.9
26	F	0615	0.5	1212	4.0	1816	0.9		
27	SA	0033	4.0	0651	0.4	1248	4.0	1849	0.9
28	SU	0107	4.0	0723	0.4	1323	4.0	1918	0.9
29	M	0139	4.0	0752	0.4	1357	3.9	1946	0.9
30	TU	0210	4.0	0820	0.5	1430	3.8	2015	0.9
31	W	0241	3.9	0849	0.5	1502	3.7	[illegible]	[illegible]

FEBRUARY

Date	Day	Time	m	Time	m	Time	m	Time	m
1	TH	0313	3.8	0919	0.6	1535	3.6	2123	1.1
2	F ☾	0347	3.7	0954	0.7	1613	3.5	2204	1.2
3	SA	0428	3.6	1037	0.9	1702	3.4	2258	1.3
4	SU	0523	3.5	1141	1.1	1807	3.3		
5	M	0021	1.4	0636	3.4	1312	1.1	1924	3.3
6	TU	0158	1.2	0759	3.4	1429	1.1	2044	3.4
7	W	0309	1.0	0916	3.6	1533	1.0	2155	3.6
8	TH	0411	0.7	1018	3.9	1628	0.9	2251	3.9
9	F ●	0506	0.5	1111	4.1	1717	0.8	2340	4.1
10	SA	0556	0.3	1200	4.3	1803	0.7		
11	SU	0025	4.3	0644	0.1	1246	4.4	1848	0.6
12	M	0109	4.4	0729	0.0	1331	4.5	1931	0.6
13	TU	0152	4.5	0812	0.0	1416	4.4	2013	0.6
14	W	0234	4.4	0853	0.1	1501	4.2	2055	0.7
15	TH	0315	4.3	0934	0.2	1546	4.0	2139	0.8
16	F ☽	0358	4.2	1017	0.5	1635	3.8	2229	0.9
17	SA	0447	3.9	1108	0.7	1730	3.5	2330	1.0
18	SU	0550	3.6	1211	1.0	1839	3.3		
19	M	0043	1.1	0715	3.4	1330	1.2	2007	3.3
20	TU	0218	1.1	0842	3.5	1506	1.2	2124	3.4
21	W	0347	0.9	0950	3.6	1610	1.1	2220	3.6
22	TH	0443	0.7	1042	3.8	1653	1.0	2304	3.8
23	F	0525	0.5	1123	3.9	1727	1.0	2342	3.9
24	SA ○	0558	0.4	1158	3.9	1757	0.9		
25	SU	0015	4.0	0628	0.4	1230	4.0	1828	0.8
26	M	0045	4.1	0656	0.4	1301	4.0	1856	0.8
27	TU	0115	4.1	0722	0.4	1332	4.0	1923	0.8
28	W	0144	4.1	0748	0.4	1401	3.9	1951	0.8
29	TH	0213	4.0	0813	0.5	1429	3.8	2020	0.8

MARCH

Date	Day	Time	m	Time	m	Time	m	Time	m
1	F	0242	3.9	0839	0.6	1500	3.7	2052	0.9
2	SA	0313	3.9	0909	0.7	1535	3.6	2128	1.0
3	SU ☾	0351	3.7	0947	0.9	1619	3.5	2216	1.1
4	M	0441	3.6	1045	1.1	1719	3.3	2332	1.2
5	TU	0551	3.4	1228	1.3	1842	3.2		
6	W	0126	1.2	0728	3.3	1405	1.2	2019	3.3
7	TH	0248	0.9	0900	3.6	1515	1.0	2137	3.5
8	F	0354	0.6	1004	3.9	1611	0.8	2233	3.8
9	SA	0449	0.3	1056	4.2	1659	0.7	2321	4.1
10	SU ●	0538	0.1	1142	4.3	1743	0.6		
11	M	0004	4.3	0623	0.0	1226	4.5	1827	0.5
12	TU	0045	4.5	0705	-0.1	1309	4.5	1909	0.5
13	W	0126	4.6	0745	0.0	1352	4.4	1950	0.5
14	TH	0207	4.5	0821	0.1	1434	4.2	2031	0.6
15	F	0247	4.4	0857	0.4	1516	4.0	2113	0.7
16	SA	0328	4.2	0935	0.6	1600	3.7	2200	0.8
17	SU ☽	0416	3.8	1024	1.0	1652	3.4	2257	0.9
18	M	0519	3.5	1131	1.2	1801	3.2		
19	TU	0013	1.1	0652	3.3	1258	1.4	1936	3.1
20	W	0202	1.1	0825	3.4	1446	1.4	2100	3.3
21	TH	0332	0.8	0934	3.6	1550	1.2	2156	3.6
22	F	0423	0.6	1022	3.8	1630	1.1	2240	3.8
23	SA	0500	0.5	1100	3.9	1701	0.9	2315	3.9
24	SU	0529	0.4	1133	3.9	1731	0.9	2347	4.0
25	M ○	0555	0.4	1203	3.9	1800	0.8		
26	TU	0016	4.1	0622	0.4	1233	4.0	1830	0.7
27	W	0045	4.1	0649	0.4	1302	4.0	1858	0.7
28	TH	0114	4.1	0714	0.4	1331	4.0	1927	0.7
29	F	0144	4.1	0738	0.5	1400	3.9	1956	0.7
30	SA	0214	4.0	0805	0.6	1431	3.8	2028	0.8
31	SU	0247	3.9	0836	0.7	1507	3.7	2105	0.8

APRIL

Date	Day	Time	m	Time	m	Time	m	Time	m
1	M	0327	3.8	0917	0.9	1550	3.5	2154	0.9
2	TU ☾	0419	3.6	1019	1.2	1651	3.3	2312	1.1
3	W	0530	3.4	1205	1.3	1815	3.2		
4	TH	0104	1.0	0710	3.4	1340	1.2	1955	3.3
5	F	0225	0.8	0841	3.6	1449	1.0	2111	3.6
6	SA	0331	0.5	0943	3.9	1545	0.8	2207	3.9
7	SU	0424	0.2	1033	4.2	1633	0.7	2253	4.2
8	M ●	0511	0.1	1118	4.3	1718	0.6	2336	4.4
9	TU	0555	0.0	1201	4.4	1802	0.5		
10	W	0017	4.5	0636	0.0	1243	4.4	1846	0.4
11	TH	0058	4.6	0714	0.1	1325	4.3	1928	0.4
12	F	0139	4.5	0749	0.3	1406	4.1	2010	0.5
13	SA	0220	4.3	0824	0.6	1447	3.9	2051	0.6
14	SU	0303	4.1	0902	0.8	1530	3.7	2136	0.7
15	M ☽	0351	3.8	0949	1.1	1619	3.4	2231	0.9
16	TU	0455	3.4	1054	1.4	1726	3.2	2343	1.0
17	W	0622	3.3	1218	1.5	1850	3.1		
18	TH	0120	1.0	0748	3.3	1355	1.5	2014	3.3
19	F	0249	0.9	0858	3.5	1506	1.3	2116	3.5
20	SA	0343	0.7	0947	3.7	1551	1.1	2201	3.7
21	SU	0419	0.6	1026	3.8	1627	1.0	2237	3.8
22	M	0449	0.5	1059	3.9	1659	0.8	2310	4.0
23	TU ○	0518	0.5	1130	3.9	1731	0.8	2341	4.0
24	W	0547	0.5	1201	4.0	1802	0.7		
25	TH	0013	4.1	0615	0.5	1231	4.0	1834	0.7
26	F	0045	4.1	0641	0.5	1304	4.0	1905	0.6
27	SA	0118	4.1	0709	0.6	1337	3.9	1938	0.7
28	SU	0153	4.0	0741	0.7	1412	3.8	2013	0.7
29	M	0231	3.9	0819	0.8	1451	3.7	2056	0.7
30	TU	0316	3.8	0908	1.0	1538	3.5	2152	0.8

MAY

Date	Day	Time	m	Time	m	Time	m	Time	m
1	W ☾	0411	3.7	1017	1.2	1641	3.4	2314	0.9
2	TH	0524	3.5	1149	1.3	1801	3.3		
3	F	0046	0.8	0655	3.6	1311	1.2	1927	3.5
4	SA	0159	0.6	0813	3.8	1417	1.0	2038	3.7
5	SU	0301	0.4	0915	4.0	1514	0.9	2135	4.0
6	M	0355	0.2	1007	4.1	1605	0.7	2224	4.2
7	TU	0442	0.2	1053	4.2	1653	0.6	2308	4.4
8	W ●	0526	0.2	1137	4.3	1740	0.5	2351	4.5
9	TH	0607	0.3	1219	4.3	1826	0.4		
10	F	0033	4.5	0647	0.4	1301	4.2	1911	0.4
11	SA	0116	4.4	0724	0.6	1343	4.1	1955	0.5
12	SU	0159	4.2	0801	0.8	1424	3.9	2037	0.6
13	M	0243	4.0	0839	1.0	1506	3.7	2120	0.7
14	TU	0332	3.7	0923	1.2	1554	3.5	2210	0.8
15	W ☽	0433	3.5	1019	1.4	1654	3.4	2312	0.9
16	TH	0544	3.3	1131	1.5	1802	3.3		
17	F	0028	0.9	0654	3.3	1255	1.5	1910	3.3
18	SA	0140	0.9	0800	3.4	1406	1.3	2014	3.4
19	SU	0239	0.8	0856	3.6	1501	1.2	2107	3.6
20	M	0325	0.7	0941	3.7	1546	1.0	2151	3.8
21	TU	0404	0.6	1019	3.8	1625	0.9	2230	3.9
22	W	0440	0.6	1055	3.9	1702	0.8	2307	4.0
23	TH ○	0514	0.6	1131	3.9	1738	0.7	2345	4.1
24	F	0546	0.6	1207	4.0	1814	0.7		
25	SA	0022	4.1	0618	0.7	1245	4.0	1852	0.6
26	SU	0101	4.1	0652	0.7	1324	4.0	1931	0.6
27	M	0141	4.1	0731	0.8	1405	3.9	2013	0.6
28	TU	0225	4.0	0817	0.9	1449	3.8	2102	0.6
29	W	0314	3.9	0911	1.0	1539	3.7	2202	0.6
30	TH ☾	0411	3.8	1016	1.1	1638	3.6	2313	0.6
31	F	0518	3.7	1128	1.2	1745	3.6		

JUNE

Date	Day	Time	m	Time	m	Time	m	Time	m
1	SA	0024	0.5	0632	3.7	1239	1.1	1856	3.7
2	SU	0130	0.5	0742	3.8	1344	1.0	2003	3.8
3	M	0229	0.4	0846	3.9	1443	0.9	2104	4.0
4	TU	0324	0.4	0941	4.0	1539	0.8	2157	4.1
5	W	0415	0.5	1031	4.1	1633	0.7	2245	4.3
6	TH ●	0502	0.5	1117	4.1	1724	0.5	2331	4.3
7	F	0547	0.6	1202	4.1	1814	0.5		
8	SA	0015	4.3	0629	0.7	1244	4.1	1902	0.4
9	SU	0100	4.2	0709	0.8	1327	4.0	1946	0.5
10	M	0144	4.1	0747	0.9	1408	3.9	2027	0.5
11	TU	0229	3.9	0823	1.0	1449	3.8	2106	0.6
12	W	0315	3.8	0902	1.1	1532	3.7	2148	0.7
13	TH	0405	3.6	0945	1.2	1621	3.6	2236	0.8
14	F ☽	0500	3.5	1038	1.3	1715	3.5	2334	0.8
15	SA	0557	3.4	1145	1.4	1812	3.5		
16	SU	0038	0.9	0654	3.4	1302	1.4	1910	3.5
17	M	0137	0.9	0751	3.5	1407	1.3	2008	3.6
18	TU	0232	0.9	0846	3.6	1502	1.1	2103	3.7
19	W	0322	0.8	0937	3.7	1551	1.0	2153	3.8
20	TH	0407	0.8	1023	3.8	1636	0.9	2239	3.9
21	F	0449	0.8	1107	3.9	1719	0.7	2323	4.0
22	SA ○	0528	0.8	1151	4.0	1801	0.6		
23	SU	0006	4.1	0607	0.8	1234	4.1	1846	0.5
24	M	0050	4.2	0648	0.8	1318	4.1	1931	0.4
25	TU	0135	4.2	0732	0.8	1403	4.1	2018	0.4
26	W	0222	4.2	0818	0.8	1448	4.0	2107	0.4
27	TH	0311	4.1	0908	0.9	1535	4.0	2159	0.4
28	F ☾	0404	4.0	1002	1.0	1625	4.0	2255	0.4
29	SA	0501	3.9	1101	1.1	1720	3.9	2355	0.5
30	SU	0603	3.8	1205	1.1	1822	3.9		

SUNRISE AND SUNSET TIMES

WALTON-ON-THE-NAZE
At 51°51'N 1°17'E

		Sunrise	Sunset
UT			
Jan	01	0802	1555
	15	0755	1614
Feb	01	0734	1643
	15	0709	1709
Mar	01	0640	1735
	15	0609	1800
BST (UT+1)			
Apr	01	0630	1929
	15	0558	1952
May	01	0526	2020
	15	0502	2042
Jun	01	0442	2104
	15	0435	2116
Jul	01	0440	2117
	15	0454	2107
Aug	01	0517	2044
	15	0539	2020
Sep	01	0607	1942
	15	0630	1909
Oct	01	0656	1832
	15	0719	1801
UT			
Nov	01	0649	1627
	15	0714	1604
Dec	01	0740	1548
	15	[illegible]	[illegible]

WALTON-ON-THE-NAZE

LAT 51°51′N
LONG 1°17′E

TIMES AND HEIGHTS OF HIGH AND LOW WATER (Heights in Metres)

TIME ZONE UT
For Summer Time (area enclosed in shaded box) add 1 hour

2024

JULY

Date	Day	Time	m	Time	m	Time	m	Time	m
1	M	0056	0.5	0710	3.7	1310	1.1	1930	3.9
2	TU	0156	0.6	0817	3.7	1416	1.0	2037	3.9
3	W	0257	0.7	0921	3.8	1521	0.9	2138	4.0
4	TH	0357	0.8	1017	3.9	1623	0.8	2232	4.1
5	F ●	0450	0.8	1107	3.9	1719	0.6	2321	4.1
6	SA	0537	0.9	1152	4.0	1810	0.5		
7	SU	0006	4.1	0619	0.9	1234	4.0	1856	0.5
8	M	0050	4.1	0658	0.9	1315	4.0	1937	0.5
9	TU	0132	4.1	0733	1.0	1353	4.0	2013	0.5
10	W	0212	4.0	0805	1.0	1429	4.0	2045	0.5
11	TH	0252	3.9	0837	1.0	1506	3.9	2118	0.6
12	F	0331	3.7	0912	1.1	1544	3.8	2154	0.7
13	SA ☽	0412	3.6	0951	1.2	1626	3.7	2236	0.8
14	SU	0457	3.5	1039	1.3	1714	3.6	2329	0.9
15	M	0549	3.4	1142	1.4	1811	3.5		
16	TU	0036	1.0	0649	3.4	1307	1.4	1915	3.5
17	W	0144	1.1	0753	3.4	1419	1.3	2020	3.5
18	TH	0245	1.0	0858	3.5	1520	1.1	2122	3.7
19	F	0341	1.0	0958	3.7	1614	0.9	2218	3.9
20	SA	0431	0.9	1050	3.9	1704	0.7	2308	4.0
21	SU O	0516	0.9	1138	4.0	1751	0.5	2355	4.2
22	M	0559	0.8	1223	4.1	1837	0.4		
23	TU	0040	4.3	0642	0.8	1307	4.2	1924	0.3
24	W	0126	4.4	0725	0.7	1351	4.3	2009	0.2
25	TH	0212	4.4	0809	0.8	1434	4.3	2053	0.2
26	F	0258	4.3	0853	0.8	1517	4.3	2138	0.3
27	SA	0345	4.1	0939	0.9	1601	4.2	2225	0.4
28	SU ☾	0435	3.9	1031	1.0	1650	4.1	2318	0.6
29	M	0531	3.7	1131	1.1	1748	3.9		
30	TU	0018	0.8	0637	3.6	1239	1.1	1901	3.8
31	W	0126	1.0	0752	3.5	1354	1.1	2019	3.7

AUGUST

Date	Day	Time	m	Time	m	Time	m	Time	m
1	TH	0241	1.1	0908	3.6	1516	1.0	2130	3.8
2	F	0352	1.1	1010	3.7	1627	0.8	2229	3.9
3	SA	0447	1.1	1101	3.9	1720	0.6	2318	4.0
4	SU ●	0530	1.0	1144	4.0	1804	0.5		
5	M	0000	4.1	0607	1.0	1223	4.1	1842	0.4
6	TU	0037	4.1	0641	0.9	1258	4.1	1917	0.4
7	W	0114	4.1	0712	0.9	1331	4.1	1946	0.5
8	TH	0148	4.0	0741	0.9	1402	4.1	2014	0.5
9	F	0222	4.0	0809	1.0	1434	4.1	2040	0.6
10	SA	0253	3.8	0839	1.0	1505	4.0	2108	0.7
11	SU	0325	3.7	0913	1.1	1538	3.8	2140	0.8
12	M ☽	0400	3.6	0952	1.2	1616	3.7	2219	1.0
13	TU	0444	3.5	1041	1.3	1707	3.5	2316	1.2
14	W	0545	3.3	1159	1.4	1816	3.4		
15	TH	0053	1.3	0702	3.3	1338	1.4	1940	3.4
16	F	0214	1.3	0824	3.4	1452	1.1	2058	3.6
17	SA	0320	1.1	0936	3.6	1554	0.9	2201	3.8
18	SU	0414	1.0	1032	3.8	1647	0.6	2253	4.1
19	M O	0500	0.9	1120	4.1	1735	0.4	2339	4.3
20	TU	0543	0.8	1204	4.3	1821	0.2		
21	W	0024	4.5	0626	0.7	1247	4.4	1905	0.1
22	TH	0108	4.5	0707	0.7	1328	4.5	1947	0.1
23	F	0151	4.5	0749	0.7	1409	4.5	2027	0.2
24	SA	0235	4.3	0830	0.7	1450	4.5	2106	0.3
25	SU	0319	4.1	0914	0.8	1532	4.3	2147	0.6
26	M ☾	0405	3.9	1002	0.9	1619	4.1	2237	0.8
27	TU	0458	3.6	1100	1.0	1717	3.8	2340	1.1
28	W	0605	3.4	1212	1.1	1839	3.6		
29	TH	0100	1.3	0733	3.3	1343	1.1	2011	3.6
30	F	0235	1.4	0858	3.5	1519	1.0	2127	3.8
31	SA	0349	1.3	1000	3.7	1624	0.7	2223	3.9

SEPTEMBER

Date	Day	Time	m	Time	m	Time	m	Time	m
1	SU	0437	1.1	1047	3.9	1709	0.6	2307	4.0
2	M	0514	1.0	1127	4.0	1746	0.5	2343	4.1
3	TU ●	0545	1.0	1201	4.1	1817	0.5		
4	W	0016	4.1	0616	0.9	1232	4.2	1845	0.5
5	TH	0048	4.1	0646	0.9	1301	4.2	1912	0.5
6	F	0118	4.1	0715	0.9	1330	4.2	1937	0.5
7	SA	0147	4.0	0742	0.9	1359	4.1	2001	0.6
8	SU	0215	3.9	0810	0.9	1428	4.0	2025	0.7
9	M	0244	3.8	0840	1.0	1458	3.9	2052	0.9
10	TU	0316	3.7	0914	1.1	1534	3.8	2126	1.1
11	W ☽	0356	3.6	0958	1.2	1620	3.6	2215	1.3
12	TH	0451	3.4	1106	1.3	1725	3.4	2352	1.5
13	F	0612	3.2	1301	1.3	1901	3.4		
14	SA	0144	1.4	0751	3.3	1424	1.1	2036	3.6
15	SU	0255	1.2	0910	3.6	1529	0.8	2140	3.9
16	M	0349	1.0	1007	3.9	1623	0.5	2231	4.2
17	TU	0435	0.9	1054	4.1	1710	0.3	2316	4.4
18	W O	0518	0.7	1137	4.4	1754	0.2		
19	TH	0000	4.5	0600	0.7	1219	4.6	1836	0.1
20	F	0042	4.6	0643	0.6	1259	4.7	1917	0.1
21	SA	0125	4.5	0725	0.6	1340	4.7	1955	0.3
22	SU	0207	4.3	0807	0.6	1421	4.5	2031	0.5
23	M	0249	4.1	0850	0.7	1503	4.3	2110	0.8
24	TU ☾	0333	3.8	0938	0.8	1551	4.0	2159	1.1
25	W	0425	3.6	1035	1.0	1653	3.7	2306	1.4
26	TH	0534	3.3	1149	1.1	1824	3.5		
27	F	0034	1.6	0708	3.3	1329	1.1	1957	3.5
28	SA	0216	1.5	0834	3.4	1504	0.9	2111	3.8
29	SU	0329	1.3	0935	3.7	1603	0.7	2203	3.9
30	M	0414	1.2	1021	3.9	1644	0.6	2243	4.0

OCTOBER

Date	Day	Time	m	Time	m	Time	m	Time	m
1	TU	0447	1.1	1058	4.0	1715	0.5	2316	4.1
2	W ●	0517	1.0	1130	4.1	1742	0.5	2347	4.1
3	TH	0547	0.9	1159	4.2	1808	0.5		
4	F	0016	4.1	0618	0.8	1227	4.2	1835	0.5
5	SA	0044	4.1	0647	0.8	1257	4.2	1900	0.6
6	SU	0113	4.1	0715	0.8	1326	4.2	1923	0.7
7	M	0141	4.0	0743	0.8	1356	4.1	1947	0.8
8	TU	0211	3.9	0814	0.9	1428	4.0	2016	0.9
9	W	0244	3.8	0848	1.0	1506	3.8	2054	1.1
10	TH ☽	0323	3.6	0932	1.1	1554	3.7	2146	1.3
11	F	0417	3.4	1039	1.2	1658	3.5	2317	1.5
12	SA	0536	3.3	1230	1.2	1831	3.4		
13	SU	0109	1.5	0715	3.3	1354	0.9	2007	3.7
14	M	0220	1.2	0835	3.6	1458	0.6	2111	4.0
15	TU	0316	1.0	0934	3.9	1552	0.4	2203	4.2
16	W	0404	0.9	1022	4.2	1639	0.3	2248	4.4
17	TH O	0449	0.7	1106	4.4	1723	0.2	2332	4.5
18	F	0534	0.6	1148	4.6	1805	0.2		
19	SA	0015	4.5	0619	0.6	1230	4.7	1846	0.3
20	SU	0057	4.4	0703	0.5	1312	4.6	1924	0.5
21	M	0140	4.3	0747	0.6	1355	4.5	2002	0.7
22	TU	0222	4.1	0832	0.6	1440	4.2	2042	1.0
23	W	0306	3.8	0919	0.7	1530	3.9	2130	1.3
24	TH ☾	0356	3.6	1015	0.9	1634	3.6	2233	1.5
25	F	0504	3.3	1126	1.0	1759	3.5	2356	1.7
26	SA	0628	3.3	1257	1.0	1924	3.5		
27	SU	0130	1.6	0751	3.4	1422	0.9	2036	3.7
28	M	0245	1.4	0855	3.6	1523	0.8	2128	3.8
29	TU	0335	1.3	0943	3.8	1603	0.7	2208	3.9
30	W	0412	1.1	1020	3.9	1634	0.6	2242	4.0
31	TH	0445	1.0	1053	4.0	1703	0.6	2314	4.0

NOVEMBER

Date	Day	Time	m	Time	m	Time	m	Time	m
1	F ●	0518	0.9	1124	4.1	1732	0.6	2343	4.1
2	SA	0550	0.8	1155	4.2	1800	0.7		
3	SU	0013	4.1	0621	0.8	1227	4.2	1826	0.7
4	M	0043	4.1	0652	0.7	1259	4.1	1852	0.8
5	TU	0115	4.0	0723	0.7	1333	4.1	1921	0.9
6	W	0149	4.0	0757	0.8	1410	4.0	1956	1.0
7	TH	0226	3.8	0835	0.8	1452	3.9	2040	1.1
8	F	0308	3.7	0925	0.9	1542	3.8	2139	1.3
9	SA ☽	0403	3.5	1035	0.9	1646	3.6	2301	1.4
10	SU	0516	3.4	1205	0.9	1808	3.6		
11	M	0029	1.4	0640	3.5	1320	0.7	1931	3.8
12	TU	0141	1.2	0756	3.7	1423	0.5	2037	4.0
13	W	0240	1.0	0858	4.0	1518	0.4	2132	4.2
14	TH	0333	0.9	0950	4.2	1607	0.3	2222	4.3
15	F O	0423	0.7	1037	4.4	1654	0.3	2307	4.4
16	SA	0512	0.6	1123	4.5	1738	0.4	2352	4.4
17	SU	0600	0.5	1207	4.6	1821	0.5		
18	M	0035	4.3	0649	0.5	1252	4.5	1903	0.7
19	TU	0119	4.2	0735	0.5	1337	4.4	1944	0.9
20	W	0202	4.0	0821	0.6	1424	4.1	2025	1.1
21	TH	0246	3.8	0907	0.7	1515	3.9	2109	1.3
22	F	0335	3.6	0957	0.8	1614	3.6	2202	1.5
23	SA ☾	0433	3.5	1057	0.9	1723	3.5	2307	1.6
24	SU	0540	3.4	1208	0.9	1832	3.4		
25	M	0029	1.6	0648	3.4	1317	0.9	1939	3.5
26	TU	0143	1.5	0754	3.5	1417	0.9	2037	3.6
27	W	0243	1.3	0850	3.6	1506	0.8	2124	3.7
28	TH	0330	1.2	0935	3.8	1547	0.8	2204	3.8
29	F	0412	1.0	1014	3.9	1625	0.8	2240	3.9
30	SA	0449	0.9	1051	4.0	1700	0.8	2314	4.0

DECEMBER

Date	Day	Time	m	Time	m	Time	m	Time	m
1	SU ●	0526	0.8	1128	4.1	1733	0.8	2349	4.0
2	M	0601	0.7	1205	4.1	1803	0.8		
3	TU	0024	4.1	0637	0.7	1242	4.1	1834	0.8
4	W	0102	4.1	0714	0.6	1320	4.1	1910	0.9
5	TH	0141	4.0	0753	0.6	1402	4.1	1951	0.9
6	F	0221	3.9	0837	0.6	1447	4.0	2039	1.0
7	SA	0306	3.8	0928	0.6	1537	3.9	2135	1.2
8	SU ☽	0357	3.7	1028	0.7	1635	3.8	2240	1.2
9	M	0457	3.7	1137	0.6	1742	3.8	2351	1.3
10	TU	0604	3.7	1244	0.6	1854	3.8		
11	W	0100	1.2	0716	3.8	1346	0.5	2003	3.8
12	TH	0205	1.1	0823	3.9	1444	0.5	2105	4.0
13	F	0305	0.9	0923	4.1	1539	0.5	2200	4.0
14	SA	0403	0.8	1016	4.2	1632	0.6	2250	4.1
15	SU O	0458	0.6	1106	4.3	1722	0.7	2337	4.2
16	M	0551	0.5	1153	4.4	1809	0.8		
17	TU	0022	4.2	0642	0.4	1240	4.3	1853	0.9
18	W	0107	4.1	0730	0.4	1326	4.2	1934	1.0
19	TH	0150	4.0	0814	0.5	1412	4.1	2011	1.1
20	F	0232	3.9	0855	0.5	1458	3.9	2048	1.2
21	SA	0314	3.8	0935	0.6	1547	3.7	2128	1.3
22	SU ☾	0359	3.7	1018	0.7	1638	3.6	2214	1.4
23	M	0449	3.6	1110	0.8	1732	3.4	2313	1.5
24	TU	0544	3.5	1209	0.9	1828	3.4		
25	W	0029	1.5	0644	3.4	1310	1.0	1927	3.4
26	TH	0142	1.4	0745	3.4	1408	1.0	2026	3.5
27	F	0243	1.3	0845	3.5	1502	1.0	2121	3.6
28	SA	0337	1.1	0938	3.7	1552	0.9	2209	3.7
29	SU	0424	0.9	1025	3.8	1636	0.9	2252	3.9
30	M ●	0506	0.8	1109	3.9	1715	0.9	2334	4.0
31	TU	0547	0.6	1150	4.0	1752	0.9		

LOWESTOFT
LAT 52°28′N
LONG 1°45′E

TIMES AND HEIGHTS OF HIGH AND LOW WATER (Heights in Metres)

TIME ZONE UT
For Summer Time (area enclosed in shaded box) add 1 hour

2024

JANUARY

Date	Day	Time	m
1	M	0009 0648 1304 1821	2.5 0.7 2.1 1.2
2	TU	0048 0727 1344 1859	2.5 0.8 2.1 1.2
3	W	0130 0808 1431 1944	2.4 0.9 2.0 1.3
4	TH ☽	0216 0856 1542 2034	2.3 0.9 2.0 1.4
5	F	0308 0956 1651 2136	2.3 1.0 2.1 1.4
6	SA	0414 1103 1744 2304	2.2 1.0 2.1 1.4
7	SU	0525 1159 1831	2.2 1.0 2.2
8	M	0017 0624 1248 1916	1.3 2.2 0.9 2.3
9	TU	0113 0719 1335 1959	1.1 2.3 0.9 2.3
10	W	0204 0813 1422 2040	1.0 2.3 0.9 2.4
11	TH ●	0256 0907 1510 2122	0.8 2.4 0.8 2.5
12	F	0348 0958 1558 2206	0.6 2.5 0.8 2.5
13	SA	0439 1047 1644 2250	0.5 2.5 0.8 2.6
14	SU	0529 1135 1729 2334	0.4 2.5 0.8 2.7
15	M	0617 1222 1812	0.4 2.4 0.9
16	TU	0017 0704 1310 1855	2.7 0.4 2.3 1.0
17	W	0103 0753 1404 1939	2.7 0.5 2.2 1.1
18	TH ☾	0151 0846 1519 2029	2.6 0.6 2.1 1.2
19	F	0246 0947 1634 2133	2.5 0.7 2.1 1.2
20	SA	0400 1055 1733 2303	2.4 0.9 2.1 1.2
21	SU	0522 1201 1828	2.3 1.0 2.2
22	M	0023 0636 1302 1923	1.1 2.3 1.0 2.2
23	TU	0133 0752 1359 2011	1.0 2.3 1.0 2.3
24	W	0232 0851 1447 2052	0.8 2.3 1.0 2.4
25	TH O	0320 0936 1527 2130	0.7 2.3 1.0 2.5
26	F	0401 1016 1602 2205	0.6 2.3 1.0 2.5
27	SA	0439 1052 1632 2239	0.6 2.3 1.0 2.5
28	SU	0514 1124 1658 2312	0.6 2.3 1.0 2.5
29	M	0547 1154 1725 2345	0.6 2.2 1.0 2.5
30	TU	0618 1223 1755	0.6 2.2 1.0
31	W	0020 0649 1255 [illegible]	2.5 0.7 2.1 [illegible]

FEBRUARY

Date	Day	Time	m
1	TH	0057 0722 1331 1910	2.4 0.8 2.1 1.1
2	F ☽	0136 0800 1414 1955	2.4 0.9 2.1 1.2
3	SA	0222 0846 1511 2049	2.3 1.0 2.0 1.3
4	SU	0320 0949 1640 2203	2.2 1.1 2.0 1.3
5	M	0444 1115 1746 2344	2.1 1.1 2.1 1.2
6	TU	0601 1221 1841	2.2 1.1 2.2
7	W	0050 0708 1316 1933	1.1 2.2 1.0 2.2
8	TH	0148 0810 1408 2020	0.9 2.3 0.9 2.3
9	F ●	0245 0904 1459 2105	0.7 2.4 0.8 2.5
10	SA	0338 0950 1548 2148	0.5 2.5 0.8 2.6
11	SU	0428 1034 1632 2231	0.3 2.5 0.7 2.7
12	M	0514 1116 1714 2314	0.2 2.5 0.7 2.8
13	TU	0557 1159 1753 2357	0.2 2.4 0.7 2.8
14	W	0640 1242 1832	0.3 2.3 0.8
15	TH	0040 0723 1326 1914	2.7 0.4 2.2 0.9
16	F ☾	0127 0809 1420 2002	2.6 0.6 2.1 1.0
17	SA	0224 0904 1538 2103	2.4 0.9 2.0 1.1
18	SU	0351 1024 1652 2246	2.3 1.1 2.1 1.1
19	M	0522 1147 1757	2.2 1.2 2.1
20	TU	0017 0654 1259 1904	1.0 2.2 1.2 2.2
21	W	0129 0804 1358 1957	0.9 2.2 1.2 2.2
22	TH	0223 0849 1441 2037	0.7 2.3 1.1 2.3
23	F	0306 0925 1516 2112	0.6 2.3 1.0 2.4
24	SA O	0343 0957 1546 2143	0.6 2.3 1.0 2.5
25	SU	0416 1027 1612 2214	0.5 2.3 0.9 2.5
26	M	0447 1053 1637 2246	0.5 2.3 0.8 2.5
27	TU	0516 1120 1703 2319	0.5 2.3 0.8 2.5
28	W	0544 1148 1732 2353	0.6 2.2 0.8 2.5
29	TH	0612 1219 1804	0.7 2.2 0.9

MARCH

Date	Day	Time	m
1	F	0026 0642 1252 1841	2.4 0.7 2.2 1.0
2	SA	0103 0716 1331 1923	2.3 0.8 2.1 1.0
3	SU ☽	0147 0759 1419 2015	2.2 1.0 2.1 1.1
4	M	0244 0855 1525 2125	2.1 1.1 2.0 1.2
5	TU	0414 1030 1655 2320	2.1 1.2 2.0 1.1
6	W	0551 1200 1805	2.1 1.2 2.1
7	TH	0032 0705 1301 1904	0.9 2.2 1.1 2.2
8	F	0132 0804 1355 1955	0.7 2.3 1.0 2.3
9	SA	0229 0851 1445 2041	0.5 2.4 0.8 2.5
10	SU ●	0321 0932 1531 2125	0.3 2.5 0.7 2.7
11	M	0407 1012 1613 2208	0.2 2.5 0.6 2.8
12	TU	0451 1052 1653 2252	0.1 2.5 0.6 2.8
13	W	0531 1132 1731 2335	0.2 2.4 0.6 2.8
14	TH	0611 1212 1811	0.3 2.3 0.7
15	F	0020 0651 1253 1854	2.7 0.5 2.2 0.7
16	SA	0109 0733 1339 1942	2.5 0.8 2.1 0.8
17	SU ☾	0213 0822 1438 2046	2.3 1.1 2.1 1.0
18	M	0353 0947 1602 2238	2.2 1.3 2.0 1.0
19	TU	0522 1134 1716	2.1 1.3 2.1
20	W	0002 0652 1247 1831	0.9 2.2 1.3 2.1
21	TH	0107 0751 1341 1931	0.8 2.2 1.2 2.2
22	F	0158 0831 1420 2011	0.7 2.3 1.1 2.3
23	SA	0238 0903 1452 2043	0.6 2.3 1.0 2.3
24	SU	0313 0931 1519 2114	0.6 2.3 0.9 2.4
25	M O	0344 0956 1545 2145	0.5 2.3 0.8 2.5
26	TU	0414 1020 1611 2218	0.5 2.3 0.8 2.5
27	W	0442 1047 1640 2252	0.5 2.3 0.8 2.5
28	TH	0509 1116 1710 2326	0.6 2.3 0.8 2.4
29	F	0538 1148 1743	0.7 2.3 0.8
30	SA	0000 0608 1221 1819	2.4 0.8 2.2 0.9
31	SU	0038 0643 1300 1900	2.3 0.9 2.2 0.9

APRIL

Date	Day	Time	m
1	M	0125 0726 1347 1954	2.2 1.0 2.1 1.0
2	TU ☽	0227 0823 1448 2109	2.1 1.2 2.1 1.0
3	W	0409 0952 1606 2302	2.1 1.3 2.0 0.9
4	TH	0545 1138 1726	2.2 1.2 2.1
5	F	0011 0653 1239 1830	0.8 2.3 1.1 2.2
6	SA	0110 0746 1333 1924	0.6 2.4 1.0 2.4
7	SU	0206 0829 1422 2012	0.4 2.4 0.9 2.5
8	M ●	0256 0908 1507 2059	0.3 2.5 0.7 2.7
9	TU	0341 0947 1549 2144	0.2 2.5 0.6 2.7
10	W	0424 1026 1631 2230	0.2 2.5 0.5 2.8
11	TH	0504 1105 1712 2317	0.3 2.4 0.5 2.7
12	F	0542 1145 1753	0.5 2.4 0.6
13	SA	0005 0621 1225 1839	2.5 0.7 2.3 0.6
14	SU	0100 0701 1309 1929	2.4 1.0 2.2 0.7
15	M ☾	0213 0747 1402 2036	2.2 1.2 2.2 0.9
16	TU	0345 0855 1510 2217	2.1 1.4 2.1 0.9
17	W	0504 1104 1626 2330	2.1 1.4 2.1 0.8
18	TH	0622 1212 1736	2.2 1.4 2.1
19	F	0028 0720 1305 1839	0.8 2.2 1.3 2.1
20	SA	0117 0801 1345 1926	0.7 2.2 1.2 2.2
21	SU	0159 0833 1417 2004	0.7 2.3 1.1 2.3
22	M	0234 0859 1445 2039	0.6 2.3 0.9 2.4
23	TU O	0305 0922 1514 2114	0.6 2.3 0.8 2.4
24	W	0336 0948 1544 2150	0.6 2.3 0.8 2.4
25	TH	0406 1016 1617 2226	0.6 2.4 0.7 2.4
26	F	0437 1048 1652 2303	0.6 2.4 0.7 2.4
27	SA	0509 1121 1727 2341	0.7 2.3 0.7 2.3
28	SU	0543 1158 1806	0.8 2.3 0.8
29	M	0024 0622 1238 1853	2.2 0.9 2.3 0.8
30	TU	0116 0708 1327 1951	2.2 1.1 2.2 0.9

MAY

Date	Day	Time	m
1	W ☾	0224 0806 1426 2111	2.1 1.2 2.2 0.8
2	TH	0410 0926 1533 2241	2.1 1.3 2.1 0.7
3	F	0530 1103 1647 2346	2.2 1.3 2.2 0.6
4	SA	0630 1207 1754	2.3 1.2 2.3
5	SU	0043 0720 1301 1851	0.5 2.3 1.0 2.4
6	M	0137 0803 1352 1944	0.4 2.4 0.9 2.5
7	TU	0227 0842 1441 2034	0.3 2.4 0.7 2.6
8	W ●	0314 0921 1527 2124	0.3 2.5 0.6 2.6
9	TH	0356 1001 1612 2214	0.4 2.5 0.5 2.6
10	F	0437 1042 1657 2305	0.5 2.5 0.5 2.5
11	SA	0517 1122 1741 2359	0.7 2.4 0.5 2.4
12	SU	0555 1204 1828	0.9 2.4 0.6
13	M	0056 0634 1246 1919	2.3 1.1 2.3 0.7
14	TU	0204 0717 1334 2021	2.2 1.2 2.3 0.8
15	W ☽	0320 0807 1429 2140	2.1 1.4 2.2 0.8
16	TH	0430 0942 1531 2248	2.1 1.5 2.1 0.8
17	F	0536 1116 1637 2343	2.1 1.4 2.1 0.8
18	SA	0634 1212 1738	2.1 1.4 2.1
19	SU	0030 0720 1256 1832	0.8 2.2 1.2 2.2
20	M	0112 0754 1333 1919	0.7 2.2 1.1 2.2
21	TU	0149 0822 1407 2002	0.7 2.3 1.0 2.3
22	W	0224 0848 1442 2043	0.7 2.3 0.9 2.3
23	TH O	0258 0917 1519 2124	0.7 2.4 0.8 2.3
24	F	0333 0949 1557 2205	0.7 2.4 0.7 2.3
25	SA	0410 1024 1638 2247	0.7 2.4 0.7 2.3
26	SU	0448 1101 1720 2331	0.8 2.4 0.7 2.3
27	M	0528 1141 1806	0.9 2.4 0.7
28	TU	0020 0611 1225 1857	2.3 1.0 2.4 0.7
29	W	0115 0659 1314 1955	2.2 1.1 2.3 0.7
30	TH ☾	0219 0754 1408 2104	2.2 1.2 2.3 0.7
31	F	0352 0858 1505 2214	2.2 1.3 2.3 0.6

JUNE

Date	Day	Time	m
1	SA	0505 1015 1611 2317	2.2 1.3 2.3 0.6
2	SU	0601 1126 1721	2.2 1.2 2.4
3	M	0014 0651 1227 1823	0.5 2.3 1.1 2.4
4	TU	0108 0736 1325 1920	0.5 2.3 0.9 2.5
5	W	0200 0818 1420 2017	0.5 2.4 0.8 2.5
6	TH ●	0249 0859 1512 2113	0.6 2.4 0.7 2.5
7	F	0334 0941 1601 2209	0.7 2.5 0.6 2.5
8	SA	0417 1023 1648 2302	0.8 2.5 0.5 2.4
9	SU	0456 1105 1733 2353	0.9 2.5 0.5 2.3
10	M	0534 1146 1818	1.0 2.4 0.6
11	TU	0044 0611 1225 1905	2.2 1.1 2.4 0.6
12	W	0137 0647 1307 1954	2.1 1.2 2.4 0.7
13	TH	0236 0726 1352 2048	2.1 1.3 2.3 0.8
14	F ☽	0341 0811 1441 2150	2.0 1.4 2.3 0.8
15	SA	0441 0907 1538 2249	2.0 1.4 2.2 0.9
16	SU	0534 1040 1643 2341	2.1 1.4 2.2 0.9
17	M	0622 1155 1745	2.1 1.3 2.2
18	TU	0025 0704 1245 1840	0.9 2.2 1.2 2.2
19	W	0107 0740 1330 1930	0.9 2.2 1.1 2.2
20	TH	0147 0815 1413 2019	0.8 2.3 1.0 2.2
21	F	0227 0850 1457 2106	0.8 2.4 0.9 2.3
22	SA O	0308 0927 1543 2153	0.8 2.4 0.7 2.3
23	SU	0351 1006 1630 2240	0.8 2.5 0.6 2.4
24	M	0435 1047 1718 2328	0.8 2.5 0.6 2.4
25	TU	0519 1130 1806	0.9 2.5 0.5
26	W	0015 0604 1213 1856	2.3 0.9 2.5 0.5
27	TH	0105 0649 1259 1947	2.3 1.0 2.5 0.5
28	F ☾	0200 0736 1346 2041	2.2 1.1 2.5 0.5
29	SA	0312 0828 1438 2142	2.2 1.2 2.5 0.6
30	SU	0431 0929 1540 2245	2.2 1.2 2.4 0.6

SUNRISE AND SUNSET TIMES

LOWESTOFT
At 52°28′N 1°45′E

UT		Sunrise	Sunset
Jan	01	0804	1550
	15	0756	1609
Feb	01	0734	1640
	15	0709	1706
Mar	01	0639	1732
	15	0607	1758
BST (UT+1)			
Apr	01	0627	1927
	15	0555	1952
May	01	0522	2020
	15	0457	2043
Jun	01	0436	2106
	15	0430	2117
Jul	01	0435	2119
	15	0449	2109
Aug	01	0513	2045
	15	0536	2020
Sep	01	0604	1941
	15	0627	1908
Oct	01	0654	1830
	15	0718	1758
UT			
Nov	01	0649	1623
	15	0715	1600
Dec	01	0741	1543
	15	[illegible]	[illegible]

LOWESTOFT
LAT 52°28′N
LONG 1°45′E

TIMES AND HEIGHTS OF HIGH AND LOW WATER (Heights in Metres)

TIME ZONE UT
For Summer Time (area enclosed in shaded box) add 1 hour

2024

JULY

Date	Day	Time	m	Time	m	Time	m	Time	m
1	M	0529	2.2	1045	1.2	1656	2.4	2347	0.7
2	TU	0621	2.2	1201	1.1	1805	2.4		
3	W	0045	0.8	0711	2.3	1308	1.0	1910	2.4
4	TH	0141	0.8	0759	2.4	1411	0.8	2017	2.4
5	F ●	0234	0.9	0844	2.4	1507	0.7	2118	2.4
6	SA	0321	0.9	0927	2.5	1556	0.6	2210	2.4
7	SU	0404	1.0	1008	2.5	1641	0.5	2256	2.4
8	M	0442	1.0	1048	2.5	1723	0.5	2338	2.3
9	TU	0516	1.0	1126	2.5	1802	0.5		
10	W	0018	2.2	0547	1.1	1201	2.5	1840	0.6
11	TH	0056	2.2	0617	1.1	1238	2.5	1917	0.7
12	F	0134	2.1	0651	1.2	1317	2.4	1955	0.8
13	SA ☽	0216	2.1	0730	1.2	1359	2.4	2037	0.9
14	SU	0313	2.0	0815	1.3	1448	2.3	2129	1.0
15	M	0424	2.0	0911	1.4	1549	2.2	2235	1.0
16	TU	0521	2.1	1034	1.4	1703	2.2	2338	1.0
17	W	0611	2.2	1202	1.3	1808	2.1		
18	TH	0030	1.0	0659	2.2	1259	1.2	1907	2.2
19	F	0117	1.0	0744	2.3	1350	1.0	2005	2.2
20	SA	0204	1.0	0826	2.4	1441	0.9	2059	2.3
21	SU ○	0251	0.9	0908	2.4	1532	0.7	2147	2.4
22	M	0339	0.9	0949	2.5	1621	0.5	2232	2.5
23	TU	0425	0.8	1031	2.6	1709	0.4	2315	2.5
24	W	0509	0.8	1113	2.7	1755	0.3	2359	2.4
25	TH	0551	0.9	1155	2.7	1839	0.3		
26	F	0043	2.4	0632	0.9	1238	2.7	1924	0.4
27	SA	0130	2.3	0713	1.0	1323	2.7	2011	0.5
28	SU ☾	0224	2.2	0759	1.1	1413	2.6	2105	0.7
29	M	0343	2.1	0855	1.1	1517	2.5	2212	0.8
30	TU	0453	2.2	1014	1.2	1645	2.4	2325	1.0
31	W	0552	2.2	1148	1.1	1804	2.3		

AUGUST

Date	Day	Time	m	Time	m	Time	m	Time	m
1	TH	0032	1.1	0650	2.3	1305	1.0	1926	2.3
2	F	0135	1.1	0745	2.3	1411	0.8	2033	2.3
3	SA	0230	1.1	0832	2.4	1503	0.7	2121	2.4
4	SU ●	0315	1.1	0913	2.5	1547	0.6	2201	2.4
5	M	0352	1.0	0951	2.6	1626	0.5	2238	2.4
6	TU	0425	1.0	1026	2.6	1703	0.5	2313	2.3
7	W	0454	1.0	1100	2.6	1736	0.5	2344	2.3
8	TH	0520	1.0	1134	2.6	1807	0.6		
9	F	0014	2.2	0548	1.0	1207	2.6	1838	0.7
10	SA	0044	2.2	0619	1.1	1243	2.5	1908	0.8
11	SU	0118	2.2	0656	1.1	1322	2.4	1942	0.9
12	M ☽	0158	2.1	0738	1.2	1406	2.3	2023	1.0
13	TU	0249	2.1	0830	1.3	1502	2.2	2118	1.1
14	W	0406	2.1	0938	1.4	1624	2.1	2243	1.2
15	TH	0521	2.2	1125	1.3	1746	2.1		
16	F	0000	1.2	0620	2.2	1235	1.1	1855	2.2
17	SA	0056	1.1	0713	2.3	1331	1.0	1959	2.3
18	SU	0147	1.1	0801	2.4	1425	0.8	2049	2.4
19	M ○	0237	1.0	0845	2.5	1517	0.6	2132	2.5
20	TU	0324	0.9	0927	2.6	1605	0.4	2213	2.5
21	W	0409	0.8	1008	2.8	1650	0.3	2253	2.6
22	TH	0451	0.8	1050	2.8	1733	0.2	2334	2.5
23	F	0530	0.8	1132	2.9	1814	0.3		
24	SA	0015	2.4	0610	0.8	1214	2.8	1856	0.4
25	SU	0057	2.3	0650	0.9	1300	2.7	1938	0.6
26	M ☾	0145	2.2	0737	1.0	1353	2.6	2028	0.9
27	TU	0246	2.2	0834	1.1	1510	2.4	2137	1.1
28	W	0411	2.2	1003	1.1	1650	2.3	2312	1.3
29	TH	0520	2.2	1145	1.1	1819	2.3		
30	F	0028	1.3	0627	2.3	1301	0.9	1940	2.3
31	SA	0133	1.3	0729	2.3	1401	0.8	2030	2.4

SEPTEMBER

Date	Day	Time	m	Time	m	Time	m	Time	m
1	SU	0222	1.2	0815	2.4	1447	0.7	2108	2.4
2	M	0300	1.1	0852	2.5	1526	0.6	2142	2.4
3	TU ●	0332	1.1	0925	2.6	1601	0.6	2212	2.4
4	W	0400	1.0	0958	2.6	1633	0.6	2241	2.4
5	TH	0427	0.9	1031	2.7	1703	0.6	2307	2.4
6	F	0452	0.9	1104	2.6	1730	0.6	2335	2.3
7	SA	0520	0.9	1137	2.6	1757	0.7		
8	SU	0004	2.3	0551	1.0	1211	2.5	1826	0.8
9	M	0038	2.3	0626	1.1	1248	2.4	1858	0.9
10	TU	0115	2.3	0707	1.1	1331	2.3	1937	1.1
11	W ☽	0201	2.2	0757	1.2	1426	2.2	2028	1.2
12	TH	0301	2.2	0904	1.3	1551	2.1	2144	1.4
13	F	0423	2.2	1057	1.2	1734	2.2	2333	1.3
14	SA	0539	2.2	1212	1.1	1846	2.3		
15	SU	0035	1.2	0639	2.3	1309	0.9	1944	2.4
16	M	0128	1.1	0729	2.4	1403	0.7	2029	2.5
17	TU	0217	1.0	0815	2.6	1454	0.5	2109	2.6
18	W ○	0303	0.9	0858	2.7	1540	0.3	2148	2.6
19	TH	0346	0.8	0941	2.9	1624	0.2	2227	2.6
20	F	0427	0.7	1025	2.9	1705	0.2	2306	2.6
21	SA	0507	0.7	1109	2.9	1745	0.4	2346	2.5
22	SU	0548	0.7	1154	2.8	1825	0.6		
23	M	0028	2.4	0632	0.8	1243	2.7	1907	0.8
24	TU ☾	0113	2.3	0721	0.9	1344	2.5	1954	1.1
25	W	0208	2.3	0822	1.0	1519	2.3	2101	1.4
26	TH	0324	2.2	1003	1.0	1652	2.3	2258	1.5
27	F	0443	2.2	1132	0.9	1819	2.3		
28	SA	0014	1.4	0554	2.3	1239	0.8	1927	2.4
29	SU	0114	1.3	0659	2.3	1334	0.8	2011	2.4
30	M	0158	1.3	0745	2.4	1418	0.7	2045	2.4

OCTOBER

Date	Day	Time	m	Time	m	Time	m	Time	m
1	TU	0233	1.2	0821	2.5	1454	0.6	2114	2.4
2	W ●	0303	1.1	0854	2.6	1527	0.6	2141	2.4
3	TH	0330	1.0	0926	2.6	1557	0.6	2206	2.4
4	F	0357	0.9	1000	2.6	1625	0.6	2232	2.4
5	SA	0425	0.9	1034	2.6	1652	0.7	2300	2.4
6	SU	0455	0.9	1109	2.5	1719	0.8	2331	2.4
7	M	0527	0.9	1144	2.4	1749	0.9		
8	TU	0004	2.4	0603	1.0	1221	2.4	1822	1.0
9	W	0042	2.4	0644	1.1	1306	2.3	1903	1.1
10	TH ☽	0128	2.3	0735	1.1	1404	2.2	1956	1.3
11	F	0225	2.2	0845	1.2	1535	2.2	2107	1.4
12	SA	0334	2.2	1032	1.1	1721	2.2	2258	1.4
13	SU	0454	2.3	1145	0.9	1826	2.3		
14	M	0006	1.3	0600	2.4	1241	0.7	1919	2.4
15	TU	0059	1.2	0653	2.5	1334	0.6	2002	2.5
16	W	0148	1.0	0742	2.6	1424	0.4	2041	2.6
17	TH ○	0234	0.9	0828	2.8	1511	0.3	2120	2.6
18	F	0320	0.8	0915	2.9	1555	0.3	2159	2.6
19	SA	0404	0.7	1002	2.9	1637	0.4	2239	2.6
20	SU	0447	0.7	1050	2.8	1717	0.5	2320	2.5
21	M	0532	0.7	1140	2.7	1757	0.8		
22	TU	0002	2.5	0619	0.7	1235	2.5	1839	1.0
23	W	0047	2.4	0711	0.8	1344	2.4	1925	1.3
24	TH ☾	0140	2.3	0815	0.9	1516	2.3	2025	1.5
25	F	0245	2.3	0946	0.9	1636	2.2	2222	1.6
26	SA	0358	2.3	1102	0.9	1752	2.3	2337	1.5
27	SU	0507	2.3	1202	0.8	1855	2.3		
28	M	0035	1.4	0609	2.3	1254	0.8	1940	2.3
29	TU	0120	1.3	0700	2.4	1337	0.8	2014	2.4
30	W	0156	1.2	0741	2.4	1415	0.7	2043	2.4
31	TH	0228	1.1	0818	2.5	1447	0.7	2107	2.4

NOVEMBER

Date	Day	Time	m	Time	m	Time	m	Time	m
1	F ●	0257	1.0	0854	2.5	1517	0.7	2132	2.5
2	SA	0328	0.9	0931	2.5	1547	0.7	2159	2.5
3	SU	0400	0.9	1007	2.5	1616	0.8	2230	2.5
4	M	0434	0.9	1044	2.4	1648	0.9	2303	2.5
5	TU	0510	0.9	1122	2.4	1721	0.9	2338	2.5
6	W	0549	0.9	1204	2.3	1758	1.1		
7	TH	0017	2.4	0633	1.0	1252	2.3	1843	1.2
8	F	0104	2.4	0727	1.0	1353	2.2	1936	1.3
9	SA ☽	0159	2.3	0837	1.0	1519	2.2	2042	1.4
10	SU	0300	2.3	1004	0.9	1657	2.2	2209	1.4
11	M	0408	2.3	1113	0.8	1757	2.3	2325	1.3
12	TU	0518	2.4	1210	0.6	1848	2.4		
13	W	0022	1.2	0618	2.5	1302	0.5	1932	2.5
14	TH	0115	1.1	0711	2.6	1353	0.5	2013	2.5
15	F ○	0206	0.9	0802	2.7	1442	0.5	2053	2.6
16	SA	0257	0.8	0853	2.8	1528	0.5	2134	2.6
17	SU	0346	0.7	0946	2.7	1612	0.6	2216	2.6
18	M	0433	0.6	1039	2.7	1654	0.8	2259	2.6
19	TU	0521	0.6	1134	2.5	1735	0.9	2342	2.5
20	W	0610	0.6	1232	2.4	1816	1.1		
21	TH	0027	2.5	0702	0.7	1336	2.3	1859	1.3
22	F	0115	2.4	0801	0.8	1451	2.2	1947	1.4
23	SA ☾	0208	2.4	0911	0.8	1604	2.2	2051	1.5
24	SU	0307	2.3	1020	0.9	1710	2.2	2235	1.6
25	M	0412	2.3	1118	0.9	1809	2.2	2341	1.5
26	TU	0514	2.3	1209	0.9	1858	2.2		
27	W	0032	1.4	0609	2.3	1253	0.9	1937	2.3
28	TH	0114	1.3	0658	2.3	1332	0.8	2007	2.3
29	F	0151	1.1	0743	2.4	1406	0.8	2033	2.4
30	SA	0226	1.0	0826	2.4	1440	0.8	2100	2.4

DECEMBER

Date	Day	Time	m	Time	m	Time	m	Time	m
1	SU ●	0302	0.9	0907	2.4	1513	0.8	2131	2.5
2	M	0339	0.9	0947	2.4	1548	0.9	2205	2.5
3	TU	0419	0.8	1028	2.4	1625	0.9	2241	2.5
4	W	0501	0.8	1111	2.4	1704	1.0	2320	2.5
5	TH	0545	0.8	1157	2.3	1745	1.0		
6	F	0002	2.5	0633	0.8	1246	2.3	1831	1.1
7	SA	0048	2.4	0726	0.8	1341	2.2	1920	1.2
8	SU ☽	0137	2.4	0825	0.8	1447	2.2	2016	1.3
9	M	0230	2.4	0932	0.7	1621	2.2	2120	1.3
10	TU	0329	2.4	1038	0.7	1724	2.3	2235	1.3
11	W	0439	2.5	1138	0.7	1816	2.3	2345	1.2
12	TH	0547	2.5	1234	0.6	1903	2.4		
13	F	0047	1.1	0647	2.6	1327	0.7	1948	2.4
14	SA	0146	0.9	0745	2.6	1419	0.7	2031	2.5
15	SU ○	0243	0.8	0844	2.6	1508	0.7	2115	2.5
16	M	0337	0.6	0942	2.6	1554	0.8	2159	2.6
17	TU	0427	0.6	1038	2.5	1637	0.9	2243	2.6
18	W	0515	0.5	1130	2.4	1718	1.0	2326	2.6
19	TH	0601	0.6	1220	2.3	1755	1.1		
20	F	0007	2.5	0647	0.6	1310	2.2	1832	1.2
21	SA	0049	2.5	0734	0.7	1405	2.1	1909	1.3
22	SU ☾	0132	2.4	0825	0.8	1510	2.1	1950	1.4
23	M	0218	2.4	0921	0.9	1614	2.1	2039	1.4
24	TU	0311	2.3	1023	0.9	1711	2.1	2148	1.5
25	W	0417	2.2	1120	1.0	1801	2.1	2331	1.4
26	TH	0523	2.2	1208	1.0	1846	2.2		
27	F	0029	1.3	0622	2.2	1251	1.0	1925	2.2
28	SA	0116	1.2	0715	2.2	1331	1.0	2000	2.3
29	SU	0159	1.1	0806	2.3	1409	1.0	2034	2.4
30	M ●	0241	0.9	0854	2.3	1449	0.9	2109	2.4
31	TU	0325	0.8	0938	2.3	1530	0.9	2147	2.5

IMMINGHAM
LAT 53°38′N
LONG 0°11′W

TIMES AND HEIGHTS OF HIGH AND LOW WATER (Heights in Metres)

TIME ZONE UT
For Summer Time (area enclosed in shaded box) add 1 hour

2024

JANUARY

Date	Day	Time	m
1	M	0305 0907 1458 2102	1.8 6.2 2.2 6.5
2	TU	0340 0944 1533 2141	2.0 6.0 2.4 6.3
3	W	0420 1028 1615 2227	2.1 5.8 2.6 6.1
4	TH ☽	0508 1120 1706 2322	2.3 5.7 2.8 5.9
5	F	0603 1222 1808	2.4 5.6 2.9
6	SA	0027 0704 1328 1918	5.8 2.5 5.7 2.9
7	SU	0137 0808 1431 2028	5.8 2.4 5.8 2.7
8	M	0243 0910 1528 2132	6.0 2.2 6.1 2.4
9	TU	0343 1006 1618 2231	6.2 2.0 6.4 2.0
10	W	0439 1058 1705 2326	6.5 1.7 6.7 1.6
11	TH ●	0532 1148 1750	6.8 1.5 7.0
12	F	0019 0623 1236 1834	1.3 7.0 1.4 7.2
13	SA	0109 0712 1322 1917	1.0 7.1 1.3 7.4
14	SU	0157 0759 1406 1959	0.8 7.1 1.3 7.4
15	M	0243 0845 1450 2043	0.7 7.0 1.4 7.4
16	TU	0329 0933 1533 2130	0.8 6.8 1.5 7.2
17	W	0415 1023 1619 2221	1.1 6.6 1.8 7.0
18	TH ☾	0504 1118 1710 2319	1.4 6.3 2.1 6.6
19	F	0559 1218 1811	1.8 6.0 2.4
20	SA	0026 0703 1322 1927	6.3 2.2 5.8 2.6
21	SU	0139 0814 1429 2049	6.1 2.4 5.8 2.5
22	M	0254 0921 1533 2158	6.0 2.4 6.0 2.2
23	TU	0404 1019 1627 2254	6.2 2.2 6.3 1.9
24	W	0502 1108 1713 2344	6.3 2.1 6.6 1.6
25	TH ○	0550 1153 1754	6.5 1.9 6.8
26	F	0028 0631 1233 1832	1.4 6.6 1.8 6.9
27	SA	0109 0707 1309 1907	1.3 6.6 1.7 7.0
28	SU	0145 0739 1341 1939	1.3 6.6 1.7 7.0
29	M	0217 0809 1410 2009	1.4 6.5 1.8 6.9
30	TU	0245 0837 1437 2038	1.5 6.5 1.8 6.8
31	W	0313 0907 1504 2108	1.7 6.3 2.0 6.6

FEBRUARY

Date	Day	Time	m
1	TH	0340 0939 1535 2141	1.8 6.2 2.1 6.4
2	F ☽	0413 1017 1613 2222	2.1 5.9 2.4 6.1
3	SA	0457 1105 1705 2315	2.3 5.7 2.6 5.9
4	SU	0559 1210 1817	2.5 5.5 2.8
5	M	0028 0716 1339 1940	5.7 2.6 5.5 2.8
6	TU	0207 0833 1457 2101	5.7 2.5 5.8 2.5
7	W	0329 0942 1558 2215	6.0 2.2 6.2 2.0
8	TH	0433 1042 1650 2318	6.4 1.9 6.6 1.5
9	F ●	0528 1136 1736	6.8 1.5 7.0
10	SA	0012 0618 1225 1821	1.0 7.1 1.2 7.4
11	SU	0101 0704 1311 1904	0.6 7.3 1.0 7.7
12	M	0146 0746 1353 1945	0.4 7.4 0.9 7.8
13	TU	0229 0827 1434 2027	0.3 7.3 0.9 7.8
14	W	0309 0906 1513 2109	0.5 7.1 1.1 7.5
15	TH	0347 0947 1552 2154	0.9 6.7 1.5 7.1
16	F ☾	0427 1032 1633 2246	1.5 6.3 1.9 6.6
17	SA	0511 1127 1725 2352	2.1 5.9 2.4 6.0
18	SU	0611 1237 1842	2.6 5.5 2.8
19	M	0116 0741 1355 2036	5.6 2.9 5.5 2.7
20	TU	0247 0907 1511 2151	5.6 2.8 5.7 2.3
21	W	0407 1008 1611 2245	5.9 2.5 6.1 1.9
22	TH	0502 1056 1657 2331	6.2 2.2 6.4 1.6
23	F	0542 1138 1737	6.4 1.9 6.7
24	SA ○	0011 0616 1216 1813	1.3 6.6 1.7 6.9
25	SU	0049 0646 1251 1846	1.2 6.6 1.6 7.0
26	M	0123 0713 1323 1916	1.1 6.7 1.5 7.0
27	TU	0153 0739 1349 1944	1.2 6.7 1.5 7.0
28	W	0219 0805 1413 2011	1.3 6.7 1.6 6.9
29	TH	0242 0832 1437 2038	1.5 6.6 1.7 6.7

MARCH

Date	Day	Time	m
1	F	0303 0859 1503 2107	1.6 6.4 1.8 6.6
2	SA	0328 0931 1535 2144	1.9 6.2 2.1 6.3
3	SU ☽	0403 1013 1620 2234	2.2 5.9 2.4 5.9
4	M	0502 1111 1734 2346	2.6 5.5 2.7 5.5
5	TU	0633 1244 1909	2.8 5.4 2.8
6	W	0152 0806 1431 2043	5.5 2.8 5.6 2.4
7	TH	0324 0926 1538 2204	5.9 2.4 6.1 1.8
8	F	0425 1028 1630 2305	6.4 1.9 6.7 1.2
9	SA	0517 1121 1717 2357	6.9 1.4 7.2 0.7
10	SU ●	0602 1208 1800	7.2 1.0 7.6
11	M	0043 0645 1252 1843	0.3 7.4 0.8 7.8
12	TU	0126 0724 1334 1925	0.2 7.5 0.7 7.9
13	W	0205 0800 1413 2006	0.2 7.4 0.7 7.8
14	TH	0242 0835 1450 2047	0.5 7.2 0.9 7.5
15	F	0316 0911 1525 2130	1.0 6.8 1.3 7.0
16	SA	0350 0950 1603 2219	1.6 6.3 1.8 6.4
17	SU ☾	0428 1039 1651 2328	2.3 5.8 2.4 5.7
18	M	0523 1154 1808	2.9 5.4 2.8
19	TU	0104 0703 1326 2024	5.4 3.2 5.3 2.7
20	W	0239 0849 1446 2133	5.4 3.1 5.6 2.3
21	TH	0355 0948 1547 2223	5.8 2.6 6.0 1.8
22	F	0442 1034 1633 2305	6.1 2.2 6.4 1.5
23	SA	0517 1114 1711 2344	6.4 1.9 6.7 1.3
24	SU	0548 1152 1745	6.6 1.6 6.8
25	M ○	0019 0616 1226 1817	1.1 6.7 1.5 6.9
26	TU	0052 0642 1257 1847	1.1 6.8 1.4 6.9
27	W	0122 0707 1324 1916	1.2 6.8 1.4 6.9
28	TH	0149 0734 1349 1945	1.3 6.8 1.5 6.9
29	F	0212 0800 1413 2012	1.4 6.7 1.5 6.8
30	SA	0234 0828 1441 2043	1.6 6.6 1.7 6.6
31	SU	0300 0900 1514 2122	1.8 6.3 1.9 6.2

APRIL

Date	Day	Time	m
1	M	0336 0942 1601 2215	2.2 6.0 2.2 5.8
2	TU ☽	0436 1041 1720 2336	2.6 5.6 2.5 5.5
3	W	0608 1213 1855	2.9 5.4 2.5
4	TH	0152 0746 1403 2029	5.5 2.8 5.7 2.1
5	F	0310 0905 1511 2144	6.0 2.3 6.3 1.6
6	SA	0407 1005 1604 2241	6.5 1.8 6.8 1.0
7	SU	0455 1057 1651 2331	7.0 1.3 7.3 0.6
8	M ●	0538 1144 1735	7.3 1.0 7.6
9	TU	0016 0619 1229 1820	0.4 7.4 0.7 7.8
10	W	0059 0656 1311 1903	0.3 7.4 0.6 7.8
11	TH	0138 0732 1351 1945	0.5 7.3 0.7 7.6
12	F	0214 0806 1428 2027	0.8 7.1 1.0 7.3
13	SA	0247 0841 1504 2111	1.3 6.8 1.3 6.7
14	SU	0320 0918 1543 2202	1.8 6.4 1.8 6.1
15	M ☾	0358 1004 1633 2312	2.4 5.9 2.3 5.6
16	TU	0451 1116 1749	3.0 5.5 2.6
17	W	0046 0618 1254 1949	5.3 3.3 5.4 2.6
18	TH	0208 0811 1411 2057	5.4 3.1 5.6 2.3
19	F	0316 0914 1512 2146	5.7 2.7 5.9 1.9
20	SA	0404 1000 1558 2227	6.1 2.3 6.3 1.6
21	SU	0441 1041 1637 2306	6.3 1.9 6.5 1.4
22	M	0512 1119 1711 2342	6.5 1.7 6.7 1.3
23	TU ○	0540 1154 1743	6.7 1.5 6.8
24	W	0017 0608 1227 1817	1.2 6.8 1.5 6.8
25	TH	0049 0637 1257 1850	1.2 6.8 1.4 6.8
26	F	0119 0707 1327 1923	1.3 6.8 1.4 6.8
27	SA	0146 0736 1357 1956	1.4 6.8 1.5 6.7
28	SU	0214 0807 1430 2032	1.6 6.6 1.6 6.5
29	M	0247 0843 1510 2117	1.9 6.4 1.8 6.2
30	TU	0330 0928 1606 2217	2.2 6.1 2.0 5.8

MAY

Date	Day	Time	m
1	W ☾	0432 1031 1722 2348	2.6 5.8 2.2 5.6
2	TH	0555 1158 1845	2.8 5.8 2.1
3	F	0134 0721 1330 2006	5.8 2.6 6.0 1.8
4	SA	0244 0834 1437 2113	6.2 2.2 6.4 1.4
5	SU	0340 0935 1533 2210	6.6 1.8 6.9 1.0
6	M	0427 1028 1623 2301	6.9 1.4 7.2 0.8
7	TU	0510 1118 1711 2348	7.1 1.1 7.4 0.7
8	W ●	0551 1205 1758	7.2 0.9 7.5
9	TH	0031 0630 1250 1845	0.7 7.2 0.8 7.4
10	F	0112 0707 1332 1930	0.9 7.2 0.9 7.2
11	SA	0149 0743 1412 2014	1.2 7.0 1.1 6.9
12	SU	0224 0820 1452 2100	1.6 6.7 1.4 6.5
13	M	0259 0857 1533 2150	2.0 6.4 1.8 6.0
14	TU	0338 0942 1623 2254	2.4 6.0 2.1 5.6
15	W ☽	0427 1044 1727	2.8 5.7 2.4
16	TH	0010 0535 1207 1845	5.4 3.1 5.6 2.4
17	F	0121 0658 1321 1956	5.4 3.1 5.6 2.3
18	SA	0222 0815 1422 2052	5.6 2.8 5.8 2.1
19	SU	0313 0911 1511 2138	5.9 2.5 6.1 1.8
20	M	0354 0957 1553 2221	6.1 2.2 6.3 1.7
21	TU	0429 1039 1632 2302	6.4 1.9 6.4 1.5
22	W	0502 1118 1710 2341	6.6 1.7 6.6 1.4
23	TH ○	0536 1156 1749	6.7 1.6 6.7
24	F	0018 0611 1233 1829	1.4 6.8 1.5 6.7
25	SA	0053 0646 1310 1909	1.4 6.8 1.4 6.7
26	SU	0128 0721 1349 1950	1.5 6.8 1.4 6.7
27	M	0204 0757 1430 2034	1.6 6.7 1.4 6.5
28	TU	0244 0838 1518 2124	1.8 6.6 1.5 6.3
29	W	0331 0927 1614 2226	2.1 6.4 1.7 6.0
30	TH ☾	0429 1027 1719 2345	2.3 6.3 1.7 5.9
31	F	0538 1140 1827	2.4 6.2 1.7

JUNE

Date	Day	Time	m
1	SA	0101 0650 1255 1935	6.0 2.4 6.3 1.6
2	SU	0207 0759 1402 2040	6.2 2.2 6.5 1.4
3	M	0305 0903 1502 2138	6.4 1.9 6.7 1.3
4	TU	0357 1001 1558 2232	6.6 1.6 6.9 1.2
5	W	0443 1055 1652 2322	6.8 1.4 7.0 1.2
6	TH ●	0527 1146 1744	6.9 1.2 7.0
7	F	0008 0609 1234 1834	1.3 7.0 1.1 7.0
8	SA	0051 0649 1320 1922	1.4 7.0 1.1 6.9
9	SU	0131 0728 1403 2007	1.5 6.9 1.2 6.7
10	M	0208 0805 1444 2050	1.8 6.8 1.4 6.4
11	TU	0244 0843 1525 2134	2.0 6.6 1.6 6.1
12	W	0321 0924 1608 2222	2.3 6.3 1.9 5.8
13	TH	0402 1011 1655 2315	2.5 6.1 2.1 5.6
14	F ☽	0451 1110 1747	2.7 5.9 2.2
15	SA	0013 0550 1214 1844	5.5 2.8 5.7 2.3
16	SU	0112 0654 1315 1942	5.6 2.9 5.8 2.3
17	M	0208 0800 1413 2040	5.7 2.7 5.9 2.1
18	TU	0259 0901 1506 2133	5.9 2.5 6.0 2.0
19	W	0345 0954 1555 2222	6.1 2.2 6.2 1.8
20	TH	0428 1043 1643 2308	6.4 2.0 6.4 1.7
21	F	0510 1130 1730 2352	6.6 1.7 6.5 1.6
22	SA ○	0550 1216 1817	6.7 1.5 6.7
23	SU	0034 0631 1302 1903	1.5 6.9 1.3 6.8
24	M	0116 0711 1347 1949	1.5 7.0 1.2 6.8
25	TU	0159 0752 1433 2036	1.5 7.0 1.1 6.7
26	W	0242 0835 1521 2125	1.6 7.0 1.1 6.6
27	TH	0328 0922 1611 2219	1.7 6.9 1.2 6.4
28	F ☾	0417 1015 1704 2319	1.9 6.8 1.3 6.3
29	SA	0513 1116 1801	2.1 6.6 1.5
30	SU	0022 0616 1221 1902	6.1 2.2 6.5 1.7

SUNRISE AND SUNSET TIMES

IMMINGHAM
At 53°38′N 0°11′W

UT		Sunrise	Sunset
Jan	01	0818	1551
	15	0809	1612
Feb	01	0746	1643
	15	0719	1711
Mar	01	0649	1738
	15	0615	1805
BST (UT+1)			
Apr	01	0634	1936
	15	0601	2002
May	01	0526	2031
	15	0500	2056
Jun	01	0438	2120
	15	0430	2132
Jul	01	0435	2133
	15	0450	2122
Aug	01	0516	2057
	15	0540	2029
Sep	01	0610	1951
	15	0634	1916
Oct	01	0703	1837
	15	0728	1804
UT			
Nov	01	0700	1628
	15	0727	1603
Dec	01	0754	1545
	15	0811	1540

IMMINGHAM
LAT 53°38′N
LONG 0°11′W

TIMES AND HEIGHTS OF HIGH AND LOW WATER (Heights in Metres)

TIME ZONE UT
For Summer Time (area enclosed in shaded box) add 1 hour

2024

JULY

Date	Day	Time	m	Time	m	Time	m	Time	m
1	M	0126	6.1	0724	2.3	1329	6.4	2007	1.8
2	TU	0228	6.1	0835	2.2	1437	6.4	2111	1.8
3	W	0327	6.3	0941	2.0	1543	6.5	2210	1.8
4	TH	0421	6.4	1041	1.7	1644	6.6	2304	1.8
5	F ●	0509	6.6	1136	1.5	1740	6.6	2353	1.7
6	SA	0553	6.8	1226	1.3	1831	6.7		
7	SU	0037	1.7	0635	6.9	1313	1.2	1916	6.7
8	M	0118	1.7	0714	6.9	1355	1.2	1956	6.6
9	TU	0155	1.8	0751	6.9	1433	1.3	2033	6.5
10	W	0228	1.9	0826	6.8	1508	1.5	2107	6.3
11	TH	0300	2.0	0901	6.6	1542	1.7	2141	6.1
12	F	0333	2.2	0937	6.4	1617	1.9	2218	6.0
13	SA ☽	0409	2.4	1018	6.2	1656	2.1	2302	5.8
14	SU	0452	2.6	1107	5.9	1743	2.3	2355	5.7
15	M	0546	2.7	1207	5.8	1839	2.4		
16	TU	0058	5.6	0651	2.8	1314	5.7	1942	2.5
17	W	0205	5.7	0802	2.7	1424	5.8	2047	2.4
18	TH	0307	5.9	0912	2.5	1528	6.0	2148	2.2
19	F	0401	6.2	1016	2.1	1626	6.2	2243	1.9
20	SA	0450	6.5	1113	1.8	1720	6.5	2334	1.7
21	SU ○	0535	6.8	1206	1.4	1810	6.8		
22	M	0022	1.5	0618	7.0	1256	1.0	1858	7.0
23	TU	0107	1.4	0701	7.3	1343	0.8	1944	7.1
24	W	0150	1.3	0742	7.4	1427	0.7	2027	7.1
25	TH	0232	1.2	0824	7.4	1510	0.7	2111	7.0
26	F	0314	1.3	0908	7.4	1553	0.9	2155	6.8
27	SA	0357	1.6	0955	7.2	1638	1.2	2244	6.5
28	SU ☾	0444	1.9	1048	6.8	1727	1.6	2340	6.1
29	M	0539	2.2	1151	6.4	1825	2.0		
30	TU	0044	5.9	0649	2.5	1303	6.1	1937	2.3
31	W	0154	5.8	0815	2.5	1423	6.0	2053	2.4

AUGUST

Date	Day	Time	m	Time	m	Time	m	Time	m
1	TH	0305	5.9	0933	2.3	1542	6.1	2158	2.3
2	F	0407	6.2	1036	1.9	1650	6.3	2253	2.1
3	SA	0457	6.5	1129	1.5	1742	6.5	2341	1.9
4	SU ●	0540	6.7	1217	1.3	1825	6.6		
5	M	0023	1.8	0620	6.9	1259	1.1	1902	6.7
6	TU	0102	1.7	0656	7.0	1338	1.1	1935	6.7
7	W	0137	1.7	0730	7.0	1412	1.2	2005	6.6
8	TH	0207	1.7	0802	7.0	1442	1.3	2033	6.5
9	F	0235	1.8	0832	6.8	1509	1.5	2100	6.4
10	SA	0301	1.9	0902	6.7	1536	1.8	2129	6.3
11	SU	0329	2.1	0934	6.4	1605	2.0	2204	6.1
12	M ☽	0403	2.3	1011	6.1	1642	2.3	2247	5.8
13	TU	0449	2.6	1101	5.8	1737	2.6	2348	5.6
14	W	0556	2.9	1214	5.6	1850	2.8		
15	TH	0117	5.5	0717	2.9	1353	5.5	2010	2.7
16	F	0237	5.7	0841	2.7	1514	5.8	2124	2.5
17	SA	0340	6.1	1000	2.2	1617	6.2	2226	2.1
18	SU	0431	6.5	1102	1.6	1711	6.7	2319	1.7
19	M ○	0517	7.0	1155	1.1	1759	7.0		
20	TU	0007	1.4	0600	7.3	1242	0.7	1844	7.2
21	W	0052	1.1	0642	7.6	1327	0.4	1926	7.4
22	TH	0134	1.0	0723	7.8	1409	0.4	2006	7.4
23	F	0214	1.0	0804	7.8	1448	0.5	2044	7.2
24	SA	0253	1.1	0846	7.7	1526	0.8	2123	6.9
25	SU	0332	1.4	0930	7.3	1605	1.3	2205	6.5
26	M ☾	0413	1.8	1021	6.8	1647	1.9	2257	6.1
27	TU	0503	2.3	1124	6.2	1744	2.5		
28	W	0004	5.7	0618	2.7	1247	5.7	1911	2.9
29	TH	0126	5.6	0810	2.7	1422	5.7	2044	2.9
30	F	0247	5.7	0930	2.3	1551	5.9	2150	2.6
31	SA	0353	6.1	1027	1.9	1650	6.3	2240	2.3

SEPTEMBER

Date	Day	Time	m	Time	m	Time	m	Time	m
1	SU	0441	6.5	1114	1.5	1731	6.5	2323	2.0
2	M	0520	6.8	1157	1.2	1805	6.7		
3	TU ●	0003	1.7	0557	7.0	1235	1.1	1836	6.8
4	W	0039	1.6	0631	7.1	1310	1.1	1905	6.8
5	TH	0112	1.5	0703	7.1	1341	1.1	1931	6.8
6	F	0141	1.6	0733	7.1	1409	1.3	1955	6.8
7	SA	0206	1.7	0801	7.0	1433	1.5	2021	6.7
8	SU	0229	1.8	0828	6.8	1455	1.7	2047	6.5
9	M	0253	1.9	0856	6.5	1517	2.0	2117	6.3
10	TU	0323	2.2	0929	6.2	1549	2.3	2154	6.0
11	W ☽	0405	2.5	1016	5.8	1641	2.7	2248	5.6
12	TH	0514	2.9	1129	5.5	1805	3.0		
13	F	0023	5.4	0647	2.9	1338	5.4	1941	3.0
14	SA	0210	5.6	0821	2.6	1503	5.9	2105	2.6
15	SU	0316	6.1	0945	2.0	1604	6.4	2208	2.1
16	M	0407	6.7	1043	1.4	1653	6.9	2258	1.7
17	TU	0452	7.2	1133	0.9	1738	7.2	2345	1.3
18	W ○	0534	7.6	1219	0.5	1820	7.4		
19	TH	0028	1.0	0617	7.9	1302	0.3	1859	7.5
20	F	0110	0.8	0659	8.0	1342	0.3	1936	7.5
21	SA	0150	0.8	0741	7.9	1420	0.6	2012	7.3
22	SU	0229	1.0	0823	7.7	1455	1.0	2049	7.0
23	M	0306	1.4	0907	7.2	1530	1.6	2129	6.6
24	TU ☾	0346	1.8	0958	6.6	1609	2.3	2217	6.1
25	W	0435	2.4	1106	5.9	1703	2.9	2328	5.6
26	TH	0558	2.8	1241	5.5	1843	3.3		
27	F	0101	5.5	0802	2.7	1416	5.6	2028	3.2
28	SA	0224	5.7	0914	2.3	1537	5.9	2129	2.8
29	SU	0328	6.2	1005	1.8	1627	6.3	2216	2.3
30	M	0415	6.6	1047	1.5	1703	6.6	2257	2.0

OCTOBER

Date	Day	Time	m	Time	m	Time	m	Time	m
1	TU	0453	6.9	1126	1.2	1734	6.8	2335	1.7
2	W ●	0528	7.0	1202	1.1	1802	6.9		
3	TH	0010	1.6	0601	7.1	1235	1.1	1829	6.9
4	F	0042	1.5	0632	7.1	1306	1.2	1855	6.9
5	SA	0111	1.5	0702	7.0	1334	1.4	1921	6.9
6	SU	0136	1.6	0731	6.9	1358	1.5	1947	6.8
7	M	0200	1.7	0759	6.8	1419	1.7	2013	6.7
8	TU	0226	1.9	0828	6.5	1444	2.0	2042	6.4
9	W	0257	2.1	0903	6.2	1517	2.4	2120	6.1
10	TH ☽	0341	2.4	0953	5.8	1609	2.8	2214	5.7
11	F	0453	2.7	1112	5.5	1733	3.1	2340	5.5
12	SA	0626	2.8	1324	5.5	1911	3.1		
13	SU	0135	5.7	0759	2.4	1442	6.0	2035	2.7
14	M	0243	6.3	0916	1.8	1539	6.5	2137	2.1
15	TU	0335	6.8	1013	1.3	1627	6.9	2229	1.6
16	W	0422	7.3	1102	0.8	1710	7.3	2316	1.2
17	TH ○	0506	7.7	1149	0.6	1751	7.5		
18	F	0001	1.0	0551	7.9	1232	0.5	1830	7.5
19	SA	0045	0.8	0635	7.9	1313	0.6	1907	7.5
20	SU	0127	0.9	0719	7.8	1351	0.9	1944	7.3
21	M	0207	1.0	0804	7.5	1427	1.3	2021	7.0
22	TU	0246	1.4	0850	7.0	1502	1.9	2100	6.6
23	W	0327	1.8	0943	6.4	1540	2.5	2147	6.1
24	TH ☾	0420	2.3	1053	5.8	1633	3.0	2255	5.7
25	F	0542	2.7	1224	5.5	1759	3.4		
26	SA	0029	5.6	0729	2.6	1344	5.6	1947	3.3
27	SU	0147	5.8	0837	2.3	1453	5.9	2052	2.9
28	M	0250	6.1	0927	1.9	1544	6.2	2141	2.5
29	TU	0339	6.4	1009	1.7	1623	6.5	2222	2.1
30	W	0419	6.7	1047	1.5	1656	6.7	2301	1.8
31	TH	0454	6.8	1123	1.4	1725	6.8	2337	1.7

NOVEMBER

Date	Day	Time	m	Time	m	Time	m	Time	m
1	F ●	0527	6.9	1158	1.4	1753	6.9		
2	SA	0010	1.6	0601	6.9	1231	1.4	1822	7.0
3	SU	0041	1.6	0634	6.9	1300	1.5	1851	7.0
4	M	0110	1.6	0707	6.8	1328	1.6	1920	6.9
5	TU	0139	1.7	0740	6.7	1355	1.8	1949	6.8
6	W	0210	1.8	0814	6.5	1426	2.0	2022	6.6
7	TH	0247	2.0	0855	6.2	1504	2.3	2103	6.3
8	F	0336	2.2	0949	5.9	1557	2.7	2157	6.0
9	SA ☽	0445	2.4	1109	5.7	1712	2.9	2315	5.9
10	SU	0607	2.4	1254	5.7	1837	2.9		
11	M	0049	6.0	0727	2.1	1407	6.1	1955	2.6
12	TU	0201	6.4	0837	1.7	1505	6.5	2100	2.2
13	W	0259	6.8	0936	1.3	1555	6.8	2156	1.7
14	TH	0351	7.2	1029	1.1	1640	7.1	2248	1.4
15	F ○	0440	7.5	1117	0.9	1722	7.3	2337	1.1
16	SA	0528	7.6	1203	0.9	1803	7.3		
17	SU	0023	1.0	0617	7.6	1246	1.0	1843	7.3
18	M	0108	1.0	0705	7.4	1327	1.2	1922	7.2
19	TU	0152	1.1	0752	7.2	1405	1.6	2001	7.0
20	W	0234	1.4	0840	6.8	1442	2.0	2041	6.7
21	TH	0318	1.7	0932	6.3	1521	2.4	2126	6.4
22	F	0409	2.1	1035	5.9	1608	2.8	2224	6.0
23	SA ☾	0512	2.4	1147	5.6	1710	3.1	2341	5.8
24	SU	0626	2.5	1255	5.6	1829	3.2		
25	M	0055	5.8	0736	2.4	1356	5.7	1949	3.0
26	TU	0158	6.0	0832	2.2	1450	5.9	2051	2.7
27	W	0252	6.2	0919	2.0	1536	6.2	2139	2.4
28	TH	0338	6.4	1002	1.9	1614	6.4	2222	2.1
29	F	0418	6.5	1042	1.7	1648	6.6	2301	1.9
30	SA	0456	6.6	1121	1.6	1721	6.8	2339	1.8

DECEMBER

Date	Day	Time	m	Time	m	Time	m	Time	m
1	SU ●	0534	6.7	1158	1.6	1755	6.9		
2	M	0015	1.7	0613	6.8	1232	1.6	1830	6.9
3	TU	0051	1.6	0652	6.7	1306	1.7	1904	6.9
4	W	0127	1.6	0731	6.7	1340	1.8	1938	6.9
5	TH	0205	1.6	0812	6.6	1418	1.9	2014	6.8
6	F	0248	1.7	0856	6.4	1500	2.1	2056	6.6
7	SA	0337	1.8	0949	6.2	1549	2.3	2148	6.5
8	SU ☽	0436	1.9	1055	6.0	1650	2.5	2251	6.3
9	M	0541	1.9	1212	6.0	1759	2.6		
10	TU	0004	6.3	0650	1.9	1322	6.1	1912	2.5
11	W	0117	6.5	0757	1.8	1424	6.3	2022	2.3
12	TH	0223	6.7	0901	1.6	1521	6.5	2126	2.0
13	F	0324	6.9	0958	1.5	1612	6.7	2224	1.7
14	SA	0421	7.0	1051	1.4	1659	6.9	2319	1.4
15	SU ○	0516	7.1	1141	1.4	1744	7.0		
16	M	0010	1.2	0609	7.1	1227	1.4	1827	7.1
17	TU	0058	1.1	0700	7.1	1310	1.5	1909	7.1
18	W	0144	1.2	0747	6.9	1350	1.7	1949	7.0
19	TH	0228	1.3	0832	6.7	1428	1.9	2028	6.9
20	F	0309	1.5	0916	6.4	1504	2.2	2107	6.6
21	SA	0350	1.8	1002	6.1	1542	2.4	2151	6.4
22	SU ☾	0433	2.1	1052	5.8	1626	2.7	2242	6.1
23	M	0522	2.3	1146	5.7	1718	2.9	2344	5.9
24	TU	0615	2.4	1244	5.6	1819	3.0		
25	W	0048	5.8	0715	2.5	1342	5.7	1927	2.9
26	TH	0151	5.8	0815	2.4	1438	5.8	2036	2.8
27	F	0249	5.9	0911	2.3	1529	6.1	2136	2.5
28	SA	0342	6.1	1002	2.1	1614	6.3	2227	2.2
29	SU	0430	6.3	1048	1.9	1655	6.5	2313	1.9
30	M ●	0515	6.5	1132	1.8	1735	6.7	2358	1.7
31	TU	0600	6.6	1213	1.7	1814	6.9		

RIVER TYNE (NORTH SHIELDS)

LAT 55°01′N
LONG 1°26′W

TIMES AND HEIGHTS OF HIGH AND LOW WATER (Heights in Metres)

TIME ZONE UT
For Summer Time (area enclosed in shaded box) add 1 hour

2024

JANUARY

Date	Day	Time	m	Date	Day	Time	m
1		0034	1.3	16		0053	0.6
		0640	4.4			0659	4.8
	M	1228	1.8		TU	1259	1.3
		1841	4.6			1859	5.1
2		0113	1.4	17		0142	0.8
		0722	4.2			0752	4.6
	TU	1306	1.9		W	1347	1.5
		1923	4.5			1953	4.9
3		0155	1.5	18		0235	1.0
		0808	4.1			0848	4.4
	W	1350	2.0		TH	1442	1.7
		2011	4.3		☽	2053	4.7
4		0244	1.7	19		0334	1.3
		0859	4.0			0949	4.2
	TH	1444	2.2		F	1550	1.9
	☾	2105	4.2			2201	4.5
5		0342	1.8	20		0441	1.6
		0957	3.9			1057	4.1
	F	1553	2.3		SA	1708	1.9
		2207	4.1			2317	4.3
6		0445	1.9	21		0554	1.7
		1059	4.0			1208	4.2
	SA	1709	2.2		SU	1827	1.8
		2313	4.1				
7		0549	1.8	22		0035	4.3
		1201	4.1			0705	1.8
	SU	1817	2.1		M	1311	4.3
						1937	1.6
8		0019	4.2	23		0141	4.4
		0648	1.7			0803	1.7
	M	1258	4.3		TU	1404	4.5
		1916	1.8			2033	1.4
9		0119	4.4	24		0234	4.5
		0741	1.5			0849	1.6
	TU	1347	4.5		W	1448	4.7
		2009	1.5			2118	1.2
10		0212	4.6	25		0317	4.6
		0830	1.4			0928	1.5
	W	1431	4.7		TH	1526	4.8
		2058	1.2		○	2157	1.0
11		0300	4.8	26		0355	4.7
		0917	1.2			1002	1.4
	TH	1514	4.9		F	1601	4.9
	●	2145	0.9			2233	0.9
12		0347	5.0	27		0430	4.7
		1003	1.1			1034	1.4
	F	1556	5.1		SA	1633	4.9
		2232	0.7			2305	0.9
13		0433	5.1	28		0502	4.7
		1047	1.0			1103	1.3
	SA	1639	5.2		SU	1705	4.9
		2319	0.5			2336	0.9
14		0520	5.1	29		0534	4.6
		1131	1.0			1132	1.4
	SU	1723	5.3		M	1736	4.9
15		0006	0.5	30		0007	1.0
		0609	5.0			0607	4.5
	M	1214	1.1		TU	1201	1.4
		1810	5.2			1810	4.8
				31		0039	1.1
						0641	4.4
					W	1232	1.5
						1844	4.7

FEBRUARY

Date	Day	Time	m	Date	Day	Time	m
1		0113	1.3	16		0159	1.1
		0718	4.3			0809	4.4
	TH	1306	1.7		F	1406	1.5
		1922	4.5		☽	2022	4.6
2		0151	1.5	17		0252	1.5
		0759	4.1			0907	4.1
	F	1346	1.9		SA	1510	1.8
	☾	2006	4.3			2132	4.2
3		0236	1.7	18		0401	1.9
		0848	4.0			1018	3.9
	SA	1438	2.1		SU	1639	2.0
		2102	4.1			2258	4.0
4		0336	1.9	19		0531	2.1
		0951	3.9			1143	3.9
	SU	1555	2.2		M	1819	1.9
		2215	3.9				
5		0455	2.0	20		0030	4.0
		1106	3.9			0658	2.0
	M	1729	2.1		TU	1258	4.1
		2342	4.0			1935	1.6
6		0614	1.9	21		0139	4.2
		1223	4.1			0757	1.9
	TU	1850	1.9		W	1354	4.3
						2027	1.4
7		0100	4.2	22		0228	4.4
		0722	1.7			0840	1.7
	W	1325	4.3		TH	1437	4.6
		1954	1.5			2107	1.1
8		0200	4.5	23		0306	4.5
		0818	1.4			0915	1.5
	TH	1415	4.6		F	1512	4.7
		2047	1.1			2141	1.0
9		0250	4.8	24		0339	4.6
		0907	1.2			0946	1.3
	F	1459	5.0		SA	1543	4.9
	●	2135	0.7		○	2212	0.8
10		0336	5.1	25		0408	4.7
		0951	0.9			1014	1.2
	SA	1541	5.2		SU	1612	4.9
		2221	0.3			2241	0.8
11		0420	5.2	26		0437	4.7
		1034	0.8			1041	1.1
	SU	1623	5.4		M	1640	5.0
		2306	0.2			2309	0.8
12		0504	5.2	27		0505	4.7
		1115	0.7			1108	1.1
	M	1705	5.5		TU	1709	5.0
		2349	0.2			2337	0.8
13		0547	5.1	28		0533	4.7
		1155	0.8			1135	1.2
	TU	1749	5.5		W	1739	4.9
14		0031	0.3	29		0005	1.0
		0632	4.9			0604	4.6
	W	1234	1.0		TH	1202	1.3
		1835	5.3			1810	4.7
15		0114	0.6				
		0718	4.7				
	TH	1317	1.2				
		1925	5.0				

MARCH

Date	Day	Time	m	Date	Day	Time	m
1		0035	1.1	16		0124	1.2
		0635	4.4			0732	4.4
	F	1233	1.4		SA	1339	1.4
		1844	4.6			1959	4.4
2		0107	1.4	17		0213	1.7
		0711	4.3			0829	4.1
	SA	1308	1.6		SU	1443	1.7
		1925	4.3		☽	2111	4.0
3		0145	1.7	18		0324	2.1
		0756	4.1			0942	3.9
	SU	1355	1.9		M	1619	1.9
	☾	2020	4.1			2242	3.8
4		0241	1.9	19		0511	2.3
		0858	3.9			1114	3.8
	M	1508	2.1		TU	1806	1.8
		2139	3.9				
5		0411	2.1	20		0019	3.9
		1022	3.8			0644	2.2
	TU	1655	2.1		W	1237	4.0
		2319	3.9			1918	1.6
6		0551	2.1	21		0124	4.1
		1153	3.9			0739	1.9
	W	1830	1.8		TH	1333	4.2
						2005	1.3
7		0046	4.2	22		0208	4.3
		0707	1.8			0818	1.7
	TH	1302	4.3		F	1414	4.5
		1938	1.3			2042	1.1
8		0146	4.5	23		0242	4.5
		0803	1.4			0851	1.4
	F	1354	4.7		SA	1447	4.7
		2031	0.8			2113	0.9
9		0234	4.9	24		0312	4.6
		0850	1.0			0920	1.2
	SA	1439	5.0		SU	1517	4.8
		2118	0.4			2142	0.8
10		0317	5.1	25		0340	4.7
		0932	0.8			0947	1.1
	SU	1520	5.4		M	1545	4.9
	●	2202	0.1		○	2210	0.7
11		0359	5.3	26		0406	4.8
		1013	0.6			1014	1.0
	M	1601	5.6		TU	1612	4.9
		2244	0.0			2238	0.7
12		0439	5.3	27		0433	4.8
		1052	0.5			1042	1.0
	TU	1643	5.6		W	1641	4.9
		2325	0.1			2306	0.8
13		0520	5.2	28		0501	4.7
		1131	0.6			1109	1.0
	W	1726	5.5		TH	1710	4.8
						2334	0.9
14		0004	0.3	29		0530	4.7
		0602	5.0			1138	1.1
	TH	1210	0.7		F	1742	4.7
		1812	5.2				
15		0043	0.7	30		0002	1.1
		0645	4.7			0602	4.5
	F	1251	1.0		SA	1209	1.3
		1901	4.9			1819	4.5
				31		0034	1.4
						0639	4.4
					SU	1246	1.5
						1904	4.3

APRIL

Date	Day	Time	m	Date	Day	Time	m
1		0114	1.7	16		0251	2.2
		0725	4.2			0909	3.9
	M	1337	1.7		TU	1555	1.8
		2004	4.0			2215	3.8
2		0213	2.0	17		0435	2.4
		0828	3.9			1034	3.8
	TU	1454	1.9		W	1730	1.8
	☾	2128	3.9			2343	3.8
3		0349	2.2	18		0605	2.2
		0954	3.8			1156	3.9
	W	1639	1.8		TH	1839	1.6
		2306	3.9				
4		0531	2.0	19		0047	4.0
		1125	4.0			0702	2.0
	TH	1809	1.5		F	1254	4.2
						1926	1.4
5		0027	4.2	20		0132	4.2
		0645	1.7			0742	1.7
	F	1235	4.3		SA	1337	4.4
		1915	1.1			2003	1.2
6		0124	4.6	21		0207	4.4
		0739	1.3			0816	1.5
	SA	1328	4.7		SU	1412	4.5
		2007	0.6			2036	1.0
7		0211	4.9	22		0237	4.5
		0825	1.0			0847	1.3
	SU	1413	5.1		M	1444	4.7
		2053	0.3			2106	0.9
8		0253	5.1	23		0306	4.7
		0907	0.7			0917	1.1
	M	1455	5.4		TU	1514	4.8
	●	2136	0.1		○	2136	0.8
9		0332	5.2	24		0334	4.7
		0948	0.5			0947	1.0
	TU	1537	5.5		W	1544	4.8
		2218	0.1			2206	0.8
10		0412	5.2	25		0403	4.8
		1028	0.5			1017	1.0
	W	1620	5.5		TH	1615	4.8
		2258	0.3			2236	0.9
11		0452	5.1	26		0433	4.8
		1109	0.5			1048	1.0
	TH	1705	5.3		F	1649	4.7
		2336	0.6			2307	1.0
12		0532	4.9	27		0504	4.7
		1150	0.7			1121	1.1
	F	1753	5.0		SA	1725	4.6
						2339	1.2
13		0014	1.0	28		0539	4.6
		0615	4.7			1158	1.2
	SA	1233	1.0		SU	1807	4.5
		1844	4.7				
14		0055	1.4	29		0016	1.4
		0702	4.4			0620	4.4
	SU	1322	1.3		M	1242	1.3
		1943	4.3			1858	4.3
15		0142	1.9	30		0102	1.7
		0757	4.1			0711	4.3
	M	1426	1.6		TU	1339	1.5
	☽	2053	3.9			2003	4.1

MAY

Date	Day	Time	m	Date	Day	Time	m
1		0207	1.9	16		0335	2.3
		0815	4.1			0943	3.9
	W	1454	1.6		TH	1630	1.7
	☽	2123	4.0			2244	3.8
2		0334	2.1	17		0458	2.2
		0935	4.1			1055	4.0
	TH	1623	1.5		F	1736	1.6
		2247	4.1			2349	3.9
3		0503	1.9	18		0602	2.1
		1054	4.2			1159	4.1
	F	1741	1.2		SA	1830	1.5
		2359	4.3				
4		0611	1.7	19		0040	4.1
		1202	4.5			0652	1.8
	SA	1844	0.9		SU	1249	4.2
						1914	1.3
5		0055	4.6	20		0122	4.3
		0707	1.3			0733	1.6
	SU	1257	4.8		M	1331	4.4
		1937	0.6			1952	1.2
6		0143	4.8	21		0158	4.4
		0755	1.0			0810	1.4
	M	1346	5.0		TU	1408	4.5
		2025	0.5			2028	1.1
7		0226	5.0	22		0231	4.6
		0840	0.8			0846	1.3
	TU	1431	5.2		W	1444	4.6
		2109	0.4			2103	1.0
8		0306	5.1	23		0304	4.7
		0925	0.6			0920	1.1
	W	1517	5.3		TH	1519	4.7
	●	2152	0.4		○	2137	1.0
9		0347	5.1	24		0336	4.7
		1008	0.6			0956	1.0
	TH	1603	5.2		F	1556	4.7
		2233	0.6			2212	1.0
10		0427	5.0	25		0410	4.8
		1052	0.6			1033	1.0
	F	1650	5.1		SA	1635	4.7
		2312	0.9			2249	1.1
11		0509	4.9	26		0446	4.8
		1136	0.8			1112	1.0
	SA	1739	4.8		SU	1717	4.6
		2352	1.2			2328	1.3
12		0552	4.7	27		0526	4.7
		1221	1.0			1156	1.0
	SU	1831	4.5		M	1804	4.5
13		0032	1.6	28		0010	1.4
		0639	4.5			0611	4.6
	M	1309	1.2		TU	1244	1.1
		1927	4.2			1858	4.4
14		0118	1.9	29		0101	1.6
		0731	4.3			0703	4.5
	TU	1406	1.5		W	1341	1.2
		2027	4.0			2000	4.3
15		0216	2.2	30		0200	1.8
		0833	4.1			0804	4.4
	W	1515	1.6		TH	1447	1.2
	☾	2134	3.8		☽	2109	4.2
				31		0311	1.8
						0912	4.4
					F	1559	1.2
						2218	4.2

JUNE

Date	Day	Time	m	Date	Day	Time	m
1		0425	1.8	16		0445	2.1
		1022	4.4			1050	4.0
	SA	1708	1.1		SU	1723	1.6
		2324	4.3			2338	4.0
2		0532	1.6	17		0549	2.0
		1128	4.6			1151	4.1
	SU	1810	1.0		M	1817	1.6
3		0023	4.5	18		0030	4.1
		0633	1.4			0644	1.8
	M	1228	4.7		TU	1245	4.2
		1907	0.9			1907	1.5
4		0115	4.7	19		0117	4.3
		0728	1.2			0733	1.7
	TU	1323	4.9		W	1334	4.3
		1959	0.8			1952	1.4
5		0202	4.8	20		0159	4.4
		0819	1.0			0817	1.4
	W	1415	5.0		TH	1418	4.5
		2047	0.8			2034	1.3
6		0246	4.9	21		0237	4.6
		0908	0.8			0859	1.2
	TH	1505	5.0		F	1501	4.6
	●	2131	0.9			2115	1.2
7		0328	4.9	22		0315	4.7
		0956	0.7			0940	1.1
	F	1553	4.9		SA	1543	4.7
		2214	1.0		○	2156	1.1
8		0410	4.9	23		0354	4.8
		1041	0.7			1023	0.9
	SA	1641	4.8		SU	1626	4.8
		2255	1.2			2238	1.1
9		0452	4.9	24		0434	4.9
		1126	0.8			1108	0.8
	SU	1728	4.7		M	1712	4.8
		2334	1.4			2321	1.2
10		0534	4.7	25		0516	4.9
		1209	0.9			1154	0.7
	M	1815	4.5		TU	1759	4.8
11		0012	1.6	26		0005	1.2
		0618	4.6			0602	4.9
	TU	1252	1.1		W	1241	0.7
		1903	4.3			1851	4.7
12		0052	1.8	27		0052	1.4
		0704	4.5			0651	4.8
	W	1338	1.3		TH	1333	0.8
		1952	4.1			1945	4.5
13		0137	1.9	28		0143	1.5
		0754	4.3			0745	4.8
	TH	1428	1.5		F	1428	0.9
		2044	4.0		☽	2043	4.4
14		0231	2.1	29		0240	1.6
		0849	4.2			0845	4.7
	F	1525	1.6		SA	1528	1.0
	☾	2140	3.9			2145	4.3
15		0336	2.1	30		0345	1.7
		0949	4.1			0949	4.6
	SA	1624	1.6		SU	1632	1.2
		2239	3.9			2248	4.3

SUNRISE AND SUNSET TIMES

RIVER TYNE
At 55°01′N 1°26′W

UT		Sunrise	Sunset
Jan	01	0831	1548
	15	0821	1609
Feb	01	0756	1643
	15	0728	1712
Mar	01	0656	1742
	15	0621	1810
BST (UT+1)			
Apr	01	0637	1943
	15	0602	2010
May	01	0526	2041
	15	0458	2107
Jun	01	0434	2134
	15	0426	2147
Jul	01	0431	2148
	15	0447	2136
Aug	01	0515	2108
	15	0540	2039
Sep	01	0612	1958
	15	0638	1922
Oct	01	0708	1841
	15	0735	1807
UT			
Nov	01	0710	1628
	15	0738	1602
Dec	01	0807	1542
	15	0825	1537

RIVER TYNE (NORTH SHIELDS)
LAT 55°01'N
LONG 1°26'W

TIMES AND HEIGHTS OF HIGH AND LOW WATER (Heights in Metres)

TIME ZONE UT
For Summer Time (area enclosed in shaded box) add 1 hour

2024

JULY

Date	Time	m
1 M	0454 1057 1737 2352	1.7 4.5 1.2 4.3
2 TU	0603 1207 1841	1.6 4.5 1.3
3 W	0052 0709 1312 1941	4.4 1.4 4.6 1.3
4 TH	0145 0809 1410 2034	4.6 1.2 4.7 1.3
5 F ●	0234 0902 1502 2120	4.7 1.0 4.7 1.3
6 SA	0318 0950 1549 2202	4.8 0.9 4.7 1.3
7 SU	0359 1034 1632 2241	4.9 0.8 4.7 1.3
8 M	0438 1114 1713 2316	4.9 0.8 4.7 1.4
9 TU	0515 1151 1752 2350	4.9 0.9 4.6 1.4
10 W	0553 1227 1831	4.8 1.0 4.4
11 TH	0023 0631 1303 1911	1.5 4.7 1.1 4.3
12 F	0058 0712 1342 1953	1.7 4.5 1.3 4.1
13 SA ☾	0137 0756 1425 2039	1.8 4.4 1.5 4.0
14 SU	0225 0846 1516 2132	2.0 4.2 1.7 3.9
15 M	0325 0944 1616 2231	2.1 4.0 1.8 3.9
16 TU	0439 1049 1721 2335	2.1 4.0 1.8 4.0
17 W	0553 1200 1825	2.1 4.0 1.8
18 TH	0037 0658 1305 1923	4.1 1.8 4.1 1.6
19 F	0130 0754 1359 2013	4.3 1.6 4.4 1.5
20 SA	0216 0842 1447 2100	4.5 1.3 4.6 1.3
21 SU ○	0258 0928 1531 2144	4.8 1.0 4.8 1.1
22 M	0338 1014 1615 2227	5.0 0.7 5.0 1.0
23 TU	0419 1058 1659 2310	5.1 0.5 5.0 0.9
24 W	0501 1143 1744 2352	5.2 0.4 5.0 1.0
25 TH	0545 1228 1831	5.3 0.4 4.9
26 F	0033 0631 1312 1919	1.1 5.2 0.5 4.7
27 SA	0118 0721 1400 2012	1.2 5.0 0.8 4.5
28 SU ☽	0207 0816 1454 2109	1.4 4.8 1.1 4.3
29 M	0308 0920 1557 2214	1.6 4.6 1.4 4.2
30 TU	0423 1035 1711 2326	1.8 4.3 1.7 4.2
31 W	0546 1158 1828	1.7 4.3 1.7

AUGUST

Date	Time	m
1 TH	0037 0706 1313 1936	4.3 1.6 4.3 1.7
2 F	0138 0809 1413 2030	4.4 1.3 4.5 1.6
3 SA	0227 0900 1500 2113	4.6 1.1 4.6 1.4
4 SU ●	0309 0943 1541 2150	4.8 0.9 4.7 1.3
5 M	0346 1020 1617 2223	4.9 0.8 4.7 1.3
6 TU	0419 1054 1650 2253	5.0 0.8 4.7 1.2
7 W	0452 1125 1722 2322	5.0 0.8 4.7 1.3
8 TH	0524 1156 1754 2351	4.9 0.9 4.6 1.3
9 F	0556 1226 1827	4.9 1.0 4.5
10 SA	0021 0631 1258 1903	1.4 4.7 1.2 4.3
11 SU	0054 0709 1334 1942	1.6 4.5 1.4 4.2
12 M ☾	0133 0752 1416 2029	1.8 4.3 1.7 4.0
13 TU	0222 0845 1512 2128	2.0 4.1 1.9 3.9
14 W	0334 0956 1628 2242	2.2 3.9 2.1 3.9
15 TH	0507 1123 1751	2.2 3.9 2.0
16 F	0000 0631 1244 1902	4.0 1.9 4.1 1.8
17 SA	0105 0735 1343 1958	4.3 1.6 4.4 1.6
18 SU	0155 0827 1431 2045	4.6 1.1 4.7 1.3
19 M ○	0238 0913 1515 2128	4.9 0.7 5.0 1.0
20 TU	0319 0957 1557 2209	5.2 0.4 5.2 0.8
21 W	0358 1040 1638 2250	5.4 0.2 5.3 0.7
22 TH	0439 1122 1720 2329	5.5 0.1 5.2 0.7
23 F	0522 1204 1803	5.5 0.2 5.1
24 SA	0009 0607 1245 1848	0.8 5.4 0.5 4.9
25 SU	0051 0655 1329 1937	1.1 5.1 0.9 4.6
26 M ☽	0139 0751 1420 2034	1.3 4.8 1.4 4.3
27 TU	0239 0859 1525 2143	1.6 4.4 1.8 4.1
28 W	0404 1024 1654 2306	1.9 4.1 2.1 4.0
29 TH	0544 1159 1827	1.8 4.1 2.1
30 F	0028 0708 1315 1934	4.2 1.6 4.2 1.9
31 SA	0130 0805 1408 2021	4.4 1.3 4.5 1.7

SEPTEMBER

Date	Time	m
1 SU	0216 0849 1449 2058	4.7 1.1 4.6 1.5
2 M	0253 0925 1522 2130	4.8 0.9 4.7 1.3
3 TU ●	0325 0956 1552 2159	5.0 0.8 4.8 1.2
4 W	0355 1025 1621 2226	5.0 0.7 4.8 1.1
5 TH	0424 1053 1649 2253	5.1 0.8 4.8 1.1
6 F	0453 1121 1717 2320	5.0 0.8 4.7 1.2
7 SA	0523 1149 1747 2349	4.9 1.0 4.7 1.3
8 SU	0554 1218 1819	4.8 1.2 4.5
9 M	0019 0629 1249 1855	1.5 4.6 1.5 4.4
10 TU	0054 0710 1326 1938	1.7 4.3 1.7 4.2
11 W ☽	0140 0803 1419 2037	1.9 4.1 2.0 4.0
12 TH	0250 0920 1544 2158	2.1 3.9 2.3 3.9
13 F	0434 1058 1725 2327	2.2 3.9 2.2 4.0
14 SA	0608 1225 1842	1.9 4.1 1.9
15 SU	0038 0715 1324 1938	4.3 1.4 4.5 1.6
16 M	0130 0806 1410 2023	4.7 1.0 4.9 1.2
17 TU	0213 0851 1452 2105	5.1 0.5 5.2 0.9
18 W ○	0253 0934 1532 2145	5.4 0.2 5.3 0.7
19 TH	0333 1015 1611 2225	5.6 0.1 5.4 0.6
20 F	0414 1056 1652 2305	5.7 0.1 5.3 0.6
21 SA	0457 1137 1733 2345	5.7 0.3 5.2 0.8
22 SU	0543 1217 1816	5.4 0.7 4.9
23 M	0028 0634 1259 1904	1.0 5.1 1.2 4.6
24 TU ☾	0117 0733 1348 2002	1.3 4.6 1.7 4.3
25 W	0221 0846 1458 2115	1.7 4.2 2.2 4.1
26 TH	0354 1016 1642 2245	1.9 4.0 2.4 4.0
27 F	0538 1153 1816	1.8 4.0 2.3
28 SA	0010 0654 1302 1916	4.2 1.6 4.2 2.0
29 SU	0110 0745 1349 1958	4.4 1.3 4.4 1.8
30 M	0153 0823 1424 2032	4.7 1.1 4.6 1.5

OCTOBER

Date	Time	m
1 TU	0228 0855 1454 2102	4.8 1.0 4.7 1.3
2 W ●	0258 0924 1522 2130	5.0 0.9 4.8 1.2
3 TH	0326 0952 1549 2157	5.0 0.8 4.9 1.1
4 F	0355 1019 1616 2225	5.1 0.8 4.9 1.1
5 SA	0423 1047 1644 2253	5.0 0.9 4.9 1.2
6 SU	0454 1115 1713 2322	4.9 1.1 4.8 1.3
7 M	0526 1143 1744 2354	4.8 1.3 4.7 1.4
8 TU	0601 1214 1819	4.6 1.5 4.5
9 W	0030 0645 1252 1904	1.6 4.3 1.8 4.3
10 TH ☽	0119 0742 1346 2004	1.8 4.1 2.1 4.1
11 F	0232 0903 1514 2125	2.0 3.9 2.3 4.0
12 SA	0410 1037 1659 2254	2.0 4.0 2.3 4.1
13 SU	0540 1158 1814	1.7 4.2 1.9
14 M	0005 0646 1257 1909	4.4 1.3 4.6 1.6
15 TU	0059 0737 1343 1955	4.8 0.9 4.9 1.2
16 W	0144 0823 1425 2037	5.2 0.5 5.2 0.9
17 TH ○	0226 0906 1505 2119	5.5 0.3 5.4 0.7
18 F	0308 0948 1544 2201	5.6 0.2 5.4 0.6
19 SA	0352 1029 1624 2243	5.7 0.4 5.3 0.6
20 SU	0437 1110 1705 2326	5.5 0.6 5.2 0.8
21 M	0526 1151 1749	5.3 1.0 4.9
22 TU	0012 0619 1233 1838	1.0 4.9 1.5 4.7
23 W	0104 0720 1323 1935	1.3 4.5 1.9 4.4
24 TH ☾	0209 0832 1431 2047	1.6 4.1 2.3 4.1
25 F	0336 0953 1611 2211	1.8 4.0 2.5 4.1
26 SA	0507 1120 1740 2332	1.8 4.0 2.4 4.2
27 SU	0617 1227 1839	1.6 4.2 2.1
28 M	0033 0708 1313 1923	4.4 1.4 4.4 1.9
29 TU	0118 0746 1349 1958	4.6 1.3 4.5 1.6
30 W	0154 0818 1421 2029	4.7 1.1 4.7 1.5
31 TH	0227 0848 1450 2100	4.8 1.1 4.8 1.3

NOVEMBER

Date	Time	m
1 F ●	0258 0918 1518 2130	4.9 1.0 4.9 1.2
2 SA	0328 0947 1547 2200	4.9 1.0 4.9 1.2
3 SU	0400 1017 1616 2231	4.9 1.1 4.9 1.2
4 M	0433 1047 1646 2304	4.8 1.2 4.8 1.3
5 TU	0508 1119 1720 2340	4.7 1.4 4.7 1.4
6 W	0548 1154 1758	4.6 1.6 4.6
7 TH	0022 0636 1236 1845	1.5 4.4 1.9 4.4
8 F	0114 0735 1333 1944	1.7 4.2 2.1 4.3
9 SA ☽	0223 0849 1452 2058	1.8 4.1 2.2 4.2
10 SU	0346 1010 1622 2216	1.7 4.1 2.2 4.3
11 M	0505 1123 1735 2326	1.5 4.3 1.9 4.5
12 TU	0609 1224 1833	1.2 4.6 1.6
13 W	0024 0705 1313 1924	4.8 0.9 4.9 1.3
14 TH	0115 0754 1357 2011	5.1 0.7 5.1 1.1
15 F ○	0202 0840 1439 2056	5.3 0.6 5.2 0.9
16 SA	0249 0924 1521 2142	5.4 0.6 5.3 0.7
17 SU	0336 1007 1602 2228	5.4 0.8 5.2 0.7
18 M	0425 1050 1645 2315	5.3 1.0 5.1 0.8
19 TU	0516 1132 1729	5.1 1.3 5.0
20 W	0002 0609 1214 1817	1.0 4.8 1.7 4.7
21 TH	0053 0706 1301 1911	1.2 4.5 2.0 4.5
22 F	0151 0807 1357 2012	1.5 4.2 2.2 4.3
23 SA ☾	0257 0912 1511 2121	1.7 4.0 2.4 4.2
24 SU	0410 1021 1632 2232	1.8 3.9 2.4 4.2
25 M	0516 1128 1739 2337	1.8 4.0 2.3 4.2
26 TU	0611 1223 1833	1.7 4.2 2.1
27 W	0031 0657 1306 1917	4.4 1.5 4.3 1.9
28 TH	0116 0736 1344 1956	4.5 1.4 4.5 1.7
29 F	0156 0813 1418 2032	4.6 1.3 4.7 1.5
30 SA	0232 0847 1451 2107	4.7 1.3 4.8 1.4

DECEMBER

Date	Time	m
1 SU ●	0308 0921 1523 2142	4.8 1.2 4.9 1.3
2 M	0344 0955 1555 2218	4.8 1.3 4.9 1.2
3 TU	0421 1030 1629 2255	4.8 1.3 4.9 1.2
4 W	0500 1107 1706 2336	4.7 1.4 4.8 1.2
5 TH	0542 1147 1747	4.6 1.5 4.8
6 F	0021 0631 1231 1834	1.3 4.5 1.7 4.7
7 SA	0111 0725 1323 1927	1.3 4.4 1.9 4.6
8 SU ☽	0209 0828 1424 2029	1.4 4.3 2.0 4.5
9 M	0315 0935 1536 2137	1.4 4.3 2.0 4.5
10 TU	0425 1043 1648 2246	1.4 4.3 1.9 4.6
11 W	0531 1146 1754 2351	1.3 4.5 1.7 4.7
12 TH	0631 1243 1854	1.2 4.6 1.5
13 F	0051 0728 1334 1950	4.9 1.1 4.8 1.3
14 SA	0147 0820 1421 2043	5.0 1.0 5.0 1.0
15 SU ○	0240 0908 1506 2134	5.1 1.0 5.1 0.9
16 M	0331 0954 1549 2222	5.1 1.1 5.1 0.8
17 TU	0421 1037 1632 2309	5.0 1.2 5.1 0.8
18 W	0509 1118 1715 2354	4.9 1.4 5.0 0.9
19 TH	0556 1157 1758	4.7 1.6 4.9
20 F	0037 0643 1236 1844	1.1 4.5 1.8 4.7
21 SA	0122 0731 1317 1932	1.3 4.3 2.0 4.5
22 SU ☾	0209 0821 1405 2025	1.5 4.1 2.1 4.4
23 M	0301 0915 1504 2123	1.7 4.0 2.3 4.2
24 TU	0359 1014 1615 2225	1.8 3.9 2.3 4.1
25 W	0500 1115 1726 2331	1.9 4.0 2.3 4.1
26 TH	0559 1215 1829	1.8 4.1 2.1
27 F	0033 0653 1305 1922	4.2 1.8 4.2 1.9
28 SA	0126 0740 1349 2008	4.3 1.6 4.4 1.7
29 SU	0212 0823 1428 2050	4.4 1.5 4.6 1.5
30 M ●	0253 0903 1505 2129	4.6 1.4 4.7 1.3
31 TU	0332 0942 1541 2209	4.7 1.3 4.9 1.1

LEITH
LAT 55°59′N
LONG 3°11′W

TIMES AND HEIGHTS OF HIGH AND LOW WATER (Heights in Metres)

TIME ZONE UT
For Summer Time (area enclosed in shaded box) add 1 hour

2024

JANUARY

Date	Day	Time	m	Time	m	Time	m	Time	m
1	M	0548	4.9	1100	1.8	1758	4.9	2341	1.5
2	TU	0628	4.7	1137	2.0	1839	4.8		
3	W	0022	1.7	0713	4.5	1221	2.2	1926	4.6
4	TH ☽	0110	1.8	0802	4.4	1318	2.3	2020	4.5
5	F	0208	2.0	0857	4.4	1434	2.4	2121	4.4
6	SA	0320	2.1	0957	4.4	1556	2.4	2226	4.4
7	SU	0434	2.0	1059	4.5	1704	2.2	2330	4.6
8	M	0535	1.9	1159	4.7	1800	1.9		
9	TU	0030	4.8	0628	1.7	1253	4.9	1852	1.6
10	W	0123	5.1	0717	1.5	1341	5.2	1942	1.3
11	TH ●	0211	5.3	0804	1.3	1425	5.4	2033	1.0
12	F	0256	5.5	0853	1.1	1507	5.6	2124	0.7
13	SA	0341	5.7	0940	1.0	1550	5.7	2213	0.5
14	SU	0426	5.7	1026	1.0	1634	5.7	2301	0.5
15	M	0513	5.6	1111	1.1	1721	5.7	2347	0.6
16	TU	0602	5.4	1153	1.3	1810	5.5		
17	W	0032	0.8	0654	5.2	1236	1.5	1904	5.3
18	TH ☾	0118	1.2	0751	4.9	1325	1.7	2006	5.1
19	F	0212	1.5	0854	4.7	1429	2.0	2116	4.9
20	SA	0324	1.8	0958	4.6	1550	2.0	2226	4.7
21	SU	0448	1.9	1106	4.6	1710	2.0	2338	4.7
22	M	0600	1.9	1213	4.7	1823	1.7		
23	TU	0045	4.8	0656	1.8	1311	4.9	1923	1.5
24	W	0140	5.0	0740	1.7	1359	5.1	2011	1.3
25	TH O	0225	5.1	0815	1.6	1440	5.2	2050	1.1
26	F	0304	5.2	0845	1.5	1517	5.3	2123	1.0
27	SA	0338	5.2	0914	1.4	1551	5.3	2152	1.0
28	SU	0411	5.2	0942	1.3	1622	5.3	2218	1.0
29	M	0443	5.1	1010	1.3	1654	5.2	2245	1.0
30	TU	0517	5.0	1038	1.4	1727	5.1	2313	1.2
31	W	0552	4.9	1105	1.6	1801	5.0	2342	1.4

FEBRUARY

Date	Day	Time	m	Time	m	Time	m	Time	m
1	TH	0630	4.7	1132	1.8	1838	4.8		
2	F ☽	0013	1.6	0712	4.6	1204	2.0	1921	4.6
3	SA	0053	1.8	0800	4.4	1254	2.2	2016	4.4
4	SU	0153	2.1	0900	4.3	1420	2.4	2130	4.3
5	M	0326	2.2	1011	4.3	1618	2.3	2251	4.4
6	TU	0507	2.1	1124	4.5	1740	2.0		
7	W	0006	4.6	0614	1.9	1230	4.7	1842	1.6
8	TH	0108	5.0	0708	1.6	1324	5.1	1937	1.2
9	F ●	0158	5.3	0757	1.2	1410	5.4	2029	0.7
10	SA	0242	5.6	0843	0.9	1452	5.7	2117	0.4
11	SU	0325	5.8	0928	0.7	1534	5.9	2202	0.1
12	M	0408	5.9	1011	0.6	1617	6.0	2245	0.1
13	TU	0452	5.8	1051	0.7	1701	5.9	2326	0.3
14	W	0537	5.5	1127	0.9	1747	5.7		
15	TH	0003	0.7	0625	5.2	1201	1.2	1838	5.4
16	F ☾	0036	1.2	0716	4.9	1240	1.5	1936	5.0
17	SA	0115	1.7	0815	4.6	1339	1.9	2046	4.7
18	SU	0223	2.1	0923	4.4	1521	2.2	2202	4.4
19	M	0427	2.3	1039	4.3	1712	2.1	2328	4.4
20	TU	0600	2.2	1202	4.5	1833	1.8		
21	W	0044	4.6	0656	2.0	1305	4.8	1926	1.5
22	TH	0136	4.8	0733	1.8	1351	5.0	2005	1.2
23	F	0216	5.0	0802	1.6	1428	5.2	2037	1.0
24	SA O	0249	5.1	0829	1.4	1500	5.3	2104	0.9
25	SU	0318	5.2	0856	1.2	1530	5.3	2130	0.8
26	M	0346	5.2	0924	1.1	1558	5.3	2155	0.8
27	TU	0415	5.2	0951	1.1	1627	5.3	2220	0.9
28	W	0446	5.1	1014	1.2	1657	5.2	2243	1.0
29	TH	0518	5.0	1032	1.3	1728	5.1	2301	1.2

MARCH

Date	Day	Time	m	Time	m	Time	m	Time	m
1	F	0552	4.9	1051	1.5	1803	4.9	2322	1.4
2	SA	0630	4.7	1120	1.7	1843	4.7	2353	1.7
3	SU ☽	0714	4.5	1202	1.9	1935	4.4		
4	M	0044	2.1	0810	4.3	1312	2.2	2048	4.3
5	TU	0233	2.4	0927	4.2	1543	2.3	2221	4.3
6	W	0451	2.3	1053	4.3	1729	1.9	2346	4.6
7	TH	0601	1.9	1208	4.7	1833	1.4		
8	F	0050	5.0	0654	1.5	1303	5.1	1927	0.9
9	SA	0139	5.4	0740	1.1	1348	5.5	2015	0.5
10	SU ●	0222	5.7	0824	0.7	1430	5.8	2100	0.1
11	M	0303	5.9	0907	0.5	1511	6.1	2142	-0.1
12	TU	0344	5.9	0948	0.4	1554	6.1	2223	0.0
13	W	0427	5.8	1027	0.5	1639	6.0	2300	0.3
14	TH	0510	5.5	1102	0.7	1725	5.7	2332	0.8
15	F	0555	5.2	1133	1.1	1815	5.3	2358	1.3
16	SA	0644	4.9	1209	1.5	1912	4.9		
17	SU ☾	0031	1.9	0742	4.5	1307	1.9	2021	4.5
18	M	0136	2.4	0851	4.3	1512	2.2	2139	4.2
19	TU	0413	2.6	1011	4.2	1712	2.0	2312	4.2
20	W	0545	2.4	1141	4.4	1820	1.7		
21	TH	0030	4.5	0635	2.1	1244	4.7	1906	1.5
22	F	0118	4.8	0708	1.8	1328	4.9	1940	1.2
23	SA	0153	4.9	0735	1.5	1403	5.1	2008	1.0
24	SU	0223	5.1	0802	1.3	1434	5.2	2034	0.9
25	M O	0249	5.2	0831	1.1	1502	5.3	2100	0.8
26	TU	0316	5.2	0900	1.0	1531	5.3	2126	0.8
27	W	0345	5.2	0927	1.0	1600	5.3	2151	0.8
28	TH	0415	5.2	0949	1.0	1630	5.2	2211	1.0
29	F	0447	5.1	1004	1.2	1703	5.1	2224	1.2
30	SA	0521	4.9	1024	1.3	1739	4.9	2245	1.4
31	SU	0558	4.8	1055	1.5	1823	4.7	2318	1.8

APRIL

Date	Day	Time	m	Time	m	Time	m	Time	m
1	M	0642	4.5	1140	1.8	1916	4.5		
2	TU ☽	0012	2.1	0739	4.3	1300	2.1	2029	4.3
3	W	0232	2.4	0857	4.2	1535	2.1	2200	4.3
4	TH	0431	2.2	1027	4.4	1712	1.7	2323	4.6
5	F	0536	1.8	1140	4.7	1813	1.2		
6	SA	0025	5.0	0627	1.4	1235	5.2	1905	0.7
7	SU	0114	5.4	0713	1.0	1321	5.6	1951	0.4
8	M ●	0156	5.7	0757	0.7	1404	5.9	2035	0.1
9	TU	0237	5.8	0841	0.4	1447	6.0	2117	0.1
10	W	0319	5.8	0924	0.4	1532	6.0	2157	0.2
11	TH	0401	5.7	1005	0.5	1619	5.9	2233	0.6
12	F	0445	5.5	1042	0.7	1707	5.6	2304	1.1
13	SA	0530	5.2	1116	1.1	1757	5.2	2327	1.6
14	SU	0618	4.8	1153	1.5	1854	4.8		
15	M ☾	0001	2.0	0715	4.5	1250	1.8	1958	4.4
16	TU	0106	2.5	0823	4.3	1502	2.1	2109	4.2
17	W	0332	2.6	0938	4.2	1639	1.9	2232	4.2
18	TH	0454	2.4	1059	4.3	1740	1.7	2352	4.4
19	F	0544	2.1	1204	4.5	1824	1.5		
20	SA	0041	4.6	0622	1.9	1250	4.8	1859	1.3
21	SU	0117	4.8	0655	1.6	1327	5.0	1928	1.1
22	M	0147	5.0	0727	1.3	1359	5.1	1956	1.0
23	TU O	0215	5.1	0800	1.1	1430	5.2	2025	0.9
24	W	0244	5.2	0832	1.0	1502	5.2	2054	0.9
25	TH	0315	5.2	0902	1.0	1534	5.2	2121	0.9
26	F	0347	5.2	0928	1.0	1607	5.2	2144	1.1
27	SA	0420	5.1	0950	1.1	1644	5.1	2204	1.3
28	SU	0456	5.0	1016	1.3	1725	5.0	2231	1.5
29	M	0537	4.8	1053	1.4	1812	4.8	2313	1.9
30	TU	0624	4.7	1154	1.7	1908	4.6		

MAY

Date	Day	Time	m	Time	m	Time	m	Time	m
1	W ☽	0036	2.2	0723	4.5	1331	1.8	2019	4.5
2	TH	0229	2.3	0838	4.4	1520	1.7	2140	4.5
3	F	0358	2.1	1000	4.6	1641	1.4	2254	4.8
4	SA	0500	1.8	1109	4.9	1741	1.1	2355	5.1
5	SU	0552	1.4	1205	5.2	1833	0.8		
6	M	0044	5.3	0640	1.1	1253	5.5	1922	0.5
7	TU	0129	5.5	0728	0.8	1340	5.7	2007	0.4
8	W ●	0212	5.6	0816	0.6	1427	5.8	2051	0.4
9	TH	0255	5.6	0903	0.5	1514	5.8	2132	0.6
10	F	0339	5.5	0947	0.6	1603	5.6	2209	1.0
11	SA	0424	5.3	1029	0.8	1652	5.3	2240	1.3
12	SU	0510	5.1	1107	1.1	1742	5.0	2306	1.7
13	M	0558	4.9	1145	1.4	1834	4.7	2342	2.0
14	TU	0651	4.6	1235	1.7	1930	4.5		
15	W ☾	0037	2.3	0751	4.4	1402	1.9	2030	4.3
16	TH	0210	2.5	0856	4.3	1539	1.9	2134	4.2
17	F	0345	2.4	1002	4.3	1638	1.8	2241	4.3
18	SA	0442	2.2	1105	4.4	1724	1.6	2340	4.4
19	SU	0528	2.0	1158	4.6	1803	1.5		
20	M	0025	4.6	0610	1.7	1242	4.8	1840	1.3
21	TU	0103	4.8	0649	1.5	1321	4.9	1914	1.2
22	W	0138	5.0	0727	1.3	1358	5.0	1948	1.1
23	TH O	0213	5.1	0803	1.2	1435	5.1	2023	1.1
24	F	0248	5.2	0839	1.1	1512	5.2	2057	1.1
25	SA	0324	5.2	0916	1.0	1550	5.2	2133	1.2
26	SU	0400	5.2	0955	1.1	1631	5.2	2211	1.4
27	M	0440	5.1	1038	1.1	1715	5.1	2255	1.5
28	TU	0524	5.0	1128	1.2	1804	5.0	2350	1.8
29	W	0613	4.9	1227	1.3	1900	4.8		
30	TH ☽	0054	1.9	0711	4.8	1334	1.4	2005	4.7
31	F	0206	2.0	0819	4.8	1451	1.4	2115	4.7

JUNE

Date	Day	Time	m	Time	m	Time	m	Time	m
1	SA	0318	1.9	0931	4.8	1603	1.3	2222	4.8
2	SU	0421	1.7	1037	5.0	1704	1.1	2322	5.0
3	M	0517	1.5	1136	5.2	1800	1.0		
4	TU	0015	5.1	0611	1.2	1230	5.3	1853	0.9
5	W	0105	5.3	0704	1.0	1322	5.4	1942	0.9
6	TH ●	0151	5.4	0758	0.8	1413	5.5	2028	0.9
7	F	0237	5.4	0849	0.8	1503	5.5	2110	1.1
8	SA	0323	5.4	0936	0.8	1551	5.4	2149	1.2
9	SU	0408	5.3	1019	0.9	1638	5.2	2221	1.5
10	M	0453	5.1	1057	1.1	1724	5.0	2248	1.7
11	TU	0537	5.0	1132	1.3	1809	4.8	2322	1.9
12	W	0624	4.8	1209	1.5	1856	4.6		
13	TH	0005	2.0	0713	4.6	1256	1.7	1945	4.4
14	F ☾	0101	2.2	0806	4.5	1356	1.8	2036	4.3
15	SA	0214	2.3	0902	4.4	1508	1.9	2131	4.3
16	SU	0330	2.3	0959	4.4	1612	1.8	2227	4.4
17	M	0433	2.1	1057	4.5	1705	1.7	2323	4.5
18	TU	0526	1.9	1152	4.6	1752	1.6		
19	W	0015	4.7	0613	1.7	1243	4.7	1836	1.5
20	TH	0102	4.9	0657	1.5	1330	4.9	1918	1.4
21	F	0146	5.0	0740	1.3	1414	5.1	2000	1.3
22	SA O	0227	5.2	0824	1.1	1455	5.2	2043	1.2
23	SU	0306	5.3	0910	0.9	1537	5.3	2128	1.2
24	M	0346	5.3	0957	0.8	1620	5.4	2214	1.2
25	TU	0428	5.3	1045	0.8	1705	5.3	2301	1.3
26	W	0513	5.3	1134	0.8	1754	5.2	2349	1.4
27	TH	0601	5.3	1224	0.9	1846	5.1		
28	F ☽	0038	1.6	0654	5.2	1316	1.0	1943	5.0
29	SA	0132	1.7	0754	5.1	1414	1.2	2045	4.8
30	SU	0234	1.8	0901	5.0	1519	1.4	2149	4.8

SUNRISE AND SUNSET TIMES
Leith
At 55°59′N 3°11′W

UT		Sunrise	Sunset
Jan	01	0844	1549
	15	0834	1611
Feb	01	0807	1646
	15	0738	1717
Mar	01	0704	1747
	15	0628	1816
BST (UT+1)			
Apr	01	0643	1951
	15	0607	2020
May	01	0529	2052
	15	0500	2119
Jun	01	0435	2147
	15	0426	2201
Jul	01	0431	2201
	15	0448	2149
Aug	01	0517	2120
	15	0544	2049
Sep	01	0617	2007
	15	0644	1930
Oct	01	0716	1848
	15	0744	1812
UT			
Nov	01	0720	1632
	15	0749	1605
Dec	01	0820	1544
	15	0838	1538

LEITH
LAT 55°59′N
LONG 3°11′W

TIMES AND HEIGHTS OF HIGH AND LOW WATER (Heights in Metres)

TIME ZONE UT
For Summer Time (area enclosed in shaded box) add 1 hour

2024

JULY

Day	Time	m	Day	Time	m
1 M	0341 1009 1628 2252	1.8 4.9 1.4 4.8	16 TU	0325 1001 1604 2230	2.3 4.3 2.0 4.4
2 TU	0448 1114 1734 2352	1.7 4.9 1.5 4.9	17 W	0442 1106 1713 2333	2.2 4.4 1.9 4.5
3 W	0552 1217 1833	1.5 5.0 1.4	18 TH	0544 1211 1809	2.0 4.6 1.8
4 TH	0049 0654 1315 1926	5.0 1.3 5.1 1.4	19 F	0032 0637 1307 1859	4.7 1.7 4.8 1.6
5 F ●	0140 0752 1408 2013	5.2 1.1 5.2 1.3	20 SA	0124 0726 1356 1946	5.0 1.4 5.1 1.4
6 SA	0228 0843 1456 2054	5.3 0.9 5.3 1.3	21 SU ○	0209 0815 1441 2032	5.2 1.0 5.3 1.2
7 SU	0312 0928 1540 2130	5.3 0.9 5.3 1.3	22 M	0251 0904 1523 2119	5.4 0.7 5.5 1.0
8 M	0354 1007 1621 2200	5.3 0.9 5.2 1.4	23 TU	0331 0952 1606 2204	5.6 0.5 5.6 0.9
9 TU	0434 1040 1700 2228	5.2 0.9 5.1 1.5	24 W	0413 1038 1650 2248	5.7 0.4 5.6 0.9
10 W	0513 1108 1738 2257	5.1 1.1 4.9 1.6	25 TH	0457 1122 1735 2330	5.7 0.4 5.5 1.0
11 TH	0551 1137 1817 2331	5.0 1.2 4.8 1.7	26 F	0542 1205 1823	5.6 0.6 5.3
12 F	0630 1212 1858	4.9 1.4 4.6	27 SA	0010 0632 1247 1915	1.2 5.5 0.9 5.1
13 SA ☾	0010 0714 1252 1943	1.9 4.7 1.6 4.5	28 SU ☽	0054 0727 1332 2013	1.5 5.2 1.3 4.8
14 SU	0059 0802 1343 2034	2.1 4.5 1.8 4.4	29 M	0150 0832 1433 2118	1.7 4.9 1.6 4.7
15 M	0204 0858 1446 2130	2.3 4.4 2.0 4.3	30 TU	0306 0945 1559 2226	1.9 4.7 1.9 4.6
			31 W	0434 1101 1723 2337	1.9 4.7 1.9 4.7

AUGUST

Day	Time	m	Day	Time	m
1 TH	0553 1215 1830	1.7 4.8 1.8	16 F	0525 1143 1754	2.1 4.5 2.0
2 F	0043 0702 1317 1922	4.9 1.4 4.9 1.7	17 SA	0006 0625 1248 1846	4.7 1.7 4.8 1.7
3 SA	0137 0755 1407 2003	5.1 1.2 5.1 1.5	18 SU	0103 0717 1339 1933	5.0 1.2 5.2 1.3
4 SU ●	0222 0839 1448 2038	5.2 1.0 5.2 1.4	19 M ○	0149 0805 1422 2018	5.3 0.8 5.5 1.0
5 M	0301 0915 1525 2109	5.3 0.8 5.2 1.3	20 TU	0230 0852 1504 2102	5.6 0.4 5.8 0.8
6 TU	0337 0947 1558 2136	5.4 0.8 5.2 1.2	21 W	0310 0936 1545 2145	5.9 0.2 5.9 0.6
7 W	0410 1014 1631 2203	5.4 0.8 5.2 1.2	22 TH	0351 1019 1627 2226	6.0 0.1 5.8 0.6
8 TH	0443 1038 1704 2229	5.3 0.9 5.1 1.3	23 F	0434 1100 1710 2305	6.0 0.2 5.7 0.8
9 F	0515 1103 1739 2255	5.2 1.0 4.9 1.5	24 SA	0519 1138 1756 2341	5.9 0.5 5.4 1.1
10 SA	0550 1130 1815 2322	5.0 1.2 4.8 1.7	25 SU	0608 1214 1845	5.6 1.0 5.1
11 SU	0627 1159 1855 2353	4.8 1.5 4.6 1.9	26 M ☽	0019 0703 1251 1942	1.4 5.2 1.5 4.8
12 M ☾	0709 1236 1941	4.6 1.8 4.5	27 TU	0113 0810 1350 2050	1.8 4.8 2.0 4.5
13 TU	0038 0801 1331 2038	2.2 4.4 2.1 4.3	28 W	0247 0929 1547 2205	2.1 4.5 2.3 4.4
14 W	0202 0910 1501 2145	2.4 4.3 2.3 4.3	29 TH	0443 1054 1728 2328	2.0 4.5 2.3 4.6
15 TH	0400 1027 1646 2257	2.4 4.3 2.2 4.4	30 F	0608 1217 1832	1.7 4.7 2.1
			31 SA	0037 0705 1315 1915	4.8 1.4 4.9 1.8

SEPTEMBER

Day	Time	m	Day	Time	m
1 SU	0127 0748 1357 1947	5.1 1.2 5.1 1.6	16 M	0038 0701 1316 1912	5.1 1.1 5.4 1.3
2 M	0207 0822 1432 2014	5.3 1.0 5.2 1.4	17 TU	0123 0747 1358 1954	5.5 0.6 5.7 0.9
3 TU ●	0241 0851 1502 2041	5.4 0.8 5.3 1.2	18 W ○	0204 0830 1438 2037	5.8 0.2 5.9 0.6
4 W	0312 0917 1530 2109	5.4 0.8 5.3 1.1	19 TH	0244 0913 1518 2119	6.1 0.0 6.0 0.5
5 TH	0341 0941 1559 2136	5.4 0.8 5.3 1.1	20 F	0326 0955 1600 2200	6.2 0.0 5.9 0.5
6 F	0411 1005 1630 2200	5.4 0.8 5.2 1.2	21 SA	0411 1034 1643 2239	6.1 0.3 5.7 0.7
7 SA	0442 1027 1702 2219	5.3 1.0 5.1 1.3	22 SU	0457 1110 1728 2315	5.9 0.7 5.4 1.0
8 SU	0514 1046 1736 2239	5.1 1.2 4.9 1.5	23 M	0547 1140 1817 2354	5.5 1.3 5.1 1.4
9 M	0549 1106 1813 2306	4.9 1.5 4.8 1.7	24 TU ☽	0644 1214 1915	5.1 1.9 4.7
10 TU	0630 1134 1857 2344	4.7 1.8 4.6 2.0	25 W	0053 0754 1318 2026	1.9 4.7 2.4 4.5
11 W ☾	0721 1220 1951	4.4 2.2 4.4	26 TH	0252 0914 1544 2146	2.1 4.4 2.6 4.4
12 TH	0052 0830 1412 2103	2.3 4.3 2.5 4.3	27 F	0448 1043 1717 2310	2.0 4.4 2.4 4.5
13 F	0326 0955 1628 2226	2.4 4.3 2.4 4.4	28 SA	0556 1205 1811	1.7 4.6 2.2
14 SA	0512 1119 1738 2340	2.0 4.5 2.1 4.7	29 SU	0017 0646 1256 1848	4.8 1.4 4.9 1.9
15 SU	0612 1226 1828	1.6 4.9 1.7	30 M	0104 0722 1334 1916	5.1 1.2 5.1 1.6

OCTOBER

Day	Time	m	Day	Time	m
1 TU	0141 0751 1405 1943	5.3 1.0 5.2 1.4	16 W	0053 0719 1329 1925	5.6 0.6 5.7 0.9
2 W ●	0213 0816 1432 2011	5.4 0.9 5.3 1.2	17 TH ○	0136 0803 1410 2009	5.9 0.3 5.9 0.6
3 TH	0243 0841 1459 2041	5.4 0.8 5.3 1.1	18 F	0219 0846 1451 2054	6.1 0.2 5.9 0.5
4 F	0312 0907 1527 2109	5.4 0.8 5.3 1.1	19 SA	0304 0928 1534 2138	6.2 0.3 5.9 0.5
5 SA	0341 0931 1557 2132	5.4 0.9 5.3 1.2	20 SU	0351 1008 1618 2220	6.0 0.6 5.7 0.8
6 SU	0413 0951 1629 2150	5.3 1.1 5.2 1.3	21 M	0440 1043 1704 2301	5.8 1.1 5.4 1.1
7 M	0446 1007 1702 2210	5.1 1.3 5.0 1.5	22 TU	0532 1112 1754 2344	5.4 1.6 5.1 1.5
8 TU	0523 1027 1739 2238	4.9 1.6 4.9 1.7	23 W	0630 1146 1853	5.0 2.1 4.8
9 W	0606 1057 1822 2320	4.7 1.9 4.7 1.9	24 TH ☽	0045 0737 1251 2004	1.8 4.6 2.5 4.5
10 TH ☾	0658 1143 1917	4.5 2.3 4.5	25 F	0244 0850 1507 2119	2.1 4.4 2.7 4.4
11 F	0037 0806 1355 2030	2.2 4.4 2.6 4.3	26 SA	0418 1010 1631 2234	1.9 4.4 2.5 4.5
12 SA	0303 0929 1601 2155	2.2 4.4 2.4 4.5	27 SU	0520 1127 1724 2339	1.7 4.5 2.3 4.7
13 SU	0447 1051 1709 2309	1.9 4.6 2.1 4.8	28 M	0607 1220 1803	1.6 4.8 2.0
14 M	0545 1156 1758	1.4 5.0 1.6	29 TU	0028 0642 1259 1836	5.0 1.4 4.9 1.7
15 TU	0006 0634 1246 1842	5.2 0.9 5.4 1.2	30 W	0107 0710 1330 1908	5.1 1.2 5.1 1.5
			31 TH	0141 0737 1358 1941	5.2 1.1 5.2 1.3

NOVEMBER

Day	Time	m	Day	Time	m
1 F ●	0212 0804 1427 2013	5.3 1.0 5.3 1.2	16 SA	0159 0821 1428 2035	5.9 0.6 5.8 0.7
2 SA	0244 0832 1457 2044	5.3 1.0 5.3 1.2	17 SU	0247 0905 1513 2123	5.9 0.8 5.7 0.7
3 SU	0316 0859 1528 2111	5.3 1.1 5.3 1.2	18 M	0337 0946 1559 2210	5.8 1.0 5.6 0.8
4 M	0350 0924 1601 2136	5.2 1.3 5.2 1.3	19 TU	0427 1024 1646 2254	5.6 1.4 5.4 1.1
5 TU	0426 0947 1636 2203	5.1 1.5 5.1 1.4	20 W	0519 1055 1736 2339	5.3 1.7 5.1 1.4
6 W	0506 1012 1715 2237	5.0 1.7 5.0 1.6	21 TH	0614 1128 1832	5.0 2.1 4.9
7 TH	0551 1048 1800 2330	4.8 2.0 4.8 1.8	22 F	0031 0712 1218 1934	1.7 4.7 2.4 4.7
8 F	0644 1150 1854	4.7 2.3 4.6	23 SA ☽	0150 0813 1340 2039	1.9 4.5 2.6 4.6
9 SA ☾	0055 0748 1343 2003	2.0 4.6 2.4 4.6	24 SU	0316 0917 1516 2143	2.0 4.4 2.6 4.5
10 SU	0235 0904 1519 2122	1.9 4.6 2.3 4.6	25 M	0418 1022 1619 2244	1.9 4.4 2.4 4.6
11 M	0406 1018 1628 2234	1.7 4.8 2.0 4.9	26 TU	0508 1121 1709 2339	1.8 4.5 2.2 4.7
12 TU	0508 1122 1721 2333	1.3 5.1 1.7 5.2	27 W	0548 1209 1753	1.7 4.7 2.0
13 W	0600 1215 1809	1.0 5.4 1.3	28 TH	0025 0624 1248 1834	4.9 1.5 4.9 1.7
14 TH	0023 0648 1301 1857	5.6 0.8 5.6 1.0	29 F	0106 0658 1323 1912	5.0 1.4 5.1 1.5
15 F ○	0111 0735 1345 1945	5.8 0.6 5.7 0.8	30 SA	0144 0731 1358 1948	5.1 1.3 5.2 1.4

DECEMBER

Day	Time	m	Day	Time	m
1 SU ●	0221 0804 1432 2024	5.2 1.3 5.3 1.3	16 M	0239 0849 1500 2117	5.6 1.1 5.6 0.8
2 M	0257 0838 1507 2059	5.2 1.3 5.3 1.2	17 TU	0329 0932 1546 2204	5.6 1.3 5.5 0.9
3 TU	0334 0912 1542 2136	5.2 1.4 5.3 1.2	18 W	0417 1010 1632 2248	5.4 1.4 5.4 1.0
4 W	0413 0948 1619 2217	5.2 1.5 5.2 1.3	19 TH	0504 1040 1719 2326	5.2 1.7 5.2 1.2
5 TH	0454 1027 1659 2301	5.1 1.6 5.1 1.4	20 F	0551 1108 1805	5.0 1.8 5.1
6 F	0540 1113 1745 2352	5.0 1.8 5.0 1.5	21 SA	0000 0638 1143 1854	1.4 4.8 2.0 4.9
7 SA	0630 1209 1836	4.9 2.0 4.9	22 SU ☽	0038 0726 1231 1946	1.6 4.6 2.2 4.7
8 SU ☾	0051 0728 1316 1936	1.5 4.8 2.1 4.9	23 M	0127 0816 1333 2042	1.9 4.4 2.4 4.5
9 M	0200 0834 1430 2046	1.6 4.8 2.1 4.9	24 TU	0232 0910 1453 2139	2.0 4.3 2.5 4.5
10 TU	0315 0942 1540 2157	1.5 4.8 2.0 5.0	25 W	0344 1006 1608 2238	2.1 4.3 2.4 4.5
11 W	0424 1046 1642 2301	1.4 4.9 1.8 5.1	26 TH	0447 1104 1710 2337	2.0 4.5 2.2 4.5
12 TH	0525 1144 1739	1.3 5.1 1.5	27 F	0539 1200 1802	1.9 4.6 2.0
13 F	0000 0620 1237 1835	5.3 1.2 5.3 1.3	28 SA	0031 0625 1249 1848	4.7 1.8 4.8 1.8
14 SA	0054 0713 1326 1931	5.5 1.1 5.4 1.1	29 SU	0119 0706 1334 1930	4.9 1.6 5.0 1.6
15 SU ○	0147 0803 1413 2026	5.6 1.1 5.5 0.9	30 M ●	0202 0745 1414 2010	5.0 1.5 5.2 1.3
			31 TU	0243 0825 1452 2052	5.2 1.4 5.3 1.1

ABERDEEN
LAT 57°09′N
LONG 2°05′W

TIMES AND HEIGHTS OF HIGH AND LOW WATER (Heights in Metres)

TIME ZONE UT
For Summer Time (area enclosed in shaded box) add 1 hour

2024

JANUARY

Day	Time	m
1 M	0436 1009 1632 2252	3.7 1.6 3.9 1.3
2 TU	0518 1048 1715 2335	3.6 1.7 3.8 1.4
3 W	0604 1133 1805	3.5 1.8 3.7
4 TH ☽	0025 0656 1228 1901	1.5 3.4 2.0 3.6
5 F	0121 0752 1336 2002	1.6 3.4 2.0 3.5
6 SA	0222 0854 1447 2108	1.7 3.4 2.0 3.5
7 SU	0325 0957 1556 2215	1.6 3.5 1.9 3.6
8 M	0425 1052 1655 2314	1.6 3.7 1.7 3.7
9 TU	0518 1140 1746	1.4 3.9 1.4
10 W	0006 0607 1224 1834	3.9 1.3 4.0 1.1
11 TH ●	0054 0652 1306 1920	4.1 1.1 4.2 0.9
12 F	0141 0737 1348 2006	4.2 1.0 4.4 0.7
13 SA	0227 0822 1431 2053	4.3 1.0 4.5 0.5
14 SU	0315 0906 1515 2140	4.3 1.0 4.5 0.5
15 M	0403 0951 1602 2229	4.2 1.1 4.4 0.6
16 TU	0453 1037 1651 2319	4.1 1.2 4.3 0.7
17 W	0545 1127 1745	3.9 1.4 4.2
18 TH ☾	0013 0642 1224 1846	1.0 3.7 1.5 4.0
19 F	0111 0743 1330 1954	1.2 3.6 1.7 3.8
20 SA	0218 0852 1446 2112	1.4 3.5 1.7 3.7
21 SU	0336 1003 1610 2230	1.6 3.6 1.6 3.7
22 M	0447 1106 1716 2336	1.6 3.7 1.5 3.7
23 TU	0541 1158 1809	1.5 3.9 1.3
24 W	0028 0625 1241 1853	3.8 1.5 4.0 1.1
25 TH ○	0112 0703 1319 1932	3.9 1.4 4.1 1.0
26 F	0150 0738 1354 2007	4.0 1.3 4.2 0.9
27 SA	0225 0810 1426 2041	4.0 1.3 4.2 0.9
28 SU	0257 0840 1458 2112	3.9 1.2 4.2 0.9
29 M	0329 0910 1529 2144	3.9 1.2 4.1 0.9
30 TU	0401 0940 1601 2216	3.8 1.3 4.1 1.0
31 W	0435 1012 1636 [illegible]	3.7 1.4 3.9 [illegible]

FEBRUARY

Day	Time	m
1 TH	0512 1047 1715 2328	3.6 1.5 3.8 1.4
2 F ☽	0555 1128 1801	3.5 1.7 3.6
3 SA	0014 0648 1222 1901	1.5 3.4 1.9 3.5
4 SU	0114 0751 1338 2014	1.7 3.3 2.0 3.4
5 M	0229 0902 1507 2136	1.8 3.3 1.9 3.4
6 TU	0351 1016 1630 2254	1.8 3.5 1.7 3.6
7 W	0500 1117 1732 2354	1.6 3.7 1.4 3.8
8 TH	0554 1208 1822	1.3 3.9 1.0
9 F ●	0044 0641 1252 1909	4.1 1.1 4.2 0.6
10 SA	0130 0725 1334 1954	4.3 0.9 4.4 0.4
11 SU	0214 0808 1416 2039	4.4 0.8 4.6 0.2
12 M	0257 0849 1458 2122	4.4 0.7 4.7 0.2
13 TU	0341 0930 1542 2206	4.3 0.8 4.6 0.3
14 W	0425 1011 1628 2250	4.2 0.9 4.5 0.6
15 TH	0512 1056 1718 2337	3.9 1.1 4.2 1.0
16 F ☾	0603 1148 1816	3.7 1.3 3.9
17 SA	0031 0703 1253 1927	1.4 3.5 1.6 3.6
18 SU	0138 0814 1419 2054	1.7 3.4 1.7 3.4
19 M	0314 0938 1604 2227	1.9 3.4 1.7 3.4
20 TU	0439 1052 1712 2336	1.8 3.5 1.5 3.6
21 W	0533 1147 1801	1.7 3.7 1.2
22 TH	0023 0615 1229 1841	3.7 1.5 3.9 1.0
23 F	0101 0649 1305 1915	3.8 1.3 4.0 0.9
24 SA ○	0133 0720 1336 1947	3.9 1.2 4.1 0.8
25 SU	0203 0749 1405 2016	4.0 1.1 4.2 0.7
26 M	0231 0817 1433 2044	4.0 1.0 4.2 0.7
27 TU	0258 0844 1502 2112	4.0 1.0 4.2 0.8
28 W	0327 0912 1532 2141	3.9 1.1 4.1 0.9
29 TH	0357 0940 1604 2210	3.8 1.1 4.0 1.1

MARCH

Day	Time	m
1 F	0429 1011 1639 2243	3.7 1.3 3.8 1.3
2 SA	0506 1047 1721 2323	3.6 1.4 3.6 1.5
3 SU ☽	0553 1136 1819	3.4 1.6 3.4
4 M	0020 0658 1250 1940	1.7 3.3 1.8 3.3
5 TU	0147 0819 1434 2113	1.9 3.2 1.8 3.3
6 W	0329 0944 1612 2240	1.8 3.3 1.6 3.5
7 TH	0446 1055 1716 2341	1.6 3.6 1.2 3.8
8 F	0539 1148 1806	1.3 3.9 0.8
9 SA	0029 0625 1232 1851	4.1 1.0 4.2 0.4
10 SU ●	0111 0706 1313 1934	4.3 0.7 4.5 0.1
11 M	0152 0746 1354 2016	4.5 0.6 4.7 0.0
12 TU	0233 0826 1436 2057	4.5 0.5 4.7 0.1
13 W	0313 0905 1519 2138	4.4 0.5 4.6 0.3
14 TH	0354 0946 1605 2219	4.2 0.7 4.4 0.7
15 F	0437 1029 1655 2302	3.9 0.9 4.1 1.1
16 SA	0526 1121 1755 2354	3.7 1.2 3.7 1.5
17 SU ☾	0625 1227 1908	3.4 1.5 3.4
18 M	0104 0739 1400 2040	1.9 3.3 1.7 3.2
19 TU	0255 0909 1552 2218	2.1 3.2 1.6 3.3
20 W	0424 1030 1655 2322	1.9 3.4 1.4 3.5
21 TH	0515 1126 1740	1.7 3.6 1.2
22 F	0004 0553 1206 1816	3.6 1.5 3.8 1.0
23 SA	0037 0625 1239 1848	3.8 1.3 3.9 0.8
24 SU	0106 0655 1309 1918	3.9 1.1 4.0 0.7
25 M ○	0133 0723 1338 1946	3.9 1.0 4.1 0.7
26 TU	0200 0750 1406 2013	4.0 0.9 4.1 0.7
27 W	0227 0817 1435 2040	4.0 0.9 4.1 0.7
28 TH	0254 0845 1505 2108	4.0 0.9 4.1 0.9
29 F	0324 0913 1538 2136	3.9 1.0 3.9 1.0
30 SA	0356 0945 1615 2209	3.8 1.1 3.8 1.2
31 SU	0433 1023 1700 [illegible]	3.7 1.3 3.6 1.5

APRIL

Day	Time	m
1 M	0518 1115 1802 2352	3.5 1.5 3.4 1.7
2 TU ☽	0623 1235 1927	3.3 1.6 3.3
3 W	0128 0750 1418 2058	1.9 3.2 1.6 3.3
4 TH	0311 0915 1551 2222	1.8 3.4 1.3 3.6
5 F	0425 1027 1653 2320	1.5 3.6 1.0 3.9
6 SA	0516 1122 1742	1.2 3.9 0.6
7 SU	0005 0601 1206 1827	4.1 0.9 4.3 0.3
8 M ●	0047 0642 1249 1910	4.3 0.7 4.5 0.1
9 TU	0126 0722 1331 1950	4.4 0.5 4.6 0.1
10 W	0205 0802 1414 2030	4.4 0.4 4.6 0.3
11 TH	0244 0843 1459 2110	4.3 0.5 4.5 0.6
12 F	0325 0925 1547 2150	4.1 0.6 4.2 0.9
13 SA	0408 1011 1639 2233	3.9 0.9 3.9 1.3
14 SU	0456 1103 1740 2324	3.7 1.2 3.6 1.7
15 M ☾	0554 1209 1851	3.5 1.4 3.3
16 TU	0034 0706 1335 2013	2.0 3.3 1.6 3.2
17 W	0214 0828 1517 2144	2.1 3.2 1.5 3.2
18 TH	0348 0950 1620 2246	2.0 3.3 1.4 3.4
19 F	0440 1048 1704 2329	1.7 3.5 1.2 3.5
20 SA	0519 1130 1740	1.5 3.7 1.0
21 SU	0002 0553 1205 1813	3.7 1.3 3.8 0.9
22 M	0031 0624 1237 1843	3.8 1.1 3.9 0.8
23 TU ○	0100 0654 1308 1912	3.9 1.0 4.0 0.8
24 W	0128 0723 1339 1941	4.0 0.9 4.0 0.8
25 TH	0156 0752 1410 2010	4.0 0.9 4.0 0.8
26 F	0226 0823 1444 2041	4.0 0.9 4.0 0.9
27 SA	0257 0855 1521 2114	3.9 1.0 3.9 1.1
28 SU	0332 0932 1603 2151	3.9 1.0 3.7 1.3
29 M	0412 1017 1654 2240	3.7 1.2 3.6 1.5
30 TU	0502 1116 1801 2347	3.6 1.3 3.4 1.7

MAY

Day	Time	m
1 W ☾	0608 1235 1919	3.4 1.4 3.4
2 TH	0116 0729 1402 2039	1.8 3.4 1.3 3.4
3 F	0243 0845 1521 2153	1.7 3.5 1.1 3.6
4 SA	0352 0954 1623 2251	1.5 3.7 0.8 3.8
5 SU	0446 1051 1715 2338	1.2 4.0 0.6 4.0
6 M	0533 1140 1801	1.0 4.2 0.4
7 TU	0020 0617 1226 1844	4.2 0.7 4.4 0.4
8 W ●	0100 0700 1311 1926	4.3 0.6 4.4 0.4
9 TH	0140 0743 1357 2007	4.3 0.5 4.4 0.6
10 F	0220 0827 1444 2047	4.2 0.6 4.3 0.9
11 SA	0302 0911 1534 2128	4.1 0.7 4.0 1.1
12 SU	0345 0958 1628 2211	3.9 0.9 3.8 1.4
13 M	0432 1049 1725 2300	3.7 1.1 3.5 1.7
14 TU	0527 1148 1825	3.6 1.3 3.3
15 W ☽	0000 0630 1256 1930	1.9 3.4 1.4 3.2
16 TH	0115 0737 1411 2041	2.0 3.3 1.5 3.2
17 F	0237 0848 1522 2148	2.0 3.3 1.4 3.3
18 SA	0345 0953 1614 2238	1.8 3.4 1.3 3.4
19 SU	0434 1044 1656 2318	1.6 3.5 1.2 3.6
20 M	0513 1126 1732 2353	1.4 3.7 1.1 3.7
21 TU	0549 1203 1806	1.3 3.8 1.0
22 W	0025 0623 1239 1840	3.8 1.1 3.9 0.9
23 TH ○	0057 0657 1314 1913	3.9 1.0 3.9 0.9
24 F	0130 0732 1351 1948	4.0 0.9 4.0 1.0
25 SA	0203 0808 1430 2024	4.0 0.9 3.9 1.0
26 SU	0239 0848 1512 2104	4.0 0.9 3.9 1.1
27 M	0318 0932 1559 2148	3.9 0.9 3.8 1.3
28 TU	0402 1021 1654 2240	3.9 1.0 3.7 1.4
29 W	0454 1120 1757 2342	3.8 1.0 3.6 1.6
30 TH ☾	0557 1227 1903	3.7 1.1 3.5
31 F	0054 0705 1338 2011	1.6 3.6 1.1 3.6

JUNE

Day	Time	m
1 SA	0206 0813 1446 2118	1.6 3.7 1.0 3.6
2 SU	0312 0920 1549 2219	1.5 3.8 0.9 3.8
3 M	0413 1023 1646 2310	1.3 3.9 0.8 3.9
4 TU	0507 1119 1737 2356	1.1 4.1 0.8 4.0
5 W	0558 1210 1823	0.9 4.1 0.8
6 TH ●	0039 0646 1259 1908	4.1 0.8 4.2 0.8
7 F	0121 0732 1348 1950	4.1 0.7 4.1 1.0
8 SA	0203 0817 1436 2031	4.1 0.7 4.1 1.1
9 SU	0245 0902 1525 2111	4.1 0.7 3.9 1.3
10 M	0328 0946 1613 2151	4.0 0.8 3.8 1.4
11 TU	0412 1031 1701 2234	3.9 1.0 3.6 1.6
12 W	0458 1119 1749 2321	3.7 1.1 3.4 1.7
13 TH	0549 1210 1840	3.6 1.3 3.3
14 F ☽	0016 0644 1306 1935	1.8 3.5 1.4 3.3
15 SA	0120 0741 1405 2034	1.9 3.4 1.4 3.3
16 SU	0226 0843 1504 2134	1.9 3.4 1.4 3.3
17 M	0331 0946 1600 2227	1.8 3.4 1.4 3.5
18 TU	0427 1042 1648 2312	1.6 3.5 1.3 3.6
19 W	0514 1130 1731 2353	1.5 3.6 1.2 3.7
20 TH	0556 1214 1812	1.3 3.7 1.2
21 F	0031 0636 1256 1852	3.9 1.1 3.9 1.1
22 SA ○	0108 0717 1338 1933	4.0 1.0 3.9 1.1
23 SU	0147 0800 1422 2015	4.1 0.8 4.0 1.0
24 M	0226 0844 1507 2058	4.1 0.7 4.0 1.1
25 TU	0308 0930 1555 2143	4.1 0.7 4.0 1.1
26 W	0354 1019 1646 2231	4.1 0.7 3.9 1.2
27 TH	0443 1111 1740 2324	4.0 0.7 3.8 1.3
28 F ☾	0538 1207 1837	4.0 0.8 3.7
29 SA	0023 0638 1307 1938	1.4 3.9 0.9 3.6
30 SU	0127 0742 1410 2042	1.5 3.8 1.0 3.6

SUNRISE AND SUNSET TIMES

ABERDEEN
At 57°09′N 2°05′W

UT		Sunrise	Sunset
Jan	01	0847	1537
	15	0836	1600
Feb	01	0808	1637
	15	0737	1709
Mar	01	0701	1741
	15	0624	1812
BST (UT+1)			
Apr	01	0637	1948
	15	0600	2020
May	01	0520	2053
	15	0449	2122
Jun	01	0422	2151
	15	0412	2206
Jul	01	0418	2206
	15	0435	2152
Aug	01	0506	2121
	15	0535	2049
Sep	01	0610	2005
	15	0639	1927
Oct	01	0712	1843
	15	0742	1805
UT			
Nov	01	0719	1623
	15	0751	1555
Dec	01	0822	1532
	15	0842	1525

ABERDEEN
LAT 57°09'N
LONG 2°05'W

TIMES AND HEIGHTS OF HIGH AND LOW WATER (Heights in Metres)

TIME ZONE UT
For Summer Time (area enclosed in shaded box) add 1 hour

2024

JULY

Date	Day	Time	m	Time	m	Time	m	Time	m
1	M	0234	1.5	0850	3.8	1516	1.1	2147	3.6
2	TU	0345	1.4	1001	3.8	1623	1.2	2247	3.7
3	W	0451	1.3	1107	3.8	1722	1.2	2340	3.9
4	TH	0549	1.1	1205	3.9	1812	1.2		
5	F ●	0027	4.0	0640	0.9	1257	4.0	1857	1.2
6	SA	0111	4.1	0726	0.8	1345	4.0	1939	1.2
7	SU	0152	4.1	0809	0.7	1429	4.0	2017	1.2
8	M	0232	4.1	0849	0.7	1510	3.9	2053	1.2
9	TU	0310	4.1	0928	0.8	1549	3.8	2128	1.3
10	W	0347	4.0	1005	0.9	1628	3.7	2203	1.4
11	TH	0425	3.9	1042	1.0	1707	3.6	2240	1.5
12	F	0505	3.8	1122	1.1	1749	3.5	2320	1.6
13	SA ☽	0550	3.6	1206	1.3	1835	3.4		
14	SU	0009	1.7	0641	3.5	1257	1.5	1928	3.3
15	M	0110	1.9	0739	3.4	1355	1.6	2026	3.3
16	TU	0221	1.9	0844	3.3	1459	1.6	2130	3.4
17	W	0335	1.8	0956	3.4	1605	1.6	2232	3.5
18	TH	0441	1.6	1101	3.5	1703	1.5	2324	3.7
19	F	0534	1.4	1155	3.7	1752	1.3		
20	SA	0009	3.8	0621	1.1	1242	3.9	1837	1.2
21	SU ○	0051	4.0	0705	0.9	1327	4.0	1920	1.0
22	M	0132	4.2	0749	0.6	1411	4.2	2003	0.9
23	TU	0213	4.3	0833	0.5	1455	4.2	2046	0.9
24	W	0255	4.4	0918	0.4	1540	4.2	2128	0.9
25	TH	0338	4.4	1003	0.4	1626	4.1	2211	1.0
26	F	0424	4.4	1050	0.5	1714	4.0	2258	1.1
27	SA	0514	4.2	1139	0.7	1806	3.8	2350	1.3
28	SU ☾	0610	4.0	1234	1.0	1903	3.6		
29	M	0051	1.5	0715	3.8	1335	1.3	2009	3.5
30	TU	0204	1.6	0829	3.7	1450	1.5	2121	3.5
31	W	0330	1.6	0953	3.6	1612	1.6	2232	3.6

AUGUST

Date	Day	Time	m	Time	m	Time	m	Time	m
1	TH	0449	1.4	1109	3.7	1717	1.5	2332	3.[illegible]
2	F	0547	1.2	1209	3.[illegible]	1806	1.4		
3	SA	0021	3.9	0636	1.[illegible]	1256	3.9	1848	1.3
4	SU ●	0102	4.[illegible]	0718	0.8	1337	3.9	1925	1.2
5	M	0139	4.[illegible]	0755	0.7	1413	4.0	1959	1.2
6	TU	0213	4.2	0829	0.7	1446	4.0	2030	1.[illegible]
7	W	0246	4.2	0901	0.7	1518	3.9	2100	1.[illegible]
8	TH	0317	4.[illegible]	0932	0.3	1549	3.3	2130	1.2
9	F	0350	4.[illegible]	1003	0.9	1622	3.7	2201	1.3
10	SA	0424	3.9	1036	1.[illegible]	1658	3.5	2234	1.4
11	SU	0502	3.3	1112	1.3	1739	3.5	2314	1.5
12	M ☽	0547	3.5	1155	1.5	1828	3.4		
13	TU	0004	1.3	0645	3.4	1250	1.7	1928	3.3
14	W	0117	1.3	0756	3.3	1404	1.3	2038	3.3
15	TH	0248	1.3	0918	3.3	1529	1.3	2153	3.4
16	F	0416	1.7	1039	3.4	1643	1.7	2258	3.6
17	SA	0516	1.4	1139	3.7	1736	1.4	2349	3.9
18	SU	0604	1.0	1227	4.0	1821	1.2		
19	M ○	0032	4.1	0649	0.7	1310	4.2	1904	0.9
20	TU	0112	4.4	0732	0.4	1352	4.4	1945	0.8
21	W	0153	4.6	0814	0.2	1433	4.4	2025	0.7
22	TH	0233	4.7	0856	0.2	1515	4.4	2105	0.7
23	F	0316	4.7	0938	0.3	1557	4.3	2146	0.8
24	SA	0400	4.6	1021	0.5	1642	4.1	2229	1.0
25	SU	0449	4.3	1107	0.8	1732	3.9	2320	1.2
26	M ☾	0546	4.0	1200	1.2	1830	3.6		
27	TU	0023	1.5	0656	3.7	1305	1.6	1939	3.5
28	W	0145	1.7	0820	3.5	1433	1.9	2101	3.4
29	TH	0331	1.6	0957	3.5	1611	1.9	2222	3.6
30	F	0448	1.4	1112	3.6	1711	1.7	2323	3.8
31	SA	0541	1.2	1205	3.8	1755	1.5		

SEPTEMBER

Date	Day	Time	m	Time	m	Time	m	Time	m
1	SU	0008	3.9	0623	1.0	1244	3.9	1832	1.4
2	M	0046	4.1	0659	0.8	1318	4.0	1904	1.2
3	TU ●	0118	4.2	0731	0.7	1347	4.0	1934	1.1
4	W	0148	4.3	0801	0.7	1415	4.0	2003	1.0
5	TH	0217	4.3	0829	0.7	1443	4.0	2030	1.0
6	F	0246	4.2	0857	0.8	1511	4.0	2058	1.1
7	SA	0316	4.2	0925	0.9	1541	3.9	2126	1.2
8	SU	0349	4.0	0954	1.1	1613	3.8	2157	1.3
9	M	0425	3.9	1025	1.3	1650	3.7	2233	1.5
10	TU	0507	3.6	1104	1.6	1735	3.5	2320	1.7
11	W ☾	0603	3.4	1157	1.8	1837	3.4		
12	TH	0032	1.9	0723	3.3	1321	2.0	1956	3.3
13	F	0215	1.9	0852	3.3	1504	2.0	2118	3.4
14	SA	0353	1.7	1019	3.5	1624	1.8	2231	3.6
15	SU	0455	1.3	1120	3.8	1716	1.4	2324	3.9
16	M	0543	0.9	1206	4.1	1800	1.1		
17	TU	0007	4.3	0626	0.5	1247	4.3	1841	0.9
18	W ○	0048	4.5	0708	0.3	1327	4.5	1920	0.7
19	TH	0128	4.7	0749	0.1	1406	4.6	2000	0.6
20	F	0209	4.8	0830	0.2	1446	4.5	2039	0.6
21	SA	0252	4.8	0910	0.4	1527	4.4	2121	0.7
22	SU	0338	4.6	0952	0.7	1611	4.1	2205	0.9
23	M	0429	4.3	1037	1.1	1659	3.9	2258	1.2
24	TU ☽	0529	3.9	1129	1.5	1759	3.7		
25	W	0005	1.5	0644	3.6	1239	1.9	1913	3.5
26	TH	0135	1.7	0813	3.4	1421	2.1	2039	3.4
27	F	0325	1.6	0952	3.4	1558	2.0	2203	3.6
28	SA	0433	1.4	1100	3.6	1653	1.8	2302	3.8
29	SU	0521	1.2	1145	3.8	1733	1.6	2345	3.9
30	M	0558	1.0	1220	3.9	1807	1.4		

OCTOBER

Date	Day	Time	m	Time	m	Time	m	Time	m
1	TU	0020	4.1	0631	0.9	1249	4.0	1837	1.2
2	W ●	0050	4.2	0700	0.8	1316	4.1	1906	1.1
3	TH	0119	4.2	0728	0.8	1343	4.1	1934	1.0
4	F	0148	4.3	0756	0.8	1409	4.1	2002	1.0
5	SA	0218	4.2	0823	0.9	1437	4.1	2029	1.1
6	SU	0248	4.2	0850	1.0	1506	4.0	2058	1.2
7	M	0322	4.0	0918	1.2	1538	3.9	2130	1.3
8	TU	0359	3.9	0950	1.4	1614	3.8	2207	1.5
9	W	0443	3.7	1029	1.7	1658	3.6	2257	1.6
10	TH ☾	0542	3.5	1125	1.9	1759	3.5		
11	F	0011	1.8	0704	3.3	1255	2.1	1923	3.4
12	SA	0152	1.8	0830	3.4	1438	2.0	2045	3.5
13	SU	0323	1.5	0953	3.6	1555	1.8	2157	3.7
14	M	0426	1.2	1053	3.9	1648	1.5	2253	4.0
15	TU	0515	0.8	1139	4.2	1732	1.1	2339	4.3
16	W	0558	0.5	1220	4.4	1814	0.9		
17	TH ○	0021	4.6	0641	0.3	1259	4.5	1855	0.7
18	F	0103	4.8	0722	0.3	1338	4.6	1936	0.6
19	SA	0147	4.8	0803	0.4	1418	4.5	2017	0.6
20	SU	0232	4.7	0844	0.6	1459	4.4	2101	0.7
21	M	0321	4.5	0926	1.0	1543	4.2	2149	1.0
22	TU	0415	4.2	1011	1.4	1632	4.0	2244	1.2
23	W	0518	3.8	1104	1.8	1733	3.7	2351	1.5
24	TH ☽	0631	3.5	1214	2.1	1845	3.5		
25	F	0115	1.6	0751	3.4	1346	2.2	2004	3.5
26	SA	0252	1.6	0921	3.4	1521	2.1	2125	3.6
27	SU	0400	1.5	1026	3.5	1618	1.9	2226	3.7
28	M	0446	1.3	1111	3.7	1700	1.7	2311	3.9
29	TU	0523	1.2	1145	3.8	1735	1.5	2347	4.0
30	W	0556	1.1	1215	4.0	1807	1.3		
31	TH	0019	4.1	0626	1.0	1243	4.1	1838	1.2

NOVEMBER

Date	Day	Time	m	Time	m	Time	m	Time	m
1	F ●	0051	4.2	0655	1.0	1311	4.1	1907	1.1
2	SA	0122	4.2	0724	1.0	1339	4.2	1937	1.1
3	SU	0154	4.2	0753	1.0	1409	4.2	2008	1.1
4	M	0227	4.1	0823	1.2	1439	4.1	2040	1.2
5	TU	0303	4.0	0855	1.3	1513	4.0	2116	1.3
6	W	0344	3.9	0931	1.5	1551	3.9	2158	1.4
7	TH	0431	3.7	1015	1.7	1637	3.8	2252	1.5
8	F	0533	3.6	1114	1.9	1737	3.6		
9	SA ☾	0002	1.6	0648	3.5	1234	2.0	1854	3.6
10	SU	0126	1.5	0803	3.5	1402	2.0	2008	3.6
11	M	0244	1.4	0917	3.7	1514	1.8	2117	3.8
12	TU	0349	1.1	1018	3.9	1612	1.5	2218	4.1
13	W	0442	0.9	1108	4.1	1702	1.2	2310	4.3
14	TH	0530	0.7	1152	4.3	1748	1.0	2358	4.5
15	F ○	0615	0.6	1234	4.4	1833	0.8		
16	SA	0044	4.6	0659	0.6	1314	4.5	1918	0.7
17	SU	0131	4.6	0742	0.7	1356	4.5	2003	0.7
18	M	0220	4.5	0824	1.0	1438	4.4	2050	0.8
19	TU	0311	4.3	0908	1.2	1523	4.2	2139	0.9
20	W	0406	4.1	0952	1.5	1612	4.0	2232	1.1
21	TH	0504	3.8	1041	1.8	1707	3.8	2331	1.3
22	F	0605	3.6	1140	2.0	1810	3.7		
23	SA ☽	0036	1.5	0710	3.4	1250	2.1	1916	3.6
24	SU	0148	1.6	0819	3.4	1407	2.2	2025	3.5
25	M	0258	1.6	0927	3.4	1519	2.0	2132	3.6
26	TU	0355	1.5	1020	3.5	1614	1.9	2225	3.7
27	W	0440	1.4	1102	3.7	1657	1.7	2310	3.8
28	TH	0517	1.3	1138	3.8	1735	1.5	2349	3.9
29	F	0552	1.2	1212	4.0	1810	1.4		
30	SA	0025	4.0	0626	1.2	1243	4.1	1845	1.3

DECEMBER

Date	Day	Time	m	Time	m	Time	m	Time	m
1	SU ●	0101	4.0	0658	1.2	1315	4.1	1919	1.2
2	M	0137	4.1	0732	1.2	1347	4.2	1954	1.1
3	TU	0214	4.1	0807	1.3	1421	4.2	2032	1.1
4	W	0254	4.0	0844	1.3	1458	4.1	2112	1.1
5	TH	0337	3.9	0924	1.4	1538	4.1	2157	1.2
6	F	0426	3.8	1010	1.6	1624	4.0	2249	1.2
7	SA	0522	3.7	1103	1.7	1719	3.9	2348	1.3
8	SU ☾	0624	3.7	1207	1.8	1823	3.8		
9	M	0055	1.3	0729	3.6	1318	1.8	1930	3.8
10	TU	0202	1.2	0836	3.7	1428	1.7	2038	3.9
11	W	0308	1.2	0940	3.8	1533	1.6	2144	4.0
12	TH	0410	1.1	1038	4.0	1634	1.4	2246	4.2
13	F	0506	1.0	1128	4.1	1729	1.2	2342	4.3
14	SA	0557	1.0	1215	4.2	1821	1.0		
15	SU ○	0034	4.3	0645	1.0	1259	4.3	1910	0.9
16	M	0125	4.4	0729	1.1	1342	4.4	1957	0.8
17	TU	0215	4.3	0812	1.2	1425	4.3	2044	0.8
18	W	0304	4.2	0854	1.3	1509	4.3	2129	0.9
19	TH	0353	4.0	0934	1.5	1553	4.1	2214	1.0
20	F	0441	3.8	1016	1.6	1639	4.0	2301	1.2
21	SA	0529	3.7	1059	1.8	1728	3.8	2349	1.3
22	SU ☽	0618	3.5	1149	1.9	1820	3.7		
23	M	0041	1.5	0711	3.4	1247	2.0	1917	3.6
24	TU	0138	1.6	0809	3.3	1355	2.1	2019	3.5
25	W	0239	1.7	0912	3.4	1506	2.0	2126	3.5
26	TH	0342	1.7	1010	3.5	1612	1.9	2227	3.6
27	F	0436	1.6	1100	3.6	1704	1.7	2319	3.7
28	SA	0521	1.5	1142	3.8	1747	1.6		
29	SU	0004	3.8	0602	1.4	1220	3.9	1827	1.4
30	M ●	0046	3.9	0640	1.4	1257	4.1	1906	1.2
31	TU	0126	4.0	0718	1.3	1332	4.2	1945	1.0

WICK
LAT 58°26′N
LONG 3°05′W

TIMES AND HEIGHTS OF HIGH AND LOW WATER (Heights in Metres)

TIME ZONE UT
For Summer Time (area enclosed in shaded box) add 1 hour

2024

JANUARY

Date	Day	Time	m
1	M	0224 0749 1426 2040	3.0 1.4 3.2 1.1
2	TU	0304 0826 1506 2125	2.9 1.5 3.1 1.2
3	W	0348 0909 1551 2217	2.8 1.6 3.0 1.3
4	TH ☾	0439 1005 1644 2317	2.7 1.7 2.9 1.4
5	F	0537 1121 1746	2.7 1.7 2.9
6	SA	0019 0639 1236 1852	1.4 2.7 1.7 2.9
7	SU	0120 0739 1346 1957	1.4 2.8 1.6 2.9
8	M	0217 0836 1445 2059	1.3 3.0 1.4 3.0
9	TU	0307 0927 1535 2155	1.2 3.2 1.2 3.2
10	W	0353 1014 1622 2246	1.1 3.3 1.0 3.3
11	TH ●	0437 1059 1707 2334	1.1 3.5 0.8 3.5
12	F	0521 1144 1753	1.0 3.6 0.6
13	SA	0022 0606 1228 1840	3.5 0.9 3.7 0.5
14	SU	0109 0650 1314 1927	3.5 0.9 3.7 0.5
15	M	0157 0734 1359 2016	3.4 1.0 3.7 0.5
16	TU	0245 0819 1447 2108	3.3 1.1 3.6 0.7
17	W	0335 0907 1538 2203	3.1 1.2 3.5 0.9
18	TH ☽	0429 1004 1635 2305	3.0 1.3 3.3 1.1
19	F	0528 1115 1740	2.9 1.5 3.1
20	SA	0015 0634 1238 1854	1.2 2.8 1.5 3.0
21	SU	0132 0745 1403 2014	1.4 2.9 1.4 3.0
22	M	0237 0852 1508 2124	1.4 3.0 1.3 3.0
23	TU	0328 0946 1559 2217	1.4 3.2 1.1 3.1
24	W	0410 1032 1641 2302	1.3 3.3 1.0 3.2
25	TH ○	0446 1112 1719 2341	1.2 3.4 0.9 3.2
26	F	0520 1148 1754	1.2 3.5 0.8
27	SA	0016 0552 1222 1827	3.2 1.1 3.5 0.8
28	SU	0049 0623 1255 1900	3.2 1.1 3.5 0.8
29	M	0121 0653 1326 1931	3.1 1.1 3.4 0.8
30	TU	0153 0723 1358 2003	3.1 1.1 3.3 0.9
31	W	0225 0753 1430	3.0 1.2 3.2

FEBRUARY

Date	Day	Time	m
1	TH	0300 0826 1506 2112	2.9 1.3 3.1 1.2
2	F ☾	0340 0904 1548 2158	2.8 1.4 3.0 1.3
3	SA	0428 0955 1642 2305	2.7 1.6 2.8 1.4
4	SU	0530 1123 1754	2.7 1.7 2.7
5	M	0024 0643 1301 1918	1.5 2.7 1.6 2.7
6	TU	0144 0756 1425 2038	1.5 2.8 1.4 2.9
7	W	0251 0901 1524 2143	1.3 3.0 1.2 3.1
8	TH	0343 0956 1613 2236	1.2 3.2 0.9 3.3
9	F ●	0428 1044 1658 2324	1.0 3.5 0.6 3.5
10	SA	0510 1130 1741	0.8 3.7 0.4
11	SU	0009 0552 1214 1825	3.6 0.7 3.8 0.2
12	M	0053 0633 1258 1909	3.6 0.7 3.9 0.2
13	TU	0136 0713 1341 1952	3.5 0.7 3.8 0.3
14	W	0219 0753 1425 2035	3.4 0.8 3.7 0.6
15	TH	0303 0835 1512 2121	3.2 1.0 3.5 0.9
16	F ☽	0350 0924 1605 2217	3.0 1.2 3.2 1.2
17	SA	0445 1033 1711 2331	2.8 1.4 2.9 1.5
18	SU	0553 1215 1834	2.7 1.5 2.7
19	M	0112 0716 1400 2012	1.6 2.7 1.4 2.7
20	TU	0232 0836 1506 2122	1.6 2.9 1.2 2.8
21	W	0323 0933 1552 2210	1.5 3.0 1.0 3.0
22	TH	0401 1018 1629 2250	1.3 3.2 0.9 3.1
23	F	0433 1056 1701 2324	1.2 3.3 0.8 3.1
24	SA ○	0502 1130 1732 2355	1.1 3.4 0.7 3.2
25	SU	0531 1202 1801	1.0 3.4 0.6
26	M	0024 0600 1231 1831	3.2 0.9 3.4 0.6
27	TU	0053 0628 1300 1859	3.2 0.9 3.4 0.7
28	W	0121 0655 1329 1927	3.1 0.9 3.3 0.8
29	TH	0149 0723 1358 1955	3.1 1.0 3.2 0.9

MARCH

Date	Day	Time	m
1	F	0220 0753 1431 2026	3.0 1.1 3.1 1.1
2	SA	0256 0827 1511 2103	2.9 1.2 2.9 1.2
3	SU ☾	0340 0911 1603 2157	2.8 1.4 2.8 1.4
4	M	0437 1022 1717 2340	2.7 1.5 2.6 1.6
5	TU	0556 1232 1855	2.6 1.5 2.6
6	W	0123 0723 1409 2025	1.5 2.7 1.3 2.8
7	TH	0238 0837 1509 2131	1.3 2.9 1.0 3.0
8	F	0328 0935 1556 2221	1.1 3.2 0.6 3.3
9	SA	0411 1025 1639 2306	0.9 3.5 0.4 3.5
10	SU ●	0451 1110 1721 2349	0.7 3.7 0.1 3.6
11	M	0530 1154 1802	0.5 3.9 0.1
12	TU	0030 0610 1236 1843	3.6 0.5 3.9 0.1
13	W	0110 0649 1319 1922	3.5 0.5 3.8 0.3
14	TH	0149 0728 1402 2001	3.4 0.6 3.6 0.6
15	F	0229 0809 1448 2042	3.2 0.8 3.3 1.0
16	SA	0313 0856 1541 2130	3.0 1.0 3.0 1.3
17	SU ☽	0405 1009 1650 2248	2.8 1.3 2.7 1.6
18	M	0516 1202 1821	2.6 1.4 2.6
19	TU	0052 0644 1347 2003	1.7 2.6 1.3 2.6
20	W	0218 0811 1448 2106	1.6 2.7 1.1 2.7
21	TH	0306 0910 1530 2150	1.5 2.9 1.0 2.9
22	F	0340 0953 1604 2225	1.3 3.1 0.8 3.0
23	SA	0409 1030 1633 2257	1.1 3.2 0.7 3.1
24	SU	0437 1103 1702 2327	1.0 3.3 0.6 3.1
25	M ○	0504 1134 1730 2355	0.8 3.3 0.6 3.2
26	TU	0532 1204 1758	0.8 3.4 0.6
27	W	0022 0601 1232 1826	3.2 0.8 3.3 0.6
28	TH	0049 0629 1301 1853	3.2 0.8 3.3 0.7
29	F	0118 0658 1332 1922	3.1 0.8 3.2 0.9
30	SA	0148 0729 1407 1953	3.1 0.9 3.0 1.0
31	SU	0224 0805 1450 [illegible]	3.0 1.1 2.9 [illegible]

APRIL

Date	Day	Time	m
1	M	0308 0852 1545 2126	2.8 1.2 2.7 1.5
2	TU ☾	0406 1011 1704 2320	2.7 1.4 2.6 1.6
3	W	0526 1219 1843	2.6 1.3 2.6
4	TH	0103 0655 1347 2008	1.5 2.7 1.1 2.8
5	F	0214 0809 1445 2110	1.3 2.9 0.8 3.0
6	SA	0304 0909 1532 2158	1.0 3.2 0.5 3.3
7	SU	0346 0959 1615 2242	0.8 3.4 0.2 3.4
8	M ●	0426 1046 1655 2324	0.6 3.7 0.1 3.5
9	TU	0506 1130 1735	0.5 3.8 0.1
10	W	0003 0546 1214 1815	3.5 0.4 3.8 0.3
11	TH	0042 0626 1257 1854	3.5 0.4 3.6 0.5
12	F	0121 0707 1342 1932	3.3 0.6 3.4 0.8
13	SA	0200 0751 1429 2010	3.2 0.8 3.1 1.1
14	SU	0242 0843 1523 2056	3.0 1.0 2.8 1.4
15	M ☽	0334 0958 1632 2210	2.8 1.2 2.6 1.7
16	TU	0443 1136 1757	2.7 1.3 2.5
17	W	0002 0606 1312 1928	1.7 2.6 1.2 2.5
18	TH	0139 0727 1411 2032	1.6 2.7 1.1 2.6
19	F	0230 0830 1453 2115	1.5 2.8 0.9 2.8
20	SA	0306 0917 1527 2151	1.3 2.9 0.8 2.9
21	SU	0336 0955 1558 2223	1.1 3.0 0.7 3.0
22	M	0406 1030 1628 2253	1.0 3.1 0.7 3.1
23	TU ○	0435 1102 1657 2322	0.9 3.2 0.6 3.2
24	W	0505 1134 1726 2351	0.8 3.2 0.6 3.2
25	TH	0535 1206 1755	0.7 3.2 0.7
26	F	0021 0606 1239 1825	3.2 0.8 3.2 0.8
27	SA	0052 0639 1314 1858	3.2 0.8 3.1 0.9
28	SU	0126 0716 1355 1934	3.1 0.9 3.0 1.1
29	M	0205 0759 1442 2019	3.0 1.0 2.8 1.3
30	TU	0252 0855 1542 2124	2.9 1.1 2.7 1.4

MAY

Date	Day	Time	m
1	W ☾	0352 1027 1701 2307	2.8 1.1 2.6 1.5
2	TH	0508 1201 1826	2.7 1.0 2.7
3	F	0033 0628 1317 1940	1.4 2.8 0.9 2.8
4	SA	0140 0738 1416 2040	1.2 3.0 0.6 3.0
5	SU	0233 0838 1504 2130	1.0 3.2 0.5 3.2
6	M	0318 0932 1548 2215	0.8 3.4 0.3 3.3
7	TU	0401 1022 1629 2257	0.6 3.5 0.3 3.4
8	W ●	0444 1109 1710 2338	0.5 3.6 0.4 3.4
9	TH	0526 1155 1750	0.5 3.5 0.5
10	F	0017 0611 1241 1830	3.4 0.5 3.4 0.8
11	SA	0057 0655 1326 1909	3.3 0.6 3.2 1.0
12	SU	0137 0743 1414 1949	3.2 0.7 3.0 1.2
13	M	0220 0836 1507 2034	3.0 0.9 2.8 1.4
14	TU	0310 0940 1608 2134	2.9 1.1 2.6 1.6
15	W ☽	0410 1052 1716 2255	2.8 1.1 2.5 1.7
16	TH	0521 1208 1826	2.7 1.2 2.5
17	F	0020 0630 1314 1932	1.6 2.7 1.1 2.6
18	SA	0130 0733 1403 2025	1.5 2.7 1.0 2.7
19	SU	0218 0827 1443 2107	1.4 2.8 0.9 2.8
20	M	0257 0912 1519 2143	1.2 2.9 0.9 2.9
21	TU	0333 0952 1552 2217	1.1 3.0 0.8 3.0
22	W	0407 1030 1624 2250	1.0 3.1 0.8 3.1
23	TH ○	0440 1107 1657 2324	0.9 3.1 0.8 3.2
24	F	0515 1145 1730 2358	0.8 3.2 0.8 3.2
25	SA	0551 1224 1806	0.8 3.1 0.9
26	SU	0034 0631 1305 1846	3.2 0.7 3.1 1.0
27	M	0113 0715 1351 1930	3.2 0.8 3.0 1.1
28	TU	0156 0805 1442 2020	3.1 0.8 2.9 1.2
29	W	0246 0907 1541 2124	3.0 0.9 2.8 1.3
30	TH ☾	0343 1021 1649 2241	3.0 0.9 2.8 1.4
31	F	0450 1134 1759 2355	2.9 0.8 2.8 1.3

JUNE

Date	Day	Time	m
1	SA	0559 1242 1905	3.0 0.8 2.8
2	SU	0101 0705 1343 2006	1.2 3.0 0.7 2.9
3	M	0200 0808 1436 2100	1.1 3.1 0.6 3.1
4	TU	0253 0908 1524 2149	0.9 3.2 0.6 3.2
5	W	0342 1004 1608 2235	0.8 3.3 0.7 3.3
6	TH ●	0430 1055 1651 2318	0.7 3.3 0.7 3.3
7	F	0516 1144 1732	0.6 3.3 0.8
8	SA	0000 0603 1230 1813	3.4 0.6 3.2 1.0
9	SU	0040 0649 1315 1852	3.3 0.6 3.1 1.1
10	M	0121 0734 1400 1931	3.2 0.7 3.0 1.2
11	TU	0202 0820 1445 2011	3.1 0.8 2.8 1.3
12	W	0246 0908 1534 2056	3.0 0.9 2.7 1.4
13	TH	0335 1001 1626 2152	2.9 1.0 2.6 1.5
14	F ☽	0430 1058 1723 2258	2.8 1.1 2.5 1.5
15	SA	0528 1158 1820	2.7 1.1 2.5
16	SU	0008 0628 1257 1918	1.5 2.7 1.1 2.6
17	M	0115 0727 1350 2011	1.5 2.7 1.1 2.7
18	TU	0212 0823 1437 2058	1.4 2.8 1.1 2.9
19	W	0300 0915 1518 2141	1.2 2.9 1.0 3.0
20	TH	0342 1002 1557 2221	1.1 3.0 1.0 3.1
21	F	0422 1047 1636 2301	1.0 3.1 0.9 3.2
22	SA ○	0502 1130 1715 2341	0.8 3.1 0.9 3.3
23	SU	0544 1215 1757	0.7 3.2 0.9
24	M	0022 0629 1300 1841	3.4 0.6 3.2 0.9
25	TU	0105 0715 1347 1926	3.4 0.6 3.2 1.0
26	W	0150 0805 1436 2014	3.3 0.6 3.1 1.1
27	TH	0237 0859 1529 2106	3.3 0.6 3.0 1.1
28	F ☾	0329 0958 1625 2206	3.2 0.7 2.9 1.2
29	SA	0426 1101 1725 2313	3.2 0.8 2.8 1.3
30	SU	0529 1206 1827	3.1 0.9 2.8

SUNRISE AND SUNSET TIMES

WICK
At 58°26′N 3°05′W

UT		Sunrise	Sunset
Jan	01	0901	1531
	15	0848	1556
Feb	01	0818	1635
	15	0745	1709
Mar	01	0708	1743
	15	0628	1815
BST (UT+1)			
Apr	01	0640	1954
	15	0600	2026
May	01	0518	2103
	15	0445	2134
Jun	01	0416	2206
	15	0405	2221
Jul	01	0411	2221
	15	0430	2206
Aug	01	0503	2133
	15	0534	2058
Sep	01	0611	2012
	15	0642	1932
Oct	01	0717	1846
	15	0748	1807
UT			
Nov	01	0728	1623
	15	0801	1552
Dec	01	0835	1527
	[illegible]	[illegible]	[illegible]

WICK
LAT 58°26′N
LONG 3°05′W

TIMES AND HEIGHTS OF HIGH AND LOW WATER (Heights in Metres)

TIME ZONE UT
For Summer Time (area enclosed in shaded box) add 1 hour

2024

JULY

Day	Time	m	Day	Time	m
1 M	0023 0636 1312 1932	1.3 3.0 0.9 2.9	16 TU	0008 0627 1252 1912	1.6 2.7 1.3 2.7
2 TU	0134 0746 1414 2034	1.2 3.0 1.0 3.0	17 W	0125 0736 1355 2013	1.5 2.7 1.3 2.8
3 W	0240 0855 1509 2131	1.1 3.0 1.0 3.1	18 TH	0233 0843 1451 2108	1.4 2.8 1.2 2.9
4 TH	0337 0957 1557 2220	0.9 3.1 1.0 3.2	19 F	0325 0941 1539 2157	1.2 2.9 1.1 3.1
5 F ●	0427 1050 1641 2305	0.8 3.1 1.0 3.3	20 SA	0410 1032 1623 2242	1.0 3.1 1.0 3.3
6 SA	0513 1138 1721 2347	0.7 3.2 1.0 3.4	21 SU O	0453 1119 1705 2326	0.8 3.2 0.9 3.4
7 SU	0556 1221 1759	0.6 3.1 1.1	22 M	0536 1204 1747	0.6 3.3 0.8
8 M	0027 0637 1301 1835	3.4 0.6 3.1 1.1	23 TU	0009 0620 1249 1829	3.5 0.4 3.4 0.8
9 TU	0105 0715 1339 1909	3.3 0.7 3.0 1.1	24 W	0052 0704 1334 1911	3.6 0.3 3.4 0.8
10 W	0142 0752 1416 1943	3.3 0.7 2.9 1.2	25 TH	0136 0749 1419 1954	3.6 0.3 3.3 0.9
11 TH	0219 0830 1454 2018	3.2 0.8 2.8 1.2	26 F	0221 0836 1505 2039	3.6 0.5 3.1 1.0
12 F	0257 0909 1534 2057	3.1 0.9 2.7 1.3	27 SA	0308 0926 1554 2129	3.4 0.6 3.0 1.1
13 SA ☽	0338 0954 1619 2145	2.9 1.1 2.7 1.4	28 SU ☾	0400 1023 1649 2233	3.3 0.9 2.9 1.3
14 SU	0425 1047 1711 2251	2.8 1.2 2.6 1.5	29 M	0501 1129 1752 2354	3.1 1.1 2.8 1.3
15 M	0522 1148 1810	2.7 1.3 2.6	30 TU	0613 1247 1902	2.9 1.3 2.8
			31 W	0125 0736 1405 2017	1.3 2.8 1.3 2.9

AUGUST

Day	Time	m	Day	Time	m
1 TH	0242 0857 1506 2120	1.2 2.9 1.3 3.0	16 F	0213 0820 1433 2039	1.4 2.7 1.4 2.9
2 F	0340 0958 1554 2211	1.0 3.0 1.2 3.2	17 SA	0310 0926 1525 2134	1.2 2.9 1.2 3.1
3 SA	0426 1047 1633 2255	0.8 3.1 1.2 3.3	18 SU	0356 1017 1608 2222	0.9 3.2 1.0 3.4
4 SU ●	0505 1128 1707 2334	0.7 3.1 1.1 3.4	19 M O	0438 1103 1649 2307	0.6 3.4 0.9 3.6
5 M	0541 1205 1740	0.6 3.2 1.0	20 TU	0519 1147 1729 2351	0.4 3.5 0.7 3.7
6 TU	0009 0615 1239 1812	3.4 0.6 3.2 1.0	21 W	0600 1230 1808	0.2 3.6 0.6
7 W	0043 0647 1311 1842	3.4 0.6 3.1 1.0	22 TH	0033 0642 1311 1848	3.8 0.2 3.5 0.6
8 TH	0115 0718 1342 1912	3.4 0.7 3.1 1.0	23 F	0116 0724 1353 1929	3.8 0.2 3.4 0.7
9 F	0147 0749 1413 1942	3.3 0.8 3.0 1.1	24 SA	0159 0806 1435 2010	3.7 0.5 3.3 0.9
10 SA	0219 0821 1446 2014	3.2 0.9 2.9 1.2	25 SU	0244 0851 1521 2057	3.5 0.8 3.1 1.1
11 SU	0253 0855 1524 2050	3.0 1.1 2.8 1.3	26 M ☾	0336 0943 1613 2202	3.3 1.1 2.9 1.3
12 M ☽	0333 0936 1608 2138	2.9 1.2 2.7 1.5	27 TU	0440 1054 1718 2341	3.0 1.4 2.8 1.4
13 TU	0424 1036 1705 2301	2.7 1.4 2.7 1.6	28 W	0601 1233 1838	2.8 1.6 2.8
14 W	0533 1158 1817	2.6 1.5 2.7	29 TH	0130 0741 1405 2004	1.3 2.7 1.6 2.9
15 TH	0044 0658 1322 1931	1.6 2.6 1.5 2.7	30 F	0243 0900 1503 2108	1.2 2.9 1.5 3.0
			31 SA	0334 0952 1544 2157	1.0 3.0 1.3 3.2

SEPTEMBER

Day	Time	m	Day	Time	m
1 SU	0413 1033 1617 2237	0.8 3.1 1.2 3.3	16 M	0334 0957 1547 2158	0.8 3.3 1.0 3.5
2 M	0445 1108 1646 2313	0.7 3.2 1.1 3.4	17 TU	0415 1041 1626 2243	0.5 3.5 0.8 3.7
3 TU ●	0515 1140 1715 2345	0.6 3.2 1.0 3.5	18 W O	0455 1123 1704 2326	0.2 3.6 0.6 3.9
4 W	0545 1210 1744	0.6 3.2 0.9	19 TH	0535 1204 1743	0.1 3.7 0.5
5 TH	0016 0614 1238 1813	3.5 0.6 3.2 0.9	20 F	0009 0616 1244 1824	4.0 0.2 3.6 0.5
6 F	0045 0643 1306 1841	3.4 0.7 3.2 0.9	21 SA	0052 0656 1324 1904	3.9 0.3 3.5 0.7
7 SA	0114 0710 1335 1909	3.4 0.8 3.1 1.0	22 SU	0136 0736 1405 1946	3.7 0.6 3.3 0.8
8 SU	0144 0738 1405 1939	3.2 0.9 3.1 1.1	23 M	0223 0817 1448 2035	3.5 1.0 3.2 1.1
9 M	0217 0808 1439 2013	3.1 1.1 3.0 1.3	24 TU ☽	0316 0906 1540 2148	3.2 1.4 3.0 1.3
10 TU	0256 0843 1521 2055	2.9 1.3 2.9 1.4	25 W	0425 1022 1650 2339	2.9 1.7 2.8 1.4
11 W ☾	0346 0932 1615 2205	2.8 1.5 2.7 1.6	26 TH	0555 1220 1815	2.7 1.8 2.8
12 TH	0456 1112 1730	2.6 1.7 2.7	27 F	0123 0738 1354 1942	1.3 2.7 1.7 2.9
13 F	0018 0633 1258 1857	1.6 2.6 1.6 2.8	28 SA	0228 0845 1445 2045	1.1 2.9 1.6 3.1
14 SA	0152 0803 1414 2010	1.4 2.8 1.5 2.9	29 SU	0312 0931 1522 2132	1.0 3.0 1.4 3.2
15 SU	0249 0908 1505 2109	1.1 3.0 1.2 3.2	30 M	0347 1007 1551 2210	0.9 3.1 1.2 3.3

OCTOBER

Day	Time	m	Day	Time	m
1 TU	0416 1040 1619 2244	0.8 3.2 1.1 3.4	16 W	0347 1014 1559 2216	0.4 3.5 0.8 3.8
2 W ●	0444 1110 1647 2316	0.7 3.3 1.0 3.5	17 TH O	0428 1056 1639 2301	0.3 3.6 0.7 3.9
3 TH	0512 1138 1715 2346	0.7 3.3 0.9 3.5	18 F	0508 1137 1720 2347	0.3 3.7 0.6 3.9
4 F	0540 1206 1744	0.7 3.3 0.9	19 SA	0548 1217 1801	0.4 3.7 0.6
5 SA	0015 0608 1233 1813	3.4 0.8 3.3 0.9	20 SU	0031 0629 1257 1845	3.8 0.6 3.6 0.7
6 SU	0044 0635 1301 1842	3.4 0.9 3.3 1.0	21 M	0118 0709 1338 1931	3.6 0.9 3.4 0.9
7 M	0116 0703 1331 1913	3.3 1.0 3.2 1.1	22 TU	0207 0750 1422 2025	3.4 1.2 3.2 1.1
8 TU	0150 0734 1406 1949	3.1 1.2 3.1 1.2	23 W	0303 0838 1514 2142	3.1 1.6 3.1 1.3
9 W	0232 0810 1448 2034	3.0 1.4 3.0 1.4	24 TH ☽	0412 0950 1622 2317	2.8 1.8 2.9 1.4
10 TH ☾	0325 0900 1543 2149	2.8 1.6 2.9 1.5	25 F	0535 1136 1743	2.7 1.9 2.9
11 F	0438 1044 1658 2356	2.7 1.8 2.8 1.5	26 SA	0051 0703 1315 1901	1.3 2.7 1.8 2.9
12 SA	0614 1232 1825	2.7 1.7 2.8	27 SU	0153 0810 1409 2007	1.2 2.8 1.6 3.0
13 SU	0121 0738 1345 1938	1.3 2.9 1.5 3.0	28 M	0237 0856 1447 2056	1.1 3.0 1.5 3.2
14 M	0219 0841 1436 2037	1.0 3.1 1.3 3.3	29 TU	0311 0933 1519 2136	1.0 3.1 1.3 3.3
15 TU	0306 0930 1519 2129	0.7 3.3 1.0 3.5	30 W	0341 1005 1549 2211	0.9 3.2 1.2 3.3
			31 TH	0410 1036 1619 2245	0.9 3.3 1.1 3.4

NOVEMBER

Day	Time	m	Day	Time	m
1 F ●	0439 1105 1649 2317	0.8 3.4 1.0 3.4	16 SA	0444 1112 1702 2329	0.6 3.7 0.7 3.8
2 SA	0508 1135 1720 2349	0.9 3.4 1.0 3.4	17 SU	0526 1154 1748	0.7 3.7 0.7
3 SU	0537 1204 1751	0.9 3.4 1.0	18 M	0017 0608 1235 1835	3.7 0.9 3.6 0.7
4 M	0022 0607 1234 1823	3.3 1.0 3.4 1.0	19 TU	0105 0649 1318 1925	3.5 1.1 3.5 0.9
5 TU	0057 0638 1307 1859	3.2 1.1 3.3 1.1	20 W	0155 0732 1403 2019	3.3 1.4 3.4 1.0
6 W	0135 0713 1345 1940	3.1 1.3 3.2 1.2	21 TH	0249 0817 1453 2122	3.0 1.6 3.2 1.2
7 TH	0221 0755 1429 2032	3.0 1.5 3.1 1.3	22 F	0349 0913 1552 2232	2.9 1.8 3.1 1.3
8 F	0316 0850 1524 2151	2.9 1.6 3.0 1.4	23 SA ☽	0455 1027 1659 2346	2.7 1.8 3.0 1.3
9 SA ☾	0427 1021 1634 2326	2.8 1.7 2.9 1.3	24 SU	0602 1150 1806	2.7 1.8 2.9
10 SU	0550 1153 1752	2.8 1.7 3.0	25 M	0054 0708 1306 1910	1.3 2.8 1.7 3.0
11 M	0042 0704 1304 1902	1.1 2.9 1.5 3.1	26 TU	0146 0804 1400 2007	1.2 2.9 1.6 3.0
12 TU	0144 0806 1401 2003	0.9 3.1 1.3 3.3	27 W	0228 0849 1442 2055	1.2 3.0 1.5 3.1
13 W	0234 0858 1449 2059	0.7 3.3 1.1 3.5	28 TH	0304 0927 1519 2137	1.1 3.1 1.3 3.2
14 TH	0319 0945 1534 2151	0.6 3.5 0.9 3.7	29 F	0338 1002 1555 2216	1.1 3.2 1.2 3.3
15 F O	0402 1029 1617 2241	0.6 3.6 0.8 3.8	30 SA	0410 1036 1629 2253	1.0 3.3 1.1 3.3

DECEMBER

Day	Time	m	Day	Time	m
1 SU ●	0442 1108 1703 2330	1.1 3.4 1.1 3.3	16 M	0513 1139 1743	1.0 3.6 0.7
2 M	0515 1142 1738	1.1 3.4 1.0	17 TU	0010 0555 1221 1831	3.5 1.1 3.6 0.7
3 TU	0007 0549 1216 1815	3.3 1.1 3.5 1.0	18 W	0057 0636 1304 1917	3.4 1.2 3.5 0.8
4 W	0047 0626 1253 1856	3.3 1.2 3.4 1.0	19 TH	0142 0715 1346 2003	3.2 1.3 3.5 0.9
5 TH	0129 0706 1334 1941	3.2 1.3 3.4 1.0	20 F	0228 0754 1430 2049	3.1 1.4 3.3 1.0
6 F	0215 0751 1419 2034	3.1 1.4 3.3 1.1	21 SA	0314 0835 1517 2138	2.9 1.5 3.2 1.2
7 SA	0308 0844 1510 2138	3.0 1.5 3.2 1.1	22 SU ☽	0404 0922 1608 2232	2.8 1.6 3.1 1.3
8 SU ☾	0409 0950 1610 2251	2.9 1.6 3.2 1.1	23 M	0458 1022 1704 2332	2.7 1.7 3.0 1.4
9 M	0517 1106 1717	2.9 1.6 3.2	24 TU	0555 1134 1805	2.7 1.8 2.9
10 TU	0000 0624 1217 1825	1.1 3.0 1.5 3.2	25 W	0034 0655 1250 1907	1.4 2.7 1.7 2.9
11 W	0105 0727 1323 1930	1.0 3.1 1.4 3.3	26 TH	0134 0753 1359 2008	1.4 2.8 1.6 2.9
12 TH	0203 0826 1422 2033	0.9 3.2 1.2 3.4	27 F	0225 0845 1452 2104	1.3 3.0 1.5 3.0
13 F	0256 0920 1516 2134	0.9 3.3 1.1 3.5	28 SA	0309 0930 1536 2152	1.3 3.1 1.4 3.1
14 SA	0344 1009 1606 2229	0.9 3.5 0.9 3.5	29 SU	0348 1010 1616 2235	1.2 3.2 1.2 3.2
15 SU O	0429 1055 1655 2321	0.9 3.6 0.8 3.5	30 M ●	0425 1048 1653 2317	1.2 3.4 1.1 3.3
			31 TU	0502 1126 1731 2358	1.2 3.4 0.9 3.3

LERWICK
LAT 60°09′N
LONG 1°08′W

TIMES AND HEIGHTS OF HIGH AND LOW WATER (Heights in Metres)

TIME ZONE UT
For Summer Time (area enclosed in shaded box) add 1 hour

2024

JANUARY

Day		Time	m	Time	m	Time	m	Time	m
1	M	0205	1.9	0743	1.0	1404	2.0	2029	0.8
2	TU	0244	1.8	0819	1.0	1443	2.0	2112	0.8
3	W	0325	1.7	0902	1.1	1528	1.9	2202	0.9
4	TH ☽	0412	1.7	0957	1.1	1619	1.8	2301	0.9
5	F	0508	1.7	1116	1.2	1719	1.8		
6	SA	0005	1.0	0614	1.7	1234	1.1	1832	1.8
7	SU	0104	1.0	0720	1.8	1336	1.1	1942	1.8
8	M	0157	0.9	0814	1.9	1429	1.0	2040	1.9
9	TU	0247	0.9	0902	2.0	1518	0.8	2132	2.0
10	W	0334	0.8	0947	2.1	1605	0.7	2223	2.1
11	TH ●	0420	0.8	1033	2.2	1651	0.6	2313	2.2
12	F	0505	0.7	1119	2.3	1737	0.4		
13	SA	0002	2.2	0550	0.7	1204	2.3	1824	0.4
14	SU	0051	2.2	0635	0.7	1250	2.4	1910	0.3
15	M	0139	2.1	0719	0.7	1337	2.3	1958	0.4
16	TU	0227	2.0	0804	0.8	1426	2.3	2047	0.5
17	W	0316	1.9	0852	0.8	1517	2.2	2141	0.6
18	TH ☾	0408	1.8	0947	0.9	1613	2.0	2245	0.8
19	F	0506	1.8	1059	1.0	1720	1.9		
20	SA	0002	0.9	0615	1.8	1231	1.0	1840	1.8
21	SU	0117	1.0	0726	1.8	1349	0.9	1959	1.8
22	M	0220	1.0	0829	1.9	1452	0.9	2107	1.9
23	TU	0312	1.0	0923	2.0	1543	0.8	2201	1.9
24	W	0356	0.9	1009	2.1	1626	0.7	2245	2.0
25	TH ○	0434	0.9	1050	2.2	1704	0.6	2323	2.0
26	F	0510	0.8	1127	2.2	1739	0.6	2359	2.0
27	SA	0543	0.8	1201	2.2	1813	0.5		
28	SU	0031	2.0	0614	0.8	1233	2.2	1846	0.5
29	M	0102	2.0	0644	0.8	1304	2.1	1917	0.6
30	TU	0133	1.9	0713	0.8	1335	2.1	1950	0.6
31	W	0204	1.8	0743	0.9	1407	2.0	2024	0.7

FEBRUARY

Day		Time	m	Time	m	Time	m	Time	m
1	TH	0238	1.8	0817	0.9	1444	1.9	2102	0.8
2	F ☽	0318	1.7	0858	1.0	1528	1.8	2148	0.9
3	SA	0407	1.7	0952	1.1	1624	1.7	2249	1.0
4	SU	0506	1.7	1119	1.1	1733	1.7		
5	M	0013	1.0	0618	1.7	1259	1.1	1902	1.7
6	TU	0127	1.0	0737	1.8	1408	1.0	2021	1.8
7	W	0229	0.9	0839	1.9	1505	0.8	2121	1.9
8	TH	0323	0.8	0931	2.0	1555	0.6	2214	2.1
9	F ●	0410	0.7	1020	2.2	1640	0.4	2303	2.2
10	SA	0454	0.6	1107	2.3	1724	0.2	2350	2.2
11	SU	0535	0.5	1152	2.4	1807	0.1		
12	M	0034	2.2	0617	0.5	1235	2.4	1850	0.1
13	TU	0117	2.2	0658	0.5	1319	2.4	1933	0.2
14	W	0200	2.1	0739	0.6	1403	2.3	2017	0.4
15	TH	0242	1.9	0824	0.7	1450	2.1	2104	0.6
16	F ☾	0328	1.8	0915	0.8	1543	1.9	2159	0.8
17	SA	0420	1.7	1024	0.9	1648	1.8	2321	1.0
18	SU	0530	1.7	1215	1.0	1822	1.7		
19	M	0100	1.1	0700	1.7	1344	0.9	2001	1.7
20	TU	0213	1.1	0816	1.8	1449	0.8	2108	1.7
21	W	0306	1.0	0912	1.9	1536	0.7	2153	1.8
22	TH	0346	0.9	0956	2.0	1613	0.6	2230	1.9
23	F	0420	0.8	1034	2.1	1646	0.5	2303	1.9
24	SA ○	0451	0.7	1108	2.1	1716	0.5	2335	2.0
25	SU	0521	0.7	1140	2.1	1746	0.4		
26	M	0004	2.0	0549	0.6	1209	2.1	1815	0.4
27	TU	0031	2.0	0616	0.6	1237	2.1	1843	0.5
28	W	0058	1.9	0644	0.6	1304	2.1	1913	0.5
29	TH	0125	1.9	0713	0.7	1334	2.0	1944	0.6

MARCH

Day		Time	m	Time	m	Time	m	Time	m
1	F	0155	1.8	0746	0.8	1408	1.9	2018	0.7
2	SA	0231	1.8	0824	0.9	1449	1.8	2058	0.9
3	SU ☽	0316	1.7	0913	0.9	1544	1.7	2152	1.0
4	M	0414	1.6	1028	1.0	1658	1.6	2321	1.1
5	TU	0528	1.6	1230	1.0	1838	1.6		
6	W	0108	1.0	0704	1.7	1350	0.8	2010	1.7
7	TH	0216	0.9	0819	1.8	1449	0.6	2109	1.9
8	F	0309	0.8	0914	2.0	1538	0.4	2158	2.0
9	SA	0353	0.6	1002	2.1	1621	0.2	2244	2.1
10	SU ●	0434	0.5	1047	2.3	1703	0.1	2328	2.2
11	M	0514	0.4	1131	2.4	1744	0.0		
12	TU	0009	2.2	0554	0.3	1213	2.4	1825	0.1
13	W	0049	2.1	0634	0.3	1256	2.3	1905	0.2
14	TH	0127	2.0	0716	0.4	1340	2.2	1946	0.4
15	F	0207	1.9	0800	0.5	1427	2.0	2030	0.7
16	SA	0249	1.8	0851	0.7	1520	1.8	2120	0.9
17	SU ☾	0338	1.7	1004	0.8	1626	1.6	2242	1.1
18	M	0445	1.6	1201	0.9	1813	1.5		
19	TU	0040	1.1	0632	1.6	1328	0.8	1956	1.5
20	W	0156	1.1	0754	1.7	1429	0.7	2051	1.6
21	TH	0246	1.0	0848	1.8	1512	0.6	2129	1.7
22	F	0324	0.8	0930	1.9	1547	0.5	2202	1.8
23	SA	0356	0.7	1007	1.9	1617	0.5	2233	1.9
24	SU	0425	0.6	1040	2.0	1645	0.4	2303	1.9
25	M ○	0452	0.6	1111	2.0	1713	0.4	2331	1.9
26	TU	0519	0.5	1140	2.1	1741	0.4	2357	1.9
27	W	0547	0.5	1208	2.0	1809	0.4		
28	TH	0023	1.9	0617	0.5	1235	2.0	1839	0.5
29	F	0050	1.9	0648	0.6	1306	1.9	1910	0.6
30	SA	0120	1.9	0723	0.6	1342	1.8	1945	0.7
31	SU	0156	1.8	0804	0.7	1426	1.7	2026	0.8

APRIL

Day		Time	m	Time	m	Time	m	Time	m
1	M	0239	1.7	0857	0.8	1525	1.6	2122	1.0
2	TU ☽	0337	1.6	1013	0.9	1644	1.5	2256	1.0
3	W	0456	1.6	1209	0.8	1828	1.5		
4	TH	0049	1.0	0635	1.6	1327	0.7	1953	1.7
5	F	0155	0.8	0754	1.7	1425	0.5	2048	1.8
6	SA	0245	0.7	0849	1.9	1513	0.3	2135	1.9
7	SU	0328	0.5	0937	2.1	1556	0.1	2218	2.1
8	M ●	0409	0.4	1023	2.2	1637	0.0	2300	2.1
9	TU	0449	0.3	1107	2.3	1718	0.1	2340	2.1
10	W	0530	0.2	1151	2.3	1757	0.2		
11	TH	0018	2.1	0612	0.2	1235	2.2	1838	0.3
12	F	0056	2.0	0656	0.3	1320	2.1	1919	0.6
13	SA	0135	1.9	0742	0.5	1409	1.9	2001	0.8
14	SU	0217	1.8	0837	0.6	1503	1.7	2051	1.0
15	M ☾	0306	1.7	0952	0.7	1608	1.5	2210	1.1
16	TU	0409	1.6	1129	0.8	1745	1.4		
17	W	0000	1.1	0547	1.5	1250	0.8	1917	1.5
18	TH	0118	1.0	0713	1.6	1351	0.7	2011	1.6
19	F	0211	0.9	0809	1.7	1435	0.6	2050	1.6
20	SA	0251	0.8	0853	1.7	1510	0.5	2124	1.7
21	SU	0323	0.7	0931	1.8	1540	0.5	2156	1.8
22	M	0352	0.6	1006	1.9	1609	0.4	2226	1.9
23	TU ○	0421	0.5	1038	1.9	1638	0.4	2255	1.9
24	W	0450	0.5	1109	2.0	1707	0.4	2323	1.9
25	TH	0521	0.5	1140	2.0	1738	0.5	2352	2.0
26	F	0554	0.5	1213	1.9	1810	0.5		
27	SA	0022	1.9	0630	0.5	1248	1.9	1845	0.6
28	SU	0055	1.9	0710	0.6	1329	1.8	1924	0.7
29	M	0134	1.8	0756	0.6	1420	1.7	2011	0.8
30	TU	0220	1.7	0854	0.7	1524	1.6	2114	0.9

MAY

Day		Time	m	Time	m	Time	m	Time	m
1	W ☾	0321	1.7	1010	0.7	1640	1.5	2242	1.0
2	TH	0439	1.6	1144	0.6	1809	1.6		
3	F	0017	0.9	0607	1.6	1257	0.5	1923	1.7
4	SA	0122	0.8	0722	1.8	1355	0.4	2018	1.8
5	SU	0215	0.6	0820	1.9	1445	0.3	2105	1.9
6	M	0301	0.5	0910	2.0	1529	0.2	2149	2.0
7	TU	0345	0.4	0958	2.1	1612	0.2	2231	2.0
8	W ●	0428	0.3	1046	2.2	1653	0.3	2311	2.1
9	TH	0511	0.3	1132	2.1	1734	0.4	2351	2.1
10	F	0555	0.3	1220	2.0	1815	0.5		
11	SA	0030	2.0	0642	0.3	1307	1.9	1857	0.7
12	SU	0111	2.0	0731	0.4	1356	1.8	1941	0.8
13	M	0155	1.9	0826	0.6	1447	1.6	2031	1.0
14	TU	0244	1.7	0930	0.6	1543	1.5	2136	1.0
15	W ☽	0339	1.6	1041	0.7	1651	1.4	2257	1.1
16	TH	0448	1.6	1150	0.7	1811	1.4		
17	F	0013	1.0	0615	1.6	1251	0.7	1912	1.5
18	SA	0117	0.9	0719	1.6	1342	0.6	1959	1.6
19	SU	0204	0.8	0808	1.7	1422	0.6	2038	1.7
20	M	0242	0.7	0850	1.7	1457	0.6	2114	1.8
21	TU	0316	0.7	0928	1.8	1530	0.5	2148	1.8
22	W	0350	0.6	1005	1.8	1604	0.5	2221	1.9
23	TH ○	0424	0.5	1042	1.9	1638	0.5	2254	2.0
24	F	0500	0.5	1119	1.9	1713	0.6	2328	2.0
25	SA	0538	0.5	1159	1.9	1750	0.6		
26	SU	0003	2.0	0619	0.5	1241	1.9	1831	0.7
27	M	0042	2.0	0704	0.5	1329	1.8	1916	0.7
28	TU	0125	1.9	0755	0.5	1423	1.7	2007	0.8
29	W	0216	1.8	0852	0.5	1523	1.6	2107	0.9
30	TH ☾	0317	1.8	0959	0.5	1628	1.6	2216	0.9
31	F	0424	1.7	1113	0.5	1738	1.6	2334	0.8

JUNE

Day		Time	m	Time	m	Time	m	Time	m
1	SA	0536	1.7	1223	0.5	1846	1.7		
2	SU	0044	0.8	0649	1.8	1324	0.4	1944	1.7
3	M	0143	0.7	0751	1.9	1417	0.4	2035	1.8
4	TU	0236	0.6	0847	1.9	1505	0.4	2122	1.9
5	W	0325	0.5	0941	2.0	1550	0.4	2207	2.0
6	TH ●	0413	0.4	1033	2.0	1634	0.5	2250	2.0
7	F	0459	0.4	1123	2.0	1716	0.6	2333	2.1
8	SA	0545	0.4	1211	1.9	1759	0.7		
9	SU	0014	2.0	0632	0.4	1257	1.9	1842	0.7
10	M	0056	2.0	0719	0.4	1341	1.8	1924	0.8
11	TU	0139	1.9	0806	0.5	1425	1.7	2007	0.9
12	W	0223	1.8	0855	0.6	1510	1.6	2054	0.9
13	TH	0309	1.7	0947	0.7	1558	1.5	2148	1.0
14	F ☽	0358	1.7	1042	0.7	1653	1.5	2254	1.0
15	SA	0456	1.6	1139	0.7	1757	1.5		
16	SU	0002	1.0	0607	1.6	1235	0.7	1859	1.5
17	M	0104	0.9	0713	1.6	1326	0.7	1949	1.6
18	TU	0156	0.9	0806	1.7	1412	0.7	2032	1.7
19	W	0241	0.8	0853	1.7	1454	0.7	2112	1.8
20	TH	0322	0.7	0937	1.8	1535	0.7	2151	1.9
21	F	0404	0.6	1021	1.9	1616	0.6	2231	2.0
22	SA ○	0445	0.5	1106	1.9	1657	0.6	2311	2.0
23	SU	0528	0.4	1152	1.9	1740	0.6	2353	2.1
24	M	0613	0.4	1239	1.9	1824	0.6		
25	TU	0037	2.1	0700	0.4	1328	1.9	1910	0.7
26	W	0123	2.0	0748	0.3	1418	1.8	1958	0.7
27	TH	0212	2.0	0839	0.4	1510	1.8	2048	0.7
28	F ☾	0306	1.9	0935	0.4	1604	1.7	2144	0.8
29	SA	0403	1.9	1037	0.5	1703	1.7	2250	0.8
30	SU	0507	1.8	1146	0.6	1807	1.7		

SUNRISE AND SUNSET TIMES

LERWICK
At 60°09′N 1°08′W

		Sunrise	Sunset
UT			
Jan	01	0908	1509
	15	0853	1535
Feb	01	0819	1618
	15	0743	1655
Mar	01	0703	1732
	15	0621	1807
BST (UT+1)			
Apr	01	0629	1949
	15	0547	2023
May	01	0502	2103
	15	0426	2138
Jun	01	0352	2214
	15	0339	2231
Jul	01	0345	2231
	15	0407	2213
Aug	01	0444	2136
	15	0518	2058
Sep	01	0559	2008
	15	0632	1926
Oct	01	0710	1837
	15	0744	1755
UT			
Nov	01	0728	1608
	15	0804	1534
Dec	01	0841	1506
	15	0903	1456

LERWICK
LAT 60°09′N
LONG 1°08′W

TIMES AND HEIGHTS OF HIGH AND LOW WATER (Heights in Metres)

TIME ZONE UT
For Summer Time (area enclosed in shaded box) add 1 hour

2024

JULY

Date	Time	m	Time	m	Time	m	Time	m
1 M	0007	0.8	0618	1.8	1254	0.6	1911	1.7
2 TU	0119	0.8	0729	1.8	1355	0.7	2009	1.8
3 W	0222	0.7	0835	1.8	1450	0.7	2103	1.9
4 TH	0318	0.6	0936	1.9	1539	0.7	2153	2.0
5 F	0408	0.5	1031	1.9	1624	0.7	● 2240	2.0
6 SA	0455	0.4	1119	1.9	1706	0.7	2323	2.1
7 SU	0538	0.4	1203	1.9	1746	0.7		
8 M	0003	2.1	0620	0.4	1242	1.9	1825	0.7
9 TU	0042	2.1	0659	0.4	1319	1.8	1901	0.8
10 W	0119	2.0	0737	0.5	1356	1.8	1936	0.8
11 TH	0156	1.9	0815	0.6	1432	1.7	2011	0.8
12 F	0233	1.9	0854	0.6	1510	1.6	2049	0.9
13 SA	0314	1.8	0938	0.7	1551	1.6	☽ 2136	0.9
14 SU	0359	1.7	1029	0.8	1640	1.6	2242	1.0
15 M	0453	1.6	1132	0.9	1738	1.6		
16 TU	0004	1.0	0601	1.6	1235	0.9	1847	1.6
17 W	0113	1.0	0720	1.6	1333	0.9	1950	1.7
18 TH	0211	0.9	0823	1.7	1426	0.8	2041	1.8
19 F	0302	0.8	0917	1.8	1516	0.8	2128	1.9
20 SA	0349	0.6	1007	1.9	1602	0.7	2214	2.0
21 SU	0434	0.5	1055	2.0	1647	0.7	O 2259	2.1
22 M	0518	0.4	1142	2.0	1730	0.6	2343	2.2
23 TU	0602	0.3	1229	2.0	1812	0.6		
24 W	0027	2.2	0646	0.2	1314	2.0	1855	0.6
25 TH	0112	2.2	0730	0.2	1359	2.0	1938	0.6
26 F	0157	2.2	0816	0.3	1445	1.9	2023	0.6
27 SA	0245	2.1	0905	0.4	1533	1.8	2113	0.7
28 SU	0338	2.0	1000	0.6	1626	1.7	☾ 2215	0.8
29 M	0439	1.9	1109	0.8	1728	1.7	2341	0.9
30 TU	0555	1.8	1233	0.9	1842	1.7		
31 W	0111	0.8	0722	1.7	1346	0.9	1954	1.8

AUGUST

Date	Time	m	Time	m	Time	m	Time	m
1 TH	0222	0.8	0839	1.8	1447	0.9	2055	1.9
2 F	0320	0.7	0940	1.8	1536	0.9	2147	2.0
3 SA	0406	0.6	1028	1.9	1617	0.8	2232	2.1
4 SU	0446	0.5	1109	1.9	1654	0.8	● 2311	2.1
5 M	0523	0.4	1145	1.9	1728	0.7	2347	2.1
6 TU	0557	0.4	1219	1.9	1801	0.7		
7 W	0021	2.1	0631	0.4	1250	1.9	1832	0.7
8 TH	0053	2.1	0703	0.5	1320	1.9	1902	0.7
9 F	0124	2.0	0734	0.5	1350	1.8	1932	0.8
10 SA	0155	2.0	0807	0.6	1422	1.8	2005	0.8
11 SU	0230	1.9	0843	0.7	1459	1.7	2044	0.9
12 M	0312	1.8	0925	0.9	1544	1.7	☽ 2135	1.0
13 TU	0404	1.7	1021	1.0	1638	1.6	2256	1.1
14 W	0509	1.6	1144	1.0	1745	1.6		
15 TH	0040	1.0	0637	1.6	1304	1.0	1908	1.7
16 F	0150	0.9	0804	1.7	1408	1.0	2017	1.8
17 SA	0247	0.8	0903	1.8	1502	0.9	2109	1.9
18 SU	0335	0.6	0953	1.9	1549	0.7	2157	2.1
19 M	0419	0.4	1039	2.1	1631	0.6	O 2242	2.2
20 TU	0501	0.2	1124	2.1	1712	0.5	2326	2.3
21 W	0542	0.1	1208	2.2	1752	0.5		
22 TH	0008	2.4	0624	0.1	1250	2.1	1832	0.4
23 F	0051	2.4	0706	0.2	1332	2.1	1914	0.5
24 SA	0135	2.3	0748	0.3	1414	2.0	1958	0.6
25 SU	0222	2.2	0834	0.5	1458	1.9	2047	0.7
26 M	0315	2.0	0925	0.8	1549	1.8	☾ 2150	0.8
27 TU	0418	1.8	1036	1.0	1652	1.7	2335	0.9
28 W	0545	1.7	1224	1.1	1821	1.7		
29 TH	0112	0.9	0731	1.7	1343	1.1	1945	1.8
30 F	0222	0.8	0844	1.7	1441	1.0	2046	1.9
31 SA	0313	0.7	0933	1.8	1525	0.9	2134	2.0

SEPTEMBER

Date	Time	m	Time	m	Time	m	Time	m
1 SU	0353	0.6	1012	1.9	1601	0.8	2214	2.1
2 M	0427	0.5	1046	2.0	1633	0.7	2250	2.1
3 TU	0458	0.4	1118	2.0	1703	0.7	● 2323	2.2
4 W	0528	0.4	1148	2.0	1732	0.6	2353	2.2
5 TH	0557	0.4	1216	2.0	1800	0.6		
6 F	0021	2.1	0626	0.5	1242	2.0	1829	0.7
7 SA	0049	2.1	0655	0.6	1309	1.9	1858	0.7
8 SU	0119	2.0	0725	0.7	1338	1.9	1931	0.8
9 M	0152	1.9	0758	0.8	1413	1.8	2008	0.9
10 TU	0233	1.8	0836	0.9	1455	1.8	2057	1.0
11 W	0326	1.7	0927	1.1	1550	1.7	☽ 2210	1.1
12 TH	0436	1.6	1053	1.1	1700	1.7		
13 F	0014	1.0	0611	1.6	1245	1.1	1831	1.7
14 SA	0130	0.9	0749	1.7	1352	1.0	1953	1.8
15 SU	0227	0.7	0846	1.9	1444	0.9	2048	2.0
16 M	0313	0.5	0933	2.0	1528	0.7	2135	2.2
17 TU	0356	0.3	1017	2.1	1608	0.6	2219	2.3
18 W	0437	0.2	1059	2.2	1648	0.5	O 2302	2.4
19 TH	0517	0.1	1141	2.3	1727	0.4	2345	2.5
20 F	0557	0.1	1221	2.2	1808	0.4		
21 SA	0028	2.4	0639	0.3	1300	2.2	1851	0.5
22 SU	0113	2.3	0720	0.5	1341	2.1	1936	0.6
23 M	0201	2.1	0804	0.7	1424	2.0	2028	0.7
24 TU	0257	1.9	0855	1.0	1515	1.9	☾ 2138	0.9
25 W	0404	1.7	1011	1.2	1621	1.8	2333	0.9
26 TH	0543	1.6	1211	1.2	1800	1.7		
27 F	0101	0.9	0730	1.7	1328	1.2	1927	1.8
28 SA	0206	0.8	0829	1.7	1422	1.1	2024	1.9
29 SU	0251	0.7	0909	1.8	1502	0.9	2109	2.0
30 M	0327	0.6	0943	1.9	1536	0.8	2147	2.1

OCTOBER

Date	Time	m	Time	m	Time	m	Time	m
1 TU	0359	0.5	1015	2.0	1606	0.7	2221	2.1
2 W	0427	0.5	1044	2.0	1635	0.7	● 2252	2.2
3 TH	0455	0.5	1113	2.1	1702	0.6	2322	2.2
4 F	0522	0.5	1140	2.1	1730	0.6	2351	2.2
5 SA	0550	0.6	1206	2.1	1800	0.7		
6 SU	0019	2.1	0620	0.6	1232	2.1	1831	0.7
7 M	0049	2.0	0650	0.8	1302	2.0	1906	0.8
8 TU	0124	2.0	0723	0.9	1336	2.0	1946	0.9
9 W	0207	1.8	0802	1.0	1418	1.9	2037	1.0
10 TH	0304	1.7	0856	1.1	1514	1.8	☽ 2152	1.0
11 F	0419	1.6	1023	1.2	1629	1.7	2347	1.0
12 SA	0553	1.6	1221	1.2	1800	1.7		
13 SU	0102	0.8	0725	1.8	1326	1.0	1923	1.9
14 M	0159	0.7	0820	1.9	1417	0.9	2020	2.0
15 TU	0246	0.5	0906	2.1	1501	0.7	2108	2.2
16 W	0329	0.3	0949	2.2	1542	0.6	2153	2.4
17 TH	0410	0.2	1030	2.3	1623	0.5	O 2237	2.5
18 F	0451	0.2	1111	2.3	1704	0.4	2322	2.5
19 SA	0532	0.3	1151	2.3	1747	0.4		
20 SU	0008	2.4	0613	0.5	1230	2.2	1832	0.5
21 M	0056	2.3	0656	0.7	1312	2.2	1921	0.6
22 TU	0147	2.1	0740	0.9	1357	2.1	2016	0.7
23 W	0245	1.9	0832	1.1	1450	1.9	2130	0.9
24 TH	0350	1.7	0948	1.2	1554	1.8	☾ 2308	0.9
25 F	0520	1.6	1134	1.3	1723	1.8		
26 SA	0028	0.9	0653	1.7	1252	1.2	1849	1.8
27 SU	0131	0.8	0749	1.7	1348	1.1	1948	1.9
28 M	0217	0.8	0830	1.8	1430	1.0	2033	2.0
29 TU	0253	0.7	0905	1.9	1505	0.9	2112	2.0
30 W	0324	0.7	0938	2.0	1536	0.8	2148	2.1
31 TH	0353	0.6	1009	2.1	1605	0.7	2221	2.1

NOVEMBER

Date	Time	m	Time	m	Time	m	Time	m
1 F	0421	0.6	1038	2.1	1634	0.7	● 2253	2.1
2 SA	0450	0.6	1107	2.1	1705	0.7	2324	2.1
3 SU	0520	0.7	1135	2.2	1737	0.7	2357	2.1
4 M	0551	0.8	1205	2.1	1812	0.7		
5 TU	0031	2.0	0625	0.8	1237	2.1	1851	0.8
6 W	0110	2.0	0702	0.9	1314	2.0	1936	0.8
7 TH	0158	1.9	0745	1.0	1358	2.0	2031	0.9
8 F	0258	1.8	0843	1.1	1455	1.9	2141	0.9
9 SA	0408	1.7	1001	1.2	1608	1.8	☽ 2310	0.9
10 SU	0529	1.7	1139	1.1	1728	1.8		
11 M	0026	0.8	0648	1.8	1249	1.0	1846	1.9
12 TU	0125	0.6	0746	1.9	1344	0.9	1947	2.1
13 W	0216	0.5	0835	2.0	1432	0.8	2040	2.2
14 TH	0302	0.5	0920	2.2	1517	0.6	2129	2.3
15 F	0345	0.4	1003	2.2	1602	0.5	O 2217	2.4
16 SA	0428	0.5	1045	2.3	1647	0.5	2306	2.4
17 SU	0510	0.6	1127	2.3	1733	0.5	2356	2.3
18 M	0553	0.7	1209	2.3	1820	0.5		
19 TU	0047	2.2	0638	0.8	1253	2.2	1912	0.6
20 W	0138	2.0	0724	1.0	1339	2.1	2007	0.7
21 TH	0231	1.9	0814	1.1	1430	2.0	2109	0.8
22 F	0327	1.8	0914	1.2	1526	1.9	2219	0.9
23 SA	0430	1.7	1029	1.2	1631	1.8	☾ 2330	0.9
24 SU	0544	1.7	1147	1.2	1750	1.8		
25 M	0034	0.9	0649	1.7	1255	1.1	1857	1.8
26 TU	0127	0.9	0740	1.8	1348	1.1	1950	1.9
27 W	0209	0.8	0822	1.9	1429	1.0	2034	1.9
28 TH	0245	0.8	0859	2.0	1505	0.9	2114	2.0
29 F	0317	0.8	0934	2.0	1538	0.8	2152	2.0
30 SA	0350	0.8	1007	2.1	1612	0.8	2229	2.1

DECEMBER

Date	Time	m	Time	m	Time	m	Time	m
1 SU	0423	0.8	1040	2.2	1647	0.8	● 2306	2.1
2 M	0457	0.8	1113	2.2	1724	0.7	2344	2.1
3 TU	0533	0.8	1147	2.2	1802	0.7		
4 W	0024	2.0	0611	0.9	1224	2.2	1845	0.7
5 TH	0108	2.0	0653	0.9	1304	2.1	1932	0.7
6 F	0157	1.9	0739	1.0	1351	2.1	2024	0.7
7 SA	0251	1.9	0832	1.0	1445	2.0	2123	0.8
8 SU	0351	1.8	0933	1.1	1547	2.0	☽ 2230	0.8
9 M	0456	1.8	1044	1.1	1654	1.9	2343	0.7
10 TU	0605	1.8	1202	1.0	1806	2.0		
11 W	0049	0.7	0709	1.9	1309	1.0	1915	2.0
12 TH	0147	0.7	0805	2.0	1407	0.8	2016	2.1
13 F	0239	0.7	0855	2.1	1500	0.7	2113	2.2
14 SA	0327	0.7	0942	2.2	1550	0.6	2208	2.2
15 SU	0413	0.7	1029	2.3	1639	0.6	O 2302	2.2
16 M	0457	0.8	1114	2.3	1727	0.5	2353	2.2
17 TU	0541	0.8	1158	2.3	1814	0.5		
18 W	0040	2.1	0625	0.9	1242	2.3	1902	0.6
19 TH	0126	2.0	0708	1.0	1325	2.2	1948	0.6
20 F	0210	1.9	0750	1.0	1409	2.1	2036	0.7
21 SA	0253	1.8	0834	1.1	1453	2.0	2125	0.8
22 SU	0338	1.7	0921	1.1	1541	1.9	☾ 2218	0.9
23 M	0429	1.7	1021	1.2	1635	1.8	2316	0.9
24 TU	0530	1.7	1135	1.2	1742	1.8		
25 W	0017	1.0	0637	1.7	1248	1.1	1855	1.8
26 TH	0113	1.0	0734	1.8	1347	1.1	1954	1.8
27 F	0201	1.0	0821	1.9	1435	1.0	2044	1.9
28 SA	0245	0.9	0903	2.0	1517	0.9	2129	1.9
29 SU	0325	0.9	0942	2.1	1557	0.8	2212	2.0
30 M	0405	0.9	1020	2.1	1636	0.7	● 2254	2.0
31 TU	0444	0.8	1059	2.2	1716	0.7	2337	2.1

ULLAPOOL
LAT 57°54′N
LONG 5°10′W

TIMES AND HEIGHTS OF HIGH AND LOW WATER (Heights in Metres)

TIME ZONE UT
For Summer Time (area enclosed in shaded box) add 1 hour

2024

JANUARY

Date	Time	m	Time	m	Time	m	Time	m
1 M	0401	1.8	0953	4.6	1640	1.7	2235	4.3
2 TU	0439	2.0	1033	4.5	1721	1.9	2323	4.1
3 W	0522	2.1	1122	4.3	1808	2.0		
4 TH ☾	0021	4.0	0612	2.3	1224	4.1	1903	2.2
5 F	0130	3.9	0715	2.4	1337	4.0	2009	2.2
6 SA	0236	4.0	0828	2.5	1447	4.1	2117	2.2
7 SU	0336	4.1	0938	2.3	1549	4.2	2218	2.0
8 M	0428	4.4	1038	2.1	1644	4.4	2309	1.8
9 TU	0514	4.6	1130	1.8	1734	4.6	2356	1.6
10 W	0556	4.9	1218	1.5	1821	4.8		
11 TH ●	0040	1.4	0639	5.2	1305	1.2	1906	5.0
12 F	0124	1.2	0721	5.4	1350	0.9	1951	5.1
13 SA	0208	1.0	0804	5.5	1436	0.8	2037	5.1
14 SU	0251	1.0	0849	5.5	1521	0.7	2123	5.1
15 M	0335	1.1	0935	5.4	1607	0.8	2212	4.9
16 TU	0421	1.2	1026	5.2	1654	1.0	2305	4.6
17 W	0509	1.5	1122	5.0	1744	1.3		
18 TH ☽	0005	4.4	0604	1.8	1226	4.7	1840	1.6
19 F	0115	4.2	0709	2.0	1338	4.4	1947	1.9
20 SA	0232	4.1	0828	2.2	1456	4.3	2105	2.1
21 SU	0348	4.2	0953	2.1	1611	4.3	2223	2.1
22 M	0450	4.4	1104	2.0	1712	4.4	2323	1.9
23 TU	0539	4.6	1200	1.7	1800	4.5		
24 W	0010	1.7	0620	4.8	1244	1.5	1841	4.7
25 TH ○	0051	1.6	0654	4.9	1324	1.3	1917	4.8
26 F	0127	1.4	0726	5.0	1359	1.2	1949	4.8
27 SA	0201	1.3	0755	5.1	1432	1.1	2019	4.8
28 SU	0233	1.3	0823	5.1	1504	1.1	2048	4.8
29 M	0304	1.3	0851	5.0	1535	1.2	2118	4.7
30 TU	0335	1.4	0920	4.9	1606	1.3	2150	4.5
31 W	0407	1.6	0952	4.7	1638	1.5		

FEBRUARY

Date	Time	m	Time	m	Time	m	Time	m
1 TH	0441	1.8	1028	4.5	1714	1.8	2310	4.1
2 F ☾	0520	2.0	1111	4.3	1756	2.0		
3 SA	0009	4.0	0609	2.2	1210	4.0	1850	2.2
4 SU	0128	3.9	0714	2.4	1341	3.9	2007	2.4
5 M	0247	3.9	0844	2.5	1512	3.9	2139	2.3
6 TU	0358	4.1	1011	2.2	1629	4.1	2250	2.0
7 W	0456	4.4	1116	1.9	1727	4.4	2344	1.7
8 TH	0543	4.8	1209	1.4	1814	4.8		
9 F ●	0030	1.3	0626	5.2	1255	0.9	1857	5.1
10 SA	0114	1.0	0707	5.5	1339	0.6	1937	5.3
11 SU	0155	0.7	0747	5.7	1422	0.3	2017	5.4
12 M	0236	0.6	0829	5.8	1503	0.3	2058	5.3
13 TU	0317	0.6	0911	5.6	1544	0.4	2140	5.1
14 W	0358	0.8	0956	5.4	1625	0.8	2226	4.8
15 TH	0441	1.1	1047	5.0	1709	1.2	2320	4.4
16 F ☽	0530	1.6	1150	4.5	1757	1.7		
17 SA	0031	4.1	0630	2.0	1309	4.2	1859	2.1
18 SU	0159	3.9	0755	2.3	1441	3.9	2032	2.4
19 M	0332	4.0	0947	2.3	1607	4.0	2216	2.3
20 TU	0442	4.2	1105	2.0	1709	4.2	2318	2.1
21 W	0530	4.4	1155	1.7	1753	4.4		
22 TH	0001	1.8	0608	4.6	1234	1.4	1828	4.6
23 F	0038	1.5	0638	4.8	1308	1.2	1858	4.7
24 SA ○	0111	1.3	0706	5.0	1339	1.0	1925	4.9
25 SU	0141	1.2	0731	5.1	1408	0.9	1951	4.9
26 M	0210	1.1	0756	5.1	1436	0.9	2017	4.9
27 TU	0238	1.1	0821	5.1	1504	1.0	2044	4.8
28 W	0306	1.1	0847	4.9	1531	1.1	2112	4.7
29 TH	0335	1.3	0916	4.8	1600	1.3	2143	4.5

MARCH

Date	Time	m	Time	m	Time	m	Time	m
1 F	0407	1.5	0948	4.6	1632	1.5	2220	4.3
2 SA	0442	1.7	1026	4.3	1708	1.8	2307	4.1
3 SU ☾	0525	2.0	1119	4.0	1755	2.1		
4 M	0026	3.9	0625	2.3	1257	3.7	1910	2.4
5 TU	0207	3.8	0803	2.4	1452	3.8	2113	2.4
6 W	0332	4.0	0955	2.2	1618	4.0	2237	2.1
7 TH	0436	4.4	1104	1.7	1715	4.4	2330	1.6
8 F	0524	4.8	1154	1.1	1758	4.8		
9 SA	0014	1.1	0606	5.2	1238	0.6	1837	5.2
10 SU ●	0055	0.7	0645	5.6	1319	0.3	1914	5.4
11 M	0135	0.4	0724	5.8	1359	0.1	1952	5.5
12 TU	0214	0.3	0804	5.8	1438	0.1	2030	5.4
13 W	0253	0.4	0845	5.6	1516	0.3	2109	5.1
14 TH	0333	0.6	0929	5.3	1555	0.7	2151	4.8
15 F	0416	1.0	1019	4.8	1636	1.2	2240	4.4
16 SA	0502	1.5	1125	4.3	1721	1.8	2352	4.0
17 SU ☽	0601	2.0	1251	3.9	1819	2.2		
18 M	0130	3.8	0733	2.3	1426	3.7	2002	2.5
19 TU	0309	3.8	0940	2.2	1553	3.8	2202	2.4
20 W	0421	4.0	1049	2.0	1652	4.0	2300	2.1
21 TH	0508	4.3	1133	1.6	1732	4.2	2340	1.8
22 F	0543	4.5	1209	1.4	1803	4.5		
23 SA	0014	1.5	0612	4.7	1240	1.1	1831	4.7
24 SU	0045	1.2	0638	4.9	1310	0.9	1856	4.8
25 M ○	0114	1.1	0702	5.0	1338	0.8	1921	4.9
26 TU	0142	1.0	0726	5.0	1405	0.8	1946	4.9
27 W	0210	0.9	0751	5.0	1431	0.8	2012	4.9
28 TH	0238	1.0	0818	4.9	1458	1.0	2039	4.8
29 F	0307	1.1	0847	4.7	1527	1.2	2110	4.6
30 SA	0339	1.3	0921	4.5	1559	1.4	2147	4.4
31 SU	0416	1.5	1003	4.2	1636	1.7	[illegible]	[illegible]

APRIL

Date	Time	m	Time	m	Time	m	Time	m
1 M	0501	1.8	1105	3.9	1724	2.1	2358	3.9
2 TU ☾	0603	2.1	1256	3.7	1842	2.4		
3 W	0141	3.8	0747	2.2	1439	3.7	2054	2.3
4 TH	0304	4.0	0937	1.9	1558	4.0	2214	1.9
5 F	0408	4.4	1041	1.4	1652	4.4	2306	1.5
6 SA	0457	4.8	1130	0.9	1734	4.8	2350	1.0
7 SU	0540	5.2	1213	0.5	1812	5.1		
8 M ●	0030	0.6	0620	5.5	1253	0.2	1849	5.3
9 TU	0110	0.4	0659	5.7	1332	0.1	1925	5.4
10 W	0150	0.3	0740	5.6	1411	0.2	2002	5.3
11 TH	0231	0.4	0822	5.4	1449	0.5	2041	5.1
12 F	0312	0.7	0909	5.0	1528	0.9	2123	4.7
13 SA	0355	1.0	1003	4.5	1609	1.4	2213	4.4
14 SU	0443	1.5	1111	4.1	1654	1.8	2325	4.0
15 M ☽	0543	1.9	1232	3.8	1751	2.3		
16 TU	0056	3.8	0711	2.2	1357	3.6	1927	2.5
17 W	0229	3.8	0901	2.1	1518	3.7	2119	2.4
18 TH	0341	3.9	1010	1.9	1617	3.9	2222	2.1
19 F	0431	4.1	1055	1.6	1657	4.1	2304	1.8
20 SA	0507	4.3	1132	1.4	1730	4.3	2340	1.5
21 SU	0538	4.5	1205	1.2	1758	4.6		
22 M	0012	1.3	0605	4.7	1235	1.0	1825	4.7
23 TU ○	0042	1.1	0631	4.8	1304	0.9	1850	4.8
24 W	0112	1.0	0657	4.8	1332	0.9	1917	4.9
25 TH	0142	1.0	0725	4.8	1401	0.9	1944	4.9
26 F	0213	1.0	0755	4.7	1430	1.0	2015	4.8
27 SA	0245	1.1	0830	4.6	1502	1.2	2051	4.6
28 SU	0321	1.2	0911	4.4	1538	1.4	2134	4.4
29 M	0402	1.5	1005	4.1	1620	1.7	2232	4.2
30 TU	0453	1.7	1123	3.9	1714	2.0	2354	4.0

MAY

Date	Time	m	Time	m	Time	m	Time	m
1 W ☾	0601	1.9	1254	3.8	1838	2.2		
2 TH	0119	4.0	0737	1.9	1416	3.9	2025	2.1
3 F	0233	4.2	0905	1.6	1527	4.1	2139	1.8
4 SA	0336	4.4	1008	1.3	1622	4.4	2234	1.4
5 SU	0428	4.8	1059	0.9	1706	4.7	2321	1.1
6 M	0513	5.1	1144	0.6	1746	5.0		
7 TU	0005	0.8	0556	5.3	1226	0.5	1824	5.2
8 W ●	0048	0.6	0639	5.3	1307	0.4	1903	5.2
9 TH	0130	0.5	0723	5.2	1347	0.6	1942	5.1
10 F	0213	0.6	0808	5.0	1427	0.8	2023	4.9
11 SA	0256	0.8	0858	4.7	1508	1.1	2107	4.7
12 SU	0342	1.1	0953	4.3	1549	1.5	2157	4.4
13 M	0431	1.5	1054	4.0	1635	1.8	2259	4.1
14 TU	0527	1.8	1159	3.8	1729	2.1		
15 W ☽	0011	3.9	0636	2.0	1308	3.7	1842	2.3
16 TH	0128	3.8	0757	2.0	1420	3.7	2010	2.3
17 F	0241	3.8	0909	1.9	1523	3.8	2122	2.2
18 SA	0338	3.9	1003	1.7	1611	4.0	2215	2.0
19 SU	0422	4.1	1046	1.6	1649	4.2	2257	1.7
20 M	0458	4.3	1124	1.4	1722	4.4	2334	1.5
21 TU	0530	4.4	1158	1.2	1752	4.6		
22 W	0009	1.4	0601	4.5	1230	1.1	1822	4.7
23 TH ○	0043	1.2	0633	4.6	1303	1.1	1853	4.8
24 F	0118	1.1	0707	4.6	1336	1.1	1926	4.8
25 SA	0154	1.1	0744	4.6	1411	1.1	2002	4.8
26 SU	0232	1.1	0828	4.5	1448	1.2	2045	4.7
27 M	0314	1.2	0918	4.4	1530	1.4	2134	4.6
28 TU	0400	1.3	1017	4.2	1617	1.6	2234	4.4
29 W	0454	1.4	1124	4.1	1715	1.8	2342	4.3
30 TH ☾	0558	1.5	1235	4.0	1826	1.9		
31 F	0052	4.3	0712	1.6	1345	4.0	1946	1.9

JUNE

Date	Time	m	Time	m	Time	m	Time	m
1 SA	0159	4.3	0825	1.5	1451	4.1	2058	1.8
2 SU	0302	4.5	0930	1.3	1550	4.3	2159	1.5
3 M	0359	4.6	1027	1.1	1640	4.6	2254	1.3
4 TU	0452	4.8	1118	1.0	1725	4.8	2344	1.1
5 W	0540	4.9	1205	0.9	1807	4.9		
6 TH ●	0032	0.9	0628	4.9	1249	0.9	1849	5.0
7 F	0118	0.9	0716	4.9	1331	1.0	1931	5.0
8 SA	0203	0.9	0803	4.7	1413	1.1	2013	4.9
9 SU	0248	1.0	0850	4.6	1454	1.3	2055	4.7
10 M	0332	1.1	0937	4.4	1535	1.5	2138	4.5
11 TU	0416	1.3	1024	4.2	1617	1.7	2224	4.3
12 W	0502	1.5	1114	4.0	1703	1.9	2316	4.1
13 TH	0552	1.7	1209	3.8	1755	2.1		
14 F ☽	0016	4.0	0649	1.9	1309	3.7	1856	2.2
15 SA	0122	3.9	0751	1.9	1413	3.8	2004	2.2
16 SU	0227	3.9	0854	1.9	1512	3.9	2110	2.2
17 M	0325	3.9	0950	1.8	1602	4.0	2207	2.0
18 TU	0414	4.0	1038	1.7	1644	4.2	2255	1.8
19 W	0457	4.2	1121	1.6	1722	4.4	2338	1.6
20 TH	0538	4.3	1201	1.4	1759	4.6		
21 F	0020	1.4	0618	4.5	1240	1.3	1836	4.8
22 SA ○	0101	1.2	0659	4.6	1320	1.2	1915	4.9
23 SU	0143	1.1	0743	4.6	1400	1.2	1956	4.9
24 M	0226	1.0	0828	4.6	1442	1.2	2041	4.9
25 TU	0311	0.9	0917	4.6	1526	1.2	2128	4.9
26 W	0357	1.0	1008	4.5	1613	1.3	2221	4.8
27 TH	0447	1.1	1104	4.4	1704	1.5	2318	4.7
28 F ☾	0540	1.2	1205	4.2	1801	1.6		
29 SA	0021	4.5	0639	1.3	1309	4.1	1907	1.8
30 SU	0126	4.4	0743	1.5	1416	4.1	2017	1.8

SUNRISE AND SUNSET TIMES

ULLAPOOL
At 57°54′N 5°10′W

UT		Sunrise	Sunset
Jan	01	0905	1544
	15	0853	1608
Feb	01	0824	1646
	15	0751	1719
Mar	01	0715	1752
	15	0637	1824
BST (UT+1)			
Apr	01	0649	2002
	15	0610	2033
May	01	0529	2108
	15	0457	2139
Jun	01	0429	2210
	15	0418	2225
Jul	01	0424	2225
	15	0442	2210
Aug	01	0515	2138
	15	0544	2104
Sep	01	0621	2020
	15	0651	1940
Oct	01	0725	1854
	15	0756	1816
UT			
Nov	01	0735	1633
	15	0807	1603
Dec	01	0840	1539
	15	0900	1532

ULLAPOOL
LAT 57°54′N
LONG 5°10′W

TIMES AND HEIGHTS OF HIGH AND LOW WATER (Heights in Metres)

TIME ZONE UT
For Summer Time (area enclosed in shaded box) add 1 hour

2024

JULY

Date	Day	Time	m	Time	m	Time	m	Time	m
1	M	0233	4.4	0851	1.5	1522	4.2	2129	1.8
2	TU	0340	4.4	0959	1.5	1622	4.4	2236	1.6
3	W	0442	4.4	1100	1.5	1715	4.5	2335	1.4
4	TH	0538	4.5	1153	1.4	1802	4.7		
5	F ●	0027	1.3	0628	4.6	1240	1.3	1845	4.8
6	SA	0114	1.1	0713	4.7	1323	1.3	1924	4.9
7	SU	0158	1.0	0754	4.7	1403	1.2	2001	4.9
8	M	0238	1.0	0832	4.6	1440	1.3	2036	4.8
9	TU	0316	1.1	0909	4.5	1517	1.3	2110	4.7
10	W	0353	1.2	0945	4.4	1553	1.5	2145	4.6
11	TH	0430	1.3	1023	4.2	1630	1.6	2222	4.4
12	F	0507	1.5	1106	4.1	1710	1.8	2305	4.2
13	SA ☽	0548	1.7	1158	3.9	1754	2.0	2359	4.0
14	SU	0636	1.9	1301	3.8	1848	2.2		
15	M	0108	3.9	0734	2.1	1407	3.8	1956	2.3
16	TU	0221	3.8	0843	2.1	1511	3.9	2111	2.3
17	W	0330	3.8	0953	2.1	1609	4.1	2219	2.1
18	TH	0432	4.0	1051	1.9	1658	4.3	2315	1.8
19	F	0524	4.2	1141	1.7	1742	4.5		
20	SA	0004	1.5	0610	4.4	1225	1.4	1823	4.8
21	SU ○	0050	1.2	0652	4.7	1308	1.2	1903	5.1
22	M	0134	0.9	0734	4.8	1350	1.0	1944	5.2
23	TU	0217	0.7	0816	4.9	1432	0.9	2026	5.3
24	W	0300	0.6	0859	4.9	1514	0.9	2109	5.3
25	TH	0342	0.6	0944	4.8	1557	1.0	2156	5.2
26	F	0426	0.7	1032	4.6	1642	1.2	2248	4.9
27	SA	0512	1.0	1128	4.4	1732	1.4	2348	4.6
28	SU ☾	0603	1.3	1233	4.2	1830	1.7		
29	M	0057	4.4	0702	1.7	1346	4.1	1943	2.0
30	TU	0214	4.2	0817	1.9	1504	4.1	2111	2.0
31	W	0335	4.1	0943	2.0	1617	4.2	2234	1.9

AUGUST

Date	Day	Time	m	Time	m	Time	m	Time	m
1	TH	0446	4.2	1056	1.9	1714	4.4	2337	1.6
2	F	0541	4.4	1150	1.7	1759	4.6		
3	SA	0026	1.4	0625	4.5	1234	1.5	1837	4.8
4	SU ●	0108	1.2	0702	4.7	1313	1.3	1910	4.9
5	M	0145	1.0	0735	4.7	1348	1.2	1940	5.0
6	TU	0219	0.9	0806	4.8	1421	1.2	2009	5.0
7	W	0251	0.9	0835	4.7	1452	1.2	2037	4.9
8	TH	0322	1.0	0905	4.6	1523	1.2	2106	4.8
9	F	0353	1.1	0936	4.5	1555	1.4	2136	4.6
10	SA	0424	1.3	1010	4.3	1628	1.6	2210	4.4
11	SU	0458	1.6	1051	4.1	1705	1.9	2252	4.1
12	M ☽	0536	1.9	1147	3.9	1750	2.1	2348	3.9
13	TU	0624	2.1	1305	3.8	1850	2.3		
14	W	0122	3.7	0734	2.3	1425	3.8	2017	2.4
15	TH	0257	3.7	0913	2.3	1538	4.0	2153	2.3
16	F	0416	3.9	1032	2.1	1638	4.2	2300	1.9
17	SA	0513	4.2	1126	1.8	1724	4.6	2351	1.5
18	SU	0557	4.5	1212	1.4	1805	5.0		
19	M ○	0035	1.0	0636	4.9	1253	1.0	1844	5.3
20	TU	0117	0.6	0714	5.1	1333	0.8	1923	5.6
21	W	0158	0.3	0753	5.3	1413	0.6	2002	5.7
22	TH	0238	0.2	0832	5.3	1452	0.6	2043	5.6
23	F	0318	0.3	0912	5.1	1533	0.7	2127	5.4
24	SA	0359	0.6	0956	4.8	1616	1.0	2217	5.0
25	SU	0441	1.0	1048	4.5	1703	1.4	2318	4.6
26	M ☾	0528	1.5	1158	4.2	1759	1.8		
27	TU	0038	4.2	0626	2.0	1324	4.0	1919	2.1
28	W	0208	4.0	0750	2.3	1456	4.0	2112	2.2
29	TH	0338	3.9	0943	2.3	1613	4.2	2240	2.0
30	F	0446	4.1	1055	2.1	1707	4.4	2334	1.6
31	SA	0534	4.3	1142	1.8	1747	4.6		

SEPTEMBER

Date	Day	Time	m	Time	m	Time	m	Time	m
1	SU	0014	1.4	0611	4.5	1219	1.5	1819	4.8
2	M	0050	1.1	0641	4.7	1253	1.3	1847	5.0
3	TU ●	0122	1.0	0708	4.8	1325	1.1	1913	5.1
4	W	0152	0.9	0735	4.9	1355	1.1	1938	5.1
5	TH	0220	0.9	0800	4.9	1423	1.1	2003	5.0
6	F	0248	0.9	0827	4.8	1451	1.1	2029	4.9
7	SA	0315	1.1	0854	4.7	1521	1.3	2058	4.7
8	SU	0344	1.3	0924	4.5	1552	1.5	2129	4.5
9	M	0414	1.5	1000	4.3	1627	1.8	2206	4.2
10	TU	0449	1.9	1046	4.1	1708	2.1	2258	3.9
11	W ☽	0533	2.2	1206	3.9	1805	2.3		
12	TH	0043	3.7	0641	2.5	1349	3.8	1939	2.5
13	F	0237	3.7	0846	2.5	1511	4.0	2136	2.3
14	SA	0400	3.9	1015	2.2	1614	4.3	2243	1.8
15	SU	0454	4.3	1107	1.8	1701	4.7	2331	1.3
16	M	0536	4.7	1150	1.3	1741	5.2		
17	TU	0013	0.8	0613	5.1	1230	0.9	1819	5.5
18	W ○	0053	0.4	0649	5.4	1309	0.6	1857	5.8
19	TH	0132	0.2	0725	5.5	1348	0.4	1936	5.9
20	F	0211	0.1	0802	5.5	1428	0.4	2017	5.7
21	SA	0250	0.3	0841	5.3	1508	0.6	2101	5.4
22	SU	0330	0.7	0923	5.0	1551	1.0	2152	4.9
23	M	0411	1.2	1014	4.6	1639	1.4	2259	4.4
24	TU ☾	0457	1.7	1128	4.2	1738	1.9		
25	W	0028	4.0	0556	2.2	1306	4.0	1908	2.3
26	TH	0202	3.9	0732	2.6	1443	4.0	2113	2.2
27	F	0330	3.9	0934	2.5	1557	4.2	2227	1.9
28	SA	0432	4.1	1037	2.2	1647	4.4	2312	1.7
29	SU	0513	4.4	1119	1.9	1723	4.6	2349	1.4
30	M	0545	4.6	1154	1.6	1753	4.8		

OCTOBER

Date	Day	Time	m	Time	m	Time	m	Time	m
1	TU	0021	1.2	0613	4.8	1226	1.3	1820	5.0
2	W ●	0051	1.0	0639	4.9	1256	1.2	1844	5.1
3	TH	0120	0.9	0704	5.0	1325	1.1	1908	5.1
4	F	0147	0.9	0728	5.0	1353	1.1	1933	5.0
5	SA	0214	1.0	0754	5.0	1421	1.2	1959	4.9
6	SU	0241	1.1	0821	4.9	1451	1.3	2028	4.8
7	M	0309	1.3	0850	4.7	1522	1.5	2101	4.5
8	TU	0340	1.6	0926	4.5	1558	1.7	2141	4.2
9	W	0416	1.9	1013	4.2	1642	2.0	2241	3.9
10	TH ☽	0501	2.2	1133	4.0	1741	2.3		
11	F	0034	3.7	0612	2.5	1319	3.9	1918	2.4
12	SA	0215	3.8	0821	2.5	1440	4.1	2110	2.1
13	SU	0333	4.1	0947	2.2	1543	4.4	2215	1.7
14	M	0427	4.4	1039	1.7	1631	4.8	2303	1.2
15	TU	0508	4.8	1122	1.3	1713	5.3	2345	0.8
16	W	0545	5.2	1203	0.9	1752	5.6		
17	TH ○	0025	0.4	0622	5.4	1243	0.6	1832	5.8
18	F	0105	0.3	0659	5.6	1324	0.5	1913	5.8
19	SA	0145	0.3	0736	5.5	1405	0.5	1956	5.6
20	SU	0225	0.6	0816	5.3	1448	0.8	2043	5.2
21	M	0305	0.9	0900	5.0	1533	1.1	2138	4.8
22	TU	0348	1.4	0951	4.7	1623	1.5	2249	4.3
23	W	0435	1.9	1105	4.3	1725	2.0		
24	TH ☾	0011	4.0	0534	2.3	1238	4.1	1851	2.2
25	F	0137	3.9	0704	2.6	1409	4.0	2036	2.2
26	SA	0258	3.9	0851	2.5	1522	4.2	2148	2.0
27	SU	0359	4.1	0958	2.3	1613	4.3	2235	1.8
28	M	0441	4.3	1043	2.0	1651	4.5	2313	1.6
29	TU	0514	4.5	1121	1.7	1722	4.7	2347	1.4
30	W	0542	4.7	1154	1.5	1750	4.8		
31	TH	0017	1.2	0609	4.9	1225	1.4	1816	4.9

NOVEMBER

Date	Day	Time	m	Time	m	Time	m	Time	m
1	F ●	0047	1.1	0635	5.0	1256	1.3	1842	5.0
2	SA	0115	1.1	0701	5.0	1326	1.2	1910	5.0
3	SU	0144	1.2	0728	5.0	1356	1.3	1939	4.9
4	M	0213	1.3	0758	5.0	1429	1.4	2012	4.7
5	TU	0244	1.5	0831	4.8	1504	1.5	2051	4.5
6	W	0319	1.7	0912	4.6	1543	1.7	2140	4.3
7	TH	0358	1.9	1004	4.4	1631	1.9	2249	4.1
8	F	0448	2.2	1119	4.2	1733	2.1		
9	SA ☽	0019	3.9	0601	2.4	1246	4.2	1859	2.2
10	SU	0142	4.0	0742	2.4	1401	4.3	2028	2.0
11	M	0255	4.2	0904	2.2	1505	4.6	2136	1.6
12	TU	0352	4.5	1002	1.8	1558	4.9	2228	1.3
13	W	0439	4.8	1051	1.4	1645	5.2	2315	1.0
14	TH	0519	5.1	1137	1.1	1729	5.4	2359	0.7
15	F ○	0559	5.3	1221	0.9	1813	5.6		
16	SA	0041	0.7	0639	5.4	1305	0.8	1858	5.5
17	SU	0123	0.7	0719	5.4	1350	0.8	1945	5.3
18	M	0205	0.9	0802	5.3	1435	1.0	2036	5.0
19	TU	0248	1.2	0847	5.1	1523	1.2	2131	4.7
20	W	0331	1.6	0938	4.8	1613	1.5	2231	4.4
21	TH	0418	1.9	1038	4.5	1709	1.8	2336	4.1
22	F	0512	2.2	1150	4.3	1815	2.1		
23	SA ☾	0045	3.9	0619	2.5	1307	4.1	1931	2.2
24	SU	0159	3.9	0740	2.5	1422	4.1	2043	2.1
25	M	0305	4.0	0855	2.4	1522	4.2	2142	2.0
26	TU	0356	4.2	0954	2.2	1609	4.3	2229	1.8
27	W	0436	4.4	1040	2.0	1647	4.5	2308	1.7
28	TH	0511	4.6	1120	1.9	1721	4.6	2344	1.6
29	F	0542	4.7	1156	1.7	1753	4.7		
30	SA	0017	1.5	0612	4.9	1230	1.5	1824	4.8

DECEMBER

Date	Day	Time	m	Time	m	Time	m	Time	m
1	SU ●	0049	1.4	0642	5.0	1305	1.4	1857	4.8
2	M	0122	1.4	0713	5.0	1340	1.4	1932	4.8
3	TU	0155	1.4	0747	5.0	1417	1.4	2010	4.7
4	W	0231	1.5	0826	5.0	1456	1.4	2054	4.6
5	TH	0309	1.6	0909	4.9	1539	1.5	2144	4.5
6	F	0352	1.8	1000	4.7	1627	1.6	2243	4.3
7	SA	0443	2.0	1100	4.6	1723	1.7	2350	4.2
8	SU ☽	0544	2.1	1209	4.5	1829	1.8		
9	M	0101	4.2	0658	2.2	1319	4.5	1941	1.8
10	TU	0211	4.2	0814	2.1	1425	4.6	2050	1.7
11	W	0315	4.4	0922	1.9	1526	4.8	2153	1.5
12	TH	0411	4.6	1022	1.7	1623	4.9	2248	1.3
13	F	0500	4.9	1116	1.4	1716	5.1	2339	1.2
14	SA	0545	5.1	1208	1.2	1806	5.2		
15	SU ○	0026	1.1	0630	5.2	1256	1.1	1855	5.2
16	M	0111	1.1	0713	5.3	1344	1.0	1943	5.1
17	TU	0154	1.2	0756	5.3	1430	1.1	2030	5.0
18	W	0237	1.3	0838	5.2	1515	1.2	2115	4.8
19	TH	0319	1.5	0921	5.0	1559	1.4	2201	4.5
20	F	0401	1.7	1004	4.7	1644	1.6	2248	4.3
21	SA	0444	1.9	1051	4.5	1731	1.8	2339	4.1
22	SU ☾	0531	2.2	1145	4.3	1822	2.0		
23	M	0039	4.0	0627	2.3	1252	4.1	1921	2.2
24	TU	0147	3.9	0732	2.5	1405	4.0	2027	2.2
25	W	0254	4.0	0844	2.5	1511	4.1	2131	2.2
26	TH	0351	4.1	0950	2.4	1608	4.2	2226	2.1
27	F	0438	4.3	1044	2.2	1655	4.3	2312	1.9
28	SA	0518	4.5	1130	2.0	1736	4.4	2353	1.8
29	SU	0554	4.7	1212	1.8	1814	4.6		
30	M ●	0031	1.6	0630	4.9	1251	1.6	1852	4.7
31	TU	0108	1.5	0705	5.1	1331	1.4	1929	4.8

STORNOWAY
LAT 58°12′N
LONG 6°23′W

TIMES AND HEIGHTS OF HIGH AND LOW WATER (Heights in Metres)

TIME ZONE UT
For Summer Time (area enclosed in shaded box) add 1 hour

2024

JANUARY

Day	Time	m	Day	Time	m
1 M	0351 0948 1636 2229	1.7 4.4 1.6 3.9	16 TU	0412 1019 1649 2258	1.2 4.9 1.0 4.2
2 TU	0430 1028 1718 2317	1.8 4.2 1.8 3.8	17 W	0500 1115 1739	1.4 4.7 1.2
3 W	0512 1117 1805	2.0 4.0 1.9	18 TH ☽	0000 0555 1219 1835	4.0 1.7 4.4 1.5
4 TH ☾	0017 0603 1218 1901	3.6 2.2 3.9 2.0	19 F	0112 0700 1333 1942	3.8 1.9 4.2 1.8
5 F	0126 0705 1331 2006	3.6 2.3 3.8 2.1	20 SA	0230 0819 1449 2101	3.8 2.1 4.0 1.9
6 SA	0234 0818 1441 2113	3.7 2.3 3.8 2.0	21 SU	0344 0946 1603 2218	3.9 2.0 4.0 1.9
7 SU	0333 0930 1543 2213	3.8 2.2 3.9 1.9	22 M	0446 1059 1704 2316	4.1 1.9 4.1 1.8
8 M	0425 1031 1638 2304	4.1 2.0 4.1 1.7	23 TU	0534 1154 1753	4.3 1.6 4.2
9 TU	0509 1124 1727 2350	4.3 1.7 4.2 1.5	24 W	0003 0614 1239 1834	1.6 4.5 1.4 4.3
10 W	0551 1212 1814	4.6 1.4 4.5	25 TH ○	0042 0649 1319 1909	1.5 4.6 1.3 4.4
11 TH ●	0033 0633 1258 1900	1.3 4.8 1.1 4.6	26 F	0118 0720 1354 1941	1.3 4.7 1.1 4.4
12 F	0116 0715 1344 1945	1.1 5.0 0.9 4.7	27 SA	0152 0748 1427 2011	1.3 4.8 1.1 4.4
13 SA	0159 0757 1430 2030	1.0 5.2 0.7 4.7	28 SU	0224 0816 1459 2041	1.2 4.8 1.1 4.4
14 SU	0243 0842 1515 2116	0.9 5.2 0.7 4.6	29 M	0255 0845 1530 2111	1.2 4.7 1.1 4.3
15 M	0327 0929 1601 2205	1.0 5.1 0.8 4.5	30 TU	0327 0914 1602 2143	1.3 4.6 1.3 4.1
			31 W	0359 0946 1635 [illegible]	1.5 4.4 1.4

FEBRUARY

Day	Time	m	Day	Time	m
1 TH	0433 1022 1710 2305	1.6 4.2 1.6 3.8	16 F ☽	0521 1144 1751	1.5 4.2 1.6
2 F ☾	0511 1105 1751	1.9 4.0 1.9	17 SA	0027 0621 1305 1852	3.8 1.9 3.9 2.0
3 SA	0005 0559 1204 1845	3.6 2.1 3.8 2.1	18 SU	0158 0747 1435 2025	3.6 2.2 3.7 2.2
4 SU	0125 0704 1333 2002	3.6 2.3 3.6 2.2	19 M	0328 0944 1559 2210	3.7 2.1 3.7 2.2
5 M	0245 0835 1508 2134	3.6 2.3 3.6 2.1	20 TU	0437 1101 1702 2311	3.9 1.9 3.8 1.9
6 TU	0355 1005 1624 2244	3.8 2.1 3.8 1.9	21 W	0525 1150 1747 2354	4.1 1.6 4.0 1.7
7 W	0451 1111 1721 2337	4.1 1.8 4.1 1.6	22 TH	0601 1229 1821	4.4 1.3 4.2
8 TH	0537 1204 1808	4.5 1.3 4.4	23 F	0030 0632 1303 1851	1.4 4.5 1.1 4.4
9 F ●	0023 0620 1250 1850	1.2 4.9 0.9 4.7	24 SA ○	0102 0659 1334 1918	1.2 4.7 1.0 4.5
10 SA	0106 0700 1333 1931	0.9 5.2 0.5 4.9	25 SU	0133 0724 1403 1944	1.1 4.8 0.9 4.5
11 SU	0147 0741 1416 2011	0.7 5.4 0.3 4.9	26 M	0202 0749 1431 2010	1.0 4.8 0.8 4.5
12 M	0228 0822 1457 2052	0.6 5.4 0.3 4.8	27 TU	0230 0814 1459 2036	1.0 4.7 0.9 4.4
13 TU	0308 0904 1538 2134	0.6 5.3 0.4 4.6	28 W	0259 0841 1526 2105	1.0 4.6 1.0 4.3
14 W	0350 0950 1620 2219	0.8 5.0 0.7 4.3	29 TH	0328 0909 1555 2136	1.2 4.5 1.2 4.1
15 TH	0433 1041 1703 2313	1.1 4.7 1.1 4.0			

MARCH

Day	Time	m	Day	Time	m
1 F	0359 0941 1626 2213	1.4 4.2 1.4 4.0	16 SA	0454 1119 1713 2347	1.4 4.0 1.7 3.7
2 SA	0435 1019 1702 2303	1.6 4.0 1.7 3.7	17 SU ☽	0552 1249 1808	1.8 3.6 2.1
3 SU ☾	0517 1111 1747	1.9 3.7 2.0	18 M	0130 0728 1421 1950	3.6 2.2 3.4 2.4
4 M	0023 0615 1249 1859	3.6 2.2 3.5 2.2	19 TU	0302 0940 1546 2155	3.6 2.1 3.5 2.3
5 TU	0205 0755 1449 2106	3.5 2.3 3.5 2.2	20 W	0414 1046 1647 2252	3.8 1.8 3.7 2.0
6 W	0327 0951 1613 2230	3.7 2.0 3.7 1.9	21 TH	0502 1129 1726 2332	4.0 1.5 3.9 1.7
7 TH	0429 1100 1709 2323	4.1 1.6 4.1 1.5	22 F	0536 1204 1757	4.2 1.2 4.1
8 F	0517 1149 1752	4.5 1.1 4.4	23 SA	0006 0605 1235 1824	1.4 4.4 1.0 4.3
9 SA	0006 0559 1232 1831	1.1 4.9 0.6 4.8	24 SU	0037 0631 1304 1849	1.2 4.6 0.9 4.4
10 SU ●	0047 0638 1313 1908	0.7 5.3 0.2 5.0	25 M ○	0106 0655 1332 1914	1.0 4.6 0.8 4.5
11 M	0127 0717 1353 1945	0.4 5.5 0.0 5.0	26 TU	0134 0719 1359 1939	0.9 4.7 0.7 4.5
12 TU	0206 0757 1432 2023	0.3 5.5 0.1 4.9	27 W	0202 0744 1426 2004	0.9 4.6 0.8 4.5
13 W	0245 0838 1510 2102	0.3 5.3 0.3 4.7	28 TH	0231 0810 1453 2032	0.9 4.5 0.9 4.4
14 TH	0326 0922 1549 2143	0.6 4.9 0.7 4.4	29 F	0300 0840 1521 2103	1.0 4.4 1.1 4.3
15 F	0408 1013 1629 2232	0.9 4.5 1.1 4.0	30 SA	0333 0913 1552 2140	1.2 4.2 1.3 4.1
			31 SU	0409 0955 1628 2231	1.5 3.9 1.6 3.8

APRIL

Day	Time	m	Day	Time	m
1 M	0453 1058 1714 2355	1.7 3.6 1.9 3.6	16 TU	0056 0709 1352 1911	3.6 2.0 3.3 2.4
2 TU ☾	0554 1252 1828	2.0 3.4 2.2	17 W	0221 0903 1512 2109	3.6 2.0 3.4 2.3
3 W	0137 0742 1436 2045	3.6 2.1 3.4 2.2	18 TH	0332 1008 1612 2213	3.7 1.8 3.6 2.0
4 TH	0258 0933 1553 2206	3.8 1.8 3.7 1.9	19 F	0423 1052 1653 2256	3.9 1.5 3.8 1.8
5 F	0401 1037 1647 2258	4.1 1.3 4.1 1.4	20 SA	0500 1127 1724 2332	4.0 1.3 4.0 1.5
6 SA	0450 1124 1729 2342	4.5 0.8 4.4 1.0	21 SU	0530 1200 1752	4.2 1.1 4.2
7 SU	0532 1207 1806	4.9 0.4 4.7	22 M	0004 0558 1229 1818	1.3 4.4 0.9 4.4
8 M ●	0022 0612 1247 1843	0.6 5.2 0.2 4.9	23 TU ○	0035 0623 1258 1844	1.1 4.5 0.8 4.5
9 TU	0103 0652 1326 1919	0.4 5.3 0.1 5.0	24 W	0105 0649 1326 1910	1.0 4.5 0.8 4.5
10 W	0143 0733 1405 1956	0.3 5.3 0.2 4.9	25 TH	0135 0717 1354 1937	0.9 4.5 0.8 4.5
11 TH	0223 0815 1443 2034	0.4 5.0 0.4 4.7	26 F	0206 0747 1423 2008	0.9 4.4 0.9 4.5
12 F	0304 0902 1521 2116	0.6 4.6 0.8 4.4	27 SA	0238 0822 1455 2044	1.0 4.2 1.1 4.3
13 SA	0348 0956 1600 2205	1.0 4.2 1.3 4.1	28 SU	0314 0904 1529 2127	1.2 4.0 1.3 4.1
14 SU	0436 1107 1643 2319	1.4 3.8 1.7 3.8	29 M	0355 0959 1610 2227	1.4 3.8 1.6 3.9
15 M ☽	0536 1230 1738	1.8 3.5 2.1	30 TU	0446 1117 1702 2348	1.6 3.6 1.9 3.8

MAY

Day	Time	m	Day	Time	m
1 W ☾	0555 1250 1825	1.8 3.5 2.1	16 TH	0123 0755 1414 1955	3.6 1.9 3.4 2.2
2 TH	0113 0733 1413 2014	3.8 1.8 3.5 2.1	17 F	0231 0906 1517 2111	3.6 1.8 3.5 2.1
3 F	0226 0901 1523 2130	3.9 1.5 3.8 1.8	18 SA	0328 0959 1606 2205	3.7 1.6 3.7 1.9
4 SA	0327 1003 1617 2225	4.2 1.2 4.1 1.4	19 SU	0413 1041 1644 2248	3.9 1.4 3.9 1.7
5 SU	0419 1054 1701 2313	4.5 0.8 4.4 1.0	20 M	0450 1118 1716 2327	4.0 1.3 4.1 1.5
6 M	0505 1138 1741 2357	4.8 0.5 4.6 0.8	21 TU	0522 1152 1746	4.1 1.1 4.2
7 TU	0548 1221 1818	5.0 0.4 4.8	22 W	0002 0554 1224 1816	1.3 4.2 1.0 4.4
8 W ●	0040 0631 1301 1857	0.6 5.0 0.4 4.8	23 TH ○	0036 0625 1256 1846	1.2 4.3 1.0 4.5
9 TH	0123 0715 1340 1935	0.5 4.9 0.5 4.8	24 F	0111 0659 1328 1919	1.1 4.3 1.0 4.5
10 F	0206 0801 1419 2016	0.6 4.7 0.8 4.6	25 SA	0147 0736 1403 1956	1.0 4.3 1.1 4.5
11 SA	0250 0851 1459 2100	0.8 4.3 1.1 4.4	26 SU	0225 0820 1439 2038	1.0 4.2 1.2 4.4
12 SU	0335 0946 1540 2150	1.1 4.0 1.4 4.1	27 M	0307 0910 1520 2128	1.1 4.0 1.3 4.3
13 M	0425 1049 1624 2253	1.4 3.7 1.7 3.9	28 TU	0354 1010 1606 2227	1.2 3.9 1.5 4.2
14 TU	0522 1157 1716	1.7 3.5 2.0	29 W	0448 1118 1703 2335	1.4 3.7 1.7 4.1
15 W ☽	0008 0633 1305 1827	3.7 1.8 3.4 2.2	30 TH ☾	0553 1231 1815	1.4 3.7 1.9
			31 F	0044 0708 1341 1936	4.1 1.5 3.7 1.8

JUNE

Day	Time	m	Day	Time	m
1 SA	0152 0821 1448 2048	4.1 1.4 3.8 1.7	16 SU	0220 0849 1507 2059	3.7 1.8 3.6 2.1
2 SU	0254 0925 1546 2150	4.2 1.2 4.0 1.5	17 M	0317 0945 1558 2158	3.7 1.7 3.7 1.9
3 M	0351 1021 1636 2246	4.4 1.0 4.2 1.3	18 TU	0406 1033 1640 2248	3.8 1.6 3.9 1.8
4 TU	0444 1112 1720 2337	4.5 0.9 4.4 1.1	19 W	0450 1115 1718 2332	3.9 1.5 4.1 1.6
5 W	0533 1158 1802	4.6 0.9 4.6	20 TH	0530 1155 1753	4.0 1.3 4.3
6 TH ●	0025 0621 1241 1843	0.9 4.6 0.9 4.7	21 F	0013 0611 1233 1830	1.4 4.1 1.2 4.5
7 F	0111 0708 1323 1924	0.8 4.5 0.9 4.7	22 SA ○	0055 0652 1312 1908	1.2 4.2 1.1 4.6
8 SA	0157 0755 1404 2006	0.9 4.4 1.1 4.6	23 SU	0136 0735 1351 1949	1.0 4.3 1.1 4.7
9 SU	0241 0842 1444 2048	0.9 4.2 1.2 4.5	24 M	0220 0821 1433 2033	0.9 4.3 1.1 4.7
10 M	0326 0930 1524 2132	1.1 4.0 1.4 4.3	25 TU	0304 0909 1516 2121	0.9 4.2 1.2 4.6
11 TU	0411 1018 1606 2218	1.3 3.8 1.6 4.1	26 W	0351 1001 1603 2213	0.9 4.1 1.3 4.5
12 W	0458 1109 1651 2310	1.5 3.6 1.8 3.9	27 TH	0441 1058 1654 2310	1.0 4.0 1.4 4.4
13 TH	0548 1204 1743	1.6 3.5 2.0	28 F ☾	0535 1159 1751	1.1 3.9 1.6
14 F ☽	0010 0645 1305 1843	3.8 1.8 3.4 2.1	29 SA	0013 0634 1305 1857	4.3 1.3 3.8 1.7
15 SA	0116 0747 1409 1952	3.7 1.8 3.5 2.1	30 SU	0119 0738 1413 2008	4.2 1.4 3.8 1.7

SUNRISE AND SUNSET TIMES

STORNOWAY
At 58°12′N 6°23′W

UT		Sunrise	Sunset
Jan	01	0912	1546
	15	0900	1610
Feb	01	0830	1649
	15	0757	1723
Mar	01	0720	1756
	15	0641	1829
BST (UT+1)			
Apr	01	0653	2007
	15	0614	2038
May	01	0532	2115
	15	0500	2145
Jun	01	0431	2217
	15	0420	2232
Jul	01	0426	2232
	15	0445	2217
Aug	01	0518	2145
	15	0548	2110
Sep	01	0625	2024
	15	0655	1945
Oct	01	0730	1859
	15	0801	1820
UT			
Nov	01	0741	1637
	15	0813	1606
Dec	01	0847	1542

STORNOWAY
LAT 58°12'N
LONG 6°23'W

TIMES AND HEIGHTS OF HIGH AND LOW WATER (Heights in Metres)

TIME ZONE UT
For Summer Time (area enclosed in shaded box) add 1 hour

2024

JULY

Date	Day	Time	m	Time	m	Time	m	Time	m
1	M	0226	4.1	0846	1.4	1519	3.9	2120	1.7
2	TU	0332	4.1	0953	1.4	1619	4.0	2229	1.6
3	W	0435	4.2	1054	1.4	1711	4.2	2329	1.4
4	TH	0530	4.2	1146	1.3	1756	4.4		
5	F ●	0021	1.2	0621	4.3	1231	1.2	1839	4.6
6	SA	0109	1.1	0705	4.3	1314	1.2	1917	4.6
7	SU	0152	1.0	0746	4.3	1353	1.2	1954	4.6
8	M	0232	1.0	0825	4.3	1431	1.2	2029	4.6
9	TU	0311	1.0	0902	4.2	1507	1.3	2104	4.5
10	W	0348	1.1	0938	4.0	1544	1.4	2139	4.3
11	TH	0425	1.2	1016	3.9	1621	1.5	2216	4.1
12	F	0503	1.4	1100	3.7	1700	1.7	2259	4.0
13	SA ☽	0545	1.6	1153	3.6	1744	1.9	2352	3.8
14	SU	0632	1.8	1258	3.5	1838	2.1		
15	M	0101	3.6	0730	1.9	1405	3.5	1946	2.2
16	TU	0215	3.6	0839	2.0	1509	3.6	2103	2.2
17	W	0324	3.6	0948	1.9	1606	3.8	2213	2.0
18	TH	0426	3.7	1045	1.8	1654	4.0	2310	1.8
19	F	0517	3.9	1134	1.6	1736	4.3	2359	1.5
20	SA	0603	4.1	1218	1.4	1816	4.5		
21	SU O	0044	1.2	0646	4.3	1300	1.1	1856	4.8
22	M	0128	0.9	0727	4.5	1342	1.0	1937	4.9
23	TU	0211	0.6	0809	4.6	1423	0.9	2018	5.0
24	W	0254	0.5	0852	4.6	1505	0.8	2102	5.0
25	TH	0337	0.5	0937	4.4	1548	0.9	2149	4.9
26	F	0421	0.7	1026	4.3	1633	1.1	2240	4.7
27	SA	0507	0.9	1122	4.0	1722	1.4	2340	4.4
28	SU ☾	0557	1.2	1229	3.8	1820	1.6		
29	M	0050	4.1	0657	1.6	1344	3.7	1934	1.9
30	TU	0208	3.9	0811	1.8	1502	3.8	2104	1.9
31	W	0328	3.8	0937	1.9	1613	3.9	2230	1.8

AUGUST

Date	Day	Time	m	Time	m	Time	m	Time	m
1	TH	0438	3.9	1049	1.8	1709	4.2	2333	1.5
2	F	0534	4.0	1142	1.6	1753	4.4		
3	SA	0021	1.3	0618	4.2	1225	1.4	1831	4.6
4	SU ●	0103	1.1	0655	4.3	1304	1.3	1904	4.7
5	M	0140	0.9	0728	4.4	1339	1.2	1934	4.7
6	TU	0214	0.9	0758	4.4	1412	1.1	2002	4.7
7	W	0246	0.9	0828	4.3	1444	1.1	2030	4.6
8	TH	0317	0.9	0857	4.3	1515	1.2	2059	4.5
9	F	0348	1.1	0929	4.1	1547	1.3	2129	4.3
10	SA	0420	1.3	1003	4.0	1620	1.5	2203	4.1
11	SU	0453	1.5	1045	3.8	1657	1.8	2244	3.9
12	M ☽	0531	1.7	1143	3.6	1741	2.0	2341	3.6
13	TU	0618	2.0	1304	3.5	1840	2.2		
14	W	0115	3.5	0728	2.2	1425	3.6	2010	2.3
15	TH	0254	3.5	0907	2.2	1536	3.7	2149	2.2
16	F	0411	3.6	1026	2.0	1633	4.0	2257	1.8
17	SA	0507	3.9	1119	1.7	1718	4.3	2347	1.4
18	SU	0551	4.2	1204	1.3	1759	4.7		
19	M O	0030	1.0	0631	4.5	1245	1.0	1837	5.0
20	TU	0112	0.6	0708	4.7	1325	0.7	1916	5.3
21	W	0152	0.3	0746	4.9	1405	0.6	1955	5.4
22	TH	0232	0.2	0825	4.9	1444	0.5	2036	5.3
23	F	0312	0.3	0906	4.7	1525	0.7	2120	5.1
24	SA	0353	0.5	0950	4.5	1607	0.9	2209	4.7
25	SU	0435	0.9	1042	4.2	1654	1.3	2311	4.3
26	M ☾	0521	1.4	1153	3.9	1751	1.7		
27	TU	0033	3.9	0618	1.9	1324	3.7	1912	2.0
28	W	0204	3.7	0742	2.2	1453	3.7	2111	2.1
29	TH	0331	3.7	0937	2.2	1607	3.9	2237	1.8
30	F	0440	3.8	1047	2.0	1701	4.2	2330	1.5
31	SA	0528	4.0	1133	1.7	1741	4.4		

SEPTEMBER

Date	Day	Time	m	Time	m	Time	m	Time	m
1	SU	0010	1.3	0604	4.2	1211	1.5	1813	4.6
2	M	0045	1.1	0634	4.4	1245	1.3	1841	4.7
3	TU ●	0117	0.9	0702	4.5	1316	1.1	1907	4.8
4	W	0146	0.8	0728	4.5	1346	1.0	1932	4.8
5	TH	0215	0.8	0753	4.5	1415	1.0	1957	4.7
6	F	0242	0.9	0820	4.5	1444	1.1	2022	4.6
7	SA	0310	1.0	0847	4.4	1513	1.2	2050	4.4
8	SU	0339	1.2	0918	4.2	1545	1.4	2121	4.2
9	M	0409	1.5	0953	4.0	1619	1.7	2158	3.9
10	TU	0443	1.8	1042	3.8	1700	2.0	2250	3.6
11	W ☽	0525	2.1	1206	3.6	1755	2.2		
12	TH	0038	3.4	0629	2.3	1349	3.6	1932	2.4
13	F	0236	3.4	0838	2.4	1508	3.7	2135	2.1
14	SA	0355	3.6	1008	2.1	1608	4.1	2240	1.7
15	SU	0449	4.0	1100	1.7	1654	4.4	2327	1.2
16	M	0530	4.4	1143	1.3	1734	4.9		
17	TU	0008	0.8	0608	4.7	1222	0.9	1812	5.2
18	W O	0048	0.4	0643	5.0	1301	0.6	1850	5.5
19	TH	0127	0.1	0719	5.1	1340	0.4	1929	5.5
20	F	0206	0.1	0756	5.1	1420	0.4	2010	5.4
21	SA	0244	0.3	0835	4.9	1501	0.6	2054	5.1
22	SU	0324	0.6	0917	4.6	1544	0.9	2145	4.6
23	M	0404	1.1	1007	4.2	1631	1.4	2253	4.1
24	TU ☾	0449	1.6	1123	3.9	1730	1.8		
25	W	0026	3.7	0545	2.1	1306	3.8	1903	2.1
26	TH	0158	3.6	0720	2.4	1436	3.8	2114	2.1
27	F	0324	3.6	0927	2.4	1549	4.0	2224	1.8
28	SA	0427	3.8	1029	2.1	1640	4.2	2309	1.5
29	SU	0509	4.0	1111	1.8	1717	4.4	2345	1.3
30	M	0540	4.2	1146	1.5	1746	4.5		

OCTOBER

Date	Day	Time	m	Time	m	Time	m	Time	m
1	TU	0016	1.1	0607	4.4	1218	1.3	1813	4.7
2	W ●	0046	0.9	0632	4.6	1248	1.1	1837	4.8
3	TH	0114	0.9	0657	4.6	1317	1.1	1901	4.8
4	F	0141	0.9	0721	4.7	1346	1.0	1926	4.7
5	SA	0208	0.9	0747	4.6	1414	1.1	1952	4.6
6	SU	0235	1.1	0814	4.5	1444	1.2	2020	4.4
7	M	0303	1.3	0844	4.4	1516	1.4	2053	4.2
8	TU	0334	1.5	0919	4.2	1552	1.7	2133	3.9
9	W	0408	1.8	1008	3.9	1635	1.9	2235	3.6
10	TH ☽	0451	2.1	1132	3.7	1733	2.2		
11	F	0032	3.4	0559	2.4	1316	3.7	1915	2.3
12	SA	0214	3.5	0811	2.4	1435	3.9	2108	2.0
13	SU	0329	3.8	0939	2.1	1536	4.2	2211	1.6
14	M	0422	4.1	1031	1.7	1624	4.6	2258	1.1
15	TU	0504	4.5	1114	1.3	1706	5.0	2340	0.7
16	W	0541	4.8	1156	0.9	1745	5.3		
17	TH O	0020	0.4	0617	5.0	1236	0.6	1825	5.5
18	F	0059	0.3	0653	5.2	1316	0.5	1906	5.5
19	SA	0139	0.3	0731	5.1	1358	0.5	1949	5.3
20	SU	0218	0.5	0810	5.0	1441	0.7	2036	4.9
21	M	0258	0.9	0853	4.7	1526	1.1	2132	4.4
22	TU	0339	1.4	0945	4.4	1617	1.5	2244	4.0
23	W	0425	1.8	1101	4.1	1719	1.8		
24	TH ☾	0010	3.7	0522	2.2	1237	3.9	1849	2.1
25	F	0133	3.6	0649	2.5	1401	3.9	2038	2.1
26	SA	0253	3.6	0841	2.4	1513	3.9	2146	1.9
27	SU	0354	3.8	0949	2.2	1605	4.1	2232	1.6
28	M	0437	4.0	1035	1.9	1644	4.3	2309	1.4
29	TU	0508	4.2	1112	1.7	1715	4.4	2341	1.3
30	W	0536	4.4	1146	1.5	1742	4.5		
31	TH	0012	1.1	0603	4.5	1218	1.3	1809	4.6

NOVEMBER

Date	Day	Time	m	Time	m	Time	m	Time	m
1	F ●	0041	1.1	0629	4.6	1248	1.2	1835	4.7
2	SA	0109	1.0	0655	4.7	1319	1.2	1902	4.6
3	SU	0138	1.1	0722	4.7	1350	1.2	1931	4.5
4	M	0207	1.2	0751	4.6	1422	1.3	2004	4.4
5	TU	0237	1.4	0825	4.5	1457	1.4	2044	4.2
6	W	0311	1.6	0906	4.3	1537	1.6	2134	3.9
7	TH	0349	1.8	1000	4.1	1625	1.8	2245	3.7
8	F	0437	2.1	1116	4.0	1727	2.0		
9	SA ☽	0016	3.6	0549	2.3	1241	4.0	1855	2.0
10	SU	0140	3.7	0732	2.3	1355	4.1	2025	1.8
11	M	0251	3.9	0855	2.1	1458	4.3	2131	1.5
12	TU	0348	4.2	0954	1.7	1551	4.6	2223	1.1
13	W	0435	4.5	1043	1.4	1638	4.9	2310	0.9
14	TH	0515	4.7	1129	1.1	1722	5.1	2353	0.7
15	F O	0554	5.0	1214	0.9	1806	5.2		
16	SA	0035	0.6	0633	5.1	1258	0.8	1852	5.2
17	SU	0117	0.7	0713	5.1	1343	0.8	1939	5.0
18	M	0158	0.9	0755	5.0	1429	0.9	2029	4.7
19	TU	0239	1.2	0841	4.8	1516	1.2	2124	4.4
20	W	0322	1.5	0932	4.5	1607	1.4	2226	4.0
21	TH	0408	1.8	1033	4.3	1705	1.7	2333	3.8
22	F	0500	2.1	1147	4.1	1812	1.9		
23	SA ☾	0043	3.6	0606	2.3	1303	3.9	1928	2.0
24	SU	0153	3.6	0726	2.4	1413	3.9	2041	2.0
25	M	0259	3.7	0843	2.3	1513	4.0	2139	1.9
26	TU	0351	3.8	0944	2.2	1600	4.1	2224	1.7
27	W	0431	4.0	1031	2.0	1639	4.2	2303	1.6
28	TH	0505	4.2	1112	1.8	1713	4.3	2338	1.4
29	F	0536	4.4	1149	1.6	1745	4.4		
30	SA	0010	1.3	0606	4.6	1223	1.5	1817	4.4

DECEMBER

Date	Day	Time	m	Time	m	Time	m	Time	m
1	SU ●	0043	1.3	0636	4.7	1258	1.4	1849	4.5
2	M	0115	1.3	0707	4.7	1333	1.3	1924	4.4
3	TU	0148	1.3	0741	4.7	1410	1.3	2003	4.4
4	W	0223	1.4	0820	4.7	1450	1.4	2048	4.2
5	TH	0301	1.5	0904	4.6	1533	1.4	2138	4.1
6	F	0343	1.7	0955	4.5	1622	1.5	2238	4.0
7	SA	0433	1.9	1055	4.3	1719	1.6	2346	3.9
8	SU ☽	0534	2.0	1203	4.3	1825	1.7		
9	M	0058	3.8	0649	2.1	1312	4.3	1937	1.7
10	TU	0208	3.9	0805	2.0	1418	4.3	2046	1.5
11	W	0312	4.1	0913	1.8	1519	4.5	2148	1.4
12	TH	0407	4.3	1014	1.6	1616	4.6	2243	1.2
13	F	0456	4.5	1109	1.4	1709	4.7	2333	1.1
14	SA	0541	4.7	1201	1.2	1759	4.8		
15	SU O	0019	1.1	0624	4.9	1250	1.0	1848	4.8
16	M	0103	1.1	0707	5.0	1338	1.0	1936	4.7
17	TU	0146	1.1	0749	4.9	1424	1.0	2023	4.6
18	W	0228	1.3	0832	4.9	1509	1.1	2109	4.4
19	TH	0309	1.4	0915	4.7	1554	1.3	2154	4.2
20	F	0351	1.6	0958	4.5	1639	1.5	2242	3.9
21	SA	0434	1.8	1045	4.3	1727	1.7	2334	3.8
22	SU ☾	0521	2.0	1141	4.1	1818	1.9		
23	M	0035	3.6	0615	2.2	1248	3.9	1917	2.0
24	TU	0143	3.6	0720	2.3	1359	3.8	2022	2.1
25	W	0249	3.7	0832	2.4	1504	3.8	2127	2.0
26	TH	0346	3.8	0941	2.3	1600	3.9	2221	1.9
27	F	0433	4.0	1037	2.1	1648	4.0	2307	1.8
28	SA	0513	4.2	1124	1.9	1729	4.1	2347	1.6
29	SU	0549	4.4	1206	1.7	1807	4.2		
30	M ●	0024	1.5	0624	4.6	1245	1.5	1845	4.4
31	TU	0101	1.4	0658	4.7	1325	1.3	1922	4.4

OBAN
LAT 56°25′N
LONG 5°29′W

TIMES AND HEIGHTS OF HIGH AND LOW WATER (Heights in Metres)

TIME ZONE UT
For Summer Time (area enclosed in shaded box) add 1 hour

2024

JANUARY

Date	Day	Time	m
1	M	0249 0840 1531 2104	1.4 3.7 1.8 3.4
2	TU	0328 0918 1612 2144	1.5 3.5 1.9 3.2
3	W	0410 0959 1659 2230	1.6 3.4 2.0 3.1
4	TH ☽	0455 1046 1754 2328	1.8 3.2 2.1 3.0
5	F	0546 1147 1856	1.9 3.2 2.1
6	SA	0052 0645 1313 2000	3.0 1.9 3.1 2.0
7	SU	0216 0749 1434 2058	3.0 1.8 3.2 1.8
8	M	0315 0853 1532 2149	3.2 1.7 3.4 1.6
9	TU	0403 0955 1621 2234	3.4 1.5 3.6 1.4
10	W	0448 1050 1705 2317	3.6 1.3 3.7 1.1
11	TH ●	0530 1142 1747	3.8 1.0 3.8
12	F	0000 0613 1229 1828	0.9 4.0 0.9 3.9
13	SA	0043 0655 1316 1908	0.7 4.1 0.8 3.8
14	SU	0128 0737 1402 1949	0.6 4.1 0.8 3.7
15	M	0213 0821 1449 2031	0.6 4.0 0.9 3.6
16	TU	0300 0906 1537 2116	0.7 3.9 1.1 3.4
17	W	0349 0956 1627 2204	0.9 3.6 1.3 3.2
18	TH ☾	0444 1055 1723 2303	1.1 3.4 1.5 3.0
19	F	0546 1214 1826	1.4 3.2 1.6
20	SA	0024 0700 1348 1936	2.9 1.6 3.1 1.7
21	SU	0158 0826 1510 2048	2.9 1.6 3.1 1.7
22	M	0313 0950 1612 2150	3.1 1.6 3.2 1.6
23	TU	0407 1050 1654 2240	3.3 1.5 3.4 1.4
24	W	0448 1136 1728 2322	3.5 1.4 3.5 1.2
25	TH ○	0527 1215 1800	3.7 1.3 3.6
26	F	0001 0604 1250 1832	1.1 3.9 1.3 3.7
27	SA	0039 0639 1324 1904	1.0 3.9 1.3 3.8
28	SU	0115 0712 1356 1935	1.0 4.0 1.3 3.8
29	M	0149 0744 1426 2005	1.0 3.9 1.4 3.7
30	TU	0221 0814 1455 2034	1.1 3.8 1.5 3.6
31	W	0251 0843 1521 2103	1.3 3.7 1.6 3.4

FEBRUARY

Date	Day	Time	m
1	TH	0322 0912 1548 2136	1.4 3.5 1.8 3.3
2	F ☽	0357 0946 1628 2216	1.6 3.3 1.9 3.1
3	SA	0442 1030 1731 2309	1.8 3.2 2.0 2.9
4	SU	0545 1133 1852	1.9 3.0 2.1
5	M	0048 0704 1354 2013	2.9 1.9 2.9 1.9
6	TU	0256 0828 1529 2124	3.0 1.8 3.1 1.7
7	W	0357 0947 1622 2220	3.3 1.5 3.4 1.3
8	TH	0443 1049 1704 2307	3.6 1.2 3.6 1.0
9	F ●	0525 1139 1743 2351	3.9 0.9 3.8 0.7
10	SA	0605 1224 1820	4.2 0.6 3.9
11	SU	0033 0645 1305 1856	0.4 4.3 0.5 4.0
12	M	0115 0724 1346 1933	0.3 4.3 0.5 3.9
13	TU	0157 0803 1426 2010	0.3 4.2 0.6 3.8
14	W	0241 0842 1508 2047	0.4 4.0 0.8 3.6
15	TH	0325 0924 1552 2127	0.7 3.6 1.1 3.3
16	F ☾	0414 1011 1641 2212	1.0 3.3 1.4 3.1
17	SA	0511 1114 1740 2320	1.4 2.9 1.6 2.8
18	SU	0624 1325 1853	1.7 2.8 1.8
19	M	0128 0822 1531 2022	2.8 1.8 2.8 1.8
20	TU	0411 1005 1629 2142	2.9 1.7 3.0 1.6
21	W	0442 1055 1659 2233	3.2 1.5 3.2 1.4
22	TH	0446 1132 1719 2313	3.4 1.3 3.4 1.2
23	F	0516 1204 1745 2348	3.6 1.2 3.6 1.0
24	SA ○	0548 1234 1814	3.8 1.1 3.8
25	SU	0022 0621 1301 1844	0.8 3.9 1.0 3.9
26	M	0054 0651 1329 1911	0.8 4.0 1.1 3.9
27	TU	0123 0719 1355 1937	0.8 3.9 1.1 3.8
28	W	0150 0744 1416 2001	0.9 3.9 1.2 3.7
29	TH	0214 0808 1432 2026	1.1 3.7 1.4 3.6

MARCH

Date	Day	Time	m
1	F	0239 0832 1453 2055	1.2 3.6 1.5 3.4
2	SA	0310 0902 1527 2131	1.4 3.4 1.7 3.2
3	SU ☽	0352 0941 1619 2219	1.6 3.1 1.9 3.0
4	M	0457 1039 1801 2346	1.9 2.9 2.0 2.8
5	TU	0640 1354 1940	1.9 2.7 1.9
6	W	0247 0822 1529 2104	3.0 1.8 3.0 1.6
7	TH	0345 0946 1615 2205	3.3 1.4 3.3 1.2
8	F	0429 1041 1653 2252	3.7 1.0 3.5 0.8
9	SA	0509 1126 1727 2335	4.0 0.7 3.8 0.4
10	SU ●	0547 1207 1801	4.3 0.4 4.0
11	M	0016 0625 1245 1835	0.2 4.4 0.3 4.0
12	TU	0057 0702 1322 1909	0.1 4.4 0.3 4.0
13	W	0138 0738 1400 1944	0.1 4.2 0.4 3.9
14	TH	0220 0815 1438 2019	0.4 3.9 0.7 3.7
15	F	0303 0852 1520 2055	0.7 3.6 1.0 3.4
16	SA	0350 0934 1608 2135	1.1 3.2 1.3 3.1
17	SU ☾	0446 1028 1707 2233	1.5 2.8 1.6 2.8
18	M	0602 1320 1820	1.8 2.5 1.8
19	TU	0110 0842 1522 1956	2.7 1.9 2.7 1.8
20	W	0408 1002 1612 2122	2.9 1.7 2.9 1.6
21	TH	0432 1040 1635 2212	3.1 1.5 3.1 1.3
22	F	0424 1110 1652 2250	3.3 1.3 3.3 1.1
23	SA	0451 1138 1717 2324	3.6 1.1 3.6 0.9
24	SU	0522 1205 1746 2355	3.8 1.0 3.8 0.8
25	M ○	0553 1230 1814	3.9 0.9 3.9
26	TU	0024 0622 1255 1841	0.7 3.9 0.9 3.9
27	W	0052 0649 1319 1905	0.8 3.9 1.0 3.8
28	TH	0118 0713 1339 1929	0.9 3.8 1.1 3.7
29	F	0141 0736 1356 1956	1.0 3.7 1.2 3.6
30	SA	0208 0802 1422 2026	1.2 3.5 1.4 3.4
31	SU	0242 0834 1459 2104	1.4 3.3 1.5 3.2

APRIL

Date	Day	Time	m
1	M	0328 0914 1551 2157	1.6 3.0 1.7 3.0
2	TU ☽	0442 1019 1732 2338	1.8 2.7 1.9 2.8
3	W	0635 1352 1914	1.8 2.7 1.8
4	TH	0221 0816 1506 2037	3.0 1.6 2.9 1.5
5	F	0319 0928 1552 2139	3.4 1.3 3.2 1.1
6	SA	0403 1019 1629 2228	3.8 0.9 3.5 0.7
7	SU	0444 1101 1701 2312	4.1 0.6 3.8 0.4
8	M ●	0522 1141 1734 2355	4.3 0.4 3.9 0.2
9	TU	0559 1219 1808	4.3 0.3 4.0
10	W	0036 0637 1255 1844	0.2 4.3 0.3 4.0
11	TH	0118 0713 1333 1919	0.3 4.1 0.5 3.9
12	F	0200 0749 1412 1955	0.5 3.8 0.7 3.7
13	SA	0244 0827 1454 2032	0.9 3.4 1.0 3.4
14	SU	0331 0908 1543 2115	1.2 3.0 1.3 3.1
15	M ☾	0429 1002 1640 2214	1.6 2.7 1.6 2.9
16	TU	0548 1258 1750	1.9 2.5 1.7
17	W	0033 0819 1431 1915	2.7 1.9 2.6 1.7
18	TH	0256 0928 1521 2040	2.9 1.7 2.8 1.6
19	F	0322 1005 1549 2134	3.0 1.5 3.0 1.4
20	SA	0347 1035 1613 2214	3.3 1.3 3.3 1.2
21	SU	0417 1102 1642 2248	3.5 1.2 3.5 1.0
22	M	0448 1128 1712 2320	3.6 1.0 3.7 0.9
23	TU ○	0520 1153 1741 2350	3.8 1.0 3.8 0.8
24	W	0550 1219 1809	3.8 0.9 3.8
25	TH	0019 0618 1245 1836	0.8 3.8 0.9 3.8
26	F	0049 0645 1309 1904	0.9 3.7 1.0 3.7
27	SA	0119 0713 1336 1935	1.0 3.6 1.1 3.6
28	SU	0153 0746 1410 2012	1.2 3.4 1.3 3.5
29	M	0234 0824 1453 2058	1.3 3.2 1.4 3.3
30	TU	0330 0915 1553 2200	1.5 3.0 1.6 3.1

MAY

Date	Day	Time	m
1	W ☾	0452 1034 1717 2339	1.7 2.7 1.7 3.0
2	TH	0626 1305 1844	1.6 2.7 1.6
3	F	0140 0751 1428 2003	3.2 1.5 2.9 1.4
4	SA	0243 0857 1517 2107	3.5 1.2 3.2 1.1
5	SU	0332 0948 1556 2200	3.7 0.9 3.4 0.8
6	M	0415 1032 1632 2248	4.0 0.7 3.7 0.6
7	TU	0456 1113 1707 2333	4.1 0.6 3.9 0.4
8	W ●	0535 1152 1744	4.1 0.5 3.9
9	TH	0017 0614 1230 1822	0.5 4.0 0.6 3.9
10	F	0101 0652 1309 1900	0.6 3.9 0.7 3.9
11	SA	0145 0731 1350 1939	0.8 3.6 0.9 3.7
12	SU	0230 0810 1434 2019	1.1 3.3 1.1 3.5
13	M	0318 0854 1522 2104	1.4 3.0 1.3 3.3
14	TU	0414 0948 1615 2159	1.7 2.8 1.5 3.0
15	W ☽	0524 1131 1715 2317	1.9 2.6 1.6 2.9
16	TH	0704 1324 1821	1.9 2.7 1.7
17	F	0111 0827 1417 1932	2.9 1.8 2.8 1.6
18	SA	0217 0914 1456 2034	3.0 1.7 3.0 1.5
19	SU	0258 0949 1530 2122	3.2 1.5 3.2 1.4
20	M	0335 1019 1603 2201	3.3 1.4 3.3 1.2
21	TU	0411 1047 1637 2238	3.5 1.2 3.5 1.1
22	W	0446 1115 1710 2314	3.6 1.1 3.6 1.0
23	TH ○	0521 1145 1742 2351	3.7 1.0 3.7 1.0
24	F	0554 1217 1814	3.7 1.0 3.7
25	SA	0028 0628 1250 1849	1.0 3.6 1.0 3.7
26	SU	0108 0704 1327 1928	1.0 3.5 1.0 3.6
27	M	0152 0744 1408 2011	1.1 3.4 1.1 3.5
28	TU	0241 0830 1456 2102	1.2 3.2 1.2 3.4
29	W	0339 0925 1552 2203	1.3 3.0 1.3 3.3
30	TH ☾	0447 1032 1658 2319	1.4 2.9 1.4 3.2
31	F	0601 1159 1811	1.4 2.8 1.4

JUNE

Date	Day	Time	m
1	SA	0051 0715 1332 1925	3.3 1.4 2.9 1.3
2	SU	0204 0819 1434 2033	3.4 1.3 3.1 1.1
3	M	0301 0914 1523 2133	3.6 1.1 3.3 1.0
4	TU	0351 1003 1605 2227	3.7 1.0 3.5 0.9
5	W	0436 1047 1646 2317	3.8 0.9 3.7 0.8
6	TH ●	0519 1129 1727	3.8 0.8 3.8
7	F	0004 0601 1210 1808	0.8 3.8 0.8 3.8
8	SA	0050 0641 1252 1848	0.9 3.7 0.9 3.8
9	SU	0135 0721 1334 1929	1.1 3.5 1.0 3.7
10	M	0220 0801 1417 2009	1.3 3.4 1.1 3.6
11	TU	0305 0843 1501 2051	1.5 3.2 1.2 3.4
12	W	0353 0928 1546 2136	1.6 3.0 1.4 3.3
13	TH	0444 1020 1635 2227	1.8 2.9 1.5 3.1
14	F ☽	0542 1127 1726 2326	1.9 2.8 1.6 3.0
15	SA	0646 1248 1820	1.9 2.8 1.7
16	SU	0037 0751 1351 1917	3.0 1.8 2.9 1.7
17	M	0147 0844 1441 2013	3.0 1.7 3.0 1.6
18	TU	0245 0928 1525 2107	3.2 1.6 3.2 1.5
19	W	0335 1006 1607 2158	3.3 1.4 3.3 1.4
20	TH	0420 1043 1647 2246	3.4 1.3 3.5 1.2
21	F	0502 1120 1726 2332	3.5 1.1 3.6 1.1
22	SA ○	0542 1158 1805	3.6 1.0 3.7
23	SU	0018 0622 1238 1846	1.0 3.6 0.9 3.8
24	M	0104 0702 1319 1927	0.9 3.6 0.9 3.8
25	TU	0151 0744 1403 2011	0.9 3.5 0.8 3.8
26	W	0240 0828 1449 2058	1.0 3.4 0.9 3.7
27	TH	0331 0916 1540 2151	1.1 3.2 1.0 3.5
28	F ☾	0426 1010 1635 2251	1.2 3.1 1.1 3.4
29	SA	0527 1114 1738	1.3 3.0 1.2
30	SU	0003 0632 1231 1848	3.3 1.4 2.9 1.3

SUNRISE AND SUNSET TIMES

OBAN
At 56°25′N 5°29′W

UT		Sunrise	Sunset
Jan	01	0856	1556
	15	0845	1618
Feb	01	0818	1654
	15	0748	1725
Mar	01	0714	1756
	15	0637	1825
BST (UT+1)			
Apr	01	0652	2001
	15	0615	2030
May	01	0536	2103
	15	0507	2131
Jun	01	0441	2200
	15	0432	2213
Jul	01	0437	2214
	15	0454	2201
Aug	01	0524	2131
	15	0551	2100
Sep	01	0625	2017
	15	0653	1940
Oct	01	0725	1857
	15	0754	1820
UT			
Nov	01	0731	1640
	15	0801	1612
Dec	01	0831	1550
	15	0850	1544

OBAN
LAT 56°25′N
LONG 5°29′W

TIMES AND HEIGHTS OF HIGH AND LOW WATER (Heights in Metres)

TIME ZONE UT
For Summer Time (area enclosed in shaded box) add 1 hour

2024

JULY

Date	Day	Time	m
1	M	0125 0738 1352 2002	3.3 1.4 3.0 1.3
2	TU	0237 0842 1458 2113	3.3 1.4 3.1 1.3
3	W	0339 0939 1552 2218	3.4 1.3 3.3 1.2
4	TH	0433 1030 1639 2313	3.4 1.2 3.5 1.2
5	F ●	0519 1116 1721	3.5 1.1 3.7
6	SA	0001 0600 1159 1802	1.1 3.6 1.0 3.8
7	SU	0045 0638 1240 1841	1.1 3.6 0.9 3.8
8	M	0127 0714 1320 1918	1.2 3.6 0.9 3.8
9	TU	0207 0749 1359 1955	1.3 3.5 1.0 3.8
10	W	0244 0824 1437 2030	1.4 3.4 1.1 3.6
11	TH	0321 0858 1514 2106	1.5 3.3 1.2 3.5
12	F	0358 0935 1553 2142	1.6 3.2 1.4 3.3
13	SA ☽	0439 1015 1634 2222	1.8 3.1 1.6 3.2
14	SU	0527 1104 1721 2309	1.9 2.9 1.7 3.1
15	M	0624 1213 1816	1.9 2.9 1.8
16	TU	0015 0730 1345 1918	3.0 1.9 2.9 1.8
17	W	0155 0836 1457 2025	3.0 1.8 3.0 1.8
18	TH	0312 0935 1551 2132	3.1 1.6 3.2 1.6
19	F	0409 1023 1637 2232	3.3 1.4 3.4 1.3
20	SA	0456 1106 1720 2325	3.4 1.1 3.7 1.1
21	SU ○	0539 1147 1801	3.6 0.9 3.8
22	M	0013 0619 1227 1841	0.9 3.7 0.7 4.0
23	TU	0058 0656 1308 1921	0.7 3.7 0.6 4.0
24	W	0142 0734 1350 2001	0.7 3.7 0.5 4.0
25	TH	0226 0812 1434 2043	0.7 3.6 0.6 3.9
26	F	0310 0854 1521 2127	0.8 3.4 0.7 3.7
27	SA	0357 0939 1611 2218	1.0 3.3 0.9 3.5
28	SU ☾	0450 1031 1708 2321	1.2 3.1 1.2 3.2
29	M	0550 1143 1817	1.4 2.9 1.4
30	TU	0054 0700 1323 1939	3.0 1.6 2.9 1.6
31	W	0232 0816 1458 2116	3.0 1.6 3.0 1.6

AUGUST

Date	Day	Time	m
1	TH	0353 0928 1607 2231	3.1 1.5 3.2 1.5
2	F	0446 1024 1645 2321	3.2 1.3 3.4 1.3
3	SA	0524 1110 1719	3.4 1.1 3.6
4	SU ●	0001 0556 1149 1754	1.2 3.5 1.0 3.8
5	M	0037 0627 1227 1828	1.1 3.6 0.9 3.9
6	TU	0111 0657 1303 1900	1.1 3.7 0.8 3.9
7	W	0143 0727 1336 1932	1.1 3.7 0.9 3.9
8	TH	0214 0755 1408 2001	1.2 3.7 1.0 3.8
9	F	0244 0823 1439 2030	1.3 3.6 1.1 3.7
10	SA	0312 0852 1510 2058	1.5 3.4 1.3 3.5
11	SU	0341 0923 1544 2127	1.6 3.3 1.5 3.3
12	M ☽	0417 1001 1626 2204	1.8 3.1 1.7 3.1
13	TU	0515 1052 1724 2256	2.0 2.9 1.9 2.9
14	W	0634 1244 1840	2.0 2.8 2.0
15	TH	0113 0758 1450 2004	2.8 1.9 2.9 1.9
16	F	0314 0915 1547 2127	3.0 1.7 3.2 1.7
17	SA	0409 1010 1630 2231	3.2 1.4 3.5 1.3
18	SU	0451 1054 1710 2320	3.4 1.0 3.8 1.0
19	M ○	0529 1133 1748	3.7 0.7 4.1
20	TU	0002 0604 1212 1826	0.7 3.8 0.5 4.3
21	W	0043 0638 1252 1903	0.5 3.9 0.3 4.3
22	TH	0122 0712 1333 1940	0.4 3.9 0.3 4.2
23	F	0202 0748 1415 2018	0.5 3.8 0.4 4.0
24	SA	0242 0825 1459 2058	0.7 3.6 0.6 3.8
25	SU	0326 0905 1547 2143	0.9 3.4 0.9 3.4
26	M ☾	0415 0951 1644 2241	1.2 3.1 1.3 3.0
27	TU	0515 1059 1754	1.5 2.9 1.6
28	W	0042 0628 1318 1936	2.8 1.7 2.8 1.8
29	TH	0255 0758 1543 2144	2.8 1.7 3.0 1.7
30	F	0408 0922 1632 2238	3.0 1.6 3.2 1.5
31	SA	0447 1015 1644 2315	3.2 1.3 3.5 1.3

SEPTEMBER

Date	Day	Time	m
1	SU	0509 1056 1704 2346	3.4 1.1 3.7 1.2
2	M	0532 1133 1733	3.6 0.9 3.9
3	TU ●	0015 0600 1206 1804	1.1 3.8 0.8 4.0
4	W	0043 0629 1238 1834	1.0 3.9 0.7 4.0
5	TH	0111 0657 1308 1902	1.0 3.9 0.8 4.0
6	F	0139 0722 1337 1928	1.1 3.9 0.9 3.9
7	SA	0205 0747 1403 1953	1.2 3.7 1.1 3.8
8	SU	0226 0813 1428 2016	1.4 3.6 1.3 3.6
9	M	0245 0842 1457 2043	1.5 3.4 1.6 3.4
10	TU	0313 0917 1536 2115	1.7 3.2 1.8 3.2
11	W ☽	0400 1004 1638 2203	1.9 3.0 2.0 2.9
12	TH	0548 1138 1821	2.1 2.8 2.1
13	F	0144 0728 1441 2001	2.7 2.0 3.0 2.0
14	SA	0311 0853 1531 2125	2.9 1.7 3.3 1.6
15	SU	0356 0949 1611 2218	3.2 1.3 3.7 1.2
16	M	0433 1032 1648 2302	3.5 0.9 4.0 0.8
17	TU	0507 1112 1724 2341	3.8 0.6 4.3 0.5
18	W ○	0538 1152 1800	3.9 0.3 4.4
19	TH	0019 0611 1231 1837	0.4 4.1 0.2 4.5
20	F	0056 0645 1312 1913	0.3 4.1 0.2 4.3
21	SA	0134 0720 1354 1950	0.4 4.0 0.4 4.1
22	SU	0214 0756 1438 2028	0.6 3.8 0.7 3.7
23	M	0257 0835 1527 2110	0.9 3.5 1.1 3.3
24	TU ☾	0346 0920 1625 2205	1.3 3.2 1.5 2.9
25	W	0446 1027 1741	1.6 2.9 1.8
26	TH	0049 0601 1346 2011	2.6 1.8 2.8 1.9
27	F	0252 0737 1536 2142	2.7 1.8 3.1 1.7
28	SA	0350 0901 1614 2221	3.0 1.6 3.3 1.5
29	SU	0420 0952 1615 2250	3.2 1.3 3.5 1.3
30	M	0436 1031 1635 2318	3.4 1.1 3.7 1.2

OCTOBER

Date	Day	Time	m
1	TU	0459 1106 1703 2344	3.6 0.9 3.9 1.1
2	W ●	0527 1138 1733	3.8 0.8 4.0
3	TH	0009 0556 1208 1802	1.0 3.9 0.8 4.1
4	F	0036 0623 1237 1830	1.0 4.0 0.9 4.0
5	SA	0103 0649 1304 1855	1.0 3.9 1.0 4.0
6	SU	0127 0714 1329 1919	1.2 3.8 1.2 3.8
7	M	0148 0741 1355 1943	1.3 3.7 1.4 3.6
8	TU	0210 0811 1426 2011	1.5 3.5 1.6 3.4
9	W	0241 0848 1509 2046	1.7 3.3 1.9 3.2
10	TH ☽	0329 0939 1621 2140	1.9 3.1 2.1 2.9
11	F	0508 1124 1813	2.0 2.9 2.1
12	SA	0133 0652 1410 1951	2.7 2.0 3.2 1.9
13	SU	0244 0816 1501 2102	2.9 1.7 3.5 1.5
14	M	0329 0916 1542 2152	3.2 1.3 3.8 1.2
15	TU	0405 1003 1619 2234	3.5 0.9 4.1 0.8
16	W	0437 1046 1656 2313	3.8 0.6 4.4 0.6
17	TH ○	0508 1128 1732 2351	4.0 0.4 4.5 0.5
18	F	0543 1210 1809	4.1 0.3 4.4
19	SA	0028 0619 1252 1847	0.4 4.1 0.4 4.3
20	SU	0107 0656 1335 1924	0.5 4.1 0.6 4.0
21	M	0148 0734 1421 2004	0.8 3.9 1.0 3.6
22	TU	0232 0815 1512 2046	1.0 3.6 1.3 3.3
23	W	0322 0902 1611 2141	1.3 3.3 1.7 2.9
24	TH ☾	0420 1008 1730	1.6 3.1 2.0
25	F	0030 0531 1308 1948	2.7 1.8 3.0 2.0
26	SA	0208 0656 1448 2105	2.8 1.8 3.1 1.8
27	SU	0304 0819 1520 2145	2.9 1.7 3.3 1.7
28	M	0333 0914 1536 2215	3.2 1.5 3.5 1.5
29	TU	0356 0957 1600 2242	3.4 1.3 3.6 1.3
30	W	0423 1032 1629 2308	3.6 1.1 3.8 1.2
31	TH	0453 1104 1700 2334	3.8 1.1 3.9 1.1

NOVEMBER

Date	Day	Time	m
1	F ●	0523 1135 1730	3.9 1.1 4.0
2	SA	0001 0553 1205 1800	1.1 4.0 1.1 4.0
3	SU	0030 0621 1235 1828	1.1 3.9 1.2 3.9
4	M	0057 0650 1306 1856	1.2 3.9 1.3 3.8
5	TU	0124 0721 1337 1926	1.3 3.7 1.5 3.6
6	W	0154 0756 1416 2000	1.5 3.6 1.7 3.4
7	TH	0233 0838 1507 2044	1.6 3.4 1.8 3.2
8	F	0325 0936 1622 2150	1.8 3.3 2.0 2.9
9	SA ☽	0441 1105 1753 2338	1.9 3.2 2.0 2.8
10	SU	0608 1318 1918	1.8 3.3 1.8
11	M	0157 0729 1420 2025	3.0 1.6 3.6 1.5
12	TU	0249 0836 1507 2117	3.2 1.4 3.8 1.2
13	W	0329 0931 1549 2202	3.5 1.1 4.1 1.0
14	TH	0404 1020 1629 2244	3.7 0.8 4.2 0.8
15	F ○	0441 1107 1708 2324	3.9 0.7 4.3 0.7
16	SA	0519 1152 1748	4.1 0.7 4.2
17	SU	0004 0559 1237 1828	0.7 4.1 0.7 4.1
18	M	0046 0639 1323 1908	0.8 4.1 0.9 3.9
19	TU	0128 0721 1410 1949	0.9 3.9 1.2 3.6
20	W	0213 0804 1500 2033	1.1 3.7 1.5 3.3
21	TH	0302 0851 1556 2124	1.3 3.5 1.8 3.0
22	F	0355 0947 1703 2240	1.5 3.3 2.0 2.8
23	SA ☾	0454 1104 1831	1.7 3.1 2.0
24	SU	0054 0600 1310 1958	2.8 1.8 3.1 2.0
25	M	0155 0711 1411 2052	2.9 1.8 3.2 1.9
26	TU	0238 0817 1448 2130	3.1 1.7 3.3 1.7
27	W	0313 0908 1521 2202	3.3 1.6 3.5 1.6
28	TH	0347 0950 1555 2231	3.4 1.5 3.6 1.5
29	F	0421 1027 1630 2300	3.6 1.4 3.7 1.3
30	SA	0455 1103 1705 2332	3.7 1.3 3.8 1.3

DECEMBER

Date	Day	Time	m
1	SU ●	0529 1139 1740	3.8 1.3 3.8
2	M	0004 0603 1216 1813	1.2 3.9 1.3 3.8
3	TU	0037 0637 1254 1847	1.2 3.8 1.3 3.7
4	W	0112 0713 1334 1923	1.2 3.8 1.4 3.6
5	TH	0149 0753 1418 2003	1.3 3.7 1.5 3.4
6	F	0230 0838 1508 2050	1.4 3.6 1.6 3.3
7	SA	0319 0931 1608 2146	1.5 3.5 1.7 3.1
8	SU ☽	0417 1037 1717 2254	1.5 3.4 1.7 3.0
9	M	0526 1201 1830	1.6 3.4 1.7
10	TU	0019 0641 1328 1938	3.0 1.5 3.5 1.6
11	W	0147 0754 1432 2038	3.1 1.4 3.6 1.4
12	TH	0249 0901 1525 2131	3.3 1.3 3.8 1.3
13	F	0338 1000 1612 2219	3.6 1.1 3.9 1.1
14	SA	0423 1053 1656 2305	3.8 1.0 4.0 1.0
15	SU ○	0506 1143 1739 2349	3.9 1.0 4.0 0.9
16	M	0549 1231 1820	4.0 1.0 3.9
17	TU	0032 0632 1317 1901	0.9 4.0 1.1 3.8
18	W	0115 0713 1402 1941	1.0 4.0 1.3 3.6
19	TH	0158 0755 1447 2021	1.0 3.9 1.5 3.5
20	F	0242 0836 1533 2102	1.2 3.7 1.7 3.3
21	SA	0327 0919 1620 2147	1.3 3.5 1.8 3.1
22	SU ☾	0413 1006 1712 2240	1.5 3.3 2.0 3.0
23	M	0503 1101 1811 2352	1.7 3.2 2.0 2.9
24	TU	0557 1210 1916	1.8 3.1 2.1
25	W	0116 0655 1329 2020	3.0 1.9 3.1 2.0
26	TH	0220 0756 1435 2112	3.1 1.9 3.2 1.9
27	F	0311 0856 1525 2156	3.2 1.8 3.3 1.7
28	SA	0355 0950 1610 2234	3.4 1.7 3.5 1.5
29	SU	0437 1039 1652 2311	3.5 1.5 3.6 1.4
30	M ●	0517 1124 1732 2348	3.7 1.4 3.7 1.2
31	TU	0555 1207 1809	3.8 1.3 3.7

GREENOCK
LAT 55°57'N
LONG 4°46'W

TIMES AND HEIGHTS OF HIGH AND LOW WATER (Heights in Metres)

TIME ZONE UT
For Summer Time (area enclosed in shaded box) add 1 hour

2024

JANUARY

Date	Day	Time	m	Time	m	Time	m	Time	m
1	M	0340	3.1	0858	0.9	1528	3.6	2114	0.7
2	TU	0421	3.0	0941	1.0	1607	3.5	2200	0.8
3	W	0505	3.0	1026	1.1	1649	3.3	2249	0.9
4	TH ☾	0552	2.9	1117	1.2	1737	3.2	2344	1.0
5	F	0644	2.8	1215	1.3	1831	3.1		
6	SA	0044	1.0	0746	2.8	1319	1.3	1933	3.0
7	SU	0145	1.0	0855	2.9	1425	1.2	2041	3.0
8	M	0243	1.0	0958	3.0	1524	1.0	2148	3.1
9	TU	0336	0.9	1050	3.2	1614	0.8	2248	3.2
10	W	0425	0.8	1135	3.3	1700	0.6	2343	3.3
11	TH ●	0511	0.7	1217	3.5	1745	0.4		
12	F	0034	3.3	0558	0.6	1257	3.6	1830	0.3
13	SA	0124	3.4	0644	0.5	1340	3.7	1916	0.2
14	SU	0212	3.4	0732	0.5	1423	3.8	2004	0.2
15	M	0259	3.4	0820	0.5	1508	3.8	2053	0.2
16	TU	0346	3.4	0909	0.5	1554	3.8	2145	0.2
17	W	0431	3.3	1000	0.6	1642	3.6	2241	0.4
18	TH ☽	0517	3.2	1054	0.8	1733	3.5	2342	0.5
19	F	0605	3.1	1156	0.9	1831	3.3		
20	SA	0048	0.7	0701	3.0	1309	1.0	1943	3.1
21	SU	0156	0.8	0817	2.9	1426	1.0	2113	3.0
22	M	0300	0.8	0940	3.0	1532	0.9	2230	3.0
23	TU	0357	0.8	1044	3.1	1627	0.7	2329	3.1
24	W	0446	0.7	1133	3.3	1712	0.6		
25	TH ○	0018	3.2	0531	0.7	1215	3.4	1752	0.5
26	F	0101	3.2	0611	0.6	1252	3.5	1827	0.5
27	SA	0139	3.2	0647	0.6	1326	3.6	1900	0.5
28	SU	0212	3.1	0720	0.6	1359	3.6	1932	0.5
29	M	0243	3.1	0753	0.6	1432	3.6	2005	0.5
30	TU	0316	3.1	0827	0.7	1505	3.6	2039	0.6
31	W	0350	3.1	0903	0.7	1540	3.5	[illegible]	[illegible]

FEBRUARY

Date	Day	Time	m	Time	m	Time	m	Time	m
1	TH	0424	3.1	0941	0.8	1617	3.4	2155	0.7
2	F ☾	0459	3.0	1024	0.9	1658	3.3	2241	0.8
3	SA	0539	2.9	1115	1.1	1745	3.1	2336	1.0
4	SU	0628	2.8	1217	1.2	1842	2.9		
5	M	0040	1.1	0740	2.7	1331	1.2	1955	2.8
6	TU	0155	1.1	0914	2.8	1451	1.0	2119	2.9
7	W	0309	1.0	1025	3.0	1556	0.8	2236	3.0
8	TH	0409	0.8	1117	3.2	1646	0.4	2336	3.2
9	F ●	0459	0.6	1201	3.4	1731	0.2		
10	SA	0027	3.3	0545	0.4	1245	3.6	1815	0.0
11	SU	0116	3.3	0629	0.3	1328	3.7	1858	-0.1
12	M	0202	3.4	0714	0.3	1412	3.8	1943	-0.1
13	TU	0244	3.4	0758	0.2	1455	3.8	2028	0.0
14	W	0325	3.4	0844	0.3	1538	3.8	2116	0.1
15	TH	0403	3.4	0930	0.4	1621	3.7	2206	0.3
16	F ☽	0441	3.3	1020	0.5	1705	3.4	2304	0.6
17	SA	0521	3.1	1117	0.7	1752	3.1		
18	SU	0013	0.8	0607	2.9	1236	1.0	1853	2.8
19	M	0133	1.0	0706	2.8	1410	1.0	2113	2.7
20	TU	0245	1.0	0918	2.8	1521	0.9	2232	2.8
21	W	0344	0.9	1032	3.0	1615	0.7	2325	3.0
22	TH	0434	0.7	1121	3.2	1659	0.5		
23	F	0008	3.1	0517	0.6	1202	3.4	1736	0.4
24	SA ○	0046	3.1	0554	0.5	1238	3.4	1808	0.4
25	SU	0120	3.1	0627	0.5	1311	3.5	1837	0.4
26	M	0150	3.1	0656	0.5	1340	3.5	1904	0.4
27	TU	0218	3.1	0723	0.5	1409	3.5	1932	0.4
28	W	0246	3.2	0753	0.5	1440	3.5	2002	0.4
29	TH	0315	3.2	0825	0.5	1513	3.5	2035	0.4

MARCH

Date	Day	Time	m	Time	m	Time	m	Time	m
1	F	0344	3.2	0902	0.6	1548	3.4	2114	0.5
2	SA	0414	3.1	0944	0.7	1626	3.2	2159	0.7
3	SU ☾	0447	2.9	1035	0.9	1709	3.0	2253	0.9
4	M	0527	2.8	1136	1.0	1803	2.8	2359	1.1
5	TU	0627	2.6	1254	1.1	1918	2.7		
6	W	0119	1.2	0826	2.6	1427	0.9	2103	2.7
7	TH	0250	1.1	1002	2.9	1537	0.6	2230	2.9
8	F	0354	0.8	1056	3.2	1628	0.2	2326	3.1
9	SA	0443	0.5	1142	3.4	1711	0.0		
10	SU ●	0014	3.3	0527	0.3	1226	3.6	1753	-0.2
11	M	0058	3.3	0609	0.1	1311	3.7	1835	-0.3
12	TU	0141	3.4	0651	0.1	1354	3.8	1917	-0.2
13	W	0220	3.4	0733	0.0	1437	3.8	2000	-0.1
14	TH	0256	3.4	0816	0.1	1518	3.7	2045	0.1
15	F	0332	3.4	0900	0.2	1558	3.5	2133	0.4
16	SA	0407	3.3	0947	0.4	1639	3.3	2228	0.7
17	SU ☽	0446	3.2	1043	0.7	1724	2.9	2341	1.0
18	M	0529	2.9	1212	0.9	1821	2.6		
19	TU	0110	1.1	0626	2.7	1352	0.9	2114	2.5
20	W	0223	1.1	0850	2.7	1500	0.8	2219	2.7
21	TH	0323	0.9	1009	2.9	1552	0.6	2304	2.9
22	F	0412	0.7	1057	3.1	1634	0.4	2343	3.0
23	SA	0453	0.5	1137	3.3	1709	0.4		
24	SU	0018	3.1	0529	0.5	1212	3.3	1740	0.4
25	M ○	0050	3.1	0559	0.4	1244	3.3	1807	0.4
26	TU	0120	3.2	0626	0.4	1312	3.3	1832	0.4
27	W	0148	3.2	0651	0.4	1341	3.4	1858	0.4
28	TH	0215	3.2	0720	0.4	1413	3.4	1928	0.4
29	F	0241	3.3	0754	0.4	1447	3.4	2004	0.4
30	SA	0309	3.3	0832	0.4	1523	3.3	2045	0.5
31	SU	0339	3.2	0917	0.6	1601	3.2	2133	0.7

APRIL

Date	Day	Time	m	Time	m	Time	m	Time	m
1	M	0411	3.1	1010	0.7	1644	3.0	2229	0.9
2	TU ☾	0451	2.9	1115	0.9	1739	2.8	2337	1.1
3	W	0549	2.7	1236	0.9	1858	2.7		
4	TH	0059	1.2	0748	2.7	1405	0.7	2056	2.7
5	F	0229	1.0	0932	2.9	1512	0.4	2214	2.9
6	SA	0333	0.7	1029	3.2	1603	0.1	2305	3.1
7	SU	0422	0.4	1117	3.4	1646	-0.2	2351	3.3
8	M ●	0505	0.2	1203	3.6	1728	-0.3		
9	TU	0032	3.4	0547	0.1	1248	3.6	1810	-0.2
10	W	0113	3.4	0628	0.0	1333	3.7	1851	-0.1
11	TH	0150	3.5	0708	0.0	1416	3.6	1934	0.0
12	F	0227	3.5	0750	0.1	1457	3.5	2019	0.2
13	SA	0302	3.5	0833	0.2	1538	3.3	2107	0.5
14	SU	0339	3.4	0921	0.4	1620	3.1	2201	0.8
15	M ☽	0418	3.2	1019	0.6	1707	2.8	2311	1.0
16	TU	0502	3.0	1147	0.8	1810	2.5		
17	W	0035	1.2	0600	2.8	1319	0.9	2040	2.5
18	TH	0148	1.2	0746	2.7	1424	0.7	2143	2.7
19	F	0249	1.0	0928	2.8	1516	0.6	2227	2.8
20	SA	0339	0.8	1019	3.0	1557	0.5	2305	3.0
21	SU	0421	0.6	1100	3.2	1633	0.4	2341	3.1
22	M	0456	0.5	1136	3.2	1704	0.4		
23	TU ○	0014	3.1	0528	0.4	1208	3.2	1733	0.4
24	W	0046	3.2	0555	0.4	1238	3.2	1759	0.4
25	TH	0115	3.2	0623	0.4	1311	3.3	1828	0.4
26	F	0143	3.3	0654	0.4	1346	3.3	1903	0.4
27	SA	0211	3.3	0731	0.4	1424	3.3	1944	0.5
28	SU	0242	3.4	0813	0.4	1503	3.3	2029	0.6
29	M	0315	3.3	0901	0.5	1545	3.2	2121	0.7
30	TU	0351	3.2	0958	0.6	1633	3.0	2219	0.9

MAY

Date	Day	Time	m	Time	m	Time	m	Time	m
1	W ☽	0435	3.0	1106	0.7	1732	2.8	2326	1.0
2	TH	0538	2.8	1224	0.6	1851	2.7		
3	F	0042	1.1	0724	2.8	1339	0.5	2031	2.8
4	SA	0200	0.9	0857	3.0	1442	0.2	2142	3.0
5	SU	0304	0.7	0958	3.2	1533	0.0	2234	3.1
6	M	0356	0.4	1049	3.4	1619	-0.1	2320	3.2
7	TU	0442	0.2	1137	3.5	1703	-0.1		
8	W ●	0003	3.3	0525	0.1	1224	3.5	1746	0.0
9	TH	0044	3.4	0607	0.1	1311	3.5	1829	0.1
10	F	0123	3.5	0648	0.1	1356	3.4	1913	0.3
11	SA	0200	3.5	0729	0.1	1439	3.3	1959	0.4
12	SU	0238	3.5	0813	0.2	1522	3.1	2048	0.6
13	M	0315	3.4	0902	0.4	1607	2.9	2140	0.8
14	TU	0356	3.3	0959	0.6	1657	2.7	2240	1.0
15	W ☾	0440	3.1	1109	0.7	1800	2.6	2347	1.1
16	TH	0535	2.9	1227	0.8	1921	2.5		
17	F	0056	1.1	0650	2.8	1332	0.7	2037	2.6
18	SA	0200	1.0	0820	2.8	1426	0.6	2131	2.8
19	SU	0255	0.9	0923	2.9	1511	0.5	2216	2.9
20	M	0341	0.7	1010	3.0	1550	0.5	2257	3.0
21	TU	0420	0.6	1050	3.1	1626	0.5	2336	3.1
22	W	0455	0.5	1127	3.1	1658	0.5		
23	TH ○	0012	3.2	0527	0.5	1203	3.2	1731	0.5
24	F	0045	3.3	0600	0.4	1242	3.2	1806	0.5
25	SA	0116	3.3	0637	0.4	1324	3.2	1847	0.5
26	SU	0148	3.4	0717	0.4	1406	3.2	1932	0.5
27	M	0223	3.4	0803	0.4	1450	3.2	2022	0.6
28	TU	0301	3.4	0854	0.4	1537	3.1	2115	0.7
29	W	0342	3.3	0952	0.4	1629	3.0	2212	0.8
30	TH ☽	0431	3.2	1056	0.4	1728	2.9	2313	0.8
31	F	0534	3.1	1204	0.4	1837	2.9		

JUNE

Date	Day	Time	m	Time	m	Time	m	Time	m
1	SA	0018	0.9	0657	3.0	1309	0.3	1952	2.9
2	SU	0126	0.8	0819	3.1	1409	0.2	2100	3.0
3	M	0232	0.7	0925	3.2	1504	0.2	2158	3.1
4	TU	0330	0.5	1022	3.3	1554	0.1	2250	3.2
5	W	0421	0.4	1115	3.4	1642	0.2	2337	3.3
6	TH ●	0508	0.3	1206	3.3	1727	0.2		
7	F	0020	3.4	0552	0.2	1255	3.3	1813	0.3
8	SA	0101	3.4	0634	0.2	1342	3.2	1858	0.5
9	SU	0140	3.5	0715	0.2	1427	3.1	1944	0.6
10	M	0218	3.5	0758	0.3	1511	3.0	2030	0.7
11	TU	0257	3.4	0844	0.4	1555	2.9	2117	0.7
12	W	0336	3.3	0933	0.5	1642	2.8	2206	0.8
13	TH	0418	3.2	1028	0.6	1732	2.7	2257	0.9
14	F ☾	0505	3.1	1127	0.7	1825	2.7	2353	1.0
15	SA	0600	3.0	1228	0.7	1921	2.7		
16	SU	0053	1.0	0701	2.9	1325	0.7	2020	2.8
17	M	0155	1.0	0806	2.9	1418	0.7	2118	2.8
18	TU	0252	0.9	0907	2.9	1505	0.7	2211	2.9
19	W	0341	0.8	1001	3.0	1548	0.6	2258	3.1
20	TH	0425	0.7	1049	3.1	1629	0.6	2341	3.2
21	F	0505	0.5	1135	3.1	1709	0.6		
22	SA ○	0018	3.3	0545	0.4	1221	3.1	1751	0.6
23	SU	0054	3.4	0625	0.3	1307	3.2	1836	0.5
24	M	0132	3.5	0709	0.3	1355	3.2	1923	0.5
25	TU	0211	3.5	0755	0.2	1443	3.2	2013	0.5
26	W	0252	3.5	0844	0.2	1532	3.2	2103	0.5
27	TH	0336	3.5	0938	0.2	1622	3.1	2156	0.6
28	F ☽	0424	3.4	1035	0.2	1713	3.1	2250	0.6
29	SA	0519	3.3	1136	0.3	1807	3.0	2349	0.7
30	SU	0624	3.2	1238	0.3	1906	3.0		

SUNRISE AND SUNSET TIMES

GREENOCK
At 55°57'N 4°46'W

		Sunrise	Sunset
UT			
Jan	01	0850	1556
	15	0840	1618
Feb	01	0813	1653
	15	0744	1723
Mar	01	0710	1754
	15	0634	1823
BST (UT+1)			
Apr	01	0650	1958
	15	0614	2026
May	01	0535	2058
	15	0506	2126
Jun	01	0441	2153
	15	0433	2207
Jul	01	0438	2208
	15	0454	2155
Aug	01	0523	2126
	15	0550	2055
Sep	01	0624	2013
	15	0651	1936
Oct	01	0722	1854
	15	0750	1818
UT			
Nov	01	0726	1638
	15	0756	1611
Dec	01	0826	1550

GREENOCK
LAT 55°57′N
LONG 4°46′W

TIMES AND HEIGHTS OF HIGH AND LOW WATER (Heights in Metres)

TIME ZONE UT
For Summer Time (area enclosed in shaded box) add 1 hour

2024

JULY

Date	Time	m	Date	Time	m
1 M	0053 0739 1340 2012	0.8 3.1 0.4 2.9	16 TU	0048 0705 1319 2012	1.1 2.9 0.9 2.8
2 TU	0202 0854 1440 2121	0.8 3.1 0.4 3.0	17 W	0156 0811 1419 2122	1.1 2.8 0.9 2.8
3 W	0309 1003 1536 2224	0.7 3.1 0.4 3.1	18 TH	0304 0919 1515 2224	1.0 2.9 0.8 3.0
4 TH	0408 1104 1628 2318	0.6 3.1 0.5 3.2	19 F	0401 1022 1606 2314	0.8 2.9 0.7 3.1
5 F ●	0458 1159 1717	0.4 3.1 0.5	20 SA	0448 1117 1652 2357	0.6 3.0 0.6 3.3
6 SA	0005 0544 1250 1803	3.3 0.3 3.1 0.5	21 SU ○	0531 1209 1737	0.4 3.1 0.6
7 SU	0047 0625 1337 1847	3.4 0.3 3.1 0.5	22 M	0037 0613 1258 1823	3.4 0.2 3.2 0.5
8 M	0126 0703 1420 1928	3.4 0.3 3.0 0.6	23 TU	0118 0655 1346 1908	3.5 0.1 3.2 0.4
9 TU	0203 0741 1458 2008	3.5 0.3 3.0 0.6	24 W	0159 0739 1433 1955	3.6 0.0 3.2 0.4
10 W	0239 0820 1535 2048	3.5 0.4 2.9 0.6	25 TH	0242 0825 1519 2043	3.7 0.0 3.2 0.4
11 TH	0315 0901 1613 2128	3.4 0.4 2.9 0.7	26 F	0325 0914 1603 2131	3.7 0.0 3.2 0.4
12 F	0352 0944 1653 2211	3.3 0.5 2.9 0.8	27 SA	0410 1006 1646 2222	3.6 0.2 3.2 0.5
13 SA ☾	0431 1031 1735 2257	3.2 0.6 2.9 0.9	28 SU ☽	0457 1104 1730 2317	3.4 0.3 3.1 0.6
14 SU	0515 1124 1820 2348	3.1 0.7 2.8 1.0	29 M	0550 1207 1818	3.2 0.5 3.0
15 M	0605 1220 1911	3.0 0.8 2.8	30 TU	0021 0655 1316 1917	0.8 3.0 0.6 2.9
			31 W	0140 0829 1424 2045	0.9 2.8 0.7 2.9

AUGUST

Date	Time	m	Date	Time	m
1 TH	0259 1004 1526 2212	0.9 2.9 0.7 3.0	16 F	0232 0850 1449 2155	1.1 2.7 1.0 2.9
2 F	0402 1108 1621 2311	0.7 3.0 0.7 3.1	17 SA	0342 1009 1549 2252	0.8 2.9 0.9 3.1
3 SA	0453 1200 1709 2358	0.5 3.0 0.6 3.3	18 SU	0431 1110 1637 2337	0.5 3.0 0.7 3.3
4 SU ●	0536 1247 1752	0.4 3.1 0.6	19 M ○	0513 1200 1721	0.2 3.2 0.5
5 M	0038 0613 1327 1831	3.4 0.3 3.0 0.5	20 TU	0019 0554 1246 1804	3.5 0.0 3.2 0.4
6 TU	0114 0646 1403 1906	3.5 0.3 3.0 0.6	21 W	0101 0634 1331 1847	3.6 -0.1 3.3 0.3
7 W	0147 0718 1434 1939	3.5 0.4 3.0 0.6	22 TH	0144 0716 1414 1931	3.7 -0.1 3.3 0.2
8 TH	0218 0750 1504 2013	3.5 0.4 3.0 0.6	23 F	0227 0759 1455 2016	3.8 -0.1 3.3 0.2
9 F	0250 0823 1536 2048	3.5 0.4 3.0 0.6	24 SA	0309 0845 1534 2102	3.8 0.0 3.4 0.3
10 SA	0323 0858 1610 2125	3.4 0.5 3.0 0.7	25 SU	0351 0934 1612 2151	3.7 0.2 3.3 0.4
11 SU	0358 0936 1645 2206	3.4 0.6 3.0 0.8	26 M ☽	0433 1030 1653 2245	3.5 0.5 3.2 0.7
12 M ☾	0437 1020 1724 2253	3.2 0.7 2.9 0.9	27 TU	0519 1139 1737 2356	3.2 0.8 3.1 0.9
13 TU	0522 1113 1810 2351	3.0 0.9 2.8 1.1	28 W	0616 1301 1831	2.8 1.0 2.9
14 W	0618 1218 1910	2.8 1.1 2.7	29 TH	0132 0840 1415 2013	1.0 2.6 1.0 2.8
15 TH	0104 0729 1333 2031	1.2 2.7 1.1 2.7	30 F	0253 1011 1517 2205	0.9 2.8 0.9 3.0
			31 SA	0353 1105 1609 2259	0.7 3.0 0.8 3.2

SEPTEMBER

Date	Time	m	Date	Time	m
1 SU	0440 1149 1654 2343	0.5 3.1 0.6 3.4	16 M	0408 1058 1617 2313	0.4 3.1 0.6 3.4
2 M	0519 1229 1734	0.4 3.1 0.5	17 TU	0449 1143 1700 2357	0.1 3.3 0.4 3.6
3 TU ●	0020 0553 1304 1809	3.5 0.4 3.1 0.5	18 W ○	0529 1226 1741	-0.1 3.4 0.3
4 W	0054 0622 1334 1839	3.5 0.4 3.1 0.5	19 TH	0040 0609 1307 1823	3.7 -0.2 3.4 0.2
5 TH	0124 0649 1401 1907	3.5 0.4 3.1 0.6	20 F	0124 0649 1347 1905	3.8 -0.1 3.5 0.2
6 F	0152 0716 1428 1936	3.5 0.4 3.2 0.6	21 SA	0207 0732 1426 1948	3.8 0.0 3.5 0.2
7 SA	0222 0745 1458 2008	3.5 0.5 3.2 0.6	22 SU	0249 0816 1503 2034	3.8 0.2 3.5 0.3
8 SU	0254 0816 1528 2044	3.5 0.5 3.2 0.6	23 M	0330 0904 1541 2122	3.6 0.4 3.4 0.5
9 M	0329 0852 1600 2125	3.4 0.6 3.2 0.8	24 TU ☽	0412 0959 1621 2218	3.4 0.7 3.3 0.8
10 TU	0405 0934 1635 2212	3.3 0.8 3.0 0.9	25 W	0458 1115 1706 2343	3.1 1.1 3.1 1.0
11 W ☾	0447 1026 1717 2311	3.1 1.0 2.9 1.1	26 TH	0556 1246 1802	2.7 1.2 2.9
12 TH	0541 1133 1817	2.8 1.2 2.8	27 F	0123 0852 1358 1957	1.0 2.6 1.2 2.8
13 F	0027 0656 1257 1946	1.2 2.7 1.3 2.7	28 SA	0235 0959 1458 2142	0.9 2.8 1.0 3.0
14 SA	0208 0833 1428 2126	1.1 2.7 1.2 2.9	29 SU	0331 1045 1548 2233	0.7 3.0 0.8 3.3
15 SU	0320 1003 1531 2227	0.7 2.9 0.9 3.2	30 M	0415 1123 1631 2315	0.5 3.2 0.7 3.4

OCTOBER

Date	Time	m	Date	Time	m
1 TU	0452 1159 1709 2352	0.4 3.2 0.6 3.5	16 W	0421 1117 1636 2331	0.1 3.4 0.4 3.7
2 W ●	0524 1230 1741	0.4 3.3 0.5	17 TH ○	0502 1159 1718	-0.1 3.5 0.3
3 TH	0024 0552 1258 1809	3.5 0.5 3.3 0.6	18 F	0016 0543 1239 1800	3.8 -0.1 3.5 0.2
4 F	0054 0617 1326 1835	3.5 0.5 3.3 0.6	19 SA	0102 0625 1319 1842	3.8 0.0 3.6 0.2
5 SA	0123 0643 1354 1903	3.5 0.5 3.3 0.6	20 SU	0147 0708 1358 1925	3.8 0.2 3.6 0.3
6 SU	0154 0711 1422 1935	3.5 0.6 3.4 0.6	21 M	0231 0753 1436 2010	3.7 0.4 3.6 0.4
7 M	0227 0744 1452 2013	3.5 0.6 3.4 0.7	22 TU	0313 0841 1516 2100	3.5 0.7 3.6 0.6
8 TU	0303 0822 1523 2055	3.4 0.7 3.3 0.8	23 W	0357 0937 1557 2159	3.3 1.0 3.4 0.8
9 W	0341 0907 1558 2146	3.3 0.9 3.2 1.0	24 TH ☽	0446 1050 1644 2325	3.0 1.2 3.2 1.0
10 TH ☾	0423 1001 1639 2248	3.1 1.1 3.0 1.1	25 F	0555 1215 1742	2.7 1.4 3.0
11 F	0516 1108 1737	2.9 1.3 2.9	26 SA	0055 0820 1326 1919	1.0 2.7 1.3 2.9
12 SA	0006 0633 1232 1909	1.1 2.8 1.4 2.8	27 SU	0203 0924 1426 2059	0.9 2.9 1.2 3.1
13 SU	0140 0819 1401 2050	1.0 2.8 1.2 3.0	28 M	0256 1008 1518 2154	0.8 3.0 0.9 3.3
14 M	0248 0943 1504 2155	0.7 3.0 1.0 3.3	29 TU	0341 1046 1601 2238	0.6 3.2 0.8 3.4
15 TU	0338 1034 1553 2244	0.3 3.2 0.7 3.5	30 W	0418 1120 1639 2315	0.6 3.3 0.7 3.4
			31 TH	0451 1153 1711 2349	0.6 3.4 0.6 3.5

NOVEMBER

Date	Time	m	Date	Time	m
1 F ●	0520 1224 1740	0.6 3.4 0.6	16 SA	0521 1214 1740	0.2 3.6 0.3
2 SA	0021 0548 1255 1808	3.5 0.6 3.5 0.7	17 SU	0043 0605 1255 1824	3.7 0.3 3.7 0.3
3 SU	0053 0615 1324 1838	3.5 0.7 3.5 0.7	18 M	0131 0650 1336 1908	3.7 0.4 3.7 0.4
4 M	0128 0647 1354 1913	3.5 0.7 3.5 0.7	19 TU	0217 0737 1416 1954	3.5 0.6 3.7 0.5
5 TU	0205 0723 1425 1953	3.5 0.7 3.5 0.7	20 W	0302 0826 1457 2044	3.4 0.8 3.7 0.6
6 W	0244 0805 1459 2038	3.4 0.8 3.5 0.8	21 TH	0348 0919 1540 2140	3.2 1.0 3.5 0.8
7 TH	0324 0853 1536 2131	3.3 1.0 3.4 0.9	22 F	0440 1018 1626 2248	3.0 1.2 3.4 0.9
8 F	0409 0949 1619 2234	3.2 1.2 3.2 1.0	23 SA ☽	0543 1126 1722	2.8 1.3 3.2
9 SA ☾	0504 1053 1716 2348	3.0 1.3 3.1 1.0	24 SU	0004 0703 1237 1831	1.0 2.7 1.3 3.1
10 SU	0616 1208 1838	2.9 1.3 3.1	25 M	0113 0817 1342 1950	1.0 2.8 1.3 3.1
11 M	0105 0748 1325 2009	0.8 2.9 1.2 3.2	26 TU	0210 0912 1437 2057	0.9 3.0 1.1 3.2
12 TU	0211 0906 1431 2119	0.6 3.1 1.0 3.4	27 W	0258 0957 1525 2149	0.8 3.1 1.0 3.2
13 W	0305 1001 1525 2214	0.4 3.3 0.8 3.6	28 TH	0339 1039 1606 2233	0.8 3.3 0.9 3.3
14 TH	0353 1048 1613 2305	0.2 3.4 0.5 3.7	29 F	0416 1118 1643 2313	0.7 3.4 0.8 3.3
15 F ○	0437 1132 1657 2355	0.1 3.5 0.4 3.7	30 SA	0451 1154 1716 2351	0.7 3.5 0.8 3.4

DECEMBER

Date	Time	m	Date	Time	m
1 SU ●	0523 1229 1749	0.8 3.5 0.7	16 M	0032 0553 1240 1814	3.5 0.5 3.6 0.4
2 M	0028 0556 1301 1823	3.4 0.8 3.6 0.7	17 TU	0123 0639 1322 1858	3.5 0.6 3.7 0.4
3 TU	0108 0631 1333 1901	3.4 0.8 3.6 0.7	18 W	0210 0725 1403 1942	3.4 0.7 3.7 0.5
4 W	0149 0712 1407 1942	3.4 0.8 3.6 0.7	19 TH	0255 0810 1444 2027	3.3 0.8 3.7 0.5
5 TH	0231 0756 1444 2029	3.4 0.9 3.6 0.7	20 F	0340 0856 1525 2114	3.1 0.9 3.6 0.7
6 F	0314 0845 1524 2121	3.3 0.9 3.6 0.7	21 SA	0424 0944 1608 2205	3.0 1.0 3.5 0.8
7 SA	0401 0938 1609 2219	3.2 1.0 3.5 0.7	22 SU ☽	0511 1034 1653 2301	2.9 1.1 3.4 0.9
8 SU ☾	0453 1035 1703 2322	3.1 1.1 3.4 0.7	23 M	0600 1130 1743	2.9 1.2 3.2
9 M	0552 1138 1809	3.1 1.1 3.3	24 TU	0001 0655 1233 1838	1.0 2.9 1.3 3.1
10 TU	0028 0703 1246 1927	0.7 3.0 1.1 3.3	25 W	0104 0755 1339 1938	1.0 2.9 1.2 3.0
11 W	0133 0817 1354 2042	0.6 3.1 1.0 3.3	26 TH	0203 0857 1441 2043	1.0 3.0 1.2 3.0
12 TH	0233 0923 1457 2147	0.5 3.2 0.9 3.4	27 F	0256 0955 1533 2145	1.0 3.1 1.1 3.1
13 F	0327 1019 1552 2245	0.4 3.3 0.7 3.5	28 SA	0344 1045 1618 2239	0.9 3.2 0.9 3.1
14 SA	0418 1109 1642 2340	0.4 3.4 0.5 3.5	29 SU	0426 1129 1658 2327	0.9 3.4 0.8 3.2
15 SU ○	0506 1156 1729	0.4 3.6 0.4	30 M ●	0505 1208 1736	0.8 3.5 0.7
			31 TU	0011 0543 1243 1813	3.3 0.8 3.5 0.6

LIVERPOOL (GLADSTONE DOCK)
LAT 53°24′N
LONG 3°01′W

TIMES AND HEIGHTS OF HIGH AND LOW WATER (Heights in Metres)

TIME ZONE UT
For Summer Time (area enclosed in shaded box) add 1 hour

2024

JANUARY

Date	Day	Time	m	Time	m	Time	m	Time	m
1	M	0200	8.2	0826	2.6	1413	8.4	2106	2.5
2	TU	0239	7.9	0903	2.9	1453	8.1	2144	2.7
3	W	0321	7.6	0945	3.1	1538	7.8	2228	3.0
4	TH ☾	0410	7.4	1035	3.4	1630	7.6	2322	3.2
5	F	0507	7.2	1135	3.6	1732	7.4		
6	SA	0028	3.3	0614	7.2	1247	3.5	1840	7.4
7	SU	0139	3.2	0720	7.4	1400	3.3	1946	7.6
8	M	0242	2.9	0820	7.8	1504	2.9	2045	7.9
9	TU	0337	2.5	0913	8.2	1601	2.4	2137	8.3
10	W	0428	2.1	1001	8.7	1653	2.0	2226	8.7
11	TH ●	0516	1.8	1047	9.1	1744	1.6	2314	9.0
12	F	0604	1.5	1133	9.4	1834	1.2		
13	SA	0000	9.2	0651	1.4	1219	9.6	1922	1.0
14	SU	0047	9.3	0736	1.3	1306	9.7	2009	0.9
15	M	0135	9.2	0821	1.4	1353	9.6	2054	1.1
16	TU	0222	9.0	0905	1.6	1441	9.4	2140	1.4
17	W	0310	8.7	0951	2.0	1532	9.0	2227	1.8
18	TH ☽	0402	8.3	1042	2.3	1627	8.6	2320	2.2
19	F	0501	7.9	1141	2.7	1730	8.2		
20	SA	0022	2.7	0611	7.6	1251	3.0	1842	7.9
21	SU	0134	2.9	0727	7.6	1410	2.9	1957	7.8
22	M	0245	2.8	0837	7.8	1523	2.7	2104	8.0
23	TU	0348	2.7	0934	8.2	1625	2.4	2200	8.2
24	W	0440	2.4	1022	8.5	1716	2.1	2246	8.5
25	TH O	0524	2.2	1103	8.7	1759	1.8	2325	8.6
26	F	0602	2.1	1139	8.9	1836	1.7		
27	SA	0000	8.7	0635	2.0	1212	9.0	1909	1.7
28	SU	0031	8.7	0705	2.0	1243	9.0	1939	1.7
29	M	0102	8.7	0734	2.0	1314	8.9	2007	1.8
30	TU	0133	8.5	0804	2.1	1345	8.7	2035	2.0
31	W	0205	8.3	0836	2.3	1416	8.5	[illegible]	[illegible]

FEBRUARY

Date	Day	Time	m	Time	m	Time	m	Time	m
1	TH	0238	8.1	0910	2.6	1448	8.2	2140	2.6
2	F ☾	0314	7.8	0948	2.9	1526	7.9	2220	3.0
3	SA	0359	7.5	1035	3.3	1616	7.5	2314	3.3
4	SU	0500	7.2	1142	3.5	1729	7.2		
5	M	0036	3.5	0622	7.1	1311	3.5	1859	7.2
6	TU	0203	3.3	0743	7.4	1434	3.1	2020	7.5
7	W	0312	2.8	0851	8.0	1541	2.5	2124	8.1
8	TH	0410	2.2	0946	8.6	1641	1.8	2217	8.7
9	F ●	0504	1.7	1035	9.2	1735	1.2	2305	9.2
10	SA	0554	1.2	1121	9.6	1824	0.7	2350	9.5
11	SU	0640	0.9	1206	10.0	1910	0.4		
12	M	0033	9.6	0724	0.7	1249	10.1	1953	0.3
13	TU	0116	9.6	0805	0.8	1332	10.0	2034	0.6
14	W	0158	9.3	0845	1.1	1416	9.7	2113	1.0
15	TH	0240	8.9	0925	1.5	1500	9.2	2153	1.7
16	F ☽	0325	8.4	1009	2.1	1550	8.5	2238	2.4
17	SA	0418	7.8	1103	2.7	1651	7.8	2337	3.0
18	SU	0529	7.3	1219	3.2	1812	7.3		
19	M	0101	3.4	0700	7.2	1354	3.2	1945	7.3
20	TU	0230	3.3	0824	7.5	1517	2.9	2100	7.6
21	W	0342	3.0	0925	7.9	1620	2.4	2154	8.0
22	TH	0434	2.6	1011	8.4	1707	2.0	2235	8.4
23	F	0514	2.2	1048	8.7	1745	1.7	2309	8.6
24	SA O	0548	2.0	1121	8.9	1817	1.5	2340	8.8
25	SU	0617	1.8	1151	9.0	1845	1.4		
26	M	0008	8.9	0644	1.6	1219	9.1	1912	1.4
27	TU	0036	8.9	0712	1.6	1248	9.0	1938	1.5
28	W	0104	8.8	0740	1.6	1315	8.9	2005	1.7
29	TH	0132	8.6	0810	1.8	1342	8.7	2033	1.9

MARCH

Date	Day	Time	m	Time	m	Time	m	Time	m
1	F	0201	8.4	0841	2.2	1410	8.4	2102	2.3
2	SA	0233	8.1	0913	2.6	1445	8.1	2135	2.8
3	SU ☾	0313	7.7	0954	3.0	1531	7.6	2221	3.2
4	M	0410	7.3	1055	3.4	1641	7.1	2341	3.6
5	TU	0538	7.0	1233	3.5	1827	7.0		
6	W	0129	3.5	0715	7.3	1410	3.1	2002	7.4
7	TH	0250	2.9	0830	7.9	1524	2.3	2110	8.1
8	F	0353	2.2	0928	8.6	1626	1.5	2203	8.8
9	SA	0448	1.5	1017	9.3	1719	0.8	2248	9.3
10	SU ●	0537	0.9	1101	9.8	1806	0.3	2330	9.7
11	M	0621	0.6	1144	10.2	1849	0.1		
12	TU	0011	9.8	0703	0.4	1226	10.2	1929	0.1
13	W	0051	9.7	0742	0.5	1307	10.1	2007	0.5
14	TH	0130	9.4	0821	0.8	1348	9.6	2043	1.0
15	F	0209	9.0	0859	1.4	1431	9.0	2119	1.8
16	SA	0251	8.4	0941	2.1	1518	8.3	2200	2.6
17	SU ☽	0342	7.8	1034	2.8	1620	7.5	2257	3.3
18	M	0454	7.2	1156	3.3	1747	7.0		
19	TU	0030	3.7	0632	7.0	1339	3.3	1929	7.0
20	W	0213	3.6	0801	7.3	1500	2.9	2045	7.4
21	TH	0324	3.1	0902	7.8	1558	2.3	2134	7.9
22	F	0413	2.6	0946	8.2	1641	1.9	2211	8.3
23	SA	0450	2.2	1022	8.6	1716	1.6	2243	8.6
24	SU	0521	1.9	1053	8.8	1746	1.5	2312	8.8
25	M O	0549	1.6	1122	9.0	1813	1.3	2339	8.9
26	TU	0616	1.5	1151	9.0	1840	1.3		
27	W	0006	8.9	0646	1.4	1218	9.0	1908	1.3
28	TH	0034	8.9	0716	1.5	1245	8.9	1936	1.5
29	F	0102	8.7	0746	1.7	1313	8.7	2005	1.8
30	SA	0131	8.5	0817	2.0	1344	8.4	2034	2.2
31	SU	0204	8.3	0850	2.4	1421	8.1	2107	2.7

APRIL

Date	Day	Time	m	Time	m	Time	m	Time	m
1	M	0246	7.9	0932	2.8	1512	7.6	2156	3.2
2	TU ☾	0347	7.4	1035	3.1	1627	7.1	2315	3.5
3	W	0517	7.2	1212	3.2	1810	7.0		
4	TH	0101	3.4	0652	7.4	1347	2.8	1942	7.5
5	F	0224	2.8	0805	8.1	1501	2.0	2048	8.2
6	SA	0329	2.1	0903	8.8	1602	1.3	2139	8.9
7	SU	0424	1.4	0951	9.4	1654	0.7	2223	9.4
8	M ●	0512	0.9	1036	9.8	1740	0.3	2305	9.6
9	TU	0556	0.5	1119	10.1	1822	0.2	2345	9.7
10	W	0638	0.4	1201	10.0	1901	0.3		
11	TH	0024	9.6	0719	0.5	1242	9.8	1939	0.7
12	F	0103	9.3	0758	0.9	1324	9.3	2015	1.3
13	SA	0142	8.9	0838	1.5	1407	8.7	2051	2.0
14	SU	0224	8.4	0921	2.1	1455	8.0	2131	2.8
15	M ☽	0315	7.8	1015	2.8	1556	7.3	2225	3.4
16	TU	0425	7.3	1135	3.2	1719	6.9	2355	3.8
17	W	0555	7.0	1308	3.2	1853	6.9		
18	TH	0134	3.7	0719	7.2	1420	2.9	2007	7.3
19	F	0243	3.2	0821	7.6	1516	2.5	2057	7.7
20	SA	0332	2.8	0907	8.0	1559	2.1	2135	8.1
21	SU	0410	2.4	0945	8.4	1635	1.8	2207	8.4
22	M	0443	2.0	1018	8.6	1707	1.6	2237	8.7
23	TU O	0515	1.7	1049	8.8	1738	1.4	2306	8.8
24	W	0546	1.5	1120	8.8	1808	1.4	2336	8.9
25	TH	0619	1.4	1150	8.8	1839	1.4		
26	F	0006	8.9	0653	1.5	1220	8.7	1911	1.6
27	SA	0037	8.8	0726	1.6	1253	8.6	1943	1.9
28	SU	0111	8.6	0801	1.9	1330	8.4	2016	2.2
29	M	0150	8.4	0839	2.2	1414	8.0	2056	2.6
30	TU	0238	8.0	0927	2.5	1511	7.6	2149	3.0

MAY

Date	Day	Time	m	Time	m	Time	m	Time	m
1	W ☽	0343	7.7	1033	2.8	1626	7.3	2306	3.2
2	TH	0506	7.6	1158	2.7	1754	7.4		
3	F	0035	3.1	0626	7.8	1320	2.4	1914	7.8
4	SA	0151	2.6	0735	8.3	1430	1.8	2018	8.3
5	SU	0256	2.1	0833	8.8	1530	1.3	2110	8.8
6	M	0353	1.5	0923	9.3	1623	1.0	2155	9.2
7	TU	0443	1.1	1010	9.6	1710	0.8	2238	9.4
8	W ●	0530	0.9	1055	9.7	1753	0.7	2320	9.4
9	TH	0614	0.8	1139	9.6	1834	0.9		
10	F	0000	9.4	0657	0.9	1222	9.3	1913	1.2
11	SA	0041	9.1	0740	1.2	1305	8.9	1951	1.7
12	SU	0122	8.8	0822	1.7	1350	8.4	2028	2.3
13	M	0205	8.4	0907	2.2	1437	7.9	2108	2.8
14	TU	0254	7.9	0959	2.7	1533	7.4	2158	3.3
15	W ☾	0356	7.5	1103	3.0	1640	7.0	2306	3.6
16	TH	0509	7.3	1216	3.1	1755	7.0		
17	F	0028	3.7	0621	7.3	1322	3.0	1906	7.1
18	SA	0138	3.4	0724	7.5	1419	2.7	2003	7.5
19	SU	0233	3.0	0817	7.8	1506	2.4	2047	7.8
20	M	0319	2.7	0900	8.1	1547	2.1	2125	8.2
21	TU	0400	2.3	0939	8.3	1625	1.9	2200	8.4
22	W	0438	2.0	1015	8.5	1702	1.7	2234	8.6
23	TH O	0516	1.8	1050	8.6	1738	1.6	2308	8.8
24	F	0555	1.6	1125	8.6	1814	1.6	2343	8.8
25	SA	0633	1.6	1203	8.6	1851	1.7		
26	SU	0020	8.8	0713	1.6	1242	8.6	1929	1.9
27	M	0100	8.7	0754	1.8	1326	8.4	2008	2.1
28	TU	0146	8.6	0838	1.9	1415	8.2	2054	2.4
29	W	0238	8.4	0930	2.1	1512	8.0	2148	2.6
30	TH ☽	0340	8.2	1031	2.2	1618	7.8	2254	2.8
31	F	0448	8.1	1139	2.2	1729	7.8		

JUNE

Date	Day	Time	m	Time	m	Time	m	Time	m
1	SA	0005	2.7	0557	8.2	1248	2.1	1840	7.9
2	SU	0114	2.5	0702	8.4	1354	1.9	1943	8.2
3	M	0220	2.2	0802	8.7	1456	1.7	2039	8.5
4	TU	0321	1.9	0857	8.9	1552	1.5	2129	8.8
5	W	0417	1.6	0948	9.0	1642	1.4	2216	9.0
6	TH ●	0508	1.4	1037	9.1	1729	1.4	2301	9.1
7	F	0557	1.3	1124	9.0	1812	1.5	2344	9.0
8	SA	0643	1.3	1209	8.9	1853	1.7		
9	SU	0025	8.9	0728	1.5	1252	8.6	1933	2.0
10	M	0106	8.7	0810	1.8	1335	8.3	2010	2.3
11	TU	0148	8.5	0852	2.1	1417	8.0	2048	2.7
12	W	0232	8.2	0935	2.4	1503	7.7	2128	3.0
13	TH	0321	7.9	1020	2.7	1554	7.4	2216	3.2
14	F ☾	0417	7.6	1112	2.9	1651	7.2	2313	3.4
15	SA	0517	7.4	1210	3.0	1753	7.1		
16	SU	0017	3.4	0619	7.4	1310	3.0	1855	7.3
17	M	0123	3.3	0718	7.5	1407	2.8	1952	7.5
18	TU	0223	3.0	0812	7.7	1459	2.6	2040	7.8
19	W	0316	2.7	0900	7.9	1546	2.3	2124	8.1
20	TH	0405	2.3	0944	8.1	1630	2.1	2205	8.4
21	F	0451	2.0	1026	8.4	1713	1.9	2245	8.7
22	SA O	0536	1.8	1108	8.6	1755	1.7	2326	8.9
23	SU	0621	1.6	1151	8.7	1838	1.7		
24	M	0009	9.0	0707	1.4	1235	8.8	1922	1.7
25	TU	0054	9.1	0753	1.4	1322	8.7	2006	1.7
26	W	0141	9.0	0839	1.4	1411	8.6	2052	1.9
27	TH	0231	8.9	0927	1.5	1502	8.4	2141	2.1
28	F ☽	0324	8.7	1018	1.7	1557	8.2	2234	2.3
29	SA	0421	8.6	1113	1.9	1657	8.0	2333	2.4
30	SU	0523	8.4	1213	2.1	1802	7.9		

SUNRISE AND SUNSET TIMES

LIVERPOOL
At 53°24′N 3°01′N

		Sunrise	Sunset
UT			
Jan	01	0828	1604
	15	0820	1624
Feb	01	0757	1655
	15	0730	1723
Mar	01	0700	1750
	15	0627	1816
BST (UT+1)			
Apr	01	0645	1948
	15	0612	2013
May	01	0538	2042
	15	0512	2106
Jun	01	0450	2130
	15	0443	2142
Jul	01	0448	2143
	15	0503	2133
Aug	01	0528	2107
	15	0552	2040
Sep	01	0621	2001
	15	0646	1928
Oct	01	0714	1849
	15	0739	1816
UT			
Nov	01	0711	1640
	15	0738	1615
Dec	01	0805	1557
	15	[illegible]	[illegible]

LIVERPOOL (GLADSTONE DOCK)
LAT 53°24′N
LONG 3°01′W

TIMES AND HEIGHTS OF HIGH AND LOW WATER (Heights in Metres)

TIME ZONE UT
For Summer Time (area enclosed in shaded box) add 1 hour

2024

JULY

Day	Time	m	Day	Time	m
1 M	0037	2.5	16 TU	0014	3.4
	0629	8.3		0613	7.2
	1318	2.2		1304	3.2
	1910	7.9		1853	7.2
2 TU	0147	2.5	17 W	0129	3.3
	0735	8.3		0722	7.3
	1425	2.2		1413	3.0
	2014	8.1		1958	7.5
3 W	0257	2.3	18 TH	0238	3.0
	0839	8.3		0826	7.5
	1527	2.2		1512	2.7
	2112	8.3		2054	7.9
4 TH	0400	2.1	19 F	0338	2.6
	0937	8.5		0921	7.9
	1623	2.0		1605	2.4
	2204	8.6		2143	8.3
5 F	0457	1.8	20 SA	0432	2.1
	1029	8.6		1011	8.3
	1713	1.9		1654	2.0
●	2251	8.8		2229	8.8
6 SA	0549	1.6	21 SU	0523	1.7
	1117	8.7		1056	8.7
	1758	1.9		1742	1.7
	2334	8.9	O	2313	9.1
7 SU	0635	1.5	22 M	0613	1.3
	1200	8.6		1141	9.0
	1839	1.9		1829	1.4
				2357	9.4
8 M	0014	8.9	23 TU	0700	1.0
	0718	1.6		1226	9.1
	1239	8.6		1914	1.3
	1917	2.0			
9 TU	0051	8.8	24 W	0042	9.6
	0755	1.7		0746	0.8
	1316	8.4		1310	9.2
	1951	2.2		1958	1.2
10 W	0127	8.7	25 TH	0127	9.6
	0830	1.9		0829	0.8
	1351	8.3		1355	9.1
	2023	2.3		2040	1.4
11 TH	0204	8.5	26 F	0212	9.4
	0902	2.1		0911	1.1
	1428	8.1		1440	8.8
	2056	2.5		2123	1.6
12 F	0242	8.2	27 SA	0259	9.2
	0934	2.4		0954	1.4
	1508	7.8		1528	8.5
	2133	2.8		2208	2.0
13 SA	0324	7.9	28 SU	0350	8.8
	1010	2.6		1041	1.9
	1552	7.5		1622	8.1
☾	2216	3.1	☽	2301	2.4
14 SU	0411	7.6	29 M	0448	8.3
	1056	2.9		1137	2.4
	1643	7.3		1726	7.7
	2308	3.3			
15 M	0506	7.3	30 TU	0006	2.7
	1154	3.1		0559	7.9
	1744	7.1		1246	2.8
				1843	7.6
			31 W	0126	2.9
				0718	7.7
				1405	2.9
				2000	7.7

AUGUST

Day	Time	m	Day	Time	m
1 TH	0248	2.7	16 F	0208	3.2
	0833	7.3		0800	7.3
	1517	2.7		1445	3.0
	2106	8.0		2030	7.8
2 F	0358	2.3	17 SA	0317	2.7
	0936	8.1		0905	7.8
	1617	2.5		1545	2.5
	2159	8.4		2125	8.4
3 SA	0456	2.0	18 SU	0416	2.0
	1027	8.4		0957	8.4
	1708	2.2		1639	1.9
	2244	8.7		2212	9.0
4 SU	0544	1.7	19 M	0510	1.4
	1110	8.5		1043	8.9
	1750	2.0		1728	1.5
●	2323	8.9	O	2256	9.5
5 M	0624	1.5	20 TU	0559	0.9
	1146	8.7		1125	9.3
	1826	1.9		1815	1.1
	2358	9.0		2339	9.8
6 TU	0700	1.5	21 W	0645	0.5
	1219	8.7		1208	9.6
	1858	1.9		1858	0.8
7 W	0030	9.0	22 TH	0021	10.0
	0731	1.5		0728	0.4
	1250	8.7		1249	9.6
	1927	1.9		1940	0.8
8 TH	0101	8.9	23 F	0104	10.0
	0759	1.7		0808	0.5
	1321	8.5		1330	9.4
	1955	2.0		2020	1.0
9 F	0131	8.8	24 SA	0147	9.8
	0825	1.8		0846	0.9
	1352	8.4		1412	9.1
	2024	2.2		2059	1.4
10 SA	0202	8.5	25 SU	0231	9.3
	0852	2.1		0925	1.5
	1424	8.2		1456	8.6
	2056	2.4		2142	1.9
11 SU	0234	8.2	26 M	0319	8.7
	0923	2.4		1008	2.2
	1459	7.8		1547	8.1
	2132	2.8	☽	2233	2.5
12 M	0310	7.8	27 TU	0418	8.0
	1000	2.8		1102	2.9
	1541	7.5		1654	7.5
☾	2216	3.2		2344	3.0
13 TU	0356	7.4	28 W	0537	7.4
	1049	3.3		1222	3.3
	1637	7.2		1823	7.3
	2317	3.5			
14 W	0503	7.0	29 TH	0120	3.2
	1203	3.5		0712	7.3
	1756	7.0		1357	3.4
				1952	7.5
15 TH	0042	3.6	30 F	0248	2.8
	0636	6.9		0835	7.6
	1332	3.5		1515	3.0
	1921	7.3		2100	8.0
			31 SA	0356	2.3
				0933	8.0
				1613	2.6
				2150	8.4

SEPTEMBER

Day	Time	m	Day	Time	m
1 SU	0447	1.9	16 M	0357	1.8
	1017	8.4		0938	8.7
	1657	2.2		1619	1.8
	2229	8.8		2150	9.2
2 M	0528	1.6	17 TU	0450	1.1
	1053	8.7		1021	9.2
	1733	2.0		1708	1.3
	2303	9.0		2233	9.8
3 TU	0602	1.5	18 W	0537	0.6
	1124	8.8		1103	9.6
	1803	1.8		1753	0.8
●	2334	9.1	O	2315	10.1
4 W	0631	1.4	19 TH	0621	0.3
	1153	8.9		1143	9.8
	1831	1.7		1836	0.6
				2357	10.3
5 TH	0002	9.1	20 F	0702	0.3
	0659	1.4		1223	9.8
	1220	8.9		1916	0.6
	1858	1.7			
6 F	0031	9.1	21 SA	0038	10.1
	0724	1.5		0741	0.5
	1248	8.8		1303	9.6
	1925	1.8		1956	0.9
7 SA	0058	8.9	22 SU	0120	9.8
	0749	1.7		0818	1.0
	1316	8.6		1343	9.2
	1954	2.0		2036	1.4
8 SU	0126	8.7	23 M	0204	9.2
	0816	2.0		0856	1.7
	1345	8.4		1426	8.6
	2025	2.3		2120	2.0
9 M	0154	8.3	24 TU	0253	8.5
	0845	2.4		0938	2.5
	1416	8.1		1518	8.0
	2058	2.7	☾	2214	2.7
10 TU	0227	8.0	25 W	0355	7.7
	0918	2.9		1034	3.3
	1454	7.7		1629	7.4
	2138	3.1		2334	3.2
11 W	0310	7.5	26 TH	0522	7.1
	1001	3.4		1204	3.7
	1547	7.3		1805	7.2
☽	2235	3.5			
12 TH	0415	7.0	27 F	0114	3.3
	1113	3.7		0703	7.1
	1711	7.0		1346	3.6
				1936	7.5
13 F	0006	3.7	28 SA	0235	2.8
	0600	6.8		0822	7.5
	1258	3.7		1500	3.1
	1850	7.2		2040	8.0
14 SA	0143	3.3	29 SU	0335	2.3
	0739	7.2		0914	8.0
	1421	3.2		1552	2.7
	2006	7.8		2126	8.4
15 SU	0256	2.5	30 M	0421	1.9
	0847	7.9		0953	8.4
	1524	2.5		1632	2.3
	2103	8.6		2203	8.8

OCTOBER

Day	Time	m	Day	Time	m
1 TU	0458	1.7	16 W	0422	1.0
	1026	8.7		0954	9.3
	1704	2.0		1641	1.3
	2235	9.0		2206	9.9
2 W	0529	1.5	17 TH	0509	0.6
	1054	8.9		1036	9.7
	1732	1.8		1727	0.9
●	2304	9.1	O	2249	10.1
3 TH	0556	1.5	18 F	0553	0.5
	1122	9.0		1116	9.8
	1759	1.7		1810	0.7
	2333	9.1		2332	10.2
4 F	0623	1.5	19 SA	0634	0.5
	1149	9.0		1157	9.8
	1827	1.7		1853	0.8
5 SA	0000	9.1	20 SU	0015	10.0
	0650	1.5		0714	0.9
	1217	8.9		1237	9.5
	1857	1.7		1935	1.1
6 SU	0028	8.9	21 M	0059	9.5
	0717	1.7		0753	1.4
	1244	8.8		1319	9.1
	1928	1.9		2018	1.6
7 M	0056	8.7	22 TU	0144	8.9
	0746	2.0		0832	2.1
	1313	8.6		1403	8.6
	1959	2.2		2105	2.2
8 TU	0126	8.4	23 W	0235	8.2
	0816	2.4		0915	2.8
	1345	8.3		1456	8.0
	2033	2.6		2202	2.8
9 W	0201	8.0	24 TH	0337	7.5
	0849	2.9		1012	3.5
	1425	7.9		1607	7.5
	2114	3.0	☾	2321	3.2
10 TH	0248	7.5	25 F	0459	7.1
	0934	3.4		1139	3.9
	1521	7.5		1734	7.3
☽	2213	3.4			
11 F	0357	7.1	26 SA	0047	3.2
	1045	3.7		0630	7.1
	1646	7.2		1312	3.7
	2343	3.5		1857	7.5
12 SA	0537	7.0	27 SU	0159	2.9
	1228	3.7		0746	7.4
	1821	7.4		1421	3.3
				2001	7.8
13 SU	0117	3.0	28 M	0256	2.5
	0712	7.4		0839	7.8
	1352	3.1		1512	2.9
	1936	8.0		2049	8.2
14 M	0230	2.3	29 TU	0340	2.2
	0820	8.1		0918	8.2
	1456	2.4		1552	2.5
	2034	8.7		2127	8.6
15 TU	0329	1.6	30 W	0417	1.9
	0910	8.8		0951	8.6
	1551	1.8		1626	2.2
	2122	9.4		2201	8.8
			31 TH	0449	1.8
				1021	8.8
				1657	2.0
				2233	8.9

NOVEMBER

Day	Time	m	Day	Time	m
1 F	0519	1.7	16 SA	0526	0.9
	1051	8.9		1053	9.6
	1728	1.8		1748	1.0
●	2303	8.9		2313	9.8
2 SA	0549	1.7	17 SU	0609	1.0
	1120	9.0		1136	9.6
	1800	1.8		1834	1.1
	2334	8.9		2359	9.6
3 SU	0619	1.7	18 M	0651	1.3
	1150	9.0		1219	9.4
	1833	1.8		1920	1.3
4 M	0004	8.8	19 TU	0044	9.2
	0651	1.9		0733	1.7
	1220	8.9		1302	9.1
	1907	2.0		2007	1.7
5 TU	0036	8.6	20 W	0131	8.7
	0723	2.1		0814	2.3
	1253	8.7		1348	8.7
	1942	2.2		2055	2.2
6 W	0111	8.4	21 TH	0220	8.2
	0756	2.5		0858	2.8
	1329	8.4		1439	8.2
	2020	2.5		2149	2.6
7 TH	0152	8.1	22 F	0316	7.7
	0834	2.8		0949	3.3
	1414	8.1		1539	7.8
	2105	2.8		2252	3.0
8 F	0243	7.7	23 SA	0420	7.3
	0923	3.2		1055	3.7
	1512	7.8		1648	7.5
	2206	3.0	☾		
9 SA	0351	7.4	24 SU	0000	3.1
	1032	3.5		0532	7.1
	1629	7.6		1211	3.8
☽	2324	3.1		1758	7.5
10 SU	0514	7.3	25 M	0104	3.1
	1157	3.4		0644	7.2
	1749	7.8		1319	3.6
				1904	7.6
11 M	0045	2.7	26 TU	0201	2.9
	0636	7.7		0745	7.5
	1314	3.0		1416	3.3
	1900	8.2		1959	7.9
12 TU	0154	2.2	27 W	0249	2.6
	0744	8.2		0833	7.9
	1420	2.5		1503	2.9
	2000	8.8		2046	8.1
13 W	0256	1.7	28 TH	0331	2.4
	0838	8.7		0912	8.2
	1518	1.9		1544	2.6
	2052	9.3		2126	8.4
14 TH	0350	1.3	29 F	0409	2.2
	0926	9.2		0948	8.5
	1612	1.5		1623	2.3
	2140	9.6		2203	8.5
15 F	0440	1.0	30 SA	0445	2.0
	1010	9.4		1022	8.7
	1701	1.2		1700	2.1
O	2227	9.8		2238	8.6

DECEMBER

Day	Time	m	Day	Time	m
1 SU	0520	1.9	16 M	0552	1.5
	1055	8.8		1125	9.3
	1737	2.0		1825	1.4
●	2313	8.7		2351	9.1
2 M	0555	1.9	17 TU	0636	1.7
	1129	8.9		1210	9.2
	1815	1.9		1912	1.4
	2348	8.7			
3 TU	0631	2.0	18 W	0036	8.9
	1204	8.9		0720	1.9
	1854	1.9		1252	9.1
				1958	1.6
4 W	0025	8.6	19 TH	0120	8.7
	0709	2.1		0800	2.2
	1242	8.9		1335	8.8
	1935	2.0		2042	1.9
5 TH	0105	8.5	20 F	0203	8.3
	0747	2.3		0840	2.6
	1323	8.7		1417	8.5
	2017	2.2		2125	2.3
6 F	0149	8.3	21 SA	0246	8.0
	0830	2.5		0919	2.9
	1410	8.5		1503	8.2
	2104	2.3		2209	2.7
7 SA	0240	8.1	22 SU	0333	7.7
	0918	2.8		1002	3.2
	1504	8.3		1554	7.9
	2158	2.5	☾	2256	3.0
8 SU	0339	7.9	23 M	0426	7.4
	1016	2.9		1053	3.5
	1607	8.2		1651	7.6
☽	2300	2.5		2350	3.2
9 M	0445	7.8	24 TU	0526	7.2
	1123	3.0		1155	3.6
	1714	8.2		1753	7.4
10 TU	0007	2.5	25 W	0050	3.2
	0556	7.8		0632	7.2
	1231	2.9		1302	3.6
	1821	8.4		1858	7.4
11 W	0114	2.3	26 TH	0150	3.1
	0704	8.1		0735	7.4
	1340	2.6		1407	3.4
	1925	8.6		1959	7.6
12 TH	0220	2.1	27 F	0244	2.9
	0806	8.4		0830	7.7
	1446	2.3		1502	3.1
	2025	8.8		2051	7.8
13 F	0320	1.8	28 SA	0332	2.7
	0901	8.7		0916	8.0
	1547	1.9		1552	2.7
	2121	9.1		2138	8.1
14 SA	0415	1.6	29 SU	0416	2.4
	0951	9.0		0958	8.4
	1642	1.6		1637	2.4
	2213	9.2		2219	8.3
15 SU	0505	1.5	30 M	0458	2.2
	1039	9.2		1037	8.7
	1735	1.4		1721	2.1
O	2303	9.2	●	2259	8.5
			31 TU	0539	2.0
				1115	8.9
				1805	1.8
				2338	8.7

HOLYHEAD
LAT 53°19'N
LONG 4°37'W

TIMES AND HEIGHTS OF HIGH AND LOW WATER (Heights in Metres)

TIME ZONE UT
For Summer Time (area enclosed in shaded box) add 1 hour

2024

JANUARY

Date	Day	Time	m
1	M	0117 0713 1327 1952	4.9 1.7 5.2 1.6
2	TU	0157 0754 1408 2035	4.7 1.9 5.0 1.7
3	W	0241 0839 1453 2123	4.6 2.1 4.8 1.9
4	TH	0333 0931 1547 ☾ 2219	4.4 2.3 4.7 2.0
5	F	0435 1033 1651 2321	4.4 2.4 4.6 2.1
6	SA	0543 1141 1800	4.4 2.3 4.6
7	SU	0024 0648 1247 1906	2.0 4.5 2.2 4.7
8	M	0122 0744 1345 2004	1.9 4.8 1.9 4.8
9	TU	0214 0833 1437 2055	1.7 5.0 1.6 5.0
10	W	0301 0918 1525 2142	1.4 5.3 1.3 5.3
11	TH	0346 1001 1612 ● 2228	1.2 5.5 1.0 5.4
12	F	0430 1044 1658 2313	1.0 5.8 0.8 5.5
13	SA	0515 1129 1744	0.9 5.9 0.6
14	SU	0000 0600 1215 1831	5.6 0.9 6.0 0.6
15	M	0046 0647 1301 1920	5.5 0.9 5.9 0.7
16	TU	0135 0735 1350 2011	5.3 1.1 5.8 0.9
17	W	0225 0827 1442 2105	5.1 1.3 5.5 1.1
18	TH	0321 0924 1540 ☽ 2206	4.9 1.6 5.3 1.4
19	F	0425 1031 1647 2314	4.7 1.8 5.0 1.7
20	SA	0539 1145 1803	4.6 1.9 4.8
21	SU	0025 0654 1300 1921	1.8 4.6 1.9 4.8
22	M	0133 0800 1409 2026	1.8 4.8 1.7 4.9
23	TU	0232 0853 1505 2119	1.7 5.0 1.5 5.0
24	W	0320 0938 1551 2202	1.6 5.2 1.3 5.1
25	TH	0401 1016 1631 ○ 2239	1.4 5.4 1.2 5.2
26	F	0436 1051 1706 2313	1.3 5.5 1.1 5.2
27	SA	0508 1123 1738 2345	1.2 5.5 1.1 5.2
28	SU	0540 1155 1810	1.2 5.5 1.1
29	M	0015 0612 1226 1842	5.2 1.3 5.4 1.1
30	TU	0047 0644 1258 1915	5.1 1.3 5.3 1.3
31	W	0120 0718 1331 1950	5.0 1.5 5.2 1.4

FEBRUARY

Date	Day	Time	m
1	TH	0155 0754 1407 2028	4.8 1.7 5.0 1.7
2	F	0235 0836 1448 ☾ 2113	4.6 1.9 4.8 1.9
3	SA	0323 0929 1541 2211	4.5 2.1 4.6 2.1
4	SU	0429 1038 1657 2327	4.3 2.3 4.4 2.2
5	M	0553 1202 1827	4.3 2.3 4.4
6	TU	0046 0711 1319 1945	2.1 4.5 2.0 4.6
7	W	0153 0813 1421 2044	1.8 4.8 1.6 4.9
8	TH	0247 0903 1514 2133	1.5 5.2 1.2 5.2
9	F	0334 0947 1600 ● 2217	1.1 5.6 0.7 5.5
10	SA	0418 1030 1644 2300	0.8 5.9 0.4 5.7
11	SU	0500 1113 1728 2343	0.6 6.1 0.2 5.7
12	M	0542 1156 1811	0.5 6.2 0.2
13	TU	0025 0626 1240 1856	5.7 0.5 6.1 0.4
14	W	0108 0710 1325 1941	5.5 0.7 5.9 0.7
15	TH	0153 0757 1412 2030	5.3 1.0 5.6 1.1
16	F	0241 0850 1506 ☽ 2126	4.9 1.4 5.2 1.5
17	SA	0339 0955 1613 2236	4.6 1.8 4.7 2.0
18	SU	0457 1119 1742	4.4 2.0 4.4
19	M	0000 0632 1248 1918	2.2 4.4 2.0 4.4
20	TU	0123 0751 1405 2028	2.1 4.6 1.8 4.6
21	W	0227 0847 1459 2116	1.9 4.9 1.5 4.8
22	TH	0312 0928 1540 2152	1.7 5.1 1.3 5.0
23	F	0348 1002 1614 2223	1.4 5.3 1.1 5.1
24	SA	0419 1032 1645 ○ 2251	1.2 5.4 0.9 5.2
25	SU	0447 1101 1713 2319	1.1 5.5 0.9 5.3
26	M	0515 1129 1741 2347	1.0 5.5 0.9 5.3
27	TU	0544 1158 1809	1.0 5.5 0.9
28	W	0015 0614 1228 1839	5.2 1.1 5.4 1.1
29	TH	0045 0645 1258 1910	5.1 1.2 5.3 1.3

MARCH

Date	Day	Time	m
1	F	0117 0718 1330 1943	5.0 1.4 5.1 1.5
2	SA	0152 0756 1407 2023	4.8 1.6 4.8 1.8
3	SU	0234 0844 1455 ☾ 2118	4.6 1.9 4.5 2.1
4	M	0333 0953 1610 2240	4.4 2.2 4.3 2.3
5	TU	0505 1128 1802	4.2 2.2 4.2
6	W	0018 0642 1258 1932	2.2 4.4 1.9 4.5
7	TH	0134 0751 1404 2031	1.9 4.8 1.4 4.9
8	F	0230 0843 1456 2118	1.4 5.2 0.9 5.3
9	SA	0316 0927 1541 2159	1.0 5.6 0.5 5.6
10	SU	0358 1009 1623 ● 2239	0.6 6.0 0.2 5.8
11	M	0438 1051 1704 2319	0.3 6.2 0.0 5.8
12	TU	0519 1133 1746 2359	0.2 6.3 0.1 5.8
13	W	0601 1216 1828	0.3 6.1 0.3
14	TH	0040 0645 1300 1911	5.6 0.5 5.8 0.7
15	F	0122 0731 1346 1957	5.3 0.9 5.4 1.2
16	SA	0208 0823 1439 2050	5.0 1.3 4.9 1.7
17	SU	0303 0929 1547 ☽ 2201	4.6 1.8 4.5 2.2
18	M	0420 1057 1727 2334	4.3 2.1 4.2 2.4
19	TU	0605 1233 1908	4.3 2.0 4.2
20	W	0105 0731 1347 2014	2.3 4.5 1.8 4.5
21	TH	0208 0825 1438 2056	2.0 4.8 1.5 4.7
22	F	0251 0903 1515 2129	1.7 5.0 1.2 4.9
23	SA	0324 0935 1547 2157	1.4 5.2 1.0 5.1
24	SU	0353 1004 1615 2223	1.2 5.3 0.9 5.2
25	M	0420 1032 1642 ○ 2249	1.0 5.4 0.8 5.3
26	TU	0447 1100 1709 2316	0.9 5.5 0.8 5.3
27	W	0516 1129 1737 2345	0.9 5.4 0.9 5.3
28	TH	0545 1159 1805	1.0 5.4 1.0
29	F	0015 0617 1230 1836	5.2 1.1 5.2 1.2
30	SA	0047 0651 1303 1910	5.1 1.3 5.0 1.4
31	SU	0122 0731 1342 1953	4.9 1.5 4.8 1.7

APRIL

Date	Day	Time	m
1	M	0206 0821 1434 2050	4.7 1.8 4.5 2.1
2	TU	0307 0933 1555 ☾ 2216	4.4 2.0 4.2 2.3
3	W	0438 1109 1748 2356	4.3 2.0 4.2 2.2
4	TH	0614 1236 1912	4.5 1.7 4.6
5	F	0110 0723 1340 2009	1.8 4.9 1.2 4.9
6	SA	0206 0816 1431 2054	1.3 5.3 0.7 5.3
7	SU	0251 0901 1515 2134	0.9 5.7 0.4 5.6
8	M	0333 0944 1557 ● 2213	0.5 6.0 0.2 5.7
9	TU	0414 1026 1638 2253	0.3 6.1 0.1 5.8
10	W	0455 1110 1719 2334	0.2 6.1 0.2 5.8
11	TH	0538 1154 1801	0.3 5.9 0.5
12	F	0015 0624 1239 1845	5.6 0.6 5.6 0.9
13	SA	0057 0711 1326 1931	5.3 0.9 5.2 1.4
14	SU	0143 0805 1420 2023	5.0 1.3 4.7 1.8
15	M	0237 0910 1528 ☽ 2130	4.7 1.7 4.3 2.2
16	TU	0349 1032 1700 2259	4.4 2.0 4.1 2.4
17	W	0522 1158 1834	4.3 2.0 4.2
18	TH	0025 0647 1308 1937	2.4 4.4 1.8 4.4
19	F	0129 0744 1359 2020	2.1 4.6 1.5 4.6
20	SA	0214 0825 1438 2053	1.8 4.9 1.3 4.8
21	SU	0249 0859 1511 2123	1.5 5.0 1.1 5.0
22	M	0320 0930 1540 2150	1.3 5.2 1.0 5.2
23	TU	0348 1000 1608 ○ 2218	1.1 5.3 0.9 5.3
24	W	0418 1030 1637 2247	1.0 5.3 0.9 5.3
25	TH	0448 1102 1706 2318	1.0 5.3 1.0 5.3
26	F	0521 1134 1738 2351	1.0 5.2 1.1 5.3
27	SA	0555 1209 1812	1.1 5.1 1.2
28	SU	0026 0635 1247 1852	5.2 1.2 5.0 1.5
29	M	0107 0720 1334 1940	5.0 1.4 4.7 1.7
30	TU	0156 0816 1433 2042	4.8 1.6 4.5 2.0

MAY

Date	Day	Time	m
1	W	0300 0928 1554 ☾ 2204	4.6 1.7 4.3 2.1
2	TH	0421 1052 1728 2329	4.6 1.7 4.4 2.0
3	F	0543 1209 1842	4.7 1.4 4.7
4	SA	0039 0650 1310 1939	1.7 5.0 1.1 5.0
5	SU	0134 0745 1402 2025	1.3 5.3 0.8 5.2
6	M	0223 0833 1448 2107	1.0 5.6 0.5 5.5
7	TU	0307 0919 1531 2149	0.7 5.8 0.4 5.6
8	W	0351 1005 1614 ● 2230	0.5 5.9 0.4 5.7
9	TH	0436 1051 1657 2312	0.5 5.8 0.6 5.6
10	F	0521 1137 1740 2356	0.5 5.6 0.8 5.5
11	SA	0608 1224 1824	0.7 5.3 1.1
12	SU	0039 0657 1311 1910	5.3 1.0 5.0 1.5
13	M	0125 0750 1403 2000	5.1 1.3 4.6 1.8
14	TU	0215 0848 1503 2058	4.8 1.6 4.4 2.1
15	W	0316 0956 1615 ☽ 2210	4.6 1.8 4.2 2.3
16	TH	0427 1107 1732 2326	4.4 1.9 4.2 2.3
17	F	0541 1213 1839	4.4 1.8 4.3
18	SA	0031 0644 1307 1929	2.2 4.5 1.7 4.5
19	SU	0123 0734 1351 2009	2.0 4.7 1.5 4.7
20	M	0205 0816 1429 2044	1.7 4.9 1.3 4.9
21	TU	0241 0853 1502 2116	1.5 5.0 1.2 5.0
22	W	0315 0928 1535 2148	1.3 5.1 1.2 5.2
23	TH	0350 1003 1608 ○ 2221	1.2 5.2 1.1 5.3
24	F	0425 1039 1642 2256	1.1 5.2 1.1 5.3
25	SA	0503 1117 1719 2334	1.1 5.2 1.2 5.3
26	SU	0543 1158 1800	1.1 5.1 1.2
27	M	0015 0628 1242 1845	5.3 1.1 5.0 1.4
28	TU	0101 0718 1333 1937	5.2 1.2 4.8 1.6
29	W	0153 0814 1433 2037	5.1 1.3 4.7 1.7
30	TH	0252 0919 1543 ☾ 2146	4.9 1.4 4.6 1.8
31	F	0400 1029 1657 2257	4.9 1.4 4.6 1.8

JUNE

Date	Day	Time	m
1	SA	0510 1137 1806	5.0 1.3 4.7
2	SU	0003 0616 1238 1905	1.6 5.1 1.1 4.9
3	M	0103 0715 1333 1957	1.4 5.2 1.0 5.1
4	TU	0157 0809 1424 2044	1.2 5.4 0.9 5.3
5	W	0247 0901 1511 2129	1.0 5.5 0.8 5.4
6	TH	0336 0950 1557 ● 2214	0.8 5.5 0.9 5.5
7	F	0424 1038 1641 2258	0.8 5.4 1.0 5.5
8	SA	0512 1126 1725 2341	0.8 5.3 1.1 5.4
9	SU	0558 1211 1807	0.9 5.1 1.3
10	M	0024 0644 1256 1850	5.3 1.1 4.9 1.5
11	TU	0106 0730 1341 1934	5.2 1.3 4.7 1.7
12	W	0150 0818 1428 2022	5.0 1.5 4.5 1.9
13	TH	0237 0909 1520 2114	4.8 1.7 4.4 2.1
14	F	0330 1005 1619 ☽ 2214	4.6 1.8 4.3 2.2
15	SA	0430 1105 1722 2319	4.5 1.9 4.3 2.2
16	SU	0533 1203 1822	4.5 1.8 4.4
17	M	0020 0634 1256 1916	2.2 4.5 1.8 4.5
18	TU	0114 0728 1343 2002	2.0 4.6 1.7 4.7
19	W	0202 0817 1426 2043	1.8 4.8 1.5 4.9
20	TH	0246 0900 1506 2122	1.6 4.9 1.4 5.1
21	F	0327 0942 1546 2200	1.4 5.0 1.3 5.2
22	SA	0409 1023 1626 ○ 2240	1.2 5.1 1.2 5.4
23	SU	0451 1106 1708 2322	1.0 5.2 1.1 5.5
24	M	0536 1151 1752	0.9 5.2 1.1
25	TU	0006 0622 1237 1838	5.5 0.9 5.1 1.2
26	W	0053 0711 1326 1928	5.5 0.9 5.1 1.3
27	TH	0142 0803 1419 2021	5.4 1.0 4.9 1.4
28	F	0235 0858 1517 ☾ 2119	5.3 1.1 4.8 1.5
29	SA	0333 0959 1620 2223	5.2 1.2 4.7 1.6
30	SU	0436 1103 1727 2330	5.1 1.3 4.7 1.6

SUNRISE AND SUNSET TIMES

HOLYHEAD
At 53°19'N 4°37'W

UT		Sunrise	Sunset
Jan	01	0834	1611
	15	0826	1631
Feb	01	0803	1702
	15	0736	1730
Mar	01	0706	1757
	15	0633	1823
BST (UT+1)			
Apr	01	0652	1954
	15	0619	2020
May	01	0544	2048
	15	0519	2112
Jun	01	0457	2136
	15	0450	2148
Jul	01	0455	2149
	15	0510	2139
Aug	01	0535	2114
	15	0559	2046
Sep	01	0628	2008
	15	0652	1934
Oct	01	0720	1855
	15	0745	1822
UT			
Nov	01	0717	1646
	15	0744	1622
Dec	01	0811	1604
	15	0827	1600

HOLYHEAD

LAT 53°19′N
LONG 4°37′W

TIMES AND HEIGHTS OF HIGH AND LOW WATER (Heights in Metres)

TIME ZONE UT
For Summer Time (area enclosed in shaded box) add 1 hour

2024

JULY

Date	Day	Time	m
1	M	0543 1208 1833	5.0 1.4 4.7
2	TU	0036 0652 1310 1935	1.6 5.0 1.4 4.9
3	W	0140 0756 1408 2030	1.4 5.0 1.3 5.0
4	TH	0239 0854 1501 2119	1.3 5.1 1.3 5.2
5	F ●	0332 0946 1548 2205	1.1 5.1 1.2 5.3
6	SA	0420 1033 1631 2248	1.0 5.2 1.2 5.4
7	SU	0504 1116 1712 2328	0.9 5.1 1.2 5.4
8	M	0545 1156 1750	1.0 5.1 1.3
9	TU	0006 0625 1233 1827	5.4 1.0 5.0 1.3
10	W	0042 0702 1310 1904	5.3 1.1 4.9 1.5
11	TH	0119 0741 1347 1943	5.2 1.3 4.7 1.6
12	F	0157 0820 1427 2024	5.0 1.5 4.6 1.8
13	SA ☽	0238 0904 1512 2111	4.8 1.7 4.5 2.0
14	SU	0325 0954 1607 2207	4.6 1.8 4.3 2.2
15	M	0423 1052 1711 2313	4.5 2.0 4.3 2.3
16	TU	0531 1157 1819	4.4 2.0 4.4
17	W	0023 0643 1259 1922	2.2 4.4 2.0 4.5
18	TH	0127 0747 1355 2015	2.0 4.5 1.8 4.8
19	F	0222 0841 1445 2102	1.7 4.7 1.6 5.0
20	SA	0311 0928 1530 2144	1.4 4.9 1.3 5.3
21	SU O	0356 1012 1613 2226	1.1 5.2 1.1 5.5
22	M	0440 1055 1655 2309	0.8 5.3 0.9 5.7
23	TU	0523 1139 1738 2352	0.6 5.4 0.8 5.8
24	W	0608 1223 1822	0.5 5.4 0.8
25	TH	0036 0653 1307 1908	5.8 0.5 5.3 0.9
26	F	0122 0740 1354 1956	5.8 0.7 5.2 1.1
27	SA	0210 0830 1444 2048	5.6 0.9 5.0 1.3
28	SU ☾	0303 0925 1542 2149	5.3 1.2 4.8 1.6
29	M	0404 1029 1651 2302	5.0 1.5 4.6 1.8
30	TU	0519 1142 1809	4.8 1.7 4.6
31	W	0020 0642 1256 1925	1.8 4.7 1.8 4.7

AUGUST

Date	Day	Time	m
1	TH	0136 0758 1403 2027	1.7 4.7 1.7 4.9
2	F	0241 0858 1458 2116	1.5 4.9 1.5 5.1
3	SA	0332 0945 1543 2158	1.2 5.0 1.4 5.3
4	SU ●	0414 1025 1621 2235	1.1 5.1 1.3 5.4
5	M	0451 1100 1655 2309	1.0 5.1 1.2 5.5
6	TU	0525 1133 1727 2342	0.9 5.2 1.1 5.5
7	W	0557 1204 1758	0.9 5.1 1.2
8	TH	0013 0629 1234 1831	5.4 1.0 5.1 1.3
9	F	0044 0701 1307 1904	5.3 1.2 5.0 1.4
10	SA	0117 0735 1341 1940	5.2 1.4 4.8 1.5
11	SU	0152 0811 1419 2020	5.0 1.5 4.7 1.9
12	M ☽	0231 0853 1504 2110	4.7 1.8 4.5 2.1
13	TU	0321 0947 1604 2215	4.5 2.1 4.3 2.3
14	W	0431 1059 1726 2339	4.3 2.3 4.3 2.3
15	TH	0605 1222 1847	4.2 2.2 4.4
16	F	0100 0727 1332 1952	2.1 4.4 2.0 4.7
17	SA	0204 0827 1427 2043	1.7 4.7 1.7 5.1
18	SU	0255 0915 1514 2126	1.3 5.0 1.3 5.4
19	M O	0340 0957 1555 2207	0.9 5.3 1.0 5.8
20	TU	0421 1037 1636 2248	0.5 5.5 0.7 6.0
21	W	0503 1118 1717 2330	0.3 5.7 0.5 6.1
22	TH	0544 1159 1758	0.2 5.7 0.5
23	F	0012 0627 1241 1842	6.1 0.3 5.6 0.6
24	SA	0056 0712 1324 1928	6.0 0.6 5.4 0.9
25	SU	0143 0759 1411 2019	5.7 0.9 5.1 1.2
26	M ☾	0235 0852 1507 2122	5.3 1.4 4.8 1.6
27	TU	0339 0959 1620 2244	4.8 1.9 4.5 1.9
28	W	0506 1123 1754	4.5 2.1 4.5
29	TH	0015 0646 1250 1920	2.0 4.4 2.2 4.7
30	F	0137 0803 1400 2022	1.8 4.6 2.0 4.9
31	SA	0237 0856 1451 2107	1.5 4.8 1.7 5.2

SEPTEMBER

Date	Day	Time	m
1	SU	0321 0935 1529 2142	1.2 5.0 1.5 5.4
2	M	0357 1007 1602 2214	1.1 5.1 1.3 5.5
3	TU ●	0428 1036 1631 2243	0.9 5.2 1.1 5.5
4	W	0457 1103 1659 2312	0.9 5.3 1.1 5.6
5	TH	0525 1131 1728 2341	0.9 5.3 1.1 5.5
6	F	0553 1200 1757	1.0 5.2 1.2
7	SA	0011 0622 1229 1829	5.4 1.1 5.2 1.3
8	SU	0041 0653 1301 1902	5.3 1.3 5.0 1.5
9	M	0113 0726 1336 1940	5.0 1.6 4.9 1.8
10	TU	0149 0804 1417 2027	4.8 1.9 4.6 2.1
11	W ☾	0236 0856 1514 2133	4.5 2.2 4.4 2.3
12	TH	0347 1013 1641 2306	4.2 2.4 4.3 2.4
13	F	0539 1152 1817	4.2 2.4 4.4
14	SA	0037 0711 1310 1928	2.1 4.4 2.1 4.8
15	SU	0143 0810 1406 2019	1.6 4.8 1.7 5.2
16	M	0233 0854 1451 2101	1.1 5.2 1.2 5.6
17	TU	0316 0934 1531 2142	0.7 5.5 0.8 6.0
18	W O	0356 1012 1611 2222	0.3 5.7 0.5 6.2
19	TH	0436 1051 1651 2304	0.2 5.9 0.4 6.3
20	F	0517 1132 1732 2348	0.2 5.9 0.4 6.2
21	SA	0559 1213 1816	0.3 5.7 0.6
22	SU	0032 0643 1256 1904	6.0 0.7 5.5 0.9
23	M	0120 0730 1343 1957	5.6 1.2 5.2 1.3
24	TU ☽	0213 0824 1439 2104	5.1 1.7 4.8 1.8
25	W	0322 0933 1556 2232	4.6 2.2 4.6 2.0
26	TH	0501 1106 1737	4.3 2.4 4.5
27	F	0006 0643 1236 1904	2.0 4.4 2.3 4.7
28	SA	0123 0751 1343 2002	1.8 4.6 2.1 4.9
29	SU	0217 0837 1429 2043	1.5 4.8 1.8 5.2
30	M	0257 0911 1505 2116	1.3 5.0 1.5 5.3

OCTOBER

Date	Day	Time	m
1	TU	0329 0939 1535 2145	1.1 5.2 1.3 5.5
2	W ●	0358 1006 1602 2213	1.0 5.3 1.2 5.5
3	TH	0425 1032 1630 2242	1.0 5.4 1.1 5.6
4	F	0451 1059 1658 2311	1.0 5.4 1.1 5.5
5	SA	0519 1128 1727 2341	1.1 5.4 1.2 5.4
6	SU	0547 1158 1759	1.2 5.3 1.3
7	M	0011 0618 1229 1833	5.3 1.4 5.2 1.5
8	TU	0044 0652 1304 1912	5.0 1.6 5.0 1.8
9	W	0122 0732 1347 2002	4.8 1.9 4.8 2.0
10	TH ☾	0213 0826 1446 2110	4.5 2.2 4.6 2.2
11	F	0328 0946 1611 2242	4.3 2.5 4.4 2.2
12	SA	0519 1124 1745	4.3 2.4 4.6
13	SU	0009 0645 1241 1855	1.9 4.6 2.1 4.9
14	M	0113 0742 1337 1948	1.5 5.0 1.6 5.4
15	TU	0204 0827 1423 2032	1.0 5.3 1.2 5.7
16	W	0247 0907 1504 2115	0.6 5.6 0.8 6.1
17	TH O	0328 0946 1545 2157	0.4 5.8 0.5 6.2
18	F	0409 1025 1627 2241	0.3 5.9 0.4 6.3
19	SA	0451 1106 1711 2326	0.3 5.9 0.5 6.1
20	SU	0534 1149 1757	0.6 5.8 0.7
21	M	0013 0619 1234 1847	5.8 1.0 5.6 1.0
22	TU	0103 0707 1322 1943	5.4 1.4 5.3 1.4
23	W	0159 0801 1419 2050	4.9 1.9 4.9 1.8
24	TH ☽	0309 0909 1532 2212	4.5 2.3 4.7 2.0
25	F	0440 1036 1702 2336	4.3 2.5 4.6 2.0
26	SA	0611 1200 1824	4.4 2.5 4.7
27	SU	0047 0717 1306 1923	1.9 4.6 2.2 4.9
28	M	0140 0802 1354 2007	1.7 4.8 2.0 5.1
29	TU	0221 0837 1431 2042	1.5 5.0 1.7 5.2
30	W	0254 0907 1503 2113	1.3 5.2 1.5 5.4
31	TH	0324 0934 1532 2143	1.2 5.3 1.4 5.4

NOVEMBER

Date	Day	Time	m
1	F ●	0352 1002 1602 2213	1.1 5.4 1.3 5.5
2	SA	0420 1031 1632 2244	1.2 5.5 1.2 5.4
3	SU	0450 1101 1704 2316	1.2 5.5 1.3 5.3
4	M	0521 1133 1738 2351	1.3 5.4 1.4 5.2
5	TU	0554 1208 1816	1.5 5.3 1.5
6	W	0028 0632 1247 1900	5.0 1.7 5.2 1.7
7	TH	0111 0716 1334 1952	4.8 1.9 5.0 1.9
8	F	0206 0813 1432 2059	4.6 2.2 4.8 2.0
9	SA ☾	0319 0927 1547 2218	4.4 2.3 4.7 1.9
10	SU	0450 1051 1708 2335	4.5 2.3 4.8 1.7
11	M	0608 1204 1816	4.7 2.0 5.1
12	TU	0038 0707 1302 1913	1.4 5.0 1.6 5.4
13	W	0131 0756 1352 2003	1.0 5.3 1.3 5.7
14	TH	0218 0839 1438 2050	0.8 5.6 1.0 5.9
15	F O	0303 0921 1523 2137	0.6 5.7 0.7 6.0
16	SA	0347 1004 1609 2224	0.6 5.8 0.7 6.0
17	SU	0431 1048 1656 2312	0.7 5.9 0.7 5.8
18	M	0516 1133 1745	0.9 5.8 0.8
19	TU	0000 0602 1218 1837	5.6 1.2 5.6 1.1
20	W	0051 0650 1307 1931	5.3 1.5 5.4 1.4
21	TH	0145 0741 1359 2030	4.9 1.9 5.1 1.7
22	F	0245 0839 1459 2136	4.6 2.2 4.9 1.9
23	SA ☽	0355 0947 1609 2246	4.4 2.4 4.7 2.0
24	SU	0510 1102 1720 2352	4.3 2.5 4.6 2.0
25	M	0618 1210 1825	4.4 2.4 4.7
26	TU	0048 0712 1305 1918	1.9 4.6 2.2 4.8
27	W	0135 0754 1350 2002	1.7 4.8 2.0 5.0
28	TH	0215 0831 1428 2040	1.6 5.0 1.8 5.1
29	F	0250 0904 1504 2116	1.5 5.2 1.6 5.2
30	SA	0323 0935 1538 2150	1.4 5.3 1.5 5.3

DECEMBER

Date	Day	Time	m
1	SU ●	0355 1008 1613 2225	1.4 5.4 1.4 5.3
2	M	0428 1041 1649 2301	1.4 5.5 1.3 5.3
3	TU	0503 1118 1727 2340	1.4 5.5 1.3 5.2
4	W	0541 1156 1808	1.4 5.5 1.4
5	TH	0021 0623 1238 1854	5.1 1.6 5.4 1.4
6	F	0107 0709 1326 1945	5.0 1.7 5.3 1.5
7	SA	0200 0803 1419 2043	4.8 1.9 5.1 1.6
8	SU ☾	0301 0904 1520 2148	4.7 2.0 5.1 1.6
9	M	0412 1013 1628 2256	4.7 2.0 5.1 1.5
10	TU	0523 1123 1736	4.7 1.9 5.2
11	W	0000 0629 1226 1840	1.4 4.9 1.7 5.3
12	TH	0100 0726 1325 1938	1.3 5.1 1.5 5.4
13	F	0154 0817 1419 2033	1.1 5.3 1.2 5.6
14	SA	0245 0905 1511 2126	1.0 5.5 1.0 5.6
15	SU O	0333 0951 1602 2216	1.0 5.7 0.9 5.6
16	M	0420 1037 1651 2305	1.0 5.7 0.9 5.6
17	TU	0505 1122 1739 2352	1.1 5.7 0.9 5.4
18	W	0549 1207 1826	1.3 5.6 1.1
19	TH	0038 0633 1250 1912	5.2 1.4 5.5 1.2
20	F	0123 0717 1334 1959	5.0 1.7 5.3 1.5
21	SA	0209 0802 1419 2049	4.8 1.9 5.1 1.7
22	SU ☽	0258 0852 1509 2142	4.6 2.1 4.9 1.9
23	M	0353 0948 1605 2241	4.4 2.3 4.7 2.0
24	TU	0456 1053 1709 2342	4.3 2.4 4.6 2.1
25	W	0601 1200 1814	4.4 2.4 4.6
26	TH	0040 0701 1300 1916	2.0 4.5 2.3 4.7
27	F	0132 0752 1353 2008	1.9 4.7 2.1 4.8
28	SA	0218 0835 1438 2053	1.8 4.9 1.8 4.9
29	SU	0258 0914 1520 2134	1.7 5.1 1.6 5.0
30	M ●	0337 0951 1559 2213	1.5 5.3 1.4 5.2
31	TU	0414 1028 1639 2252	1.4 5.5 1.2 5.2

MILFORD HAVEN
LAT 51°42′N
LONG 5°03′W

TIMES AND HEIGHTS OF HIGH AND LOW WATER (Heights in Metres)

TIME ZONE UT
For Summer Time (area enclosed in shaded box) add 1 hour

2024

JANUARY

Date	Day	Time	m	Time	m	Time	m	Time	m
1	M	0308	1.8	0918	6.2	1536	1.9	2139	5.8
2	TU	0343	2.0	0955	6.0	1613	2.1	2218	5.6
3	W	0423	2.3	1036	5.7	1656	2.3	2302	5.4
4	TH ☽	0510	2.5	1124	5.5	1748	2.5	2356	5.2
5	F	0610	2.6	1222	5.3	1853	2.6		
6	SA	0102	5.1	0723	2.7	1330	5.3	2005	2.6
7	SU	0213	5.3	0835	2.5	1440	5.5	2112	2.3
8	M	0317	5.6	0939	2.2	1541	5.7	2209	2.0
9	TU	0412	6.0	1035	1.9	1636	6.1	2300	1.7
10	W	0502	6.4	1126	1.5	1727	6.4	2348	1.4
11	TH ●	0551	6.7	1214	1.2	1815	6.7		
12	F	0034	1.1	0638	7.0	1301	0.9	1903	6.9
13	SA	0120	0.9	0725	7.2	1348	0.7	1950	7.0
14	SU	0205	0.8	0811	7.3	1434	0.7	2036	6.9
15	M	0251	0.9	0858	7.2	1520	0.8	2122	6.8
16	TU	0336	1.0	0945	7.0	1606	1.0	2208	6.5
17	W	0422	1.3	1033	6.7	1654	1.4	2257	6.1
18	TH ☾	0513	1.7	1125	6.3	1747	1.7	2352	5.8
19	F	0612	2.0	1225	5.9	1849	2.1		
20	SA	0057	5.5	0725	2.3	1334	5.6	2004	2.3
21	SU	0212	5.4	0846	2.3	1450	5.6	2119	2.3
22	M	0328	5.6	0959	2.2	1601	5.7	2223	2.1
23	TU	0432	5.9	1058	1.9	1700	5.9	2315	1.8
24	W	0523	6.2	1147	1.6	1747	6.2	2359	1.6
25	TH O	0606	6.4	1228	1.4	1827	6.4		
26	F	0037	1.4	0644	6.6	1304	1.3	1903	6.4
27	SA	0112	1.3	0718	6.7	1337	1.2	1936	6.5
28	SU	0144	1.3	0750	6.7	1408	1.3	2008	6.4
29	M	0215	1.3	0821	6.6	1437	1.3	2038	6.3
30	TU	0244	1.4	0851	6.5	1506	1.5	2108	6.2
31	W	0314	1.5	0921	6.3	1536	1.7		

FEBRUARY

Date	Day	Time	m	Time	m	Time	m	Time	m
1	TH	0346	1.8	0954	6.0	1608	1.9	2213	5.7
2	F ☽	0421	2.1	1030	5.8	1645	2.2	2253	5.4
3	SA	0503	2.4	1116	5.4	1733	2.5	2349	5.2
4	SU	0604	2.6	1220	5.2	1847	2.7		
5	M	0106	5.1	0736	2.7	1345	5.1	2025	2.6
6	TU	0235	5.2	0906	2.5	1511	5.4	2144	2.3
7	W	0349	5.7	1016	2.0	1620	5.8	2244	1.8
8	TH	0448	6.2	1113	1.4	1716	6.3	2336	1.3
9	F ●	0539	6.8	1203	0.9	1805	6.8		
10	SA	0023	0.8	0627	7.2	1250	0.5	1852	7.1
11	SU	0108	0.5	0712	7.5	1335	0.2	1936	7.3
12	M	0152	0.3	0756	7.6	1418	0.2	2018	7.3
13	TU	0234	0.4	0839	7.6	1500	0.3	2100	7.1
14	W	0315	0.6	0921	7.3	1540	0.7	2140	6.7
15	TH	0355	1.0	1004	6.8	1620	1.2	2223	6.3
16	F ☾	0438	1.5	1049	6.2	1704	1.8	2310	5.8
17	SA	0528	2.0	1143	5.7	1759	2.3		
18	SU	0012	5.3	0641	2.5	1256	5.2	1924	2.6
19	M	0140	5.1	0825	2.6	1430	5.1	2102	2.6
20	TU	0316	5.3	0953	2.4	1556	5.3	2215	2.3
21	W	0425	5.7	1053	2.0	1652	5.7	2306	1.9
22	TH	0512	6.1	1138	1.6	1734	6.1	2347	1.5
23	F	0551	6.4	1214	1.3	1810	6.4		
24	SA O	0021	1.3	0626	6.6	1245	1.1	1843	6.5
25	SU	0052	1.1	0657	6.7	1314	1.0	1913	6.6
26	M	0122	1.0	0726	6.8	1342	1.0	1941	6.6
27	TU	0150	1.0	0754	6.8	1409	1.0	2008	6.6
28	W	0217	1.1	0821	6.7	1435	1.2	2035	6.4
29	TH	0245	1.2	0848	6.5	1502	1.4	2103	6.2

MARCH

Date	Day	Time	m	Time	m	Time	m	Time	m
1	F	0313	1.5	0917	6.2	1530	1.7	2133	6.0
2	SA	0344	1.8	0949	5.9	1601	2.0	2208	5.7
3	SU ☽	0421	2.2	1029	5.5	1642	2.4	2257	5.3
4	M	0515	2.5	1129	5.1	1747	2.7		
5	TU	0015	5.0	0648	2.7	1305	4.9	1948	2.8
6	W	0203	5.1	0843	2.5	1451	5.2	2124	2.3
7	TH	0330	5.6	0959	1.9	1606	5.8	2227	1.7
8	F	0431	6.3	1056	1.2	1700	6.4	2319	1.1
9	SA	0521	6.9	1146	0.6	1748	6.9		
10	SU ●	0005	0.6	0608	7.4	1231	0.2	1832	7.3
11	M	0049	0.2	0651	7.7	1314	0.0	1914	7.5
12	TU	0131	0.1	0734	7.8	1355	0.0	1954	7.5
13	W	0211	0.1	0814	7.6	1433	0.2	2033	7.2
14	TH	0250	0.4	0854	7.2	1511	0.7	2111	6.8
15	F	0328	0.9	0934	6.7	1547	1.3	2150	6.3
16	SA	0407	1.5	1017	6.1	1627	1.9	2234	5.8
17	SU ☾	0454	2.1	1108	5.4	1718	2.5	2334	5.2
18	M	0607	2.6	1223	4.9	1846	2.9		
19	TU	0111	4.9	0807	2.8	1412	4.8	2043	2.8
20	W	0258	5.1	0937	2.4	1539	5.2	2156	2.4
21	TH	0404	5.6	1033	2.0	1631	5.6	2244	1.9
22	F	0448	6.0	1113	1.6	1709	6.0	2322	1.5
23	SA	0524	6.4	1146	1.3	1743	6.3	2355	1.3
24	SU	0557	6.6	1217	1.1	1814	6.5		
25	M O	0024	1.1	0627	6.7	1245	1.0	1843	6.7
26	TU	0053	0.9	0656	6.8	1312	0.9	1911	6.7
27	W	0121	0.9	0723	6.8	1338	1.0	1938	6.7
28	TH	0149	1.0	0750	6.7	1405	1.1	2005	6.6
29	F	0218	1.1	0818	6.5	1432	1.3	2033	6.4
30	SA	0247	1.4	0848	6.3	1501	1.6	2104	6.1
31	SU	0319	1.7	0922	6.0	1533	1.9	[illegible]	[illegible]

APRIL

Date	Day	Time	m	Time	m	Time	m	Time	m
1	M	0359	2.1	1004	5.6	1617	2.3	2232	5.4
2	TU ☽	0456	2.4	1108	5.1	1726	2.7	2354	5.1
3	W	0631	2.6	1248	4.9	1926	2.7		
4	TH	0141	5.2	0822	2.3	1432	5.3	2100	2.2
5	F	0306	5.7	0936	1.7	1543	5.9	2204	1.6
6	SA	0406	6.4	1032	1.1	1636	6.5	2255	1.0
7	SU	0457	7.0	1121	0.6	1723	7.0	2341	0.5
8	M ●	0542	7.4	1206	0.2	1806	7.3		
9	TU	0024	0.2	0626	7.6	1247	0.1	1847	7.4
10	W	0106	0.2	0708	7.6	1327	0.2	1927	7.4
11	TH	0146	0.3	0749	7.4	1406	0.5	2006	7.2
12	F	0225	0.6	0829	7.0	1443	0.9	2044	6.8
13	SA	0304	1.1	0909	6.5	1520	1.4	2124	6.3
14	SU	0345	1.6	0951	5.9	1600	2.0	2209	5.7
15	M ☾	0433	2.2	1042	5.3	1650	2.5	2308	5.3
16	TU	0544	2.6	1155	4.8	1813	2.9		
17	W	0038	5.0	0732	2.7	1336	4.8	2002	2.8
18	TH	0215	5.1	0857	2.5	1459	5.1	2115	2.5
19	F	0322	5.5	0952	2.1	1552	5.5	2205	2.1
20	SA	0409	5.9	1033	1.7	1632	5.9	2244	1.7
21	SU	0447	6.2	1108	1.4	1707	6.2	2319	1.4
22	M	0521	6.4	1140	1.2	1738	6.4	2351	1.2
23	TU O	0552	6.6	1211	1.1	1809	6.6		
24	W	0022	1.1	0623	6.7	1240	1.0	1839	6.7
25	TH	0052	1.0	0653	6.7	1309	1.1	1909	6.7
26	F	0123	1.1	0723	6.6	1339	1.2	1939	6.6
27	SA	0156	1.2	0755	6.5	1410	1.3	2012	6.5
28	SU	0230	1.4	0829	6.3	1444	1.6	2048	6.2
29	M	0308	1.7	0909	5.9	1523	1.9	2132	5.9
30	TU	0355	2.0	0959	5.6	1614	2.2	2230	5.6

MAY

Date	Day	Time	m	Time	m	Time	m	Time	m
1	W ☾	0458	2.2	1108	5.3	1727	2.5	2350	5.4
2	TH	0626	2.3	1238	5.2	1906	2.4		
3	F	0119	5.5	0755	2.0	1404	5.5	2029	2.1
4	SA	0235	6.0	0905	1.6	1511	5.9	2132	1.6
5	SU	0335	6.4	1002	1.1	1606	6.4	2225	1.1
6	M	0427	6.9	1052	0.8	1653	6.8	2314	0.8
7	TU	0515	7.1	1138	0.6	1738	7.1	2359	0.6
8	W ●	0600	7.2	1221	0.5	1821	7.2		
9	TH	0042	0.5	0644	7.2	1302	0.6	1903	7.1
10	F	0124	0.7	0726	7.0	1342	0.8	1944	6.9
11	SA	0206	0.9	0808	6.7	1421	1.2	2024	6.6
12	SU	0247	1.3	0850	6.2	1501	1.6	2106	6.2
13	M	0330	1.7	0934	5.8	1542	2.0	2152	5.8
14	TU	0418	2.1	1023	5.4	1630	2.4	2246	5.5
15	W ☽	0518	2.5	1124	5.0	1736	2.7	2355	5.2
16	TH	0634	2.6	1241	4.9	1857	2.7		
17	F	0114	5.2	0751	2.5	1357	5.0	2012	2.5
18	SA	0222	5.4	0853	2.2	1457	5.3	2110	2.3
19	SU	0316	5.6	0941	2.0	1543	5.6	2156	2.0
20	M	0400	5.9	1023	1.7	1623	6.0	2237	1.7
21	TU	0439	6.1	1100	1.5	1700	6.2	2314	1.5
22	W	0515	6.3	1135	1.4	1735	6.4	2351	1.3
23	TH O	0551	6.4	1210	1.3	1809	6.6		
24	F	0026	1.2	0627	6.5	1244	1.2	1845	6.6
25	SA	0103	1.2	0703	6.5	1320	1.3	1922	6.6
26	SU	0142	1.2	0742	6.4	1358	1.4	2001	6.5
27	M	0222	1.3	0823	6.3	1438	1.5	2045	6.4
28	TU	0307	1.5	0910	6.0	1524	1.7	2135	6.2
29	W	0358	1.7	1004	5.8	1618	1.9	2233	6.0
30	TH ☾	0459	1.8	1107	5.6	1723	2.1	2340	5.9
31	F	0609	1.9	1217	5.6	1839	2.1		

JUNE

Date	Day	Time	m	Time	m	Time	m	Time	m
1	SA	0051	5.9	0722	1.8	1329	5.7	1952	1.9
2	SU	0159	6.1	0828	1.6	1434	5.9	2057	1.7
3	M	0301	6.3	0928	1.4	1533	6.2	2155	1.4
4	TU	0358	6.5	1022	1.2	1625	6.5	2248	1.2
5	W	0450	6.7	1112	1.1	1715	6.7	2338	1.0
6	TH ●	0540	6.7	1158	1.0	1801	6.8		
7	F	0024	1.0	0627	6.7	1242	1.1	1846	6.8
8	SA	0109	1.0	0712	6.6	1324	1.2	1929	6.7
9	SU	0152	1.2	0754	6.4	1405	1.4	2011	6.5
10	M	0234	1.4	0836	6.2	1445	1.6	2052	6.3
11	TU	0316	1.7	0917	5.9	1525	1.9	2134	6.0
12	W	0357	1.9	1000	5.6	1606	2.1	2218	5.8
13	TH	0443	2.1	1046	5.3	1654	2.3	2308	5.5
14	F ☽	0535	2.3	1140	5.2	1751	2.5		
15	SA	0004	5.4	0635	2.4	1242	5.1	1856	2.5
16	SU	0108	5.3	0738	2.4	1347	5.2	2000	2.5
17	M	0211	5.4	0838	2.3	1446	5.4	2100	2.3
18	TU	0307	5.6	0931	2.1	1536	5.6	2152	2.0
19	W	0356	5.8	1019	1.9	1622	5.9	2240	1.8
20	TH	0441	6.0	1103	1.7	1704	6.2	2324	1.6
21	F	0524	6.2	1145	1.5	1746	6.4		
22	SA O	0007	1.4	0608	6.4	1226	1.3	1829	6.6
23	SU	0050	1.2	0651	6.5	1308	1.2	1912	6.7
24	M	0134	1.1	0736	6.5	1351	1.2	1957	6.8
25	TU	0219	1.1	0821	6.5	1436	1.2	2043	6.7
26	W	0305	1.1	0908	6.4	1522	1.3	2132	6.6
27	TH	0354	1.2	0958	6.2	1611	1.5	2223	6.4
28	F ☾	0446	1.4	1051	6.0	1705	1.7	2319	6.3
29	SA	0542	1.6	1148	5.8	1806	1.8		
30	SU	0019	6.1	0644	1.7	1251	5.7	1913	1.9

SUNRISE AND SUNSET TIMES

MILFORD HAVEN
At 51°42′N 5°03′W

Month	Day	Sunrise	Sunset
UT			
Jan	01	0827	1621
	15	0820	1640
Feb	01	0759	1709
	15	0734	1735
Mar	01	0705	1800
	15	0634	1825
BST (UT+1)			
Apr	01	0655	1954
	15	0624	2017
May	01	0551	2044
	15	0528	2107
Jun	01	0508	2129
	15	0501	2140
Jul	01	0506	2142
	15	0520	2132
Aug	01	0543	2109
	15	0605	2043
Sep	01	0633	2007
	15	0655	1935
Oct	01	0721	1858
	15	0745	1826
UT			
Nov	01	0714	1652
	15	0739	1630
Dec	01	0805	1614

MILFORD HAVEN
LAT 51°42′N
LONG 5°03′W

TIMES AND HEIGHTS OF HIGH AND LOW WATER (Heights in Metres)

TIME ZONE UT
For Summer Time (area enclosed in shaded box) add 1 hour

2024

JULY

Date	Time	m	Date	Time	m
1 M	0124 0751 1358 2023	6.0 1.8 5.7 1.9	16 TU	0056 0728 1339 2001	5.2 2.6 5.1 2.6
2 TU	0230 0858 1504 2131	5.9 1.8 5.8 1.8	17 W	0208 0840 1449 2111	5.2 2.5 5.3 2.4
3 W	0335 1000 1606 2233	6.0 1.7 6.0 1.6	18 TH	0316 0943 1550 2212	5.4 2.2 5.7 2.1
4 TH	0436 1056 1702 2327	6.1 1.6 6.3 1.5	19 F	0415 1038 1642 2304	5.7 1.9 6.1 1.7
5 F ●	0530 1145 1752	6.3 1.4 6.5	20 SA	0507 1127 1730 2353	6.1 1.6 6.4 1.3
6 SA	0016 0618 1230 1837	1.3 6.4 1.3 6.6	21 SU ○	0555 1213 1816	6.4 1.2 6.8
7 SU	0100 0702 1312 1919	1.3 6.4 1.3 6.6	22 M	0039 0641 1257 1902	1.0 6.7 1.0 7.0
8 M	0141 0742 1351 1957	1.3 6.4 1.3 6.6	23 TU	0124 0726 1342 1947	0.8 6.8 0.8 7.2
9 TU	0219 0819 1427 2034	1.3 6.3 1.4 6.4	24 W	0209 0811 1425 2032	0.6 6.9 0.8 7.2
10 W	0254 0854 1501 2109	1.5 6.1 1.6 6.3	25 TH	0253 0855 1509 2117	0.6 6.8 0.9 7.1
11 TH	0328 0929 1535 2144	1.6 5.9 1.8 6.1	26 F	0337 0939 1553 2202	0.8 6.6 1.1 6.8
12 F	0402 1005 1611 2222	1.8 5.7 2.0 5.8	27 SA	0421 1025 1639 2251	1.1 6.3 1.4 6.5
13 SA ☽	0439 1045 1652 2304	2.0 5.5 2.2 5.6	28 SU ☾	0509 1115 1730 2345	1.5 6.0 1.8 6.0
14 SU	0523 1132 1742 2354	2.3 5.3 2.4 5.4	29 M	0604 1214 1836	1.9 5.6 2.1
15 M	0619 1229 1847	2.5 5.1 2.6	30 TU	0050 0715 1326 1958	5.7 2.2 5.4 2.3
			31 W	0206 0836 1447 2122	5.5 2.3 5.5 2.2

AUGUST

Date	Time	m	Date	Time	m
1 TH	0326 0950 1601 2230	5.5 2.1 5.8 1.9	16 F	0246 0918 1526 2152	5.2 2.5 5.5 2.2
2 F	0433 1050 1659 2325	5.8 1.9 6.1 1.6	17 SA	0357 1020 1625 2249	5.6 2.0 6.0 1.6
3 SA	0526 1139 1746	6.1 1.6 6.4	18 SU	0453 1111 1715 2338	6.1 1.5 6.6 1.1
4 SU ●	0010 0610 1220 1827	1.4 6.3 1.4 6.6	19 M ○	0541 1157 1801	6.6 1.0 7.1
5 M	0049 0648 1257 1903	1.2 6.4 1.2 6.7	20 TU	0023 0626 1241 1845	0.7 7.0 0.7 7.4
6 TU	0123 0722 1331 1936	1.2 6.5 1.2 6.7	21 W	0108 0709 1324 1929	0.4 7.2 0.5 7.6
7 W	0155 0754 1402 2008	1.2 6.5 1.2 6.7	22 TH	0150 0751 1406 2011	0.3 7.3 0.4 7.6
8 TH	0225 0825 1432 2038	1.2 6.4 1.3 6.5	23 F	0232 0832 1447 2053	0.3 7.2 0.6 7.4
9 F	0253 0854 1501 2107	1.4 6.2 1.5 6.3	24 SA	0312 0912 1528 2135	0.6 6.9 0.9 7.0
10 SA	0322 0924 1531 2138	1.6 6.0 1.7 6.1	25 SU	0352 0954 1610 2220	1.1 6.5 1.4 6.4
11 SU	0352 0956 1604 2212	1.8 5.8 2.0 5.8	26 M ☾	0435 1040 1658 2312	1.6 6.0 1.9 5.8
12 M ☽	0426 1033 1643 2253	2.2 5.5 2.3 5.5	27 TU	0527 1139 1805	2.2 5.5 2.4
13 TU	0509 1123 1738 2350	2.5 5.2 2.7 5.1	28 W	0020 0645 1303 1949	5.3 2.6 5.2 2.6
14 W	0613 1234 1904	2.8 5.0 2.8	29 TH	0155 0828 1443 2125	5.1 2.7 5.3 2.4
15 TH	0112 0753 1407 2041	5.0 2.8 5.1 2.6	30 F	0328 0948 1559 2230	5.3 2.4 5.7 2.0
			31 SA	0429 1044 1651 2318	5.7 1.9 6.1 1.6

SEPTEMBER

Date	Time	m	Date	Time	m
1 SU	0514 1127 1731 2355	6.1 1.6 6.5 1.3	16 M	0434 1051 1654 2318	6.3 1.4 6.8 0.9
2 M	0552 1203 1807	6.4 1.3 6.7	17 TU	0520 1137 1739	6.8 0.8 7.3
3 TU ●	0027 0625 1234 1839	1.2 6.6 1.2 6.8	18 W ○	0002 0603 1219 1822	0.4 7.3 0.5 7.7
4 W	0057 0656 1304 1909	1.1 6.7 1.1 6.8	19 TH	0044 0645 1301 1905	0.2 7.5 0.3 7.8
5 TH	0125 0724 1333 1937	1.1 6.7 1.1 6.8	20 F	0126 0725 1342 1946	0.1 7.5 0.3 7.7
6 F	0152 0752 1400 2004	1.1 6.6 1.2 6.7	21 SA	0206 0805 1422 2027	0.3 7.3 0.5 7.4
7 SA	0218 0819 1427 2031	1.3 6.5 1.3 6.5	22 SU	0245 0845 1502 2109	0.7 7.0 1.0 6.9
8 SU	0244 0846 1455 2059	1.5 6.3 1.6 6.3	23 M	0323 0926 1544 2153	1.3 6.5 1.5 6.3
9 M	0312 0915 1526 2129	1.8 6.0 1.9 5.9	24 TU ☾	0405 1012 1633 2245	1.9 6.0 2.1 5.6
10 TU	0342 0948 1601 2207	2.1 5.7 2.3 5.5	25 W	0457 1112 1747 2359	2.5 5.4 2.7 5.1
11 W ☽	0420 1033 1652 2301	2.5 5.3 2.7 5.1	26 TH	0624 1247 1945	2.9 5.1 2.8
12 TH	0519 1145 1819	2.9 5.0 2.9	27 F	0146 0819 1433 2117	4.9 2.9 5.3 2.5
13 F	0032 0716 1335 2018	4.9 3.0 5.0 2.7	28 SA	0317 0935 1542 2213	5.3 2.4 5.7 2.0
14 SA	0225 0857 1505 2134	5.1 2.6 5.5 2.1	29 SU	0410 1024 1628 2254	5.7 2.0 6.2 1.6
15 SU	0341 1001 1605 2230	5.7 2.0 6.2 1.5	30 M	0450 1103 1705 2328	6.2 1.6 6.5 1.4

OCTCBER

Date	Time	m	Date	Time	m
1 TU	0524 1136 1738 2358	6.5 1.4 6.7 1.2	16 W	0453 1111 1712 2336	6.9 0.8 7.4 0.5
2 W ●	0555 1206 1809	6.6 1.2 6.8	17 TH ○	0536 1155 1756	7.3 0.5 7.7
3 TH	0026 0625 1234 1838	1.1 6.8 1.1 6.9	18 F	0018 0619 1237 1840	0.3 7.5 0.4 7.7
4 F	0053 0653 1302 1905	1.1 6.8 1.1 6.8	19 SA	0100 0700 1319 1922	0.3 7.5 0.4 7.6
5 SA	0120 0720 1330 1932	1.1 6.8 1.2 6.8	20 SU	0140 0740 1401 2004	0.6 7.3 0.7 7.2
6 SU	0146 0747 1358 1959	1.3 6.6 1.4 6.6	21 M	0220 0822 1443 2047	1.0 7.0 1.2 6.7
7 M	0213 0814 1427 2028	1.5 6.5 1.6 6.3	22 TU	0301 0904 1527 2133	1.5 6.5 1.7 6.1
8 TU	0241 0844 1459 2100	1.8 6.2 1.9 6.0	23 W	0344 0953 1619 2226	2.1 6.0 2.3 5.5
9 W	0312 0920 1537 2140	2.1 5.9 2.3 5.6	24 TH ☾	0437 1054 1733 2339	2.6 5.5 2.7 5.0
10 TH ☽	0353 1007 1632 2238	2.5 5.5 2.7 5.2	25 F	0601 1221 1917	2.9 5.2 2.8
11 F	0456 1123 1801	2.9 5.2 2.8	26 SA	0115 0745 1355 2040	4.9 2.9 5.3 2.6
12 SA	0012 0652 1309 1954	5.0 2.9 5.2 2.6	27 SU	0238 0857 1503 2135	5.2 2.6 5.7 2.2
13 SU	0201 0831 1437 2108	5.2 2.5 5.7 2.0	28 M	0334 0947 1551 2217	5.6 2.2 6.0 1.8
14 M	0314 0934 1537 2203	5.8 1.9 6.3 1.4	29 TU	0415 1027 1630 2252	6.0 1.8 6.3 1.6
15 TU	0407 1025 1627 2251	6.4 1.3 6.9 0.9	30 W	0450 1102 1704 2324	6.3 1.6 6.6 1.4
			31 TH	0522 1134 1736 2354	6.5 1.4 6.7 1.3

NOVEMBER

Date	Time	m	Date	Time	m
1 F ●	0552 1205 1806	6.7 1.3 6.7	16 SA	0555 1217 1818	7.3 0.7 7.4
2 SA	0023 0622 1235 1836	1.3 6.8 1.3 6.7	17 SU	0038 0639 1301 1904	0.7 7.3 0.8 7.2
3 SU	0052 0652 1305 1906	1.3 6.8 1.3 6.7	18 M	0121 0723 1346 1949	0.9 7.1 1.0 6.9
4 M	0121 0722 1337 1937	1.4 6.7 1.5 6.5	19 TU	0203 0807 1431 2033	1.2 6.9 1.3 6.5
5 TU	0151 0754 1411 2010	1.6 6.5 1.7 6.3	20 W	0245 0852 1517 2120	1.6 6.5 1.7 6.0
6 W	0224 0828 1448 2047	1.8 6.3 1.9 6.0	21 TH	0330 0939 1607 2210	2.0 6.1 2.2 5.6
7 TH	0301 0909 1532 2133	2.1 6.0 2.2 5.7	22 F	0420 1033 1707 2309	2.4 5.7 2.5 5.3
8 F	0348 1002 1630 2236	2.4 5.7 2.4 5.4	23 SA ☾	0523 1138 1820	2.7 5.5 2.7
9 SA ☽	0453 1116 1750 2359	2.7 5.5 2.5 5.2	24 SU	0020 0640 1253 1935	5.1 2.8 5.4 2.6
10 SU	0626 1242 1920	2.7 5.6 2.3	25 M	0135 0754 1402 2037	5.2 2.7 5.5 2.4
11 M	0126 0754 1400 2032	5.4 2.4 5.9 1.9	26 TU	0238 0854 1459 2127	5.4 2.5 5.7 2.2
12 TU	0237 0900 1503 2131	5.9 1.9 6.4 1.5	27 W	0328 0942 1545 2210	5.7 2.2 6.0 1.9
13 W	0334 0955 1556 2222	6.4 1.4 6.8 1.1	28 TH	0410 1024 1626 2247	6.0 1.9 6.2 1.7
14 TH	0424 1044 1646 2310	6.8 1.1 7.2 0.8	29 F	0447 1102 1703 2323	6.3 1.7 6.4 1.6
15 F ○	0510 1131 1733 2355	7.1 0.8 7.3 0.7	30 SA	0523 1138 1739 2357	6.5 1.6 6.5 1.5

DECEMBER

Date	Time	m	Date	Time	m
1 SU ●	0557 1214 1813	6.6 1.5 6.5	16 M	0024 0628 1252 1855	1.1 7.0 1.1 6.8
2 M	0030 0632 1249 1849	1.5 6.7 1.4 6.5	17 TU	0109 0714 1338 1940	1.2 7.0 1.1 6.7
3 TU	0104 0707 1325 1925	1.5 6.7 1.5 6.5	18 W	0152 0758 1422 2023	1.3 6.8 1.3 6.5
4 W	0140 0744 1404 2004	1.5 6.6 1.5 6.4	19 TH	0233 0840 1505 2105	1.5 6.6 1.5 6.2
5 TH	0219 0825 1446 2047	1.7 6.5 1.6 6.2	20 F	0314 0922 1546 2146	1.8 6.4 1.8 5.9
6 F	0301 0910 1532 2135	1.8 6.3 1.8 6.0	21 SA	0355 1005 1629 2230	2.0 6.1 2.1 5.6
7 SA	0349 1002 1626 2231	2.0 6.1 1.9 5.8	22 SU ☾	0438 1050 1716 2318	2.3 5.8 2.3 5.4
8 SU ☽	0446 1103 1729 2336	2.2 6.0 2.0 5.6	23 M	0529 1142 1811	2.5 5.5 2.5
9 M	0554 1210 1840	2.3 5.9 2.0	24 TU	0016 0630 1243 1915	5.2 2.7 5.4 2.6
10 TU	0046 0710 1319 1950	5.6 2.2 6.0 1.9	25 W	0123 0738 1350 2021	5.2 2.7 5.3 2.6
11 W	0156 0820 1426 2055	5.8 2.0 6.2 1.7	26 TH	0229 0845 1453 2121	5.3 2.6 5.5 2.4
12 TH	0259 0924 1527 2154	6.1 1.7 6.4 1.5	27 F	0325 0943 1547 2211	5.5 2.3 5.7 2.2
13 F	0357 1021 1623 2248	6.4 1.5 6.6 1.3	28 SA	0414 1032 1634 2256	5.8 2.1 5.9 1.9
14 SA	0450 1115 1717 2337	6.7 1.2 6.8 1.2	29 SU	0458 1117 1717 2336	6.1 1.8 6.1 1.7
15 SU ○	0540 1205 1807	6.9 1.1 6.9	30 M ●	0539 1158 1758	6.4 1.6 6.3
			31 TU	0015 0619 1238 1839	1.5 6.6 1.4 6.5

BRISTOL (AVONMOUTH)
LAT 51°30'N
LONG 2°44'W

TIMES AND HEIGHTS OF HIGH AND LOW WATER (Heights in Metres)

TIME ZONE UT
For Summer Time (area enclosed in shaded box) add 1 hour

2024

JANUARY

Date	Day	Time	m	Time	m	Time	m	Time	m
1	M	0416	2.7	1010	11.5	1635	2.9	2231	11.1
2	TU	0445	2.8	1043	11.1	1706	3.0	2304	10.7
3	W	0519	3.0	1119	10.8	1743	3.2	2343	10.4
4	TH ☽	0601	3.3	1203	10.4	1829	3.5		
5	F	0032	10.0	0654	3.7	1300	10.1	1926	3.8
6	SA	0135	9.8	0802	3.9	1409	10.1	2040	3.9
7	SU	0251	10.0	0923	3.8	1524	10.3	2202	3.7
8	M	0405	10.5	1038	3.3	1633	10.9	2314	3.1
9	TU	0507	11.2	1142	2.7	1732	11.5		
10	W	0013	2.5	0601	12.0	1238	2.1	1826	12.2
11	TH ●	0107	2.0	0650	12.7	1333	1.7	1917	12.7
12	F	0200	1.7	0738	13.1	1427	1.4	2006	13.0
13	SA	0251	1.5	0826	13.4	1518	1.2	2053	13.2
14	SU	0337	1.3	0912	13.5	1604	1.1	2139	13.2
15	M	0419	1.3	0957	13.4	1645	1.1	2222	13.0
16	TU	0457	1.5	1041	13.1	1722	1.4	2304	12.6
17	W	0533	1.8	1126	12.6	1759	1.8	2348	12.0
18	TH ☾	0611	2.3	1214	11.9	1839	2.4		
19	F	0037	11.2	0654	2.9	1312	11.1	1927	3.0
20	SA	0139	10.6	0750	3.5	1424	10.5	2032	3.6
21	SU	0256	10.2	0920	3.9	1538	10.4	2203	3.7
22	M	0409	10.4	1048	3.6	1646	10.7	2316	3.3
23	TU	0512	10.9	1152	3.0	1744	11.2		
24	W	0014	2.7	0606	11.5	1245	2.5	1836	11.7
25	TH ○	0106	2.2	0654	12.1	1336	2.1	1922	12.1
26	F	0155	1.9	0736	12.4	1423	1.9	2003	12.3
27	SA	0239	1.8	0816	12.5	1505	2.0	2040	12.3
28	SU	0318	1.9	0851	12.5	1540	2.1	2112	12.1
29	M	0348	2.1	0922	12.3	1605	2.3	2141	11.9
30	TU	0408	2.2	0950	12.0	1622	2.4	2207	11.7
31	W	0427	2.3	1017	11.8	1642	2.4	[illegible]	[illegible]

FEBRUARY

Date	Day	Time	m	Time	m	Time	m	Time	m
1	TH	0452	2.4	1045	11.5	1709	2.5	2304	11.1
2	F ☽	0524	2.6	1119	11.1	1743	2.8	2342	10.6
3	SA	0604	3.1	1204	10.5	1826	3.3		
4	SU	0032	10.1	0656	3.7	1304	10.0	1926	3.9
5	M	0142	9.7	0815	4.1	1424	9.8	2101	4.1
6	TU	0316	9.8	0959	3.8	1559	10.2	2242	3.6
7	W	0441	10.6	1118	3.0	1714	11.1	2354	2.8
8	TH	0544	11.7	1224	2.2	1814	12.0		
9	F ●	0055	2.1	0638	12.7	1324	1.5	1906	12.9
10	SA	0153	1.4	0728	13.5	1421	1.0	1955	13.5
11	SU	0245	0.9	0814	14.0	1511	0.5	2041	13.9
12	M	0331	0.6	0859	14.2	1555	0.3	2123	13.9
13	TU	0411	0.6	0941	14.2	1632	0.5	2202	13.7
14	W	0444	0.8	1020	13.8	1702	0.9	2239	13.2
15	TH	0511	1.3	1059	13.0	1729	1.5	2315	12.3
16	F ☾	0538	2.0	1138	12.0	1758	2.3	2354	11.3
17	SA	0610	2.8	1224	10.8	1836	3.2		
18	SU	0043	10.2	0655	3.7	1335	9.8	1932	4.0
19	M	0211	9.4	0809	4.5	1513	9.4	2111	4.5
20	TU	0346	9.5	1030	4.3	1629	9.8	2257	3.8
21	W	0456	10.3	1137	3.4	1731	10.7	2357	2.9
22	TH	0552	11.2	1230	2.5	1821	11.5		
23	F	0048	2.1	0639	12.0	1318	1.9	1905	12.1
24	SA ○	0136	1.6	0720	12.5	1404	1.6	1944	12.5
25	SU	0221	1.4	0756	12.7	1447	1.5	2018	12.5
26	M	0301	1.4	0829	12.7	1522	1.7	2048	12.4
27	TU	0333	1.7	0859	12.5	1549	2.0	2115	12.2
28	W	0353	1.9	0924	12.3	1602	2.2	2139	12.0
29	TH	0405	2.0	0948	12.1	1613	2.2	2202	11.8

MARCH

Date	Day	Time	m	Time	m	Time	m	Time	m
1	F	0424	2.0	1014	11.8	1636	2.2	2230	11.5
2	SA	0452	2.2	1046	11.4	1706	2.4	2305	11.0
3	SU ☽	0526	2.7	1127	10.8	1743	3.0	2352	10.3
4	M	0610	3.4	1224	10.0	1835	3.8		
5	TU	0057	9.6	0720	4.1	1344	9.5	2001	4.4
6	W	0237	9.5	0928	4.1	1538	9.8	2223	3.9
7	TH	0423	10.4	1106	3.1	1702	10.9	2342	2.8
8	F	0530	11.7	1214	2.1	1800	12.2		
9	SA	0044	1.8	0623	12.9	1312	1.2	1851	13.2
10	SU ●	0139	1.0	0711	13.8	1406	0.5	1937	13.9
11	M	0229	0.5	0756	14.4	1453	0.1	2020	14.3
12	TU	0313	0.2	0838	14.6	1534	0.0	2100	14.3
13	W	0351	0.2	0918	14.4	1608	0.3	2137	13.9
14	TH	0421	0.6	0955	13.8	1634	0.9	2211	13.2
15	F	0444	1.3	1030	12.9	1656	1.6	2243	12.3
16	SA	0505	2.0	1105	11.7	1720	2.4	2316	11.1
17	SU ☾	0533	2.9	1144	10.4	1754	3.4	2359	9.9
18	M	0614	3.9	1247	9.2	1847	4.3		
19	TU	0129	9.0	0729	4.7	1452	8.8	2030	4.8
20	W	0325	9.2	1014	4.5	1608	9.5	2237	4.0
21	TH	0434	10.1	1116	3.4	1708	10.5	2334	2.9
22	F	0528	11.1	1205	2.4	1756	11.5		
23	SA	0023	2.0	0613	12.0	1251	1.7	1837	12.2
24	SU	0109	1.5	0652	12.5	1336	1.4	1914	12.5
25	M ○	0154	1.2	0727	12.7	1418	1.3	1947	12.6
26	TU	0234	1.3	0800	12.7	1454	1.5	2018	12.5
27	W	0307	1.5	0829	12.5	1522	1.8	2045	12.4
28	TH	0329	1.8	0855	12.3	1536	2.1	2109	12.2
29	F	0341	1.9	0920	12.2	1546	2.1	2133	12.0
30	SA	0400	1.9	0948	11.9	1609	2.1	2203	11.7
31	SU	0427	2.0	1022	11.5	1639	2.3	2240	11.2

APRIL

Date	Day	Time	m	Time	m	Time	m	Time	m
1	M	0501	2.5	1105	10.8	1716	2.9	2328	10.4
2	TU ☽	0546	3.2	1202	10.0	1807	3.7		
3	W	0035	9.7	0655	4.0	1325	9.4	1934	4.4
4	TH	0219	9.6	0910	3.9	1523	9.9	2207	3.8
5	F	0403	10.5	1048	2.9	1642	11.1	2323	2.6
6	SA	0508	11.9	1153	1.8	1739	12.3		
7	SU	0021	1.6	0601	13.0	1248	1.0	1828	13.4
8	M ●	0114	0.9	0648	13.9	1339	0.4	1912	14.0
9	TU	0202	0.4	0732	14.3	1426	0.1	1954	14.2
10	W	0246	0.2	0814	14.4	1506	0.2	2033	14.1
11	TH	0324	0.4	0853	14.1	1540	0.6	2110	13.7
12	F	0355	0.9	0930	13.4	1606	1.2	2144	12.9
13	SA	0418	1.6	1005	12.4	1627	1.9	2216	12.0
14	SU	0439	2.3	1039	11.3	1651	2.6	2249	10.9
15	M ☾	0508	3.0	1117	10.1	1725	3.5	2330	9.8
16	TU	0550	3.9	1217	9.0	1818	4.4		
17	W	0059	9.0	0706	4.6	1420	8.8	1956	4.8
18	TH	0252	9.2	0917	4.5	1533	9.4	2156	4.1
19	F	0357	10.0	1038	3.5	1630	10.3	2258	3.1
20	SA	0450	10.9	1128	2.6	1718	11.2	2347	2.3
21	SU	0535	11.7	1215	2.0	1800	11.9		
22	M	0033	1.7	0615	12.2	1258	1.6	1837	12.3
23	TU ○	0117	1.5	0652	12.4	1340	1.5	1912	12.5
24	W	0157	1.5	0726	12.5	1418	1.6	1944	12.5
25	TH	0232	1.6	0758	12.4	1448	1.8	2014	12.4
26	F	0300	1.8	0829	12.3	1510	2.0	2043	12.2
27	SA	0321	1.9	0859	12.1	1528	2.1	2113	12.1
28	SU	0345	1.9	0932	11.9	1553	2.1	2147	11.8
29	M	0415	2.1	1011	11.5	1626	2.4	2229	11.3
30	TU	0453	2.5	1057	10.9	1707	2.9	2320	10.6

MAY

Date	Day	Time	m	Time	m	Time	m	Time	m
1	W ☾	0542	3.1	1156	10.2	1803	3.6		
2	TH	0030	10.1	0657	3.6	1317	9.9	1934	4.0
3	F	0206	10.2	0847	3.4	1456	10.3	2135	3.4
4	SA	0332	10.9	1014	2.6	1610	11.2	2249	2.5
5	SU	0437	11.9	1119	1.8	1708	12.2	2348	1.7
6	M	0531	12.8	1216	1.2	1758	13.1		
7	TU	0041	1.1	0620	13.5	1307	0.8	1844	13.6
8	W ●	0131	0.8	0706	13.7	1354	0.6	1927	13.7
9	TH	0217	0.7	0749	13.7	1436	0.7	2007	13.6
10	F	0257	0.9	0831	13.3	1513	1.1	2046	13.1
11	SA	0332	1.4	0910	12.7	1543	1.7	2123	12.5
12	SU	0359	2.0	0947	11.9	1608	2.2	2157	11.7
13	M	0424	2.6	1024	11.0	1635	2.8	2233	10.9
14	TU	0455	3.1	1103	10.2	1710	3.4	2317	10.1
15	W ☽	0539	3.7	1156	9.5	1800	4.0		
16	TH	0024	9.5	0642	4.1	1320	9.1	1915	4.3
17	F	0158	9.4	0759	4.1	1439	9.4	2036	4.1
18	SA	0305	9.9	0915	3.7	1538	10.0	2151	3.5
19	SU	0400	10.5	1025	3.1	1629	10.7	2253	2.8
20	M	0448	11.1	1122	2.6	1715	11.4	2346	2.3
21	TU	0532	11.6	1212	2.2	1756	11.9		
22	W	0033	1.9	0613	12.0	1257	1.9	1836	12.2
23	TH ○	0116	1.7	0652	12.2	1339	1.8	1913	12.4
24	F	0157	1.7	0730	12.2	1416	1.9	1949	12.4
25	SA	0234	1.7	0808	12.2	1450	1.9	2025	12.3
26	SU	0308	1.8	0847	12.1	1520	2.0	2103	12.2
27	M	0342	1.9	0927	11.9	1552	2.2	2144	11.9
28	TU	0418	2.1	1011	11.6	1629	2.4	2230	11.6
29	W	0501	2.3	1059	11.3	1714	2.7	2323	11.2
30	TH ☾	0553	2.6	1156	10.9	1811	3.1		
31	F	0026	10.9	0659	2.8	1303	10.7	1926	3.2

JUNE

Date	Day	Time	m	Time	m	Time	m	Time	m
1	SA	0142	10.9	0814	2.8	1420	10.8	2052	3.1
2	SU	0256	11.2	0930	2.5	1531	11.2	2208	2.6
3	M	0401	11.7	1040	2.2	1633	11.8	2313	2.1
4	TU	0500	12.2	1141	1.8	1728	12.3		
5	W	0009	1.7	0553	12.6	1235	1.5	1817	12.7
6	TH ●	0102	1.5	0642	12.8	1325	1.4	1903	12.9
7	F	0151	1.4	0729	12.8	1411	1.4	1947	12.9
8	SA	0236	1.6	0813	12.5	1453	1.6	2029	12.6
9	SU	0317	1.9	0856	12.2	1529	2.0	2109	12.2
10	M	0351	2.3	0936	11.7	1559	2.4	2146	11.7
11	TU	0420	2.6	1013	11.2	1627	2.7	2223	11.2
12	W	0449	2.9	1050	10.7	1700	3.0	2302	10.7
13	TH	0526	3.2	1130	10.2	1740	3.3	2348	10.3
14	F ☽	0611	3.4	1218	9.9	1831	3.6		
15	SA	0044	10.0	0705	3.5	1318	9.7	1933	3.8
16	SU	0150	9.9	0806	3.6	1424	9.9	2040	3.7
17	M	0253	10.1	0911	3.4	1527	10.2	2148	3.4
18	TU	0352	10.5	1019	3.1	1624	10.7	2253	2.9
19	W	0446	11.0	1122	2.7	1716	11.3	2349	2.4
20	TH	0536	11.5	1216	2.3	1803	11.8		
21	F	0040	2.0	0623	11.8	1305	2.0	1847	12.2
22	SA ○	0129	1.8	0709	12.1	1352	1.9	1931	12.5
23	SU	0216	1.7	0755	12.3	1437	1.9	2015	12.6
24	M	0302	1.7	0841	12.3	1520	1.9	2059	12.6
25	TU	0346	1.7	0926	12.4	1600	1.9	2144	12.5
26	W	0428	1.7	1011	12.3	1640	2.0	2229	12.4
27	TH	0510	1.7	1056	12.1	1722	2.1	2317	12.1
28	F ☾	0554	1.9	1144	11.7	1807	2.3		
29	SA	0009	11.7	0642	2.2	1237	11.4	1900	2.7
30	SU	0110	11.4	0736	2.5	1340	11.0	2004	3.0

SUNRISE AND SUNSET TIMES

BRISTOL (AVONMOUTH)
At 51°30'N 2°44'W

		Sunrise	Sunset
UT			
Jan	01	0817	1613
	15	0810	1632
Feb	01	0749	1701
	15	0725	1726
Mar	01	0656	1751
	15	0625	1816
BST (UT+1)			
Apr	01	0646	1944
	15	0615	2008
May	01	0543	2034
	15	0519	2056
Jun	01	0459	2119
	15	0453	2130
Jul	01	0458	2131
	15	0511	2122
Aug	01	0535	2059
	15	0557	2033
Sep	01	0624	1957
	15	0646	1925
Oct	01	0712	1848
	15	0735	1817
UT			
Nov	01	0705	1644
	15	0729	1621
Dec	01	0754	1605
	15	0810	1602

BRISTOL (AVONMOUTH)
LAT 51°30′N
LONG 2°44′W

TIMES AND HEIGHTS OF HIGH AND LOW WATER (Heights in Metres)

TIME ZONE UT
For Summer Time (area enclosed in shaded box) add 1 hour

2024

JULY

Date	Day	Time	m	Time	m	Time	m	Time	m
1	M	0218	11.1	0841	2.8	1450	10.9	2124	3.1
2	TU	0327	11.1	0959	2.9	1559	11.0	2240	2.9
3	W	0432	11.3	1109	2.7	1701	11.4	2344	2.6
4	TH	0531	11.6	1209	2.4	1756	11.8		
5	F ●	0040	2.2	0625	11.9	1303	2.1	1847	12.2
6	SA	0132	2.0	0715	12.1	1354	1.9	1933	12.4
7	SU	0222	1.9	0802	12.1	1440	1.9	2017	12.4
8	M	0308	2.0	0845	12.1	1521	2.0	2057	12.3
9	TU	0347	2.2	0923	11.9	1555	2.2	2133	12.0
10	W	0417	2.4	0957	11.6	1621	2.4	2206	11.7
11	TH	0440	2.6	1027	11.3	1645	2.6	2237	11.4
12	F	0505	2.7	1058	11.0	1714	2.7	2310	11.0
13	SA ☽	0535	2.8	1132	10.6	1749	3.0	2348	10.6
14	SU	0613	3.0	1214	10.3	1833	3.3		
15	M	0036	10.2	0702	3.4	1307	9.9	1933	3.7
16	TU	0138	10.0	0805	3.7	1417	9.8	2049	3.8
17	W	0251	10.0	0924	3.7	1533	10.1	2207	3.5
18	TH	0403	10.4	1040	3.3	1641	10.7	2315	2.9
19	F	0507	11.0	1145	2.7	1738	11.5		
20	SA	0014	2.3	0603	11.6	1242	2.3	1829	12.2
21	SU ○	0110	1.9	0655	12.2	1338	1.9	1918	12.7
22	M	0206	1.6	0744	12.6	1431	1.7	2005	13.1
23	TU	0259	1.3	0832	12.9	1520	1.4	2051	13.3
24	W	0346	1.1	0917	13.1	1603	1.3	2135	13.4
25	TH	0427	1.0	1000	13.1	1640	1.3	2217	13.2
26	F	0504	1.1	1041	12.8	1714	1.5	2259	12.8
27	SA	0538	1.5	1122	12.3	1748	1.9	2344	12.2
28	SU ☾	0613	2.0	1206	11.6	1825	2.5		
29	M	0034	11.4	0655	2.6	1259	10.9	1914	3.2
30	TU	0140	10.6	0750	3.3	1412	10.2	2029	3.9
31	W	0259	10.2	0917	3.8	1533	10.1	2218	3.8

AUGUST

Date	Day	Time	m	Time	m	Time	m	Time	m
1	TH	0414	10.3	1047	3.5	1644	10.5	2329	3.2
2	F	0519	10.3	1153	2.9	1745	11.3		
3	SA	0027	2.6	0616	11.4	1248	2.3	1836	11.9
4	SU ●	0119	2.1	0705	11.9	1339	1.9	1922	12.4
5	M	0209	1.8	0749	12.2	1427	1.7	2003	12.6
6	TU	0255	1.7	0828	12.3	1509	1.7	2040	12.6
7	W	0334	1.8	0903	12.2	1544	1.8	2113	12.4
8	TH	0404	2.1	0932	12.0	1608	2.1	2141	12.1
9	F	0423	2.3	0958	11.8	1624	2.3	2207	11.8
10	SA	0436	2.5	1023	11.5	1643	2.4	2232	11.5
11	SU	0457	2.5	1050	11.1	1709	2.6	2302	11.0
12	M ☽	0526	2.8	1123	10.7	1743	3.0	2340	10.5
13	TU	0604	3.2	1208	10.1	1829	3.7		
14	W	0035	9.9	0657	3.8	1312	9.6	1943	4.2
15	TH	0153	9.5	0824	4.2	1446	9.6	2130	4.1
16	F	0331	9.8	1009	3.9	1616	10.3	2253	3.3
17	SA	0448	10.7	1125	3.1	1721	11.4		
18	SU	0000	2.4	0549	11.6	1229	2.3	1815	12.4
19	M ○	0100	1.7	0642	12.5	1328	1.7	1904	13.2
20	TU	0157	1.2	0730	13.1	1422	1.3	1950	13.8
21	W	0249	0.8	0816	13.6	1510	0.9	2034	14.1
22	TH	0334	0.5	0859	13.7	1551	0.8	2116	14.1
23	F	0412	0.6	0939	13.6	1625	0.9	2156	13.8
24	SA	0444	0.9	1016	13.2	1654	1.3	2235	13.2
25	SU	0511	1.5	1053	12.5	1719	1.9	2314	12.2
26	M ☾	0538	2.2	1131	11.6	1748	2.7	2358	11.0
27	TU	0612	3.1	1218	10.5	1829	3.7		
28	W	0103	9.9	0703	4.0	1340	9.6	1940	4.6
29	TH	0245	9.4	0844	4.6	1520	9.5	2214	4.4
30	F	0405	9.7	1038	4.0	1634	10.2	2320	3.4
31	SA	0509	10.6	1139	3.0	1732	11.2		

SEPTEMBER

Date	Day	Time	m	Time	m	Time	m	Time	m
1	SU	0012	2.5	0602	11.5	1231	2.2	1821	12.1
2	M	0101	1.8	0647	12.2	1319	1.6	1903	12.7
3	TU ●	0147	1.4	0726	12.6	1405	1.3	1941	12.9
4	W	0231	1.3	0802	12.7	1446	1.3	2015	12.9
5	TH	0309	1.5	0834	12.5	1521	1.6	2045	12.7
6	F	0339	1.8	0901	12.3	1546	2.0	2111	12.3
7	SA	0357	2.3	0925	12.0	1557	2.3	2133	12.0
8	SU	0403	2.4	0947	11.7	1611	2.4	2156	11.7
9	M	0420	2.4	1012	11.4	1634	2.5	2224	11.3
10	TU	0447	2.6	1043	10.9	1705	2.9	2302	10.7
11	W ☽	0520	3.1	1126	10.2	1744	3.6	2354	9.9
12	TH	0606	3.9	1228	9.5	1845	4.4		
13	F	0111	9.3	0722	4.6	1407	9.3	2059	4.5
14	SA	0310	9.5	0949	4.3	1557	10.2	2241	3.5
15	SU	0434	10.6	1114	3.2	1704	11.5	2348	2.4
16	M	0533	11.9	1216	2.2	1756	12.7		
17	TU	0045	1.5	0623	12.9	1311	1.5	1844	13.6
18	W ○	0138	0.8	0709	13.7	1402	0.9	1929	14.2
19	TH	0227	0.4	0752	14.1	1448	0.6	2012	14.5
20	F	0311	0.3	0834	14.1	1528	0.6	2053	14.4
21	SA	0347	0.5	0912	13.9	1602	0.9	2131	13.9
22	SU	0417	1.0	0949	13.3	1628	1.5	2208	13.0
23	M	0440	1.8	1024	12.4	1650	2.2	2245	11.9
24	TU ☾	0504	2.6	1100	11.3	1716	3.1	2326	10.5
25	W	0536	3.5	1144	10.1	1755	4.1		
26	TH	0032	9.3	0626	4.5	1322	9.1	1910	5.0
27	F	0234	8.9	0828	5.1	1506	9.4	2204	4.6
28	SA	0347	9.6	1023	4.1	1613	10.2	2301	3.4
29	SU	0447	10.6	1117	3.0	1708	11.3	2348	2.4
30	M	0536	11.6	1205	2.1	1754	12.2		

OCTOBER

Date	Day	Time	m	Time	m	Time	m	Time	m
1	TU	0033	1.6	0618	12.3	1250	1.5	1834	12.8
2	W ●	0117	1.3	0655	12.7	1334	1.2	1910	13.0
3	TH	0159	1.2	0729	12.8	1415	1.3	1943	12.9
4	F	0237	1.4	0800	12.7	1450	1.6	2013	12.7
5	SA	0307	1.8	0828	12.4	1516	2.0	2039	12.4
6	SU	0325	2.2	0853	12.1	1529	2.3	2103	12.1
7	M	0333	2.4	0915	11.9	1544	2.4	2127	11.8
8	TU	0352	2.4	0942	11.6	1608	2.5	2159	11.4
9	W	0419	2.6	1016	11.1	1640	2.9	2238	10.7
10	TH ☽	0453	3.1	1101	10.4	1720	3.5	2331	9.9
11	F	0538	3.9	1204	9.7	1820	4.3		
12	SA	0048	9.3	0653	4.6	1342	9.5	2030	4.5
13	SU	0248	9.6	0927	4.3	1533	10.3	2219	3.4
14	M	0411	10.8	1051	3.2	1638	11.6	2324	2.3
15	TU	0509	12.0	1151	2.1	1731	12.8		
16	W	0019	1.4	0558	13.1	1243	1.4	1819	13.7
17	TH ○	0110	0.8	0643	13.8	1333	0.9	1904	14.3
18	F	0158	0.5	0726	14.1	1419	0.7	1947	14.4
19	SA	0241	0.5	0807	14.1	1500	0.8	2028	14.2
20	SU	0318	0.8	0846	13.8	1535	1.2	2108	13.6
21	M	0349	1.4	0924	13.1	1604	1.8	2147	12.7
22	TU	0415	2.1	1000	12.2	1629	2.5	2225	11.5
23	W	0440	2.9	1037	11.2	1657	3.4	2307	10.3
24	TH ☾	0513	3.7	1124	10.1	1739	4.2		
25	F	0012	9.3	0605	4.6	1301	9.3	1853	4.9
26	SA	0205	9.0	0742	5.0	1436	9.5	2124	4.6
27	SU	0314	9.6	0944	4.3	1538	10.2	2223	3.7
28	M	0410	10.4	1040	3.3	1631	11.1	2312	2.7
29	TU	0459	11.3	1128	2.4	1717	11.9	2356	2.0
30	W	0541	12.0	1214	1.8	1757	12.4		
31	TH	0039	1.6	0619	12.5	1256	1.6	1835	12.7

NOVEMBER

Date	Day	Time	m	Time	m	Time	m	Time	m
1	F ●	0121	1.5	0654	12.7	1337	1.6	1909	12.7
2	SA	0159	1.6	0727	12.6	1414	1.7	1942	12.5
3	SU	0231	1.9	0758	12.5	1444	2.0	2012	12.3
4	M	0255	2.2	0826	12.2	1506	2.2	2041	12.1
5	TU	0313	2.4	0854	12.0	1528	2.4	2111	11.8
6	W	0336	2.5	0926	11.7	1556	2.5	2147	11.4
7	TH	0406	2.7	1005	11.3	1631	2.8	2231	10.9
8	F	0444	3.1	1053	10.7	1716	3.3	2325	10.3
9	SA ☽	0533	3.7	1156	10.2	1819	3.8		
10	SU	0036	9.9	0646	4.2	1320	10.1	1957	3.9
11	M	0210	10.1	0841	4.0	1454	10.7	2135	3.3
12	TU	0333	10.9	1011	3.2	1603	11.6	2246	2.5
13	W	0435	11.9	1115	2.4	1700	12.6	2345	1.7
14	TH	0528	12.7	1211	1.7	1751	13.3		
15	F ○	0038	1.2	0616	13.4	1302	1.3	1839	13.7
16	SA	0127	0.9	0700	13.7	1350	1.1	1924	13.8
17	SU	0212	0.9	0743	13.7	1435	1.2	2008	13.6
18	M	0253	1.2	0825	13.4	1514	1.5	2051	13.0
19	TU	0329	1.7	0906	12.8	1549	2.1	2133	12.3
20	W	0359	2.3	0946	12.1	1619	2.7	2213	11.5
21	TH	0429	2.9	1026	11.3	1651	3.3	2256	10.6
22	F	0503	3.5	1112	10.5	1731	3.9	2348	9.8
23	SA ☾	0549	4.1	1216	9.9	1827	4.3		
24	SU	0105	9.4	0654	4.4	1342	9.7	1939	4.4
25	M	0220	9.6	0812	4.3	1448	10.1	2057	4.0
26	TU	0320	10.0	0929	3.8	1542	10.6	2208	3.5
27	W	0411	10.7	1033	3.2	1632	11.2	2305	2.9
28	TH	0458	11.3	1126	2.6	1716	11.6	2354	2.4
29	F	0540	11.9	1213	2.2	1758	12.0		
30	SA	0038	2.1	0620	12.2	1257	1.9	1837	12.2

DECEMBER

Date	Day	Time	m	Time	m	Time	m	Time	m
1	SU ●	0120	1.9	0657	12.4	1338	1.9	1915	12.3
2	M	0158	2.0	0733	12.4	1416	2.0	1952	12.2
3	TU	0233	2.1	0809	12.3	1451	2.1	2029	12.1
4	W	0304	2.3	0845	12.2	1524	2.2	2108	11.9
5	TH	0334	2.4	0924	12.0	1559	2.4	2148	11.7
6	F	0409	2.6	1006	11.7	1638	2.6	2232	11.4
7	SA	0449	2.8	1053	11.4	1723	2.8	2322	11.1
8	SU ☽	0537	3.1	1148	11.1	1818	3.0		
9	M	0019	10.8	0637	3.4	1254	10.9	1924	3.2
10	TU	0129	10.7	0751	3.5	1409	11.0	2041	3.1
11	W	0246	10.8	0919	3.3	1522	11.4	2201	2.9
12	TH	0357	11.3	1037	2.9	1627	11.9	2310	2.4
13	F	0458	11.9	1140	2.4	1725	12.4		
14	SA	0008	2.0	0551	12.5	1235	1.9	1818	12.8
15	SU ○	0101	1.6	0640	12.9	1327	1.7	1907	12.9
16	M	0150	1.5	0727	13.1	1417	1.6	1955	12.9
17	TU	0236	1.6	0812	13.0	1503	1.8	2040	12.7
18	W	0318	1.8	0855	12.7	1543	2.1	2123	12.3
19	TH	0354	2.2	0936	12.3	1617	2.5	2203	11.8
20	F	0424	2.6	1015	11.8	1646	2.9	2240	11.2
21	SA	0454	2.9	1053	11.3	1717	3.1	2317	10.7
22	SU ☾	0528	3.2	1133	10.8	1755	3.4	2358	10.2
23	M	0611	3.5	1222	10.3	1841	3.6		
24	TU	0050	9.9	0704	3.8	1322	10.0	1937	3.8
25	W	0155	9.8	0807	3.9	1429	10.0	2042	3.9
26	TH	0305	10.0	0917	3.8	1533	10.3	2153	3.6
27	F	0407	10.4	1027	3.4	1631	10.7	2301	3.1
28	SA	0501	11.0	1128	2.8	1723	11.2	2358	2.6
29	SU	0549	11.6	1221	2.3	1810	11.7		
30	M ●	0047	2.2	0633	12.1	1309	2.0	1855	12.0
31	TU	0134	2.0	0716	12.4	1357	1.9	1939	12.3

COBH
LAT 51°51′N
LONG 8°18′W

TIMES AND HEIGHTS OF HIGH AND LOW WATER (Heights in Metres)

TIME ZONE UT
For Summer Time (area enclosed in shaded box) add 1 hour

2024

JANUARY

Date	Day	Time	m	Time	m	Time	m	Time	m
1	M	0232	1.0	0834	3.7	1458	1.2	2044	3.6
2	TU	0311	1.1	0914	3.6	1540	1.3	2126	3.5
3	W	0355	1.2	0957	3.6	1626	1.4	2213	3.5
4	TH ☽	0446	1.3	1045	3.5	1720	1.4	2307	3.4
5	F	0545	1.4	1140	3.4	1822	1.5		
6	SA	0007	3.4	0650	1.4	1241	3.4	1927	1.4
7	SU	0113	3.4	0754	1.4	1345	3.5	2028	1.3
8	M	0218	3.5	0856	1.2	1447	3.6	2127	1.2
9	TU	0319	3.7	0954	1.1	1545	3.7	2222	1.0
10	W	0415	3.9	1048	0.9	1638	3.9	2312	0.8
11	TH ●	0506	4.0	1137	0.7	1727	4.0	2357	0.6
12	F	0554	4.2	1222	0.5	1813	4.1		
13	SA	0041	0.5	0640	4.2	1306	0.5	1858	4.1
14	SU	0126	0.4	0726	4.2	1351	0.5	1943	4.0
15	M	0212	0.4	0812	4.2	1437	0.5	2030	4.0
16	TU	0259	0.5	0900	4.1	1524	0.7	2117	3.9
17	W	0348	0.6	0948	3.9	1613	0.8	2206	3.7
18	TH ☾	0440	0.8	1039	3.8	1706	1.0	2258	3.6
19	F	0538	1.0	1136	3.6	1806	1.1	2359	3.5
20	SA	0644	1.1	1241	3.4	1915	1.2		
21	SU	0110	3.4	0758	1.2	1352	3.4	2029	1.2
22	M	0225	3.4	0912	1.2	1500	3.5	2138	1.1
23	TU	0333	3.6	1016	1.0	1600	3.6	2236	1.0
24	W	0429	3.8	1107	0.9	1650	3.7	2322	0.8
25	TH ○	0515	3.9	1149	0.8	1732	3.8		
26	F	0000	0.7	0555	4.0	1224	0.8	1809	3.9
27	SA	0033	0.7	0630	4.0	1255	0.8	1842	3.9
28	SU	0103	0.7	0703	4.0	1324	0.8	1913	3.9
29	M	0132	0.7	0735	3.9	1353	0.9	1944	3.8
30	TU	0202	0.8	0806	3.9	1426	1.0	2016	3.8
31	W	0235	0.9	0839	3.8	1500	1.1		

FEBRUARY

Date	Day	Time	m	Time	m	Time	m	Time	m
1	TH	0312	1.0	0915	3.7	1537	1.2	2130	3.6
2	F ☽	0353	1.2	0954	3.6	1619	1.3	2214	3.5
3	SA	0442	1.3	1042	3.5	1713	1.4	2309	3.4
4	SU	0546	1.4	1142	3.3	1827	1.5		
5	M	0018	3.3	0705	1.5	1254	3.3	1948	1.5
6	TU	0137	3.3	0823	1.4	1413	3.3	2100	1.3
7	W	0254	3.5	0934	1.1	1527	3.5	2203	1.0
8	TH	0359	3.8	1034	0.8	1626	3.8	2257	0.7
9	F ●	0452	4.0	1124	0.5	1715	4.0	2344	0.4
10	SA	0540	4.2	1209	0.3	1800	4.1		
11	SU	0027	0.2	0624	4.3	1251	0.2	1843	4.2
12	M	0109	0.1	0708	4.3	1333	0.2	1925	4.2
13	TU	0152	0.2	0751	4.3	1415	0.3	2007	4.1
14	W	0235	0.3	0834	4.1	1457	0.4	2049	4.0
15	TH	0320	0.4	0917	4.0	1541	0.6	2132	3.8
16	F ☾	0406	0.7	1003	3.7	1627	0.9	2219	3.6
17	SA	0458	1.0	1054	3.4	1722	1.1	2316	3.3
18	SU	0601	1.2	1159	3.2	1832	1.3		
19	M	0033	3.2	0723	1.3	1324	3.1	2001	1.4
20	TU	0206	3.2	0857	1.3	1445	3.2	2128	1.2
21	W	0321	3.4	1008	1.1	1548	3.4	2229	1.0
22	TH	0416	3.6	1057	0.9	1636	3.6	2313	0.7
23	F	0459	3.8	1136	0.7	1716	3.8	2348	0.6
24	SA ○	0536	4.0	1208	0.6	1751	3.9		
25	SU	0016	0.6	0610	4.0	1234	0.6	1822	3.9
26	M	0040	0.6	0640	4.0	1258	0.6	1850	3.9
27	TU	0104	0.6	0707	4.0	1324	0.7	1917	3.9
28	W	0131	0.7	0734	3.9	1353	0.8	1946	3.8
29	TH	0202	0.8	0803	3.8	1424	0.9	2016	3.8

MARCH

Date	Day	Time	m	Time	m	Time	m	Time	m
1	F	0236	0.9	0835	3.8	1456	1.0	2050	3.7
2	SA	0313	1.0	0911	3.6	1532	1.2	2130	3.6
3	SU ☽	0358	1.2	0956	3.5	1620	1.4	2223	3.4
4	M	0500	1.4	1057	3.2	1735	1.5	2335	3.2
5	TU	0624	1.5	1217	3.1	1910	1.5		
6	W	0104	3.2	0754	1.4	1348	3.1	2033	1.3
7	TH	0233	3.4	0911	1.1	1509	3.4	2141	0.9
8	F	0340	3.7	1013	0.7	1609	3.7	2236	0.5
9	SA	0433	4.0	1104	0.4	1656	4.0	2323	0.2
10	SU ●	0519	4.2	1148	0.1	1740	4.2		
11	M	0006	0.0	0602	4.4	1229	0.0	1821	4.3
12	TU	0047	0.0	0644	4.4	1310	0.0	1901	4.3
13	W	0129	0.0	0725	4.3	1350	0.1	1941	4.2
14	TH	0210	0.1	0805	4.1	1430	0.3	2021	4.0
15	F	0253	0.4	0846	3.9	1512	0.5	2102	3.8
16	SA	0338	0.6	0929	3.6	1557	0.8	2147	3.5
17	SU ☾	0428	0.9	1018	3.3	1650	1.1	2242	3.2
18	M	0530	1.2	1123	3.0	1800	1.4		
19	TU	0006	3.0	0655	1.4	1301	2.9	1936	1.4
20	W	0150	3.0	0838	1.3	1427	3.0	2111	1.2
21	TH	0301	3.3	0947	1.0	1528	3.3	2209	0.9
22	F	0352	3.6	1034	0.8	1614	3.6	2250	0.7
23	SA	0434	3.8	1111	0.6	1652	3.8	2323	0.6
24	SU	0510	3.9	1141	0.6	1726	3.9	2350	0.5
25	M ○	0542	3.9	1206	0.5	1755	3.9		
26	TU	0011	0.5	0611	3.9	1228	0.6	1823	3.9
27	W	0034	0.6	0636	3.9	1254	0.6	1849	3.9
28	TH	0102	0.6	0702	3.9	1322	0.7	1916	3.9
29	F	0133	0.7	0730	3.8	1353	0.8	1947	3.8
30	SA	0208	0.8	0803	3.7	1427	0.9	2021	3.7
31	SU	0247	1.0	0841	3.6	1505	1.1	[illegible]	3.6

APRIL

Date	Day	Time	m	Time	m	Time	m	Time	m
1	M	0334	1.1	0928	3.4	1556	1.3	2158	3.4
2	TU ☽	0437	1.3	1032	3.2	1711	1.4	2311	3.2
3	W	0600	1.4	1154	3.0	1843	1.4		
4	TH	0043	3.2	0728	1.2	1326	3.1	2007	1.1
5	F	0210	3.4	0845	0.9	1445	3.4	2114	0.8
6	SA	0315	3.7	0946	0.6	1543	3.7	2210	0.4
7	SU	0407	4.0	1037	0.3	1631	4.0	2259	0.2
8	M ●	0453	4.2	1123	0.1	1715	4.2	2343	0.0
9	TU	0537	4.3	1205	0.0	1757	4.3		
10	W	0025	0.0	0619	4.3	1246	0.0	1837	4.2
11	TH	0107	0.0	0700	4.2	1327	0.1	1917	4.1
12	F	0149	0.2	0740	4.0	1408	0.3	1957	4.0
13	SA	0232	0.4	0821	3.8	1451	0.6	2038	3.7
14	SU	0317	0.7	0903	3.5	1536	0.8	2124	3.5
15	M ☾	0407	1.0	0952	3.2	1630	1.1	2219	3.2
16	TU	0509	1.2	1056	3.0	1739	1.3	2342	3.0
17	W	0627	1.3	1230	2.9	1905	1.3		
18	TH	0119	3.0	0757	1.3	1354	3.0	2029	1.2
19	F	0226	3.2	0904	1.1	1453	3.2	2127	0.9
20	SA	0317	3.5	0952	0.9	1538	3.5	2210	0.8
21	SU	0358	3.6	1031	0.7	1618	3.7	2245	0.7
22	M	0435	3.8	1103	0.6	1652	3.8	2313	0.6
23	TU ○	0508	3.8	1131	0.6	1723	3.8	2339	0.6
24	W	0538	3.8	1158	0.6	1752	3.9		
25	TH	0006	0.6	0606	3.8	1227	0.6	1822	3.9
26	F	0037	0.6	0634	3.8	1259	0.7	1853	3.9
27	SA	0112	0.7	0707	3.8	1334	0.8	1928	3.8
28	SU	0150	0.8	0745	3.7	1413	0.9	2007	3.7
29	M	0234	0.9	0828	3.6	1458	1.0	2054	3.6
30	TU	0327	1.0	0920	3.4	1554	1.1	2151	3.5

MAY

Date	Day	Time	m	Time	m	Time	m	Time	m
1	W ☾	0430	1.2	1024	3.2	1705	1.2	2302	3.3
2	TH	0545	1.2	1140	3.2	1824	1.2		
3	F	0024	3.4	0705	1.1	1301	3.3	1940	1.0
4	SA	0141	3.5	0815	0.8	1412	3.5	2045	0.7
5	SU	0244	3.8	0915	0.6	1511	3.8	2142	0.4
6	M	0338	4.0	1009	0.4	1602	4.0	2233	0.3
7	TU	0427	4.1	1057	0.2	1650	4.1	2321	0.2
8	W ●	0513	4.2	1143	0.2	1734	4.2		
9	TH	0005	0.2	0557	4.1	1226	0.2	1817	4.1
10	F	0048	0.2	0639	4.0	1308	0.3	1858	4.0
11	SA	0131	0.4	0720	3.9	1351	0.5	1939	3.9
12	SU	0215	0.6	0801	3.7	1435	0.7	2022	3.7
13	M	0300	0.8	0844	3.5	1521	0.9	2108	3.5
14	TU	0350	1.0	0932	3.3	1613	1.1	2201	3.3
15	W ☽	0446	1.2	1028	3.1	1714	1.2	2308	3.1
16	TH	0552	1.3	1141	3.0	1823	1.2		
17	F	0027	3.1	0702	1.2	1257	3.0	1931	1.2
18	SA	0134	3.2	0803	1.1	1359	3.2	2027	1.0
19	SU	0227	3.4	0854	1.0	1448	3.4	2114	0.9
20	M	0312	3.5	0938	0.9	1531	3.5	2155	0.8
21	TU	0353	3.6	1017	0.8	1611	3.7	2232	0.7
22	W	0430	3.7	1054	0.7	1649	3.8	2307	0.7
23	TH ○	0505	3.8	1130	0.7	1725	3.8	2343	0.7
24	F	0540	3.8	1207	0.7	1801	3.9		
25	SA	0020	0.7	0616	3.8	1245	0.7	1839	3.9
26	SU	0100	0.7	0655	3.8	1325	0.7	1919	3.8
27	M	0143	0.7	0738	3.7	1409	0.8	2003	3.8
28	TU	0231	0.8	0826	3.6	1458	0.9	2053	3.7
29	W	0324	0.9	0919	3.5	1553	0.9	2150	3.6
30	TH ☾	0423	1.0	1018	3.4	1655	1.0	2253	3.5
31	F	0528	1.0	1124	3.4	1802	0.9		

JUNE

Date	Day	Time	m	Time	m	Time	m	Time	m
1	SA	0001	3.5	0637	0.9	1231	3.5	1911	0.8
2	SU	0109	3.6	0743	0.8	1337	3.6	2015	0.7
3	M	0211	3.7	0844	0.7	1437	3.7	2114	0.6
4	TU	0308	3.8	0941	0.6	1534	3.8	2210	0.5
5	W	0402	3.9	1034	0.5	1627	3.9	2302	0.4
6	TH ●	0452	3.9	1124	0.5	1716	4.0	2349	0.4
7	F	0539	3.9	1210	0.5	1801	4.0		
8	SA	0034	0.5	0623	3.9	1253	0.5	1844	3.9
9	SU	0116	0.6	0705	3.8	1336	0.6	1925	3.8
10	M	0159	0.7	0745	3.7	1418	0.7	2007	3.7
11	TU	0241	0.8	0826	3.5	1502	0.9	2050	3.6
12	W	0326	1.0	0909	3.4	1547	1.0	2136	3.4
13	TH	0414	1.1	0956	3.3	1636	1.1	2226	3.3
14	F ☽	0506	1.2	1048	3.2	1730	1.2	2322	3.3
15	SA	0602	1.2	1147	3.2	1828	1.2		
16	SU	0022	3.3	0700	1.2	1248	3.2	1924	1.2
17	M	0122	3.3	0754	1.2	1346	3.3	2017	1.1
18	TU	0216	3.4	0845	1.1	1439	3.4	2107	1.0
19	W	0305	3.5	0935	1.0	1529	3.6	2156	0.9
20	TH	0353	3.6	1024	0.9	1617	3.7	2242	0.8
21	F	0438	3.7	1109	0.8	1703	3.8	2327	0.7
22	SA ○	0522	3.8	1153	0.7	1746	3.9		
23	SU	0009	0.6	0605	3.8	1235	0.6	1829	3.9
24	M	0053	0.6	0648	3.8	1318	0.6	1913	3.9
25	TU	0137	0.6	0734	3.8	1403	0.6	1959	3.9
26	W	0225	0.6	0821	3.8	1451	0.6	2048	3.9
27	TH	0314	0.7	0911	3.7	1541	0.7	2139	3.8
28	F ☾	0406	0.7	1003	3.6	1634	0.7	2233	3.7
29	SA	0502	0.8	1058	3.6	1733	0.8	2331	3.6
30	SU	0603	0.9	1158	3.5	1836	0.9		

SUNRISE AND SUNSET TIMES

COBH
At 51°51′N 8°18′W

UT		Sunrise	Sunset
Jan	01	0841	1633
	15	0834	1652
Feb	01	0812	1722
	15	0748	1748
Mar	01	0719	1813
	15	0647	1838
BST (UT+1)			
Apr	01	0708	2007
	15	0637	2031
May	01	0604	2058
	15	0540	2120
Jun	01	0520	2143
	15	0513	2154
Jul	01	0518	2155
	15	0532	2146
Aug	01	0556	2122
	15	0618	2056
Sep	01	0645	2020
	15	0708	1948
Oct	01	0734	1911
	15	0758	1839
UT			
Nov	01	0728	1705
	15	0753	1642
Dec	01	0818	1626

COBH
LAT 51°51′N
LONG 8°18′W

TIMES AND HEIGHTS OF HIGH AND LOW WATER (Heights in Metres)

TIME ZONE UT
For Summer Time (area enclosed in shaded box) add 1 hour

2024

JULY

Date	Time	m	Time	m	Time	m	Time	m
1 M	0034	3.6	0708	0.9	1301	3.5	1943	0.9
2 TU	0138	3.6	0813	0.9	1406	3.6	2049	0.8
3 W	0242	3.6	0917	0.9	1511	3.6	2152	0.8
4 TH	0342	3.6	1018	0.8	1611	3.7	2249	0.7
5 F ●	0438	3.7	1111	0.7	1704	3.8	2338	0.6
6 SA	0526	3.8	1158	0.6	1750	3.9		
7 SU	0021	0.6	0610	3.8	1240	0.6	1831	3.9
8 M	0101	0.7	0649	3.8	1318	0.6	1910	3.9
9 TU	0138	0.7	0726	3.7	1356	0.7	1947	3.8
10 W	0215	0.8	0803	3.6	1432	0.8	2024	3.7
11 TH	0252	0.9	0840	3.6	1509	0.9	2102	3.6
12 F	0330	1.0	0919	3.5	1547	1.0	2142	3.5
13 SA ☽	0412	1.1	1001	3.4	1630	1.1	2225	3.4
14 SU	0459	1.2	1048	3.4	1719	1.2	2313	3.4
15 M	0554	1.3	1142	3.3	1818	1.3		
16 TU	0010	3.3	0656	1.3	1244	3.3	1923	1.3
17 W	0115	3.3	0800	1.3	1351	3.3	2026	1.2
18 TH	0221	3.4	0901	1.2	1455	3.5	2127	1.1
19 F	0323	3.5	0959	1.0	1553	3.6	2223	0.9
20 SA	0418	3.6	1051	0.8	1645	3.8	2312	0.7
21 SU O	0507	3.8	1138	0.6	1732	4.0	2358	0.5
22 M	0553	3.9	1221	0.5	1817	4.1		
23 TU	0041	0.4	0637	3.9	1304	0.4	1901	4.1
24 W	0124	0.4	0721	3.9	1347	0.3	1945	4.1
25 TH	0208	0.4	0806	3.9	1432	0.4	2030	4.0
26 F	0253	0.5	0851	3.9	1518	0.5	2116	3.9
27 SA	0340	0.6	0938	3.8	1606	0.6	2204	3.8
28 SU ☾	0429	0.7	1027	3.7	1658	0.8	2257	3.6
29 M	0524	0.9	1122	3.5	1758	1.0	2358	3.4
30 TU	0630	1.1	1228	3.4	1910	1.1		
31 W	0109	3.3	0745	1.1	1344	3.3	2029	1.1

AUGUST

Date	Time	m	Time	m	Time	m	Time	m
1 TH	0224	3.3	0903	1.1	1500	3.4	2144	1.0
2 F	0331	3.4	1011	0.9	1603	3.6	2243	0.8
3 SA	0427	3.6	1105	0.7	1654	3.8	2330	0.7
4 SU ●	0514	3.7	1148	0.6	1737	3.9		
5 M	0009	0.6	0555	3.8	1224	0.6	1815	3.9
6 TU	0042	0.6	0630	3.8	1256	0.6	1849	3.9
7 W	0112	0.7	0703	3.8	1326	0.6	1921	3.9
8 TH	0141	0.8	0734	3.8	1355	0.7	1952	3.8
9 F	0212	0.8	0806	3.7	1425	0.8	2024	3.7
10 SA	0245	0.9	0840	3.6	1458	0.9	2057	3.7
11 SU	0320	1.1	0917	3.6	1535	1.1	2134	3.6
12 M ☽	0400	1.2	0958	3.5	1619	1.2	2218	3.4
13 TU	0449	1.3	1048	3.3	1716	1.4	2313	3.3
14 W	0557	1.4	1153	3.2	1831	1.4		
15 TH	0022	3.2	0718	1.4	1310	3.2	1951	1.4
16 F	0144	3.2	0832	1.3	1429	3.3	2102	1.2
17 SA	0300	3.4	0936	1.0	1534	3.6	2203	0.9
18 SU	0401	3.6	1031	0.7	1627	3.9	2254	0.6
19 M O	0450	3.8	1118	0.5	1714	4.1	2339	0.4
20 TU	0534	4.0	1201	0.3	1757	4.2		
21 W	0021	0.2	0617	4.1	1242	0.2	1839	4.3
22 TH	0102	0.2	0659	4.1	1324	0.1	1921	4.2
23 F	0144	0.2	0741	4.1	1407	0.2	2004	4.1
24 SA	0226	0.3	0823	4.0	1450	0.4	2047	4.0
25 SU	0311	0.5	0907	3.8	1536	0.6	2132	3.8
26 M ☾	0357	0.7	0954	3.6	1626	0.8	2222	3.5
27 TU	0451	1.0	1049	3.4	1726	1.1	2324	3.2
28 W	0558	1.2	1202	3.2	1844	1.3		
29 TH	0048	3.1	0726	1.3	1336	3.2	2022	1.3
30 F	0215	3.2	0900	1.2	1455	3.3	2141	1.1
31 SA	0323	3.4	1007	0.9	1554	3.6	2235	0.9

SEPTEMBER

Date	Time	m	Time	m	Time	m	Time	m
1 SU	0414	3.6	1055	0.7	1639	3.8	2316	0.7
2 M	0457	3.8	1133	0.6	1718	3.9	2350	0.6
3 TU ●	0533	3.9	1204	0.5	1752	4.0		
4 W	0017	0.6	0606	3.9	1229	0.5	1823	4.0
5 TH	0041	0.6	0635	3.9	1252	0.6	1850	3.9
6 F	0106	0.7	0702	3.8	1317	0.7	1917	3.9
7 SA	0133	0.8	0731	3.8	1345	0.8	1944	3.8
8 SU	0203	0.9	0801	3.7	1417	0.9	2015	3.7
9 M	0237	1.0	0835	3.6	1453	1.1	2050	3.6
10 TU	0314	1.2	0914	3.5	1535	1.2	2133	3.5
11 W ☽	0401	1.4	1004	3.3	1631	1.4	2229	3.3
12 TH	0510	1.5	1112	3.2	1751	1.5	2344	3.1
13 F	0641	1.5	1238	3.1	1921	1.5		
14 SA	0115	3.1	0804	1.3	1407	3.3	2038	1.2
15 SU	0239	3.4	0912	1.0	1513	3.7	2140	0.8
16 M	0338	3.7	1006	0.6	1604	4.0	2231	0.5
17 TU	0426	4.0	1054	0.3	1650	4.2	2315	0.3
18 W O	0510	4.2	1137	0.1	1732	4.3	2357	0.1
19 TH	0552	4.3	1219	0.1	1814	4.4		
20 F	0037	0.1	0633	4.3	1300	0.1	1855	4.3
21 SA	0118	0.2	0714	4.2	1342	0.2	1937	4.2
22 SU	0201	0.3	0756	4.1	1426	0.4	2019	4.0
23 M	0245	0.6	0840	3.9	1512	0.7	2103	3.7
24 TU ☾	0332	0.8	0927	3.6	1602	1.0	2153	3.4
25 W	0427	1.1	1024	3.3	1704	1.2	2257	3.1
26 TH	0538	1.3	1147	3.1	1828	1.4		
27 F	0033	3.0	0716	1.4	1328	3.1	2014	1.3
28 SA	0203	3.1	0849	1.2	1441	3.3	2123	1.1
29 SU	0305	3.4	0947	0.9	1533	3.6	2212	0.9
30 M	0352	3.6	1031	0.7	1615	3.8	2250	0.7

OCTOEER

Date	Time	m	Time	m	Time	m	Time	m
1 TU	0432	3.8	1106	0.6	1651	4.0	2322	0.6
2 W ●	0506	3.9	1135	0.6	1724	4.0	2347	0.6
3 TH	0537	3.9	1158	0.6	1752	4.0		
4 F	0008	0.7	0605	3.9	1219	0.7	1818	4.0
5 SA	0032	0.7	0631	3.9	1243	0.7	1843	3.9
6 SU	0100	0.8	0659	3.9	1313	0.8	1910	3.9
7 M	0130	0.9	0729	3.8	1346	1.0	1941	3.8
8 TU	0204	1.0	0803	3.7	1424	1.1	2018	3.7
9 W	0244	1.2	0845	3.6	1509	1.3	2103	3.5
10 TH ☽	0335	1.4	0938	3.4	1609	1.4	2202	3.3
11 F	0446	1.5	1048	3.3	1727	1.5	2319	3.2
12 SA	0614	1.5	1214	3.2	1854	1.4		
13 SU	0049	3.2	0736	1.3	1340	3.4	2011	1.1
14 M	0210	3.5	0843	0.9	1445	3.8	2112	0.8
15 TU	0309	3.8	0938	0.6	1536	4.0	2203	0.5
16 W	0358	4.1	1027	0.3	1623	4.3	2249	0.3
17 TH O	0443	4.2	1113	0.2	1707	4.4	2333	0.2
18 F	0527	4.3	1157	0.1	1750	4.4		
19 SA	0015	0.2	0610	4.3	1239	0.2	1832	4.3
20 SU	0057	0.3	0652	4.2	1323	0.3	1914	4.1
21 M	0141	0.4	0735	4.1	1408	0.5	1956	3.9
22 TU	0226	0.7	0820	3.8	1455	0.8	2041	3.7
23 W	0315	0.9	0909	3.6	1547	1.1	2131	3.4
24 TH ☾	0412	1.2	1008	3.3	1649	1.3	2235	3.1
25 F	0523	1.4	1129	3.1	1809	1.5		
26 SA	0006	3.0	0652	1.4	1300	3.2	1939	1.4
27 SU	0132	3.1	0813	1.2	1408	3.4	2045	1.2
28 M	0232	3.4	0909	1.0	1458	3.6	2132	1.0
29 TU	0318	3.6	0952	0.9	1540	3.8	2211	0.9
30 W	0358	3.8	1029	0.8	1617	3.9	2244	0.8
31 TH	0433	3.9	1059	0.7	1651	4.0	2312	0.8

NOVEMBER

Date	Time	m	Time	m	Time	m	Time	m
1 F ●	0505	3.9	1125	0.7	1721	4.0	2338	0.8
2 SA	0535	4.0	1151	0.8	1748	4.0		
3 SU	0005	0.8	0605	4.0	1219	0.8	1816	3.9
4 M	0036	0.9	0636	3.9	1252	0.9	1846	3.9
5 TU	0110	0.9	0709	3.9	1329	1.0	1921	3.8
6 W	0148	1.0	0748	3.8	1411	1.1	2002	3.7
7 TH	0233	1.2	0833	3.7	1500	1.3	2051	3.6
8 F	0328	1.3	0928	3.5	1559	1.4	2151	3.4
9 SA ☽	0434	1.4	1035	3.4	1710	1.4	2303	3.3
10 SU	0551	1.3	1151	3.5	1828	1.3		
11 M	0021	3.4	0706	1.2	1307	3.6	1940	1.1
12 TU	0134	3.6	0812	0.9	1411	3.8	2041	0.9
13 W	0236	3.8	0910	0.7	1506	4.0	2135	0.6
14 TH	0329	4.0	1003	0.5	1556	4.2	2226	0.5
15 F O	0419	4.2	1052	0.4	1644	4.3	2313	0.4
16 SA	0506	4.3	1140	0.3	1730	4.3	2358	0.4
17 SU	0552	4.3	1225	0.4	1814	4.2		
18 M	0042	0.4	0637	4.2	1310	0.5	1858	4.1
19 TU	0126	0.6	0721	4.1	1355	0.7	1941	3.9
20 W	0212	0.8	0807	3.9	1442	0.9	2025	3.7
21 TH	0301	1.0	0856	3.7	1532	1.1	2113	3.4
22 F	0355	1.1	0950	3.4	1628	1.3	2208	3.2
23 SA ☾	0456	1.3	1054	3.3	1733	1.4	2316	3.1
24 SU	0606	1.4	1207	3.3	1843	1.4		
25 M	0032	3.2	0715	1.3	1314	3.3	1946	1.3
26 TU	0137	3.3	0812	1.2	1408	3.5	2038	1.2
27 W	0229	3.5	0900	1.1	1455	3.6	2122	1.1
28 TH	0314	3.6	0942	1.0	1537	3.7	2202	1.0
29 F	0355	3.8	1021	0.9	1616	3.8	2239	0.9
30 SA	0434	3.9	1056	0.9	1652	3.9	2314	0.9

DECEMBER

Date	Time	m	Time	m	Time	m	Time	m
1 SU ●	0511	4.0	1131	0.9	1725	3.9	2348	0.8
2 M	0546	4.0	1207	0.9	1759	3.9		
3 TU	0024	0.9	0623	4.0	1243	0.9	1835	3.9
4 W	0102	0.9	0701	4.0	1323	0.9	1913	3.9
5 TH	0143	0.9	0743	3.9	1407	1.0	1957	3.8
6 F	0230	1.0	0830	3.8	1456	1.1	2046	3.7
7 SA	0321	1.1	0922	3.8	1549	1.2	2141	3.6
8 SU ☽	0419	1.1	1020	3.7	1649	1.2	2242	3.5
9 M	0523	1.2	1124	3.7	1755	1.2	2348	3.5
10 TU	0631	1.1	1230	3.7	1903	1.1		
11 W	0055	3.6	0738	1.0	1334	3.8	2009	1.0
12 TH	0200	3.7	0841	0.9	1435	3.9	2109	0.9
13 F	0301	3.9	0941	0.8	1532	4.0	2206	0.7
14 SA	0359	4.0	1037	0.7	1627	4.0	2258	0.6
15 SU O	0452	4.1	1129	0.6	1717	4.1	2347	0.6
16 M	0541	4.2	1216	0.6	1803	4.1		
17 TU	0031	0.6	0627	4.1	1300	0.6	1846	4.0
18 W	0115	0.6	0711	4.1	1343	0.7	1927	3.9
19 TH	0158	0.7	0754	3.9	1426	0.9	2008	3.7
20 F	0242	0.9	0837	3.8	1510	1.0	2050	3.6
21 SA	0327	1.0	0922	3.6	1555	1.2	2134	3.5
22 SU ☾	0415	1.2	1010	3.5	1644	1.3	2223	3.4
23 M	0507	1.3	1101	3.4	1738	1.4	2318	3.3
24 TU	0605	1.4	1159	3.4	1836	1.4		
25 W	0019	3.3	0704	1.4	1300	3.4	1935	1.4
26 TH	0124	3.4	0800	1.3	1359	3.4	2030	1.3
27 F	0223	3.5	0855	1.3	1453	3.5	2122	1.2
28 SA	0317	3.6	0946	1.1	1543	3.7	2211	1.1
29 SU	0407	3.8	1034	1.0	1629	3.8	2256	0.9
30 M ●	0452	3.9	1117	0.9	1711	3.9	2336	0.8
31 TU	0535	4.0	1158	0.8	1750	3.9		

DUBLIN (NORTH WALL)
LAT 53°21′N
LONG 6°13′W

TIMES AND HEIGHTS OF HIGH AND LOW WATER (Heights in Metres)

TIME ZONE UT
For Summer Time (area enclosed in shaded box) add 1 hour

2024

JANUARY

Date	Time	m	Date	Time	m
1 M	0241 0816 1454 2059	3.5 1.3 3.8 1.1	**16** TU	0256 0825 1506 2105	3.9 0.9 4.2 0.6
2 TU	0326 0901 1539 2145	3.4 1.4 3.7 1.2	**17** W	0351 0921 1602 2203	3.7 1.1 4.1 0.8
3 W	0415 0951 1627 2233	3.3 1.5 3.5 1.3	**18** TH ☽	0450 1022 1702 2304	3.6 1.2 3.9 1.0
4 TH ☾	0510 1048 1720 2327	3.3 1.6 3.4 1.4	**19** F	0556 1128 1810	3.5 1.3 3.7
5 F	0611 1149 1821	3.3 1.7 3.4	**20** SA	0010 0705 1239 1923	1.2 3.5 1.4 3.6
6 SA	0024 0713 1250 1927	1.4 3.3 1.7 3.4	**21** SU	0124 0812 1354 2036	1.3 3.6 1.4 3.6
7 SU	0121 0809 1347 2028	1.4 3.4 1.6 3.4	**22** M	0236 0915 1503 2142	1.4 3.6 1.3 3.6
8 M	0216 0859 1440 2122	1.3 3.6 1.4 3.6	**23** TU	0334 1011 1559 2239	1.3 3.8 1.1 3.6
9 TU	0305 0944 1528 2212	1.2 3.7 1.2 3.7	**24** W	0420 1058 1645 2323	1.2 3.9 1.0 3.7
10 W	0350 1027 1613 2258	1.1 3.9 1.0 3.8	**25** TH ○	0459 1136 1724 2358	1.1 4.0 0.9 3.7
11 TH ●	0433 1109 1658 2343	0.9 4.1 0.7 3.9	**26** F	0533 1208 1800	1.1 4.0 0.8
12 F	0515 1152 1743	0.8 4.2 0.5	**27** SA	0026 0604 1237 1835	3.6 1.0 4.0 0.8
13 SA	0028 0558 1236 1830	4.0 0.8 4.3 0.4	**28** SU	0056 0635 1309 1908	3.6 1.0 4.0 0.8
14 SU	0114 0644 1324 1919	4.0 0.8 4.3 0.4	**29** M	0127 0705 1342 1940	3.6 1.0 3.9 0.8
15 M	0204 0732 1414 2011	3.9 0.8 4.3 0.5	**30** TU	0202 0737 1418 2013	3.6 1.0 3.8 0.9
			31 W	0239 0812 1457	3.6 1.1 3.7

FEBRUARY

Date	Time	m	Date	Time	m
1 TH	0319 0852 1539 2128	3.5 1.2 3.6 1.1	**16** F ☽	0408 0948 1630 2224	3.6 1.0 3.8 1.1
2 F ☾	0405 0936 1625 2214	3.4 1.4 3.5 1.3	**17** SA	0513 1054 1741 2330	3.4 1.3 3.5 1.4
3 SA	0457 1028 1720 2310	3.3 1.5 3.3 1.4	**18** SU	0628 1210 1902	3.4 1.4 3.4
4 SU	0600 1138 1829	3.2 1.6 3.2	**19** M	0054 0744 1340 2023	1.6 3.4 1.4 3.3
5 M	0024 0716 1300 1952	1.6 3.2 1.6 3.2	**20** TU	0225 0855 1457 2137	1.6 3.5 1.3 3.4
6 TU	0140 0825 1412 2101	1.5 3.4 1.4 3.4	**21** W	0325 0956 1550 2232	1.4 3.7 1.1 3.5
7 W	0244 0921 1512 2157	1.3 3.6 1.1 3.6	**22** TH	0409 1044 1632 2313	1.3 3.8 0.9 3.6
8 TH	0336 1010 1602 2246	1.1 3.9 0.8 3.8	**23** F	0444 1121 1706 2342	1.1 3.9 0.8 3.6
9 F ●	0421 1054 1646 2329	0.8 4.1 0.5 4.0	**24** SA ○	0514 1150 1738	1.0 3.9 0.7
10 SA	0502 1137 1729	0.6 4.3 0.2	**25** SU	0005 0543 1215 1808	3.6 0.9 3.9 0.7
11 SU	0011 0543 1219 1813	4.1 0.5 4.4 0.1	**26** M	0028 0609 1241 1835	3.6 0.8 3.9 0.7
12 M	0054 0625 1303 1858	4.1 0.4 4.4 0.1	**27** TU	0054 0634 1311 1901	3.7 0.8 3.9 0.7
13 TU	0138 0709 1350 1945	4.0 0.5 4.4 0.3	**28** W	0124 0702 1345 1930	3.7 0.8 3.8 0.8
14 W	0224 0757 1439 2034	3.9 0.6 4.2 0.5	**29** TH	0159 0735 1422 2004	3.7 0.9 3.7 0.8
15 TH	0314 0850 1531 2127	3.8 0.8 4.0 0.8			

MARCH

Date	Time	m	Date	Time	m
1 F	0238 0812 1503 2043	3.6 1.0 3.6 1.0	**16** SA	0330 0923 1604 2150	3.6 0.9 3.6 1.2
2 SA	0321 0854 1548 2128	3.5 1.1 3.5 1.2	**17** SU ☽	0432 1028 1718 2254	3.4 1.2 3.3 1.5
3 SU ☾	0410 0945 1642 2222	3.3 1.3 3.3 1.4	**18** M	0553 1145 1843	3.3 1.4 3.2
4 M	0510 1051 1752 2341	3.2 1.5 3.1 1.6	**19** TU	0018 0715 1321 2009	1.7 3.3 1.4 3.2
5 TU	0630 1228 1927	3.1 1.5 3.1	**20** W	0202 0831 1437 2122	1.7 3.4 1.2 3.3
6 W	0114 0755 1353 2045	1.6 3.3 1.3 3.3	**21** TH	0303 0933 1528 2213	1.5 3.6 1.0 3.4
7 TH	0228 0859 1458 2143	1.4 3.5 0.9 3.6	**22** F	0345 1020 1607 2249	1.3 3.7 0.8 3.5
8 F	0322 0951 1547 2230	1.0 3.8 0.6 3.8	**23** SA	0419 1055 1639 2315	1.1 3.8 0.7 3.6
9 SA	0405 1036 1630 2311	0.7 4.1 0.2 4.0	**24** SU	0449 1124 1708 2337	0.9 3.8 0.7 3.6
10 SU ●	0445 1118 1711 2351	0.5 4.3 0.0 4.1	**25** M ○	0516 1149 1735 2358	0.8 3.8 0.6 3.7
11 M	0523 1159 1752	0.3 4.4 0.0	**26** TU	0540 1214 1759	0.7 3.8 0.6
12 TU	0029 0604 1241 1834	4.1 0.2 4.4 0.0	**27** W	0021 0604 1242 1825	3.7 0.7 3.8 0.7
13 W	0109 0646 1326 1918	4.0 0.3 4.3 0.2	**28** TH	0051 0631 1316 1855	3.7 0.7 3.8 0.7
14 TH	0152 0733 1414 2004	3.9 0.4 4.1 0.5	**29** F	0127 0705 1355 1931	3.7 0.8 3.7 0.8
15 F	0239 0825 1506 2054	3.8 0.7 3.9 0.9	**30** SA	0207 0744 1437 2012	3.7 0.9 3.6 1.0
			31 SU	0251 0829 1524 [illegible]	3.5 1.0 3.4 [illegible]

APRIL

Date	Time	m	Date	Time	m
1 M	0341 0924 1621 2159	3.4 1.2 3.3 1.4	**16** TU	0521 1120 1817 2341	3.3 1.2 3.1 1.7
2 TU ☾	0441 1038 1736 2321	3.2 1.3 3.1 1.6	**17** W	0640 1245 1937	3.3 1.3 3.1
3 W	0600 1212 1908	3.2 1.3 3.2	**18** TH	0115 0754 1358 2047	1.7 3.4 1.2 3.2
4 TH	0052 0726 1334 2024	1.5 3.3 1.1 3.4	**19** F	0223 0855 1451 2136	1.5 3.5 1.0 3.4
5 F	0204 0833 1437 2122	1.3 3.6 0.7 3.6	**20** SA	0309 0943 1531 2211	1.3 3.6 0.9 3.5
6 SA	0259 0927 1527 2209	1.0 3.9 0.4 3.8	**21** SU	0346 1020 1605 2239	1.1 3.7 0.8 3.6
7 SU	0343 1014 1610 2250	0.7 4.1 0.2 4.0	**22** M	0417 1052 1634 2305	0.9 3.7 0.7 3.6
8 M ●	0424 1057 1650 2328	0.4 4.3 0.0 4.1	**23** TU ○	0445 1120 1700 2327	0.8 3.8 0.7 3.7
9 TU	0503 1139 1730	0.3 4.3 0.0	**24** W	0509 1147 1725 2352	0.8 3.8 0.7 3.8
10 W	0005 0544 1222 1811	4.1 0.2 4.3 0.2	**25** TH	0535 1218 1753	0.8 3.8 0.7
11 TH	0044 0627 1307 1853	4.0 0.3 4.2 0.4	**26** F	0024 0606 1254 1827	3.8 0.7 3.7 0.8
12 F	0126 0714 1356 1939	3.9 0.4 4.0 0.7	**27** SA	0102 0643 1335 1906	3.8 0.8 3.7 0.9
13 SA	0212 0807 1448 2028	3.8 0.6 3.7 1.0	**28** SU	0144 0727 1421 1952	3.7 0.9 3.6 1.1
14 SU	0303 0905 1547 2123	3.6 0.9 3.5 1.3	**29** M	0232 0819 1513 2046	3.6 1.0 3.5 1.2
15 M ☽	0403 1009 1658 2226	3.5 1.1 3.2 1.6	**30** TU	0325 0922 1613 2151	3.5 1.1 3.3 1.4

MAY

Date	Time	m	Date	Time	m
1 W ☾	0427 1036 1726 2307	3.4 1.1 3.3 1.5	**16** TH	0559 1158 1849	3.4 1.2 3.1
2 TH	0541 1156 1845	3.4 1.1 3.3	**17** F	0013 0707 1304 1951	1.7 3.4 1.2 3.2
3 F	0024 0657 1308 1956	1.4 3.5 0.9 3.5	**18** SA	0123 0806 1401 2042	1.6 3.5 1.1 3.3
4 SA	0132 0803 1409 2053	1.2 3.7 0.7 3.6	**19** SU	0219 0856 1446 2123	1.4 3.5 1.0 3.4
5 SU	0228 0900 1501 2143	1.0 3.9 0.4 3.8	**20** M	0302 0939 1523 2158	1.3 3.6 0.9 3.6
6 M	0317 0951 1547 2226	0.7 4.1 0.3 3.9	**21** TU	0338 1016 1556 2229	1.1 3.6 0.9 3.6
7 TU	0402 1038 1630 2307	0.5 4.2 0.3 4.0	**22** W	0410 1050 1626 2256	1.0 3.7 0.9 3.7
8 W ●	0445 1124 1711 2346	0.4 4.2 0.3 4.0	**23** TH ○	0439 1122 1656 2327	0.9 3.7 0.9 3.8
9 TH	0528 1209 1752	0.4 4.1 0.5	**24** F	0511 1158 1729	0.9 3.7 0.9
10 F	0026 0614 1254 1834	4.0 0.4 4.0 0.6	**25** SA	0002 0548 1237 1808	3.9 0.8 3.7 0.9
11 SA	0108 0702 1342 1919	3.9 0.5 3.8 0.9	**26** SU	0043 0630 1322 1851	3.9 0.8 3.7 1.0
12 SU	0154 0754 1434 2007	3.8 0.7 3.6 1.1	**27** M	0129 0719 1411 1940	3.9 0.8 3.6 1.1
13 M	0243 0850 1530 2100	3.7 0.8 3.4 1.3	**28** TU	0219 0816 1506 2037	3.8 0.9 3.6 1.2
14 TU	0341 0949 1632 2159	3.6 1.0 3.3 1.5	**29** W	0314 0919 1605 2139	3.8 0.9 3.5 1.3
15 W ☽	0448 1052 1741 2303	3.5 1.1 3.1 1.6	**30** TH ☾	0414 1025 1709 2245	3.7 0.9 3.5 1.3
			31 F	0519 1133 1817 2352	3.7 0.9 3.5 1.3

JUNE

Date	Time	m	Date	Time	m
1 SA	0626 1238 1922	3.7 0.8 3.5	**16** SU	0021 0711 1301 1945	1.6 3.4 1.3 3.3
2 SU	0056 0732 1339 2022	1.2 3.8 0.7 3.6	**17** M	0118 0805 1352 2034	1.5 3.4 1.2 3.4
3 M	0156 0833 1435 2116	1.1 3.9 0.7 3.7	**18** TU	0210 0855 1437 2116	1.4 3.5 1.2 3.5
4 TU	0252 0931 1526 2206	0.9 4.0 0.6 3.8	**19** W	0256 0940 1518 2155	1.3 3.5 1.1 3.6
5 W	0343 1024 1613 2251	0.8 4.0 0.6 3.9	**20** TH	0336 1022 1556 2230	1.2 3.6 1.1 3.7
6 TH ●	0432 1114 1657 2333	0.7 4.0 0.7 3.9	**21** F	0414 1102 1633 2307	1.1 3.7 1.0 3.9
7 F	0519 1200 1739	0.7 3.9 0.8	**22** SA ○	0453 1142 1712 2346	0.9 3.7 0.9 4.0
8 SA	0012 0606 1244 1820	4.0 0.7 3.8 0.9	**23** SU	0535 1225 1753	0.8 3.8 0.9
9 SU	0053 0653 1329 1901	3.9 0.7 3.7 1.0	**24** M	0029 0621 1310 1838	4.0 0.7 3.8 0.9
10 M	0136 0741 1415 1946	3.9 0.8 3.6 1.1	**25** TU	0115 0710 1359 1926	4.1 0.7 3.8 0.9
11 TU	0222 0831 1504 2034	3.8 0.8 3.5 1.3	**26** W	0205 0805 1451 2019	4.1 0.7 3.7 1.0
12 W	0312 0923 1556 2126	3.7 1.0 3.3 1.4	**27** TH	0258 0903 1545 2116	4.0 0.7 3.7 1.1
13 TH	0407 1016 1652 2222	3.6 1.1 3.2 1.5	**28** F ☾	0354 1003 1643 2216	4.0 0.7 3.6 1.1
14 F ☽	0507 1110 1752 2321	3.5 1.2 3.2 1.6	**29** SA	0453 1104 1745 2318	3.9 0.8 3.6 1.2
15 SA	0610 1206 1851	3.4 1.2 3.2	**30** SU	0557 1206 1849	3.8 0.9 3.6

SUNRISE AND SUNSET TIMES

DUBLIN
At 53°21′N 6°13′W

UT		Sunrise	Sunset
Jan	01	0840	1617
	15	0832	1637
Feb	01	0809	1708
	15	0743	1736
Mar	01	0712	1803
	15	0639	1829
BST (UT+1)			
Apr	01	0658	2000
	15	0625	2026
May	01	0551	2054
	15	0525	2118
Jun	01	0503	2143
	15	0456	2155
Jul	01	0501	2156
	15	0516	2145
Aug	01	0541	2120
	15	0605	2053
Sep	01	0634	2014
	15	0659	1940
Oct	01	0727	1901
	15	0752	1829
UT			
Nov	01	0724	1652
	15	0750	1628
Dec	01	0817	1610

DUBLIN (NORTH WALL)

LAT 53°21′N
LONG 6°13′W

TIMES AND HEIGHTS OF HIGH AND LOW WATER (Heights in Metres)

TIME ZONE UT
For Summer Time (area enclosed in shaded box) add 1 hour

2024

JULY

Date	Day	Time	m	Time	m	Time	m	Time	m
1	M	0023	1.2	0705	3.8	1309	1.0	1954	3.6
2	TU	0129	1.2	0813	3.8	1412	1.0	2055	3.7
3	W	0234	1.2	0918	3.8	1511	1.0	2150	3.8
4	TH	0334	1.1	1017	3.8	1602	1.0	2240	3.8
5	F ●	0427	0.9	1109	3.8	1647	1.0	2323	3.9
6	SA	0514	0.8	1153	3.8	1728	1.0		
7	SU	0000	4.0	0558	0.8	1232	3.7	1805	1.0
8	M	0037	4.0	0640	0.7	1309	3.7	1842	1.0
9	TU	0114	3.9	0721	0.8	1348	3.6	1920	1.1
10	W	0154	3.9	0803	0.8	1428	3.5	2000	1.1
11	TH	0235	3.8	0847	0.9	1509	3.4	2043	1.2
12	F	0319	3.7	0931	1.0	1554	3.3	2130	1.3
13	SA ☽	0406	3.6	1018	1.2	1643	3.3	2222	1.5
14	SU	0459	3.4	1108	1.3	1739	3.2	2319	1.6
15	M	0601	3.3	1202	1.4	1842	3.2		
16	TU	0020	1.6	0711	3.3	1258	1.4	1943	3.3
17	W	0121	1.6	0815	3.3	1355	1.4	2038	3.4
18	TH	0219	1.5	0911	3.4	1447	1.3	2126	3.6
19	F	0310	1.3	1001	3.6	1534	1.2	2209	3.8
20	SA	0356	1.1	1045	3.7	1616	1.0	2250	3.9
21	SU ○	0439	0.8	1128	3.8	1656	0.9	2330	4.1
22	M	0522	0.6	1210	3.9	1737	0.8		
23	TU	0011	4.2	0606	0.5	1253	3.9	1820	0.7
24	W	0055	4.3	0653	0.4	1338	3.9	1905	0.7
25	TH	0142	4.3	0743	0.4	1426	3.9	1954	0.8
26	F	0233	4.2	0836	0.5	1516	3.8	2047	0.9
27	SA	0326	4.1	0932	0.7	1610	3.7	2144	1.0
28	SU ☾	0423	4.0	1030	0.9	1710	3.6	2246	1.2
29	M	0528	3.8	1133	1.1	1818	3.5	2355	1.3
30	TU	0644	3.6	1243	1.3	1930	3.5		
31	W	0110	1.4	0802	3.6	1356	1.4	2038	3.6

AUGUST

Date	Day	Time	m	Time	m	Time	m	Time	m
1	TH	0227	1.3	0914	3.6	1502	1.3	2140	3.7
2	F	0333	1.2	1015	3.6	1555	1.2	2232	3.8
3	SA	0424	1.0	1106	3.7	1638	1.1	2314	3.9
4	SU ●	0506	0.8	1146	3.7	1714	1.0	2348	4.0
5	M	0543	0.8	1217	3.7	1747	1.0		
6	TU	0016	4.0	0619	0.7	1244	3.6	1818	0.9
7	W	0047	4.0	0653	0.7	1314	3.6	1849	0.9
8	TH	0121	3.9	0726	0.8	1348	3.6	1922	1.0
9	F	0157	3.9	0801	0.9	1424	3.6	1957	1.1
10	SA	0235	3.8	0837	1.0	1502	3.5	2035	1.2
11	SU	0317	3.6	0917	1.1	1545	3.4	2118	1.3
12	M ☽	0404	3.5	1002	1.3	1634	3.3	2209	1.5
13	TU	0500	3.3	1059	1.5	1734	3.2	2316	1.7
14	W	0614	3.2	1209	1.6	1851	3.2		
15	TH	0039	1.7	0742	3.2	1321	1.3	2005	3.3
16	F	0153	1.5	0850	3.3	1425	1.5	2102	3.5
17	SA	0254	1.2	0944	3.5	1517	1.2	2149	3.8
18	SU	0343	0.9	1029	3.8	1600	1.0	2231	4.0
19	M ○	0425	0.6	1110	3.9	1639	0.7	2311	4.2
20	TU	0505	0.3	1150	4.0	1718	0.6	2351	4.4
21	W	0546	0.2	1230	4.1	1758	0.5		
22	TH	0031	4.4	0629	0.2	1311	4.1	1841	0.5
23	F	0116	4.4	0715	0.3	1355	4.0	1926	0.6
24	SA	0204	4.3	0804	0.5	1443	3.9	2017	0.8
25	SU	0256	4.1	0858	0.7	1535	3.7	2114	1.0
26	M ☾	0353	3.9	0956	1.0	1634	3.6	2219	1.2
27	TU	0504	3.6	1101	1.3	1748	3.4	2333	1.4
28	W	0631	3.4	1218	1.6	1908	3.4		
29	TH	0101	1.5	0756	3.4	1346	1.6	2024	3.5
30	F	0227	1.3	0913	3.5	1454	1.5	2129	3.7
31	SA	0327	1.1	1012	3.6	1543	1.3	2220	3.9

SEPTEMBER

Date	Day	Time	m	Time	m	Time	m	Time	m
1	SU	0412	0.9	1056	3.6	1621	1.2	2259	4.0
2	M	0448	0.8	1130	3.7	1654	1.0	2329	4.0
3	TU ●	0521	0.7	1155	3.7	1724	0.9	2354	4.0
4	W	0551	0.7	1217	3.7	1752	0.9		
5	TH	0020	4.0	0620	0.7	1241	3.7	1819	0.9
6	F	0050	3.9	0647	0.8	1311	3.7	1847	0.9
7	SA	0123	3.9	0715	0.8	1345	3.7	1919	1.0
8	SU	0200	3.8	0748	1.0	1423	3.6	1955	1.1
9	M	0241	3.6	0827	1.1	1505	3.5	2036	1.2
10	TU	0327	3.5	0912	1.3	1552	3.4	2126	1.4
11	W ☽	0421	3.3	1008	1.6	1650	3.2	2232	1.6
12	TH	0536	3.1	1129	1.7	1807	3.2		
13	F	0009	1.7	0717	3.1	1256	1.7	1933	3.3
14	SA	0134	1.5	0831	3.3	1407	1.5	2037	3.6
15	SU	0238	1.1	0926	3.6	1459	1.2	2126	3.9
16	M	0325	0.7	1010	3.8	1541	0.9	2209	4.1
17	TU	0406	0.4	1049	4.0	1619	0.6	2249	4.4
18	W ○	0444	0.1	1127	4.1	1657	0.4	2328	4.5
19	TH	0524	0.0	1204	4.2	1735	0.3		
20	F	0008	4.5	0605	0.1	1244	4.1	1817	0.3
21	SA	0052	4.4	0648	0.3	1326	4.1	1903	0.5
22	SU	0139	4.3	0734	0.5	1413	3.9	1954	0.7
23	M	0232	4.0	0826	0.9	1504	3.8	2052	1.0
24	TU ☾	0332	3.7	0925	1.2	1605	3.6	2159	1.2
25	W	0449	3.5	1032	1.5	1722	3.5	2315	1.4
26	TH	0618	3.3	1153	1.7	1845	3.4		
27	F	0050	1.4	0747	3.3	1327	1.7	2003	3.6
28	SA	0212	1.3	0901	3.4	1433	1.6	2108	3.7
29	SU	0306	1.1	0954	3.6	1519	1.4	2158	3.9
30	M	0348	0.9	1034	3.7	1557	1.2	2235	4.0

OCTOBER

Date	Day	Time	m	Time	m	Time	m	Time	m
1	TU	0422	0.8	1104	3.7	1629	1.0	2305	4.0
2	W ●	0453	0.7	1127	3.7	1659	0.9	2330	4.0
3	TH	0521	0.7	1149	3.8	1726	0.9	2355	4.0
4	F	0546	0.7	1212	3.8	1751	0.9		
5	SA	0023	3.9	0611	0.8	1240	3.8	1818	0.9
6	SU	0055	3.9	0638	0.9	1314	3.8	1849	1.0
7	M	0133	3.8	0712	1.0	1353	3.7	1927	1.1
8	TU	0215	3.6	0752	1.2	1436	3.6	2010	1.2
9	W	0302	3.5	0839	1.4	1524	3.5	2103	1.4
10	TH ☽	0359	3.3	0940	1.6	1622	3.4	2214	1.5
11	F	0516	3.1	1104	1.8	1735	3.3	2347	1.5
12	SA	0650	3.2	1230	1.7	1857	3.4		
13	SU	0109	1.3	0805	3.4	1339	1.5	2004	3.6
14	M	0212	1.0	0900	3.7	1432	1.2	2057	3.9
15	TU	0300	0.6	0945	3.9	1515	0.9	2143	4.2
16	W	0343	0.3	1024	4.1	1556	0.6	2225	4.4
17	TH ○	0422	0.2	1103	4.2	1635	0.4	2307	4.5
18	F	0502	0.1	1141	4.2	1716	0.3	2350	4.5
19	SA	0542	0.2	1221	4.2	1759	0.4		
20	SU	0035	4.3	0625	0.4	1304	4.1	1846	0.5
21	M	0124	4.2	0711	0.7	1351	4.0	1939	0.7
22	TU	0218	3.9	0802	1.1	1443	3.9	2037	0.9
23	W	0320	3.6	0900	1.4	1544	3.7	2142	1.2
24	TH ☾	0435	3.4	1006	1.6	1657	3.6	2254	1.3
25	F	0556	3.3	1121	1.8	1814	3.5		
26	SA	0018	1.4	0719	3.3	1247	1.8	1928	3.6
27	SU	0135	1.3	0829	3.4	1356	1.6	2032	3.7
28	M	0232	1.1	0920	3.6	1446	1.4	2122	3.8
29	TU	0315	1.0	0959	3.7	1527	1.2	2202	3.9
30	W	0350	0.9	1029	3.7	1601	1.1	2235	3.9
31	TH	0421	0.8	1056	3.8	1632	1.0	2305	3.9

NOVEMBER

Date	Day	Time	m	Time	m	Time	m	Time	m
1	F ●	0450	0.8	1121	3.8	1701	1.0	2333	3.9
2	SA	0515	0.9	1146	3.9	1727	1.0		
3	SU	0001	3.8	0541	0.9	1214	3.9	1756	1.0
4	M	0035	3.8	0611	1.0	1250	3.9	1829	1.0
5	TU	0114	3.7	0647	1.1	1330	3.8	1910	1.1
6	W	0158	3.6	0730	1.3	1416	3.7	1957	1.2
7	TH	0249	3.5	0821	1.4	1506	3.7	2055	1.3
8	F	0348	3.4	0924	1.6	1603	3.6	2203	1.3
9	SA ☽	0458	3.3	1039	1.7	1709	3.5	2321	1.3
10	SU	0616	3.4	1156	1.6	1820	3.6		
11	M	0035	1.1	0726	3.5	1302	1.4	1926	3.8
12	TU	0138	0.9	0824	3.7	1358	1.2	2023	4.0
13	W	0231	0.7	0914	3.9	1448	1.0	2116	4.1
14	TH	0318	0.5	0959	4.0	1534	0.8	2205	4.3
15	F ○	0402	0.4	1041	4.1	1618	0.6	2252	4.3
16	SA	0444	0.4	1123	4.2	1703	0.5	2339	4.3
17	SU	0526	0.5	1205	4.2	1748	0.5		
18	M	0026	4.2	0609	0.7	1249	4.2	1837	0.6
19	TU	0115	4.0	0654	0.9	1336	4.1	1929	0.7
20	W	0209	3.8	0743	1.2	1427	4.0	2024	0.9
21	TH	0307	3.6	0837	1.4	1523	3.8	2123	1.1
22	F	0411	3.4	0937	1.6	1626	3.7	2225	1.2
23	SA ☾	0520	3.3	1043	1.7	1734	3.6	2332	1.3
24	SU	0629	3.3	1153	1.8	1840	3.6		
25	M	0041	1.3	0733	3.4	1303	1.7	1942	3.6
26	TU	0143	1.3	0827	3.5	1403	1.6	2036	3.6
27	W	0233	1.2	0911	3.6	1450	1.4	2122	3.7
28	TH	0314	1.1	0949	3.7	1530	1.3	2202	3.7
29	F	0348	1.1	1023	3.8	1605	1.2	2239	3.8
30	SA	0419	1.1	1054	3.9	1637	1.1	2312	3.8

DECEMBER

Date	Day	Time	m	Time	m	Time	m	Time	m
1	SU ●	0449	1.1	1123	3.9	1707	1.1	2345	3.8
2	M	0519	1.1	1155	3.9	1740	1.1		
3	TU	0021	3.8	0553	1.1	1232	4.0	1817	1.0
4	W	0101	3.7	0631	1.1	1314	4.0	1900	1.0
5	TH	0147	3.7	0716	1.2	1400	3.9	1949	1.0
6	F	0238	3.6	0807	1.3	1450	3.9	2044	1.0
7	SA	0333	3.6	0905	1.4	1544	3.8	2144	1.0
8	SU ☽	0434	3.5	1008	1.5	1642	3.8	2249	1.0
9	M	0538	3.5	1115	1.5	1744	3.8	2356	1.0
10	TU	0644	3.6	1221	1.4	1848	3.8		
11	W	0101	1.0	0747	3.7	1323	1.3	1952	3.9
12	TH	0201	0.9	0844	3.8	1422	1.1	2053	4.0
13	F	0257	0.8	0937	3.9	1517	1.0	2151	4.0
14	SA	0347	0.8	1026	4.0	1608	0.8	2245	4.1
15	SU ○	0434	0.8	1112	4.1	1657	0.7	2334	4.1
16	M	0517	0.8	1156	4.2	1744	0.7		
17	TU	0021	4.0	0559	0.9	1238	4.2	1831	0.7
18	W	0107	3.9	0641	1.0	1322	4.1	1917	0.7
19	TH	0154	3.8	0724	1.1	1407	4.0	2006	0.8
20	F	0243	3.6	0811	1.3	1456	3.9	2056	0.9
21	SA	0334	3.5	0903	1.4	1547	3.8	2147	1.1
22	SU ☾	0430	3.4	0958	1.5	1642	3.6	2241	1.2
23	M	0529	3.3	1058	1.7	1743	3.5	2339	1.4
24	TU	0630	3.3	1201	1.7	1844	3.4		
25	W	0038	1.4	0728	3.3	1304	1.7	1944	3.4
26	TH	0137	1.4	0820	3.4	1405	1.6	2039	3.4
27	F	0230	1.4	0908	3.6	1456	1.5	2129	3.5
28	SA	0315	1.3	0950	3.7	1539	1.4	2213	3.6
29	SU	0353	1.3	1028	3.8	1616	1.2	2253	3.7
30	M ●	0428	1.2	1103	3.9	1651	1.1	2331	3.7
31	TU	0502	1.1	1138	4.0	1726	1.0		

BELFAST
LAT 54°36′N
LONG 5°55′W

TIMES AND HEIGHTS OF HIGH AND LOW WATER (Heights in Metres)

TIME ZONE UT
For Summer Time (area enclosed in shaded box) add 1 hour

2024

SUNRISE AND SUNSET TIMES

BELFAST
At 54°36′N 5°55′ W

UT		Sunrise	Sunset
Jan	01	0846	1609
	15	0837	1630
Feb	01	0813	1703
	15	0745	1732
Mar	01	0713	1800
	15	0638	1828
BST (UT+1)			
Apr	01	0656	2000
	15	0621	2027
May	01	0545	2058
	15	0518	2123
Jun	01	0455	2149
	15	0447	2202
Jul	01	0452	2203
	15	0507	2151
Aug	01	0535	2124
	15	0600	2055
Sep	01	0631	2015
	15	0656	1940
Oct	01	0726	1900
	15	0753	1825
UT			
Nov	01	0726	1647
	15	0754	1622
Dec	01	0823	1603
	15	0840	1558

JANUARY

Day	Time	m	Day	Time	m
1 M	0217 0806 1431 2030	3.0 1.0 3.5 0.8	16 TU	0230 0820 1439 2100	3.3 0.7 3.7 0.4
2 TU	0301 0848 1512 2112	3.0 1.1 3.4 0.8	17 W	0324 0911 1532 2155	3.2 0.8 3.6 0.5
3 W	0348 0933 1557 2159	2.9 1.1 3.3 0.9	18 TH ☽	0419 1006 1628 2257	3.1 0.8 3.5 0.6
4 TH ☾	0439 1023 1647 2252	2.9 1.2 3.2 1.0	19 F	0518 1109 1734	3.1 1.0 3.3
5 F	0534 1122 1745 2354	2.8 1.3 3.1 1.0	20 SA	0005 0623 1222 1851	0.8 3.0 1.0 3.2
6 SA	0632 1233 1847	2.9 1.3 3.1	21 SU	0113 0731 1335 2006	0.9 3.0 1.0 3.1
7 SU	0103 0731 1344 1949	1.0 2.9 1.2 3.1	22 M	0215 0835 1442 2110	0.9 3.1 1.0 3.1
8 M	0203 0826 1441 2046	1.0 3.1 1.1 3.2	23 TU	0311 0931 1541 2204	0.9 3.3 0.8 3.2
9 TU	0255 0917 1531 2137	0.9 3.2 0.9 3.3	24 W	0359 1020 1629 2251	0.9 3.4 0.7 3.2
10 W	0341 1002 1617 2225	0.8 3.3 0.7 3.4	25 TH ○	0441 1104 1709 2333	0.9 3.5 0.7 3.1
11 TH ●	0426 1045 1702 2312	0.7 3.5 0.6 3.4	26 F	0519 1143 1744	0.8 3.6 0.6
12 F	0510 1128 1746 2359	0.7 3.6 0.4 3.4	27 SA	0009 0554 1218 1817	3.1 0.8 3.6 0.6
13 SA	0555 1213 1832	0.7 3.7 0.4	28 SU	0042 0628 1252 1849	3.0 0.8 3.6 0.6
14 SU	0047 0642 1259 1920	3.4 0.7 3.7 0.3	29 M	0114 0701 1326 1921	3.0 0.8 3.5 0.6
15 M	0138 0730 1348 2009	3.3 0.7 3.7 0.3	30 TU	0147 0735 1359 1955	3.0 0.8 3.5 0.6
			31 W	0221 0812 1433 [illegible]	3.0 0.8 3.4 0.6

FEBRUARY

Day	Time	m	Day	Time	m
1 TH	0257 0852 1509 2113	3.0 0.9 3.3 0.7	16 F ☽	0344 0933 1602 2220	3.2 0.7 3.4 0.7
2 F ☾	0336 0935 1552 2158	2.9 1.0 3.2 0.9	17 SA	0437 1035 1703 2335	3.0 0.9 3.1 0.9
3 SA	0425 1026 1647 2253	2.9 1.1 3.0 1.0	18 SU	0540 1158 1823	2.9 1.0 2.9
4 SU	0528 1131 1756	2.8 1.3 2.9	19 M	0049 0700 1318 1955	1.1 2.9 1.0 2.8
5 M	0004 0637 1308 1909	1.1 2.8 1.3 2.9	20 TU	0158 0817 1432 2102	1.1 3.0 0.9 2.9
6 TU	0134 0745 1421 2018	1.1 2.9 1.1 3.0	21 W	0300 0916 1536 2155	1.0 3.2 0.8 3.0
7 W	0238 0849 1517 2120	1.0 3.0 0.8 3.1	22 TH	0350 1005 1622 2238	0.9 3.3 0.6 3.0
8 TH	0329 0943 1606 2212	0.8 3.2 0.6 3.2	23 F	0429 1047 1655 2316	0.8 3.4 0.6 3.0
9 F ●	0415 1029 1650 2259	0.7 3.4 0.3 3.3	24 SA ○	0501 1124 1723 2350	0.7 3.5 0.5 3.0
10 SA	0458 1113 1733 2344	0.6 3.6 0.2 3.4	25 SU	0531 1158 1750	0.7 3.5 0.5
11 SU	0541 1158 1816	0.5 3.7 0.1	26 M	0019 0602 1228 1820	3.0 0.7 3.4 0.5
12 M	0030 0624 1243 1900	3.4 0.4 3.8 0.1	27 TU	0045 0633 1255 1850	3.0 0.6 3.4 0.5
13 TU	0117 0708 1331 1944	3.3 0.4 3.8 0.1	28 W	0109 0705 1323 1921	3.0 0.6 3.4 0.5
14 W	0205 0754 1419 2031	3.3 0.4 3.7 0.3	29 TH	0135 0738 1354 1955	3.1 0.6 3.4 0.5
15 TH	0254 0841 1509 2121	3.2 0.5 3.6 0.5			

MARCH

Day	Time	m	Day	Time	m
1 F	0207 0815 1430 2033	3.1 0.7 3.3 0.6	16 SA	0312 0905 1540 2146	3.2 0.6 3.2 0.9
2 SA	0245 0855 1514 2116	3.0 0.8 3.2 0.8	17 SU ☽	0403 1008 1638 2303	3.1 0.8 3.0 1.1
3 SU ☾	0329 0942 1608 2208	2.9 1.0 3.0 1.0	18 M	0502 1135 1800	3.0 1.0 2.7
4 M	0427 1045 1720 2317	2.8 1.1 2.8 1.2	19 TU	0022 0622 1257 1942	1.2 2.9 1.0 2.7
5 TU	0548 1242 1839	2.7 1.2 2.8	20 W	0134 0752 1414 2047	1.2 2.9 0.9 2.8
6 W	0111 0708 1403 1956	1.2 2.7 0.9 2.8	21 TH	0240 0853 1517 2136	1.1 3.1 0.7 2.9
7 TH	0222 0822 1500 2104	1.0 2.9 0.6 3.0	22 F	0331 0941 1558 2216	0.9 3.2 0.6 3.0
8 F	0315 0922 1549 2156	0.8 3.2 0.3 3.2	23 SA	0408 1021 1627 2250	0.8 3.3 0.5 3.0
9 SA	0400 1010 1632 2240	0.6 3.4 0.1 3.3	24 SU	0437 1057 1652 2321	0.7 3.4 0.5 3.0
10 SU ●	0441 1054 1713 2323	0.4 3.6 0.0 3.4	25 M ○	0505 1129 1719 2349	0.6 3.3 0.5 3.0
11 M	0521 1138 1753	0.3 3.7 0.0	26 TU	0534 1156 1748	0.6 3.3 0.5
12 TU	0007 0602 1223 1834	3.4 0.3 3.8 0.0	27 W	0010 0605 1219 1818	3.1 0.6 3.3 0.5
13 W	0052 0643 1310 1916	3.4 0.3 3.7 0.1	28 TH	0030 0636 1247 1849	3.1 0.6 3.3 0.5
14 TH	0138 0727 1358 2001	3.4 0.3 3.6 0.3	29 F	0058 0709 1322 1923	3.2 0.6 3.3 0.6
15 F	0225 0813 1448 2049	3.3 0.4 3.5 0.6	30 SA	0133 0744 1402 2002	3.2 0.6 3.2 0.7
			31 SU	0213 0825 1449 2046	3.1 0.7 3.1 0.8

APRIL

Day	Time	m	Day	Time	m
1 M	0258 0914 1548 2140	3.0 0.9 2.9 1.0	16 TU	0430 1109 1732 2347	3.1 0.9 2.6 1.3
2 TU ☾	0356 1020 1701 2251	2.9 1.0 2.8 1.2	17 W	0537 1225 1914	2.9 0.9 2.6
3 W	0515 1222 1819	2.8 1.0 2.7	18 TH	0056 0710 1335 2018	1.3 2.9 0.8 2.7
4 TH	0043 0639 1341 1938	1.2 2.8 0.8 2.8	19 F	0201 0817 1434 2105	1.2 3.0 0.7 2.8
5 F	0158 0757 1437 2044	1.0 3.0 0.5 3.0	20 SA	0254 0907 1516 2143	1.0 3.1 0.6 2.9
6 SA	0252 0858 1525 2133	0.8 3.2 0.2 3.2	21 SU	0334 0947 1548 2216	0.9 3.2 0.6 3.0
7 SU	0338 0947 1608 2217	0.6 3.5 0.0 3.4	22 M	0406 1022 1617 2246	0.8 3.3 0.5 3.1
8 M ●	0419 1031 1648 2259	0.4 3.6 0.0 3.4	23 TU ○	0436 1053 1646 2313	0.7 3.3 0.5 3.1
9 TU	0458 1116 1727 2343	0.3 3.7 0.0 3.5	24 W	0507 1121 1717 2336	0.6 3.3 0.6 3.2
10 W	0538 1202 1807	0.3 3.7 0.1	25 TH	0538 1147 1748	0.6 3.3 0.6
11 TH	0027 0620 1249 1850	3.5 0.3 3.6 0.3	26 F	0000 0612 1219 1822	3.2 0.6 3.3 0.6
12 F	0113 0705 1338 1935	3.4 0.3 3.5 0.5	27 SA	0032 0646 1259 1858	3.3 0.6 3.3 0.7
13 SA	0159 0752 1428 2024	3.4 0.4 3.3 0.8	28 SU	0111 0724 1344 1940	3.3 0.6 3.2 0.8
14 SU	0246 0845 1520 2121	3.3 0.6 3.1 1.0	29 M	0155 0809 1437 2029	3.2 0.7 3.1 0.9
15 M ☽	0335 0949 1617 2232	3.2 0.8 2.8 1.2	30 TU	0245 0904 1539 2127	3.1 0.8 2.9 1.1

MAY

Day	Time	m	Day	Time	m
1 W ☾	0344 1016 1648 2239	3.0 0.9 2.8 1.2	16 TH	0457 1143 1810	3.1 0.9 2.6
2 TH	0454 1153 1802	3.0 0.8 2.8	17 F	0008 0603 1246 1926	1.3 3.0 0.9 2.7
3 F	0005 0613 1309 1916	1.2 3.0 0.6 2.9	18 SA	0109 0717 1341 2016	1.2 3.0 0.8 2.8
4 SA	0121 0730 1406 2017	1.0 3.1 0.4 3.1	19 SU	0205 0816 1428 2057	1.1 3.0 0.7 2.9
5 SU	0219 0832 1455 2107	0.8 3.3 0.2 3.3	20 M	0251 0902 1506 2132	1.0 3.1 0.7 3.0
6 M	0309 0923 1540 2152	0.6 3.5 0.2 3.4	21 TU	0331 0941 1541 2206	0.9 3.2 0.6 3.1
7 TU	0354 1010 1621 2236	0.5 3.6 0.2 3.5	22 W	0406 1017 1614 2238	0.8 3.3 0.6 3.2
8 W ●	0437 1056 1703 2321	0.4 3.6 0.3 3.5	23 TH ○	0441 1050 1648 2308	0.7 3.3 0.6 3.3
9 TH	0520 1143 1745	0.4 3.6 0.4	24 F	0517 1123 1724 2338	0.7 3.3 0.7 3.3
10 F	0005 0604 1230 1830	3.5 0.4 3.5 0.6	25 SA	0554 1201 1802	0.6 3.3 0.7
11 SA	0051 0650 1319 1917	3.5 0.4 3.3 0.7	26 SU	0015 0634 1244 1844	3.4 0.6 3.2 0.8
12 SU	0136 0738 1408 2006	3.5 0.5 3.2 0.9	27 M	0058 0717 1334 1931	3.4 0.6 3.2 0.8
13 M	0222 0830 1459 2100	3.4 0.6 3.0 1.0	28 TU	0145 0806 1429 2024	3.4 0.6 3.1 0.9
14 TU	0309 0929 1552 2200	3.3 0.7 2.8 1.2	29 W	0236 0904 1529 2122	3.3 0.6 3.0 1.0
15 W ☽	0400 1035 1653 2305	3.2 0.8 2.7 1.3	30 TH ☾	0332 1009 1633 2225	3.3 0.6 2.9 1.0
			31 F	0434 1121 1741 2332	3.2 0.6 2.9 1.0

JUNE

Day	Time	m	Day	Time	m
1 SA	0544 1230 1847	3.2 0.5 3.0	16 SU	0008 0613 1245 1902	1.2 3.0 0.9 2.8
2 SU	0039 0700 1331 1947	0.9 3.2 0.5 3.1	17 M	0111 0714 1338 1956	1.2 3.0 0.9 2.9
3 M	0143 0806 1424 2040	0.8 3.3 0.4 3.2	18 TU	0207 0811 1424 2044	1.1 3.0 0.8 3.0
4 TU	0241 0902 1513 2129	0.7 3.4 0.4 3.3	19 W	0255 0901 1506 2128	1.0 3.1 0.8 3.1
5 W	0333 0953 1600 2216	0.6 3.5 0.4 3.4	20 TH	0339 0946 1546 2208	0.9 3.2 0.7 3.2
6 TH ●	0422 1042 1645 2303	0.6 3.5 0.5 3.5	21 F	0420 1027 1626 2245	0.8 3.3 0.7 3.3
7 F	0509 1130 1730 2349	0.5 3.4 0.6 3.5	22 SA ○	0501 1107 1707 2322	0.7 3.3 0.7 3.4
8 SA	0555 1217 1815	0.5 3.3 0.8	23 SU	0543 1148 1749	0.6 3.3 0.7
9 SU	0033 0641 1303 1901	3.6 0.5 3.2 0.9	24 M	0001 0626 1233 1835	3.4 0.5 3.2 0.8
10 M	0117 0726 1349 1947	3.6 0.6 3.1 0.9	25 TU	0046 0711 1323 1923	3.5 0.5 3.2 0.8
11 TU	0200 0811 1435 2033	3.5 0.6 3.0 1.0	26 W	0133 0800 1416 2014	3.5 0.4 3.1 0.8
12 W	0244 0858 1523 2120	3.4 0.7 2.9 1.1	27 TH	0223 0852 1512 2107	3.5 0.4 3.1 0.8
13 TH	0330 0948 1613 2210	3.3 0.8 2.8 1.1	28 F ☾	0315 0947 1611 2202	3.5 0.4 3.1 0.8
14 F ☽	0420 1043 1707 2306	3.2 0.9 2.7 1.2	29 SA	0411 1048 1711 2301	3.4 0.5 3.0 0.9
15 SA	0514 1145 1804	3.1 0.9 2.7	30 SU	0515 1154 1813	3.3 0.6 3.0

BELFAST
LAT 54°36′N
LONG 5°55′W

TIMES AND HEIGHTS OF HIGH AND LOW WATER (Heights in Metres)

TIME ZONE UT
For Summer Time (area enclosed in shaded box) add 1 hour

2024

JULY

Day	Time	m	Time	m	Time	m	Time	m
1 M	0006	0.9	0628	3.2	1259	0.6	1916	3.1
2 TU	0115	0.9	0742	3.2	1400	0.6	2016	3.2
3 W	0221	0.8	0847	3.2	1455	0.7	2111	3.3
4 TH	0321	0.8	0944	3.3	1546	0.7	2203	3.4
5 F ●	0414	0.7	1035	3.3	1633	0.7	2251	3.5
6 SA	0503	0.6	1123	3.2	1718	0.8	2336	3.5
7 SU	0547	0.6	1207	3.1	1801	0.8		
8 M	0017	3.6	0628	0.5	1247	3.1	1842	0.9
9 TU	0057	3.6	0706	0.6	1326	3.0	1920	0.9
10 W	0137	3.5	0742	0.6	1406	2.9	1958	0.9
11 TH	0216	3.5	0818	0.6	1448	2.9	2036	0.9
12 F	0257	3.4	0856	0.7	1533	2.9	2117	1.0
13 SA ☽	0340	3.3	0939	0.8	1621	2.9	2203	1.1
14 SU	0427	3.1	1027	0.9	1711	2.8	2256	1.2
15 M	0520	3.0	1125	1.0	1806	2.8		
16 TU	0003	1.2	0621	2.9	1238	1.0	1903	2.9
17 W	0122	1.2	0724	2.9	1345	1.0	2000	3.0
18 TH	0225	1.1	0826	3.0	1439	0.9	2054	3.1
19 F	0317	0.9	0921	3.1	1526	0.8	2141	3.2
20 SA	0404	0.7	1009	3.2	1610	0.8	2224	3.3
21 SU O	0447	0.6	1052	3.3	1653	0.7	2304	3.4
22 M	0530	0.4	1135	3.3	1735	0.7	2346	3.5
23 TU	0612	0.3	1219	3.3	1820	0.6		
24 W	0030	3.6	0656	0.2	1306	3.3	1905	0.6
25 TH	0116	3.6	0740	0.2	1356	3.2	1952	0.6
26 F	0205	3.6	0827	0.3	1447	3.2	2041	0.6
27 SA	0255	3.6	0918	0.4	1541	3.2	2132	0.7
28 SU ☾	0348	3.5	1014	0.5	1637	3.1	2229	0.8
29 M	0447	3.3	1122	0.7	1738	3.1	2339	0.9
30 TU	0559	3.1	1235	0.9	1846	3.0		
31 W	0057	1.0	0726	3.0	1343	0.9	1957	3.1

AUGUST

Day	Time	m	Time	m	Time	m	Time	m
1 TH	0211	0.9	0841	3.0	1444	0.9	2100	3.2
2 F	0317	0.8	0940	3.1	1537	0.9	2154	3.4
3 SA	0412	0.7	1030	3.1	1624	0.9	2240	3.5
4 SU ●	0457	0.6	1114	3.1	1705	0.8	2322	3.5
5 M	0534	0.6	1153	3.1	1741	0.8		
6 TU	0000	3.5	0607	0.6	1227	3.0	1815	0.8
7 W	0035	3.5	0637	0.6	1300	3.0	1847	0.8
8 TH	0109	3.5	0706	0.6	1333	3.0	1920	0.8
9 F	0144	3.4	0738	0.6	1408	3.0	1955	0.8
10 SA	0219	3.4	0812	0.6	1446	3.0	2034	0.9
11 SU	0255	3.3	0850	0.7	1527	3.0	2116	1.0
12 M ☽	0335	3.2	0933	0.9	1614	2.9	2204	1.1
13 TU	0426	3.0	1024	1.0	1710	2.9	2304	1.3
14 W	0531	2.9	1131	1.2	1813	2.8		
15 TH	0042	1.3	0643	2.8	1311	1.2	1918	2.9
16 F	0202	1.1	0754	2.9	1418	1.1	2021	3.0
17 SA	0259	0.9	0900	3.0	1509	0.9	2116	3.2
18 SU	0347	0.6	0952	3.2	1554	0.8	2202	3.4
19 M O	0430	0.4	1035	3.3	1635	0.6	2244	3.5
20 TU	0511	0.2	1116	3.4	1716	0.6	2326	3.7
21 W	0551	0.1	1159	3.4	1756	0.5		
22 TH	0010	3.7	0631	0.1	1243	3.4	1839	0.5
23 F	0056	3.8	0713	0.1	1330	3.4	1924	0.5
24 SA	0144	3.7	0757	0.3	1419	3.3	2011	0.6
25 SU	0234	3.6	0845	0.5	1511	3.3	2101	0.7
26 M ☾	0327	3.4	0939	0.7	1605	3.2	2200	0.8
27 TU	0426	3.2	1050	1.0	1706	3.1	2319	1.0
28 W	0539	3.0	1216	1.1	1819	3.0		
29 TH	0047	1.1	0720	2.8	1330	1.2	1942	3.1
30 F	0207	1.0	0837	2.9	1436	1.1	2047	3.2
31 SA	0317	0.8	0933	3.0	1531	1.0	2139	3.4

SEPTEMBER

Day	Time	m	Time	m	Time	m	Time	m
1 SU	0408	0.6	1018	3.1	1614	0.9	2223	3.5
2 M	0445	0.6	1057	3.1	1647	0.9	2302	3.5
3 TU ●	0512	0.6	1131	3.1	1716	0.8	2337	3.5
4 W	0536	0.6	1202	3.1	1744	0.8		
5 TH	0007	3.5	0603	0.6	1228	3.1	1814	0.8
6 F	0036	3.4	0630	0.6	1254	3.1	1845	0.8
7 SA	0105	3.4	0700	0.6	1322	3.1	1919	0.8
8 SU	0137	3.4	0733	0.7	1354	3.2	1955	0.8
9 M	0212	3.3	0810	0.7	1430	3.1	2035	0.9
10 TU	0252	3.2	0851	0.9	1514	3.1	2122	1.1
11 W ☽	0344	3.0	0940	1.1	1611	2.9	2221	1.3
12 TH	0454	2.9	1045	1.3	1726	2.8		
13 F	0007	1.3	0612	2.8	1236	1.4	1841	2.9
14 SA	0140	1.1	0729	2.8	1357	1.2	1951	3.0
15 SU	0237	0.8	0839	3.0	1450	1.0	2051	3.3
16 M	0325	0.5	0931	3.2	1534	0.8	2138	3.5
17 TU	0407	0.3	1013	3.4	1613	0.6	2221	3.7
18 W O	0446	0.1	1053	3.5	1651	0.5	2304	3.8
19 TH	0524	0.1	1135	3.5	1730	0.4	2349	3.8
20 F	0602	0.1	1219	3.5	1812	0.4		
21 SA	0035	3.8	0644	0.2	1305	3.5	1857	0.5
22 SU	0124	3.7	0728	0.4	1353	3.5	1944	0.6
23 M	0215	3.6	0816	0.7	1444	3.4	2036	0.7
24 TU ☾	0310	3.4	0910	1.0	1538	3.3	2138	0.9
25 W	0410	3.1	1024	1.2	1638	3.2	2304	1.1
26 TH	0527	2.8	1154	1.4	1752	3.1		
27 F	0032	1.1	0712	2.8	1310	1.4	1920	3.1
28 SA	0154	1.0	0823	2.9	1419	1.2	2025	3.2
29 SU	0300	0.8	0915	3.0	1513	1.1	2115	3.4
30 M	0346	0.7	0956	3.1	1553	1.0	2158	3.5

OCTOBER

Day	Time	m	Time	m	Time	m	Time	m
1 TU	0418	0.6	1031	3.1	1622	0.9	2235	3.5
2 W ●	0439	0.6	1103	3.2	1648	0.9	2308	3.5
3 TH	0502	0.7	1130	3.2	1715	0.8	2337	3.5
4 F	0529	0.7	1154	3.2	1744	0.8		
5 SA	0002	3.4	0557	0.7	1216	3.3	1815	0.8
6 SU	0029	3.4	0627	0.7	1243	3.3	1848	0.8
7 M	0102	3.4	0700	0.8	1316	3.3	1924	0.9
8 TU	0141	3.3	0737	0.8	1355	3.3	2005	0.9
9 W	0226	3.2	0820	1.0	1439	3.2	2053	1.1
10 TH ☽	0321	3.0	0911	1.2	1535	3.1	2155	1.2
11 F	0431	2.9	1018	1.4	1649	3.0	2334	1.2
12 SA	0548	2.8	1153	1.4	1807	3.0		
13 SU	0110	1.0	0705	2.9	1325	1.3	1922	3.1
14 M	0208	0.7	0813	3.1	1421	1.0	2024	3.4
15 TU	0256	0.5	0904	3.3	1506	0.8	2114	3.6
16 W	0338	0.3	0948	3.5	1546	0.6	2159	3.8
17 TH O	0417	0.2	1029	3.6	1625	0.5	2244	3.9
18 F	0455	0.2	1112	3.7	1706	0.5	2330	3.9
19 SA	0536	0.3	1156	3.7	1749	0.5		
20 SU	0017	3.8	0619	0.5	1242	3.7	1836	0.5
21 M	0108	3.7	0705	0.7	1331	3.6	1925	0.6
22 TU	0201	3.5	0754	0.9	1422	3.5	2019	0.8
23 W	0256	3.3	0851	1.2	1514	3.4	2123	0.9
24 TH ☾	0356	3.0	1002	1.4	1611	3.3	2243	1.0
25 F	0510	2.8	1122	1.5	1718	3.2		
26 SA	0001	1.1	0645	2.8	1234	1.5	1841	3.1
27 SU	0115	1.0	0754	2.8	1341	1.4	1950	3.2
28 M	0218	0.9	0844	3.0	1436	1.2	2043	3.3
29 TU	0303	0.8	0924	3.1	1518	1.1	2126	3.4
30 W	0335	0.8	0958	3.2	1550	1.0	2203	3.4
31 TH	0401	0.8	1029	3.3	1619	0.9	2236	3.5

Day	Time	m	Time	m	Time	m	Time	m
1 F ●	0429	0.8	1058	3.3	1649	0.9	2306	3.4
2 SA	0458	0.8	1124	3.4	1720	0.9	2334	3.4
3 SU	0529	0.8	1149	3.4	1753	0.9		
4 M	0003	3.4	0601	0.8	1218	3.5	1828	0.9
5 TU	0040	3.4	0636	0.9	1254	3.5	1905	0.9
6 W	0123	3.3	0716	1.0	1336	3.4	1948	0.9
7 TH	0212	3.2	0802	1.1	1423	3.3	2039	1.0
8 F	0308	3.1	0857	1.2	1518	3.2	2144	1.1
9 SA ☽	0414	3.0	1003	1.3	1622	3.2	2305	1.0
10 SU	0525	2.9	1120	1.4	1735	3.1		
11 M	0027	0.9	0638	3.0	1237	1.2	1850	3.3
12 TU	0129	0.7	0743	3.2	1340	1.1	1955	3.4
13 W	0221	0.5	0835	3.4	1433	0.9	2050	3.6
14 TH	0307	0.4	0922	3.5	1520	0.7	2139	3.7
15 F O	0350	0.4	1007	3.6	1604	0.6	2227	3.8
16 SA	0432	0.4	1052	3.7	1649	0.6	2315	3.7
17 SU	0516	0.6	1138	3.7	1735	0.5		
18 M	0004	3.7	0602	0.7	1225	3.7	1823	0.6
19 TU	0055	3.5	0649	0.9	1314	3.7	1914	0.6
20 W	0147	3.4	0740	1.0	1402	3.7	2007	0.7
21 TH	0240	3.2	0834	1.2	1452	3.6	2106	0.9
22 F	0335	3.0	0934	1.3	1543	3.4	2211	1.0
23 SA ☾	0435	2.9	1039	1.4	1640	3.3	2317	1.0
24 SU	0547	2.8	1145	1.4	1743	3.2		
25 M	0021	1.0	0701	2.8	1247	1.4	1854	3.2
26 TU	0119	1.0	0756	2.9	1345	1.3	1955	3.2
27 W	0209	1.0	0841	3.0	1434	1.2	2044	3.3
28 TH	0250	0.9	0919	3.2	1516	1.1	2127	3.3
29 F	0325	0.9	0954	3.3	1552	1.0	2205	3.4
30 SA	0359	0.9	1028	3.4	1627	0.9	2241	3.4

Day	Time	m	Time	m	Time	m	Time	m
1 SU ●	0433	0.9	1101	3.5	1702	0.9	2315	3.4
2 M	0508	0.9	1131	3.5	1739	0.8	2348	3.4
3 TU	0545	0.9	1203	3.5	1817	0.8		
4 W	0026	3.3	0624	0.9	1240	3.5	1859	0.8
5 TH	0110	3.3	0707	1.0	1323	3.5	1944	0.8
6 F	0200	3.2	0755	1.0	1410	3.5	2035	0.8
7 SA	0254	3.1	0848	1.1	1501	3.4	2132	0.8
8 SU ☽	0352	3.1	0946	1.1	1558	3.4	2235	0.8
9 M	0456	3.0	1048	1.2	1701	3.3	2342	0.8
10 TU	0603	3.1	1155	1.1	1813	3.3		
11 W	0048	0.7	0708	3.2	1301	1.1	1925	3.4
12 TH	0147	0.7	0807	3.3	1404	1.0	2028	3.5
13 F	0241	0.6	0900	3.4	1501	0.8	2124	3.5
14 SA	0331	0.6	0950	3.5	1553	0.7	2216	3.6
15 SU O	0418	0.7	1039	3.6	1642	0.6	2307	3.5
16 M	0505	0.7	1127	3.7	1730	0.6	2357	3.5
17 TU	0552	0.8	1214	3.7	1818	0.6		
18 W	0045	3.3	0639	0.9	1259	3.7	1905	0.6
19 TH	0133	3.2	0725	1.0	1344	3.7	1952	0.7
20 F	0220	3.1	0811	1.1	1428	3.6	2038	0.7
21 SA	0306	3.0	0857	1.1	1514	3.5	2126	0.8
22 SU ☾	0353	2.9	0945	1.2	1602	3.4	2218	0.9
23 M	0444	2.9	1039	1.3	1654	3.2	2316	1.0
24 TU	0539	2.8	1143	1.3	1751	3.1		
25 W	0019	1.1	0638	2.9	1250	1.3	1852	3.1
26 TH	0117	1.1	0738	2.9	1350	1.3	1954	3.1
27 F	0209	1.1	0833	3.1	1442	1.2	2049	3.2
28 SA	0254	1.0	0921	3.2	1528	1.0	2138	3.2
29 SU	0335	0.9	1005	3.3	1609	0.9	2221	3.3
30 M ●	0415	0.9	1043	3.4	1649	0.8	2301	3.3
31 TU	0454	0.9	1118	3.5	1728	0.7	2338	3.3

GALWAY
LAT 53°16′N
LONG 9°03′W

TIMES AND HEIGHTS OF HIGH AND LOW WATER (Heights in Metres)

TIME ZONE UT
For Summer Time (area enclosed in shaded box) add 1 hour

2024

SUNRISE AND SUNSET TIMES

GALWAY
At 53°16′N 9°03′W

UT		Sunrise	Sunset
Jan	01	0851	1629
	15	0843	1649
Feb	01	0820	1720
	15	0754	1747
Mar	01	0723	1814
	15	0651	1841
BST (UT+1)			
Apr	01	0710	2012
	15	0637	2037
May	01	0602	2106
	15	0537	2129
Jun	01	0515	2154
	15	0508	2206
Jul	01	0513	2207
	15	0528	2156
Aug	01	0553	2131
	15	0616	2104
Sep	01	0646	2025
	15	0710	1952
Oct	01	0738	1913
	15	0803	1840
UT			
Nov	01	0735	1704
	15	0801	1640
Dec	01	0828	1622
	15	0845	1618

JANUARY

Date	Day	Time m	Time m	Time m	Time m
1	M	0146 1.7	0819 4.6	1415 1.5	2052 4.4
2	TU	0225 1.9	0901 4.4	1457 1.7	2135 4.2
3	W	0308 2.1	0946 4.2	1542 1.9	2223 4.1
4	TH ☾	0359 2.2	1036 4.1	1637 2.0	2315 4.0
5	F	0508 2.3	1131 4.0	1753 2.1	
6	SA	0012 4.0	0639 2.3	1233 4.0	1910 2.0
7	SU	0113 4.1	0742 2.1	1341 4.1	2007 1.9
8	M	0213 4.3	0834 1.9	1442 4.3	2055 1.7
9	TU	0304 4.6	0921 1.6	1534 4.6	2139 1.5
10	W	0352 4.9	1005 1.3	1622 4.8	2222 1.3
11	TH ●	0439 5.1	1048 1.0	1710 5.0	2304 1.1
12	F	0525 5.3	1131 0.8	1757 5.1	2347 1.0
13	SA	0611 5.4	1215 0.6	1843 5.2	
14	SU	0031 0.9	0659 5.5	1258 0.6	1931 5.1
15	M	0116 1.0	0746 5.4	1344 0.7	2018 5.0
16	TU	0203 1.1	0834 5.2	1432 0.9	2108 4.8
17	W	0254 1.3	0926 4.9	1523 1.2	2201 4.5
18	TH ☽	0351 1.6	1022 4.6	1621 1.5	2300 4.3
19	F	0457 1.8	1128 4.3	1728 1.8	
20	SA	0011 4.2	0616 1.9	1248 4.1	1850 1.9
21	SU	0129 4.2	0741 1.9	1404 4.2	2008 2.0
22	M	0234 4.3	0851 1.7	1505 4.3	2107 1.8
23	TU	0328 4.5	0945 1.5	1557 4.5	2154 1.7
24	W	0414 4.7	1027 1.3	1641 4.7	2231 1.5
25	TH ○	0455 4.9	1101 1.2	1722 4.8	2304 1.4
26	F	0533 5.0	1131 1.1	1800 4.9	2337 1.3
27	SA	0610 5.1	1201 1.0	1835 4.9	
28	SU	0010 1.2	0645 5.0	1233 1.0	1911 4.8
29	M	0043 1.3	0719 4.9	1306 1.1	1944 4.7
30	TU	0116 1.4	0753 4.8	1339 1.2	2018 4.6
31	W	0149 1.5	0826 4.6	1413 1.4	[illegible]

FEBRUARY

Date	Day	Time m	Time m	Time m	Time m
1	TH	0226 1.7	0903 4.4	1450 1.6	2135 4.2
2	F ☾	0307 1.9	0947 4.2	1533 1.8	2223 4.1
3	SA	0355 2.1	1042 4.0	1624 2.1	2319 4.0
4	SU	0453 2.3	1145 3.9	1727 2.2	
5	M	0022 4.0	0637 2.3	1256 3.9	1940 2.2
6	TU	0132 4.1	0817 2.0	1412 4.1	2043 1.9
7	W	0239 4.4	0911 1.6	1517 4.4	2132 1.6
8	TH	0335 4.8	0958 1.2	1610 4.8	2216 1.2
9	F ●	0425 5.2	1041 0.8	1657 5.1	2257 0.9
10	SA	0511 5.5	1121 0.5	1741 5.3	2337 0.7
11	SU	0556 5.7	1201 0.3	1825 5.4	
12	M	0016 0.5	0641 5.7	1240 0.3	1909 5.4
13	TU	0057 0.6	0725 5.6	1321 0.4	1953 5.2
14	W	0139 0.7	0810 5.4	1403 0.7	2037 5.0
15	TH	0225 1.0	0858 5.0	1449 1.1	2124 4.6
16	F ☽	0316 1.4	0949 4.6	1542 1.6	2216 4.3
17	SA	0421 1.8	1050 4.1	1651 2.0	2322 4.0
18	SU	0546 2.0	1224 3.9	1820 2.2	
19	M	0110 3.9	0720 2.1	1357 3.9	1949 2.2
20	TU	0227 4.1	0851 1.8	1501 4.1	2100 2.0
21	W	0321 4.3	0942 1.6	1549 4.3	2145 1.8
22	TH	0405 4.6	1018 1.3	1630 4.6	2218 1.5
23	F	0443 4.8	1045 1.1	1706 4.8	2247 1.3
24	SA ○	0518 5.0	1109 0.9	1740 4.9	2316 1.1
25	SU	0552 5.0	1136 0.8	1813 4.9	2346 1.0
26	M	0624 5.0	1205 0.8	1844 4.9	
27	TU	0016 1.0	0656 5.0	1235 0.8	1915 4.8
28	W	0047 1.0	0724 4.8	1306 1.0	1944 4.7
29	TH	0119 1.2	0752 4.7	1339 1.1	2014 4.5

MARCH

Date	Day	Time m	Time m	Time m	Time m
1	F	0154 1.3	0823 4.5	1415 1.4	2050 4.3
2	SA	0234 1.6	0905 4.2	1456 1.7	2136 4.1
3	SU ☾	0318 1.9	1001 4.0	1543 2.0	2235 3.9
4	M	0413 2.1	1110 3.8	1643 2.3	2344 3.8
5	TU	0527 2.2	1226 3.7	1927 2.3	
6	W	0101 3.9	0805 1.9	1355 4.0	2032 1.9
7	TH	0221 4.3	0859 1.4	1507 4.4	2120 1.5
8	F	0321 4.8	0944 0.9	1556 4.8	2201 1.0
9	SA	0409 5.2	1024 0.5	1639 5.2	2240 0.6
10	SU ●	0453 5.6	1102 0.2	1721 5.5	2317 0.3
11	M	0536 5.8	1139 0.0	1802 5.6	2355 0.2
12	TU	0618 5.8	1216 0.1	1843 5.5	
13	W	0033 0.3	0702 5.6	1253 0.3	1924 5.3
14	TH	0113 0.5	0746 5.3	1333 0.7	2007 5.0
15	F	0156 0.9	0831 4.9	1417 1.2	2051 4.6
16	SA	0246 1.3	0921 4.4	1509 1.7	2140 4.3
17	SU ☽	0354 1.8	1020 4.0	1624 2.1	2239 3.9
18	M	0525 2.0	1209 3.7	1758 2.3	
19	TU	0056 3.7	0654 2.0	1347 3.8	1921 2.3
20	W	0212 3.9	0841 1.8	1445 4.0	2037 2.0
21	TH	0303 4.2	0922 1.5	1530 4.3	2119 1.7
22	F	0345 4.5	0950 1.3	1608 4.5	2151 1.4
23	SA	0421 4.7	1014 1.0	1642 4.7	2220 1.2
24	SU	0455 4.8	1039 0.9	1713 4.8	2249 1.0
25	M ○	0527 4.9	1106 0.7	1744 4.9	2318 0.8
26	TU	0558 4.9	1135 0.7	1814 4.9	2348 0.8
27	W	0628 4.9	1204 0.8	1843 4.9	
28	TH	0019 0.9	0656 4.8	1235 0.9	1910 4.8
29	F	0052 1.0	0723 4.6	1309 1.1	1939 4.6
30	SA	0128 1.1	0754 4.5	1346 1.3	2014 4.4
31	SU	0208 1.4	0837 4.2	1427 1.6	[illegible]

APRIL

Date	Day	Time m	Time m	Time m	Time m
1	M	0253 1.7	0935 3.9	1515 2.0	2203 3.9
2	TU ☾	0350 1.9	1047 3.7	1619 2.2	2316 3.8
3	W	0509 2.1	1206 3.7	1907 2.2	
4	TH	0035 3.9	0745 1.7	1340 4.0	2012 1.8
5	F	0200 4.3	0838 1.2	1448 4.4	2058 1.3
6	SA	0300 4.7	0921 0.8	1534 4.9	2138 0.8
7	SU	0347 5.2	1000 0.4	1615 5.2	2216 0.5
8	M ●	0430 5.5	1036 0.1	1655 5.5	2253 0.2
9	TU	0513 5.6	1112 0.1	1735 5.5	2330 0.2
10	W	0556 5.6	1148 0.2	1816 5.5	
11	TH	0009 0.3	0639 5.4	1226 0.5	1858 5.3
12	F	0050 0.6	0724 5.1	1306 0.9	1940 5.0
13	SA	0134 0.9	0810 4.7	1351 1.4	2025 4.6
14	SU	0226 1.4	0900 4.3	1445 1.8	2114 4.2
15	M ☽	0337 1.7	0958 3.9	1607 2.2	2210 3.9
16	TU	0502 1.9	1140 3.6	1732 2.3	
17	W	0018 3.7	0617 1.9	1319 3.7	1844 2.3
18	TH	0141 3.8	0728 1.8	1415 3.9	1947 2.0
19	F	0233 4.0	0826 1.6	1500 4.2	2037 1.7
20	SA	0315 4.3	0903 1.3	1537 4.4	2115 1.4
21	SU	0351 4.5	0935 1.1	1610 4.6	2148 1.2
22	M	0424 4.6	1005 1.0	1640 4.7	2219 1.0
23	TU ○	0456 4.7	1035 0.9	1711 4.8	2250 0.9
24	W	0528 4.8	1104 0.8	1741 4.9	2320 0.8
25	TH	0559 4.8	1134 0.9	1811 4.8	2353 0.9
26	F	0630 4.7	1208 1.0	1841 4.8	
27	SA	0029 0.9	0702 4.6	1244 1.1	1914 4.7
28	SU	0108 1.1	0740 4.4	1324 1.4	1954 4.5
29	M	0151 1.3	0826 4.2	1408 1.6	2043 4.3
30	TU	0240 1.5	0925 4.0	1502 1.9	2145 4.1

MAY

Date	Day	Time m	Time m	Time m	Time m
1	W ☽	0341 1.7	1033 3.8	1613 2.1	2255 4.0
2	TH	0501 1.8	1148 3.8	1803 2.1	
3	F	0011 4.1	0706 1.5	1312 4.1	1939 1.7
4	SA	0131 4.3	0806 1.2	1417 4.5	2028 1.3
5	SU	0232 4.7	0851 0.8	1506 4.8	2110 0.9
6	M	0322 5.0	0931 0.5	1549 5.1	2150 0.6
7	TU	0407 5.3	1009 0.4	1630 5.3	2229 0.4
8	W ●	0452 5.3	1046 0.4	1711 5.4	2309 0.4
9	TH	0536 5.3	1124 0.6	1753 5.3	2350 0.5
10	F	0621 5.1	1205 0.9	1835 5.1	
11	SA	0033 0.8	0707 4.9	1247 1.2	1919 4.9
12	SU	0120 1.1	0754 4.6	1334 1.5	2005 4.6
13	M	0213 1.4	0843 4.3	1429 1.9	2053 4.3
14	TU	0317 1.6	0937 4.0	1541 2.1	2146 4.1
15	W ☾	0428 1.8	1042 3.8	1656 2.2	2248 3.8
16	TH	0534 1.9	1222 3.7	1801 2.2	
17	F	0040 3.8	0635 1.8	1328 3.9	1900 2.1
18	SA	0146 3.9	0729 1.7	1416 4.0	1952 1.8
19	SU	0232 4.0	0816 1.5	1455 4.2	2036 1.6
20	M	0311 4.2	0856 1.4	1529 4.4	2114 1.4
21	TU	0347 4.4	0931 1.2	1602 4.6	2149 1.2
22	W	0421 4.5	1004 1.1	1635 4.7	2222 1.1
23	TH ○	0456 4.6	1036 1.1	1708 4.8	2256 1.0
24	F	0532 4.7	1109 1.1	1743 4.9	2333 0.9
25	SA	0609 4.7	1147 1.1	1820 4.8	
26	SU	0012 1.0	0649 4.6	1227 1.2	1900 4.8
27	M	0056 1.0	0733 4.5	1312 1.4	1945 4.7
28	TU	0143 1.1	0822 4.3	1401 1.5	2036 4.5
29	W	0235 1.3	0917 4.2	1458 1.7	2133 4.4
30	TH ☽	0334 1.4	1018 4.1	1605 1.8	2236 4.3
31	F	0442 1.4	1126 4.1	1721 1.8	2345 4.3

JUNE

Date	Day	Time m	Time m	Time m	Time m
1	SA	0559 1.4	1238 4.2	1843 1.6	
2	SU	0058 4.4	0717 1.3	1343 4.4	1950 1.4
3	M	0203 4.6	0816 1.1	1437 4.7	2042 1.1
4	TU	0258 4.8	0903 1.0	1524 4.9	2128 0.9
5	W	0348 4.9	0946 0.9	1609 5.1	2212 0.8
6	TH ●	0436 5.0	1028 0.9	1653 5.1	2255 0.8
7	F	0523 5.0	1109 1.0	1737 5.1	2339 0.8
8	SA	0609 4.9	1151 1.2	1820 5.0	
9	SU	0022 0.9	0654 4.8	1234 1.4	1904 4.9
10	M	0107 1.1	0739 4.6	1318 1.6	1947 4.7
11	TU	0153 1.3	0824 4.4	1405 1.8	2032 4.5
12	W	0243 1.5	0911 4.2	1459 2.0	2120 4.3
13	TH	0337 1.7	1000 4.0	1601 2.1	2210 4.1
14	F ☾	0437 1.8	1054 3.9	1708 2.2	2305 3.9
15	SA	0538 1.9	1154 3.9	1810 2.1	
16	SU	0007 3.8	0637 1.9	1300 3.9	1906 2.0
17	M	0120 3.9	0730 1.8	1355 4.1	1956 1.9
18	TU	0217 4.0	0818 1.7	1440 4.3	2041 1.7
19	W	0303 4.2	0900 1.6	1521 4.5	2123 1.5
20	TH	0346 4.4	0939 1.4	1600 4.7	2202 1.3
21	F	0427 4.5	1016 1.3	1640 4.8	2241 1.1
22	SA ○	0510 4.7	1055 1.2	1722 4.9	2322 1.0
23	SU	0553 4.7	1136 1.2	1805 5.0	
24	M	0004 0.9	0637 4.8	1219 1.2	1849 5.0
25	TU	0048 0.8	0723 4.7	1305 1.2	1935 5.0
26	W	0135 0.8	0811 4.6	1353 1.3	2024 4.9
27	TH	0224 0.9	0901 4.5	1446 1.4	2117 4.7
28	F ☽	0317 1.1	0956 4.4	1544 1.5	2214 4.5
29	SA	0415 1.2	1056 4.3	1648 1.6	2317 4.4
30	SU	0518 1.4	1202 4.3	1758 1.6	

GALWAY
LAT 53°16′N
LONG 9°03′W

TIMES AND HEIGHTS OF HIGH AND LOW WATER (Heights in Metres)

TIME ZONE UT
For Summer Time (area enclosed in shaded box) add 1 hour

2024

JULY

Date	Day	Time	m
1	M	0027 0628 1311 1914	4.3 1.5 4.3 1.6
2	TU	0140 0743 1414 2023	4.3 1.5 4.5 1.4
3	W	0242 0845 1509 2119	4.4 1.5 4.6 1.3
4	TH	0338 0936 1558 2208	4.6 1.4 4.8 1.1
5	F ●	0428 1021 1644 2251	4.7 1.3 4.9 1.0
6	SA	0515 1102 1728 2332	4.8 1.3 5.0 1.0
7	SU	0559 1140 1809	4.8 1.3 5.0
8	M	0009 0641 1217 1850	1.0 4.8 1.3 5.0
9	TU	0046 0721 1255 1929	1.0 4.7 1.4 4.8
10	W	0123 0800 1333 2008	1.1 4.6 1.5 4.7
11	TH	0202 0839 1412 2048	1.3 4.4 1.7 4.5
12	F	0242 0920 1453 2131	1.5 4.2 1.9 4.3
13	SA ☾	0323 1004 1539 2217	1.7 4.1 2.0 4.1
14	SU	0410 1052 1637 2308	1.9 4.0 2.2 3.9
15	M	0509 1145 1804	2.0 3.9 2.2
16	TU	0005 0635 1244 1918	3.8 2.1 4.0 2.1
17	W	0111 0744 1347 2015	3.9 2.0 4.1 1.9
18	TH	0219 0838 1444 2105	4.0 1.8 4.3 1.7
19	F	0316 0925 1533 2150	4.2 1.6 4.6 1.4
20	SA	0406 1007 1620 2233	4.5 1.4 4.9 1.1
21	SU ○	0452 1048 1705 2314	4.7 1.2 5.1 0.8
22	M	0537 1128 1749 2355	4.9 1.0 5.3 0.6
23	TU	0621 1210 1834	5.0 0.9 5.3
24	W	0036 0706 1252 1920	0.5 5.0 0.8 5.3
25	TH	0119 0751 1336 2006	0.5 5.0 0.9 5.2
26	F	0204 0837 1424 2054	0.6 4.8 1.1 5.0
27	SA	0251 0927 1516 2147	0.9 4.6 1.3 4.7
28	SU ☽	0344 1021 1616 2247	1.2 4.4 1.6 4.4
29	M	0444 1125 1727	1.6 4.2 1.8
30	TU	0001 0557 1246 1854	4.1 1.8 4.1 1.8
31	W	0126 0725 1402 2020	4.0 1.9 4.2 1.7

AUGUST

Date	Day	Time	m
1	TH	0238 0842 1503 2123	4.1 1.8 4.4 1.5
2	F	0334 0936 1553 2210	4.3 1.7 4.6 1.2
3	SA	0422 1017 1637 2248	4.5 1.5 4.8 1.1
4	SU ●	0505 1052 1718 2319	4.7 1.3 5.0 0.9
5	M	0544 1123 1755 2347	4.8 1.2 5.0 0.9
6	TU	0621 1155 1831	4.8 1.1 5.0
7	W	0017 0656 1227 1905	0.9 4.8 1.1 4.9
8	TH	0050 0730 1300 1939	0.9 4.7 1.2 4.8
9	F	0123 0803 1333 2013	1.1 4.6 1.4 4.6
10	SA	0156 0839 1408 2050	1.3 4.4 1.6 4.4
11	SU	0232 0918 1447 2133	1.5 4.2 1.8 4.1
12	M ☾	0312 1004 1532 2223	1.7 4.1 2.0 3.9
13	TU	0359 1057 1627 2322	2.0 3.9 2.2 3.8
14	W	0456 1157 1841	2.2 3.9 2.3
15	TH	0028 0720 1304 1958	3.7 2.2 4.0 2.0
16	F	0145 0824 1415 2052	3.9 2.0 4.2 1.7
17	SA	0258 0913 1514 2138	4.2 1.7 4.6 1.2
18	SU	0350 0956 1602 2220	4.5 1.3 5.0 0.8
19	M ○	0435 1036 1647 2300	4.9 0.9 5.3 0.5
20	TU	0518 1114 1730 2338	5.1 0.7 5.5 0.2
21	W	0600 1152 1814	5.3 0.5 5.6
22	TH	0016 0642 1231 1858	0.2 5.3 0.5 5.6
23	F	0055 0725 1312 1942	0.2 5.2 0.6 5.4
24	SA	0137 0808 1357 2029	0.5 5.0 0.8 5.0
25	SU	0221 0855 1446 2120	0.9 4.7 1.2 4.6
26	M ☽	0312 0946 1547 2220	1.3 4.4 1.6 4.2
27	TU	0415 1049 1708 2344	1.8 4.1 1.9 3.9
28	W	0540 1232 1847	2.1 3.9 2.0
29	TH	0126 0718 1359 2029	3.8 2.2 4.0 1.8
30	F	0237 0841 1458 2124	4.0 2.0 4.3 1.5
31	SA	0328 0929 1544 2202	4.3 1.7 4.6 1.2

SEPTEMBER

Date	Day	Time	m
1	SU	0410 1004 1624 2232	4.5 1.4 4.8 1.0
2	M	0448 1032 1700 2254	4.7 1.2 5.0 0.8
3	TU ●	0522 1059 1734 2318	4.8 1.1 5.0 0.8
4	W	0555 1127 1806 2346	4.9 1.0 5.0 0.7
5	TH	0626 1157 1838	4.9 0.9 4.9
6	F	0016 0657 1228 1909	0.8 4.8 1.0 4.8
7	SA	0047 0728 1300 1939	0.9 4.7 1.1 4.6
8	SU	0120 0759 1335 2011	1.1 4.5 1.4 4.4
9	M	0155 0835 1413 2051	1.4 4.3 1.6 4.1
10	TU	0234 0919 1456 2143	1.7 4.1 1.9 3.9
11	W ☾	0319 1015 1549 2248	2.0 3.9 2.1 3.7
12	TH	0416 1120 1701 2359	2.3 3.8 2.3 3.6
13	F	0705 1232 1942	2.4 3.9 2.0
14	SA	0123 0809 1352 2035	3.8 2.0 4.2 1.5
15	SU	0247 0857 1456 2120	4.2 1.6 4.6 1.0
16	M	0334 0938 1543 2200	4.6 1.1 5.1 0.6
17	TU	0415 1015 1626 2237	5.0 0.7 5.4 0.2
18	W ○	0454 1051 1708 2313	5.3 0.4 5.7 0.0
19	TH	0534 1128 1750 2350	5.5 0.2 5.7 0.0
20	F	0615 1207 1833	5.5 0.3 5.6
21	SA	0027 0657 1247 1919	0.2 5.4 0.5 5.4
22	SU	0108 0740 1331 2006	0.6 5.1 0.8 4.9
23	M	0152 0825 1421 2057	1.1 4.7 1.2 4.5
24	TU ☽	0244 0916 1526 2158	1.6 4.3 1.7 4.0
25	W	0355 1018 1658 2338	2.0 4.0 2.0 3.7
26	TH	0529 1225 1832	2.3 3.8 2.0
27	F	0121 0658 1346 2021	3.8 2.3 4.0 1.7
28	SA	0223 0821 1440 2104	4.0 2.0 4.3 1.5
29	SU	0309 0905 1523 2135	4.3 1.7 4.5 1.2
30	M	0348 0937 1601 2159	4.5 1.4 4.7 1.0

OCTOBER

Date	Day	Time	m
1	TU	0423 1004 1635 2222	4.7 1.2 4.8 0.9
2	W ●	0454 1031 1707 2247	4.8 1.0 4.9 0.8
3	TH	0525 1059 1738 2315	4.9 0.9 4.9 0.8
4	F	0555 1129 1809 2345	4.9 0.9 4.9 0.8
5	SA	0624 1200 1840	4.9 0.9 4.8
6	SU	0015 0654 1232 1909	0.9 4.8 1.1 4.6
7	M	0049 0724 1307 1941	1.1 4.6 1.3 4.4
8	TU	0125 0758 1346 2021	1.4 4.4 1.5 4.1
9	W	0204 0842 1430 2116	1.7 4.2 1.8 3.9
10	TH ☾	0251 0941 1525 2223	2.0 4.0 2.0 3.7
11	F	0351 1050 1641 2336	2.3 3.8 2.1 3.6
12	SA	0640 1203 1918	2.4 3.9 1.9
13	SU	0102 0745 1324 2011	3.8 2.0 4.2 1.4
14	M	0222 0832 1430 2055	4.3 1.5 4.7 0.9
15	TU	0308 0912 1518 2133	4.7 1.0 5.1 0.5
16	W	0348 0949 1601 2209	5.1 0.6 5.4 0.2
17	TH ○	0427 1026 1644 2245	5.4 0.4 5.6 0.2
18	F	0508 1104 1727 2322	5.5 0.3 5.7 0.2
19	SA	0549 1144 1812	5.5 0.3 5.5
20	SU	0001 0632 1225 1859	0.5 5.4 0.6 5.2
21	M	0043 0716 1311 1947	0.9 5.1 0.9 4.8
22	TU	0130 0802 1404 2040	1.3 4.8 1.3 4.4
23	W	0224 0853 1514 2141	1.8 4.4 1.7 4.0
24	TH ☽	0341 0953 1639 2318	2.2 4.1 1.9 3.8
25	F	0507 1148 1757	2.3 3.9 1.9
26	SA	0053 0622 1315 1914	3.8 2.3 4.0 1.8
27	SU	0152 0729 1410 2012	4.0 2.1 4.2 1.6
28	M	0238 0820 1454 2049	4.2 1.8 4.3 1.4
29	TU	0317 0859 1531 2119	4.4 1.6 4.5 1.2
30	W	0351 0931 1605 2147	4.6 1.3 4.7 1.1
31	TH	0422 1002 1637 2216	4.7 1.2 4.8 1.0

NOVEMBER

Date	Day	Time	m
1	F ●	0452 1032 1709 2246	4.9 1.1 4.8 1.0
2	SA	0523 1103 1742 2317	4.9 1.0 4.8 1.0
3	SU	0555 1136 1815 2349	4.9 1.0 4.7 1.1
4	M	0626 1210 1848	4.8 1.1 4.6
5	TU	0024 0658 1248 1924	1.3 4.7 1.3 4.4
6	W	0103 0735 1329 2007	1.5 4.5 1.4 4.2
7	TH	0145 0821 1416 2100	1.7 4.3 1.6 4.0
8	F	0236 0918 1513 2204	2.0 4.2 1.8 3.9
9	SA ☾	0340 1024 1628 2313	2.2 4.1 1.9 3.8
10	SU	0511 1134 1825	2.2 4.1 1.7
11	M	0030 0703 1249 1934	4.0 1.9 4.3 1.4
12	TU	0143 0757 1357 2021	4.3 1.5 4.7 1.0
13	W	0235 0842 1451 2102	4.7 1.1 5.0 0.8
14	TH	0320 0923 1538 2142	5.1 0.8 5.3 0.6
15	F ○	0402 1003 1624 2221	5.3 0.6 5.4 0.5
16	SA	0445 1044 1710 2301	5.4 0.5 5.4 0.7
17	SU	0528 1127 1757 2343	5.4 0.6 5.3 0.9
18	M	0613 1212 1844	5.3 0.8 5.1
19	TU	0027 0658 1300 1934	1.2 5.1 1.0 4.8
20	W	0115 0745 1353 2025	1.5 4.8 1.3 4.5
21	TH	0210 0835 1454 2121	1.8 4.5 1.6 4.2
22	F	0316 0929 1604 2227	2.1 4.3 1.8 4.0
23	SA ☽	0429 1032 1712 2352	2.2 4.0 1.9 3.9
24	SU	0537 1209 1813	2.3 3.9 1.9
25	M	0101 0638 1321 1910	3.9 2.2 4.0 1.8
26	TU	0154 0732 1412 1958	4.1 2.0 4.1 1.7
27	W	0237 0818 1454 2039	4.3 1.8 4.3 1.5
28	TH	0313 0859 1530 2116	4.4 1.6 4.4 1.4
29	F	0346 0935 1606 2150	4.6 1.4 4.6 1.3
30	SA	0420 1010 1642 2223	4.8 1.3 4.7 1.3

DECEMBER

Date	Day	Time	m
1	SU ●	0455 1044 1718 2256	4.9 1.2 4.7 1.3
2	M	0530 1119 1756 2332	4.9 1.2 4.7 1.3
3	TU	0605 1157 1833	4.9 1.2 4.7
4	W	0010 0643 1237 1914	1.4 4.9 1.2 4.6
5	TH	0052 0723 1321 1958	1.5 4.8 1.3 4.4
6	F	0137 0809 1408 2047	1.6 4.6 1.4 4.3
7	SA	0228 0901 1502 2143	1.8 4.5 1.5 4.2
8	SU ☾	0328 1000 1604 2245	1.9 4.4 1.6 4.1
9	M	0436 1104 1713 2352	1.9 4.4 1.6 4.2
10	TU	0552 1213 1829	1.9 4.4 1.5
11	W	0102 0709 1324 1939	4.4 1.7 4.5 1.4
12	TH	0204 0810 1427 2034	4.6 1.4 4.8 1.2
13	F	0256 0902 1521 2121	4.9 1.2 5.0 1.1
14	SA	0345 0949 1611 2207	5.1 1.0 5.1 1.1
15	SU ○	0431 1035 1700 2251	5.2 0.9 5.1 1.1
16	M	0517 1121 1748 2335	5.3 0.9 5.1 1.2
17	TU	0602 1205 1834	5.3 0.9 5.0
18	W	0018 0647 1249 1921	1.3 5.2 1.0 4.9
19	TH	0102 0730 1334 2006	1.5 5.0 1.2 4.7
20	F	0147 0815 1421 2053	1.7 4.8 1.4 4.4
21	SA	0236 0900 1512 2140	1.9 4.5 1.6 4.2
22	SU ☽	0331 0949 1609 2231	2.1 4.3 1.8 4.1
23	M	0436 1042 1711 2327	2.2 4.1 2.0 4.0
24	TU	0542 1142 1813	2.3 4.0 2.0
25	W	0032 0644 1255 1911	4.0 2.2 3.9 2.0
26	TH	0136 0740 1402 2003	4.1 2.1 4.0 1.9
27	F	0227 0829 1453 2049	4.2 1.9 4.2 1.8
28	SA	0311 0914 1537 2132	4.4 1.7 4.4 1.7
29	SU	0351 0955 1618 2211	4.6 1.5 4.5 1.5
30	M ●	0431 1034 1659 2248	4.8 1.3 4.7 1.4
31	TU	0510 1112 1740 2325	5.0 1.2 4.8 1.3

ESBJERG
LAT 55°28′N
LONG 8°27′E

TIMES AND HEIGHTS OF HIGH AND LOW WATER (Heights in Metres)

TIME ZONE
European Standard Time (UT+0100)
For Summer Time (area enclosed in shaded box) add 1 hour

2024

SUNRISE AND SUNSET TIMES

ESBJERG
At 55°28′N 8°27′E

		Sunrise	Sunset
European Standard Time (UT+0100)			
Jan	01	0854	1606
	15	0844	1627
Feb	01	0819	1702
	15	0750	1732
Mar	01	0717	1801
	15	0641	1830
European Summer Time (UT+0200)			
Apr	01	0657	2004
	15	0622	2032
May	01	0544	2104
	15	0516	2130
Jun	01	0452	2157
	15	0443	2210
Jul	01	0449	2211
	15	0505	2159
Aug	01	0533	2131
	15	0559	2101
Sep	01	0632	2020
	15	0658	1943
Oct	01	0729	1902
	15	0757	1826
European Standard Time (UT+0100)			
Nov	01	0732	1647
	15	0800	1621
Dec	01	0830	1600

JANUARY

Date	Day	Time	m	Time	m	Time	m	Time	m
1	M	0527	2.1	1204	0.3	1757	1.7		
2	TU	0000	0.4	0604	2.1	1242	0.4	1836	1.7
3	W	0039	0.4	0645	2.0	1322	0.4	1921	1.7
4	TH ☽	0123	0.5	0732	2.0	1408	0.4	2013	1.7
5	F	0212	0.5	0825	2.0	1459	0.5	2113	1.7
6	SA	0309	0.6	0925	1.9	1557	0.5	2217	1.7
7	SU	0414	0.6	1031	1.9	1659	0.5	2323	1.8
8	M	0523	0.5	1142	1.9	1801	0.4		
9	TU	0027	1.9	0630	0.5	1252	1.9	1859	0.4
10	W	0125	1.9	0730	0.4	1356	1.9	1952	0.3
11	TH ●	0218	2.0	0824	0.3	1452	1.9	2040	0.3
12	F	0305	2.1	0914	0.2	1543	1.9	2126	0.3
13	SA	0349	2.1	1001	0.1	1629	1.9	2211	0.3
14	SU	0431	2.1	1047	0.1	1712	1.9	2255	0.3
15	M	0512	2.2	1132	0.1	1755	1.9	2339	0.2
16	TU	0556	2.2	1219	0.1	1839	1.8		
17	W	0026	0.2	0643	2.2	1307	0.2	1927	1.8
18	TH ☾	0115	0.3	0735	2.2	1359	0.2	2020	1.8
19	F	0209	0.3	0833	2.1	1455	0.3	2118	1.8
20	SA	0309	0.4	0940	2.0	1555	0.4	2223	1.8
21	SU	0416	0.4	1055	2.0	1700	0.4	2331	1.8
22	M	0528	0.4	1209	1.9	1804	0.5		
23	TU	0036	1.9	0638	0.4	1316	1.9	1903	0.5
24	W	0134	1.9	0739	0.3	1413	1.9	1954	0.4
25	TH ○	0224	2.0	0831	0.3	1500	1.8	2039	0.4
26	F	0307	2.0	0915	0.3	1540	1.8	2119	0.4
27	SA	0343	2.1	0955	0.3	1613	1.8	2156	0.3
28	SU	0414	2.1	1031	0.3	1641	1.8	2231	0.3
29	M	0441	2.1	1104	0.3	1707	1.8	2304	0.3
30	TU	0509	2.1	1137	0.3	1734	1.8	2337	0.3
31	W	0539	2.1	1209	0.3	1806	1.8		

FEBRUARY

Date	Day	Time	m	Time	m	Time	m	Time	m
1	TH	0011	0.3	0614	2.1	1243	0.4	1842	1.8
2	F	0048	0.4	0654	2.0	1322	0.4	1925	1.8
3	SA ☽	0131	0.4	0741	2.0	1407	0.4	2016	1.8
4	SU	0221	0.5	0836	1.9	1501	0.5	2116	1.8
5	M	0321	0.5	0941	1.8	1605	0.5	2224	1.8
6	TU	0436	0.6	1100	1.8	1719	0.6	2341	1.8
7	W	0559	0.5	1229	1.8	1830	0.5		
8	TH	0055	1.9	0710	0.4	1343	1.9	1931	0.4
9	F ●	0157	2.0	0809	0.3	1442	1.9	2023	0.3
10	SA	0249	2.1	0859	0.1	1532	1.9	2110	0.3
11	SU	0336	2.2	0945	0.1	1617	2.0	2155	0.2
12	M	0418	2.2	1029	0.0	1657	1.9	2237	0.1
13	TU	0459	2.3	1112	0.0	1735	1.9	2320	0.1
14	W	0540	2.3	1155	0.1	1813	1.9		
15	TH	0004	0.1	0623	2.2	1240	0.2	1854	1.9
16	F ☾	0050	0.2	0710	2.1	1327	0.3	1940	1.8
17	SA	0140	0.2	0804	2.0	1419	0.4	2035	1.8
18	SU	0238	0.4	0910	1.9	1518	0.5	2141	1.8
19	M	0348	0.5	1033	1.8	1628	0.6	2259	1.8
20	TU	0511	0.5	1154	1.8	1742	0.6		
21	W	0013	1.8	0627	0.5	1302	1.8	1846	0.6
22	TH	0116	1.9	0728	0.4	1358	1.8	1939	0.5
23	F	0209	2.0	0817	0.3	1444	1.8	2024	0.4
24	SA ○	0252	2.1	0859	0.3	1523	1.9	2103	0.3
25	SU	0329	2.1	0935	0.2	1556	1.9	2138	0.3
26	M	0359	2.1	1008	0.2	1623	1.9	2210	0.3
27	TU	0424	2.1	1038	0.3	1647	1.9	2241	0.3
28	W	0449	2.1	1107	0.3	1710	1.9	2312	0.3
29	TH	0515	2.1	1137	0.3	1737	1.9	2344	0.3

MARCH

Date	Day	Time	m	Time	m	Time	m	Time	m
1	F	0546	2.0	1209	0.3	1808	1.9		
2	SA	0019	0.3	0623	2.0	1245	0.4	1846	1.8
3	SU ☽	0059	0.4	0706	1.9	1327	0.4	1933	1.8
4	M	0146	0.4	0759	1.9	1418	0.5	2029	1.8
5	TU	0245	0.5	0905	1.8	1523	0.6	2139	1.8
6	W	0404	0.6	1032	1.7	1645	0.6	2303	1.8
7	TH	0537	0.5	1214	1.7	1805	0.6		
8	F	0028	1.9	0651	0.4	1327	1.8	1909	0.5
9	SA	0135	2.0	0749	0.2	1424	1.9	2003	0.3
10	SU ●	0230	2.1	0839	0.1	1513	2.0	2050	0.2
11	M	0318	2.2	0924	0.0	1555	2.0	2134	0.1
12	TU	0401	2.3	1006	0.0	1633	2.0	2216	0.1
13	W	0441	2.3	1048	0.1	1709	2.0	2258	0.1
14	TH	0520	2.2	1129	0.1	1744	1.9	2341	0.1
15	F	0600	2.1	1210	0.2	1821	1.9		
16	SA	0025	0.1	0644	2.0	1254	0.4	1903	1.9
17	SU ☾	0114	0.3	0735	1.9	1343	0.5	1953	1.8
18	M	0211	0.4	0842	1.8	1441	0.6	2100	1.8
19	TU	0326	0.5	1013	1.7	1556	0.7	2228	1.8
20	W	0455	0.5	1133	1.7	1718	0.7	2347	1.8
21	TH	0609	0.5	1239	1.7	1824	0.6		
22	F	0051	1.9	0706	0.4	1333	1.8	1917	0.5
23	SA	0144	2.0	0753	0.3	1419	1.8	2001	0.4
24	SU	0228	2.1	0833	0.3	1458	1.9	2039	0.3
25	M ○	0306	2.1	0908	0.2	1531	1.9	2114	0.3
26	TU	0337	2.1	0939	0.2	1600	1.9	2146	0.3
27	W	0403	2.1	1009	0.3	1624	1.9	2217	0.3
28	TH	0427	2.0	1038	0.3	1647	1.9	2247	0.3
29	F	0453	2.0	1107	0.3	1712	1.9	2319	0.3
30	SA	0523	2.0	1139	0.4	1741	1.9	2355	0.3
31	SU	0559	1.9	1216	0.4	1816	1.9		

APRIL

Date	Day	Time	m	Time	m	Time	m	Time	m
1	M	0035	0.4	0642	1.9	1258	0.5	1901	1.8
2	TU ☽	0124	0.4	0735	1.8	1349	0.6	1957	1.8
3	W	0226	0.5	0845	1.7	1456	0.7	2109	1.8
4	TH	0350	0.5	1023	1.7	1620	0.7	2237	1.8
5	F	0518	0.4	1157	1.7	1740	0.6		
6	SA	0002	1.9	0627	0.3	1304	1.8	1844	0.4
7	SU	0110	2.0	0724	0.2	1400	1.9	1937	0.3
8	M ●	0206	2.1	0813	0.1	1447	2.0	2026	0.2
9	TU	0256	2.2	0858	0.1	1529	2.0	2111	0.1
10	W	0340	2.2	0941	0.1	1606	2.0	2154	0.1
11	TH	0421	2.2	1021	0.2	1641	2.0	2237	0.1
12	F	0500	2.1	1101	0.2	1714	2.0	2319	0.1
13	SA	0539	2.0	1142	0.3	1749	1.9		
14	SU	0004	0.2	0620	1.9	1224	0.4	1829	1.9
15	M ☾	0053	0.3	0709	1.8	1310	0.6	1918	1.9
16	TU	0151	0.4	0815	1.7	1406	0.7	2022	1.8
17	W	0305	0.5	0944	1.6	1520	0.7	2149	1.8
18	TH	0428	0.6	1100	1.6	1642	0.7	2310	1.8
19	F	0537	0.5	1202	1.7	1749	0.6		
20	SA	0014	1.9	0633	0.4	1256	1.8	1843	0.5
21	SU	0108	2.0	0719	0.4	1343	1.8	1929	0.4
22	M	0155	2.0	0759	0.3	1424	1.9	2009	0.4
23	TU	0235	2.0	0834	0.3	1501	2.0	2046	0.3
24	W ○	0309	2.0	0907	0.3	1532	2.0	2120	0.3
25	TH	0340	2.0	0939	0.3	1559	1.9	2153	0.3
26	F	0408	2.0	1010	0.3	1624	1.9	2226	0.3
27	SA	0436	1.9	1042	0.4	1651	1.9	2301	0.3
28	SU	0508	1.9	1117	0.4	1721	1.9	2339	0.3
29	M	0545	1.8	1155	0.5	1757	1.9		
30	TU	0023	0.4	0630	1.8	1240	0.5	1843	1.9

MAY

Date	Day	Time	m	Time	m	Time	m	Time	m
1	W ☾	0115	0.4	0727	1.7	1334	0.6	1940	1.9
2	TH	0221	0.4	0841	1.7	1440	0.6	2052	1.9
3	F	0338	0.4	1012	1.7	1557	0.6	2215	1.9
4	SA	0454	0.4	1129	1.7	1710	0.5	2334	2.0
5	SU	0558	0.3	1233	1.8	1814	0.4		
6	M	0042	2.1	0654	0.2	1328	1.9	1910	0.3
7	TU	0141	2.1	0745	0.2	1417	1.9	2001	0.2
8	W ●	0234	2.1	0831	0.2	1501	1.9	2048	0.2
9	TH	0321	2.1	0915	0.2	1540	2.0	2134	0.1
10	F	0404	2.0	0956	0.3	1615	2.0	2218	0.2
11	SA	0443	1.9	1036	0.4	1649	2.0	2302	0.2
12	SU	0521	1.9	1116	0.4	1724	2.0	2347	0.3
13	M	0601	1.8	1158	0.5	1803	2.0		
14	TU	0036	0.4	0646	1.7	1242	0.6	1849	1.9
15	W ☽	0130	0.5	0743	1.6	1333	0.6	1945	1.9
16	TH	0234	0.5	0856	1.6	1437	0.7	2056	1.8
17	F	0344	0.6	1008	1.6	1549	0.7	2214	1.8
18	SA	0449	0.5	1111	1.7	1658	0.7	2322	1.9
19	SU	0545	0.5	1207	1.7	1757	0.6		
20	M	0020	1.9	0633	0.4	1258	1.8	1847	0.5
21	TU	0111	1.9	0717	0.4	1343	1.9	1933	0.4
22	W	0157	2.0	0756	0.3	1424	1.9	2014	0.4
23	TH ○	0238	2.0	0834	0.3	1501	1.9	2053	0.3
24	F	0316	1.9	0910	0.3	1534	1.9	2130	0.3
25	SA	0351	1.9	0946	0.4	1604	1.9	2209	0.3
26	SU	0426	1.8	1022	0.4	1635	1.9	2248	0.3
27	M	0503	1.8	1101	0.5	1708	1.9	2331	0.3
28	TU	0543	1.7	1143	0.5	1747	1.9		
29	W	0018	0.3	0630	1.7	1229	0.5	1834	1.9
30	TH ☾	0111	0.3	0727	1.7	1323	0.5	1931	2.0
31	F	0212	0.4	0834	1.7	1423	0.5	2037	2.0

JUNE

Date	Day	Time	m	Time	m	Time	m	Time	m
1	SA	0317	0.3	0946	1.7	1530	0.5	2150	2.0
2	SU	0423	0.3	1053	1.7	1637	0.5	2303	2.0
3	M	0525	0.3	1155	1.8	1742	0.4		
4	TU	0012	2.0	0623	0.3	1253	1.8	1842	0.3
5	W	0116	2.0	0716	0.3	1347	1.9	1938	0.3
6	TH ●	0214	2.0	0806	0.3	1435	1.9	2030	0.2
7	F	0306	1.9	0852	0.4	1517	1.9	2118	0.2
8	SA	0352	1.9	0935	0.4	1555	1.9	2204	0.2
9	SU	0432	1.8	1016	0.4	1630	2.0	2249	0.3
10	M	0508	1.7	1055	0.5	1704	2.0	2333	0.3
11	TU	0543	1.7	1135	0.5	1740	2.0		
12	W	0017	0.4	0621	1.7	1217	0.5	1821	2.0
13	TH	0103	0.4	0704	1.6	1301	0.5	1908	1.9
14	F ☽	0152	0.5	0755	1.6	1351	0.6	2001	1.9
15	SA	0246	0.5	0855	1.6	1447	0.6	2101	1.9
16	SU	0343	0.6	0959	1.7	1550	0.6	2207	1.8
17	M	0440	0.6	1101	1.7	1654	0.6	2312	1.8
18	TU	0535	0.5	1159	1.8	1754	0.6		
19	W	0015	1.8	0627	0.5	1253	1.8	1850	0.5
20	TH	0113	1.9	0715	0.4	1342	1.9	1940	0.4
21	F	0205	1.9	0800	0.4	1427	1.9	2027	0.4
22	SA ○	0254	1.9	0843	0.4	1508	1.9	2111	0.3
23	SU	0339	1.9	0925	0.4	1546	1.9	2155	0.3
24	M	0421	1.8	1006	0.4	1622	2.0	2238	0.3
25	TU	0502	1.8	1048	0.4	1659	2.0	2322	0.3
26	W	0543	1.8	1131	0.4	1740	2.0		
27	TH	0009	0.3	0627	1.7	1217	0.4	1826	2.1
28	F ☾	0058	0.3	0716	1.7	1307	0.4	1918	2.1
29	SA	0151	0.3	0810	1.7	1401	0.4	2017	2.1
30	SU	0248	0.3	0909	1.7	1500	0.4	2122	2.0

ESBJERG
LAT 55°28′N
LONG 8°27′E

TIMES AND HEIGHTS OF HIGH AND LOW WATER (Heights in Metres)

TIME ZONE
European Standard Time (UT+0100)
For Summer Time (area enclosed in shaded box) add 1 hour

2024

JULY

Day	Time	m	Day	Time	m
1 M	0348	0.3	16 TU	0326	0.6
	1011	1.8		0941	1.7
	1604	0.4		1543	0.6
	2233	2.0		2200	1.8
2 TU	0450	0.4	17 W	0426	0.6
	1116	1.8		1045	1.7
	1711	0.4		1652	0.6
	2346	1.9		2311	1.8
3 W	0552	0.4	18 TH	0531	0.6
	1219	1.8		1152	1.8
	1818	0.4		1803	0.6
4 TH	0058	1.9	19 F	0027	1.8
	0651	0.5		0633	0.5
	1320	1.8		1256	1.8
	1920	0.3		1908	0.5
5 F ●	0202	1.9	20 SA	0136	1.8
	0745	0.5		0729	0.5
	1414	1.9		1352	1.9
	2017	0.3		2004	0.4
6 SA	0257	1.8	21 SU O	0234	1.8
	0833	0.5		0820	0.4
	1501	1.9		1442	2.0
	2107	0.3		2053	0.3
7 SU	0342	1.8	22 M	0324	1.9
	0918	0.5		0906	0.4
	1541	2.0		1526	2.0
	2153	0.3		2139	0.2
8 M	0421	1.7	23 TU	0409	1.9
	0958	0.5		0949	0.4
	1616	2.0		1607	2.0
	2234	0.3		2223	0.2
9 TU	0453	1.7	24 W	0450	1.8
	1037	0.4		1032	0.3
	1647	2.0		1646	2.1
	2314	0.3		2307	0.2
10 W	0522	1.7	25 TH	0529	1.8
	1114	0.4		1114	0.3
	1718	2.0		1727	2.1
	2351	0.4		2350	0.2
11 TH	0551	1.7	26 F	0608	1.8
	1150	0.4		1158	0.3
	1752	2.0		1810	2.1
12 F	0029	0.4	27 SA	0036	0.2
	0624	1.7		0650	1.8
	1228	0.4		1245	0.3
	1830	2.0		1858	2.1
13 SA ☽	0107	0.4	28 SU ☾	0124	0.2
	0703	1.7		0736	1.8
	1308	0.5		1335	0.3
	1914	2.0		1951	2.1
14 SU	0147	0.5	29 M	0215	0.3
	0749	1.7		0829	1.8
	1353	0.5		1430	0.3
	2002	1.9		2053	2.0
15 M	0233	0.5	30 TU	0312	0.4
	0842	1.7		0929	1.8
	1444	0.6		1533	0.4
	2058	1.8		2205	1.9
			31 W	0416	0.5
				1038	1.8
				1646	0.4
				2329	1.8

AUGUST

Day	Time	m	Day	Time	m
1 TH	0524	0.6	16 F	0438	0.6
	1151	1.8		1055	1.8
	1802	0.4		1723	0.6
				2350	1.7
2 F	0046	1.8	17 SA	0555	0.6
	0630	0.6		1212	1.8
	1259	1.8		1841	0.5
	1910	0.4			
3 SA	0151	1.8	18 SU	0111	1.8
	0729	0.6		0702	0.5
	1358	1.9		1319	1.9
	2007	0.4		1941	0.3
4 SU ●	0244	1.8	19 M O	0212	1.8
	0818	0.5		0756	0.4
	1447	1.9		1415	2.0
	2055	0.3		2032	0.2
5 M	0328	1.8	20 TU	0303	1.9
	0901	0.5		0844	0.3
	1527	2.0		1503	2.1
	2137	0.3		2118	0.1
6 TU	0403	1.8	21 W	0347	1.9
	0940	0.4		0929	0.3
	1600	2.0		1547	2.1
	2214	0.3		2201	0.1
7 W	0431	1.8	22 TH	0427	1.9
	1016	0.4		1011	0.2
	1628	2.0		1627	2.2
	2248	0.3		2244	0.1
8 TH	0456	1.8	23 F	0504	1.9
	1050	0.3		1053	0.2
	1654	2.0		1707	2.2
	2321	0.3		2325	0.1
9 F	0520	1.8	24 SA	0540	1.9
	1123	0.3		1136	0.1
	1723	2.0		1749	2.2
	2352	0.4			
10 SA	0547	1.8	25 SU	0008	0.2
	1156	0.3		0618	1.9
	1755	2.0		1221	0.2
				1834	2.1
11 SU	0024	0.4	26 M ☾	0053	0.3
	0620	1.8		0700	1.9
	1231	0.4		1309	0.2
	1833	2.0		1925	2.0
12 M ☽	0058	0.4	27 TU	0142	0.4
	0659	1.8		0749	1.8
	1310	0.4		1403	0.3
	1917	1.9		2025	1.9
13 TU	0138	0.5	28 W	0237	0.5
	0746	1.8		0849	1.8
	1355	0.5		1508	0.4
	2007	1.8		2146	1.8
14 W	0226	0.5	29 TH	0344	0.6
	0840	1.8		1005	1.8
	1449	0.5		1629	0.5
	2107	1.8		2319	1.7
15 TH	0325	0.6	30 F	0501	0.7
	0943	1.8		1129	1.8
	1558	0.6		1752	0.5
	2220	1.7			
			31 SA	0034	1.7
				0613	0.7
				1241	1.9
				1858	0.4

SEPTEMBER

Day	Time	m	Day	Time	m
1 SU	0134	1.7	16 M	0047	1.8
	0712	0.6		0634	0.5
	1339	1.9		1249	2.0
	1951	0.3		1916	0.3
2 M	0224	1.8	17 TU	0147	1.9
	0800	0.5		0731	0.4
	1427	2.0		1348	2.1
	2035	0.3		2007	0.1
3 TU ●	0304	1.8	18 W O	0237	1.9
	0842	0.4		0820	0.3
	1507	2.0		1438	2.2
	2114	0.3		2053	0.1
4 W	0338	1.8	19 TH	0320	2.0
	0919	0.3		0905	0.2
	1539	2.0		1523	2.2
	2148	0.3		2136	0.0
5 TH	0405	1.8	20 F	0359	2.0
	0953	0.3		0948	0.1
	1605	2.0		1605	2.2
	2219	0.3		2217	0.1
6 F	0429	1.9	21 SA	0435	2.0
	1024	0.3		1030	0.1
	1629	2.0		1646	2.2
	2248	0.3		2258	0.1
7 SA	0451	1.9	22 SU	0510	2.0
	1055	0.3		1113	0.1
	1655	2.0		1727	2.1
	2317	0.3		2340	0.2
8 SU	0515	1.9	23 M	0546	1.9
	1126	0.3		1158	0.1
	1725	2.0		1810	2.0
	2346	0.4			
9 M	0545	1.9	24 TU ☾	0023	0.3
	1159	0.3		0627	1.9
	1759	1.9		1246	0.2
				1900	1.9
10 TU	0019	0.4	25 W	0110	0.5
	0620	1.9		0715	1.9
	1237	0.4		1341	0.3
	1841	1.9		2003	1.8
11 W ☽	0058	0.5	26 TH	0205	0.6
	0703	1.9		0816	1.8
	1320	0.4		1451	0.5
	1930	1.8		2134	1.7
12 TH	0144	0.5	27 F	0315	0.7
	0755	1.8		0939	1.8
	1414	0.5		1617	0.5
	2031	1.7		2302	1.6
13 F	0242	0.6	28 SA	0438	0.7
	0858	1.8		1107	1.8
	1524	0.6		1736	0.5
	2148	1.7			
14 SA	0358	0.7	29 SU	0010	1.7
	1013	1.8		0550	0.7
	1656	0.5		1216	1.9
	2326	1.7		1837	0.4
15 SU	0524	0.6	30 M	0107	1.8
	1136	1.9		0648	0.6
	1816	0.4		1313	2.0
				1926	0.3

OCTOBER

Day	Time	m	Day	Time	m
1 TU	0154	1.8	16 W	0117	1.9
	0735	0.4		0702	0.3
	1400	2.0		1320	2.1
	2008	0.3		1938	0.1
2 W ●	0234	1.9	17 TH O	0207	2.0
	0817	0.4		0753	0.2
	1440	2.1		1413	2.2
	2045	0.2		2025	0.1
3 TH	0308	1.9	18 F	0251	2.0
	0854	0.3		0840	0.1
	1513	2.1		1501	2.2
	2118	0.2		2109	0.1
4 F	0337	1.9	19 SA	0331	2.0
	0927	0.3		0925	0.1
	1541	2.0		1545	2.2
	2148	0.3		2151	0.1
5 SA	0402	1.9	20 SU	0407	2.0
	0959	0.3		1009	0.1
	1606	2.0		1626	2.1
	2217	0.3		2233	0.2
6 SU	0425	1.9	21 M	0443	2.0
	1030	0.3		1054	0.1
	1631	2.0		1708	2.0
	2246	0.3		2314	0.3
7 M	0449	1.9	22 TU	0520	2.0
	1101	0.3		1139	0.2
	1701	1.9		1751	1.9
	2316	0.4		2356	0.4
8 TU	0518	1.9	23 W	0600	2.0
	1135	0.3		1229	0.3
	1735	1.9		1841	1.8
	2350	0.4			
9 W	0552	1.9	24 TH ☾	0043	0.5
	1213	0.4		0648	1.9
	1816	1.8		1325	0.4
				1944	1.7
10 TH ☽	0029	0.5	25 F	0137	0.6
	0633	1.9		0749	1.9
	1259	0.4		1435	0.5
	1906	1.8		2111	1.6
11 F	0117	0.6	26 SA	0245	0.7
	0725	1.9		0909	1.9
	1355	0.5		1554	0.5
	2009	1.7		2230	1.6
12 SA	0216	0.6	27 SU	0404	0.7
	0829	1.9		1033	1.9
	1509	0.5		1705	0.5
	2131	1.7		2334	1.7
13 SU	0333	0.7	28 M	0515	0.6
	0945	1.9		1140	1.9
	1636	0.4		1803	0.4
	2306	1.7			
14 M	0456	0.6	29 TU	0029	1.8
	1107	1.9		0614	0.5
	1748	0.3		1237	2.0
				1852	0.3
15 TU	0019	1.8	30 W	0117	1.9
	0605	0.5		0704	0.4
	1219	2.0		1326	2.0
	1847	0.2		1934	0.3
			31 TH	0159	1.9
				0747	0.3
				1408	2.0
				2012	0.2

NOVEMBER

Day	Time	m	Day	Time	m
1 F ●	0236	2.0	16 SA	0224	2.0
	0826	0.3		0818	0.1
	1445	2.0		1443	2.1
	2046	0.2		2045	0.2
2 SA	0309	2.0	17 SU	0306	2.0
	0902	0.3		0907	0.1
	1517	2.0		1530	2.0
	2118	0.3		2128	0.2
3 SU	0338	2.0	18 M	0346	2.0
	0936	0.3		0953	0.1
	1546	2.0		1614	2.0
	2149	0.3		2211	0.3
4 M	0404	2.0	19 TU	0423	2.0
	1009	0.3		1039	0.2
	1615	1.9		1656	1.9
	2221	0.3		2253	0.4
5 TU	0430	2.0	20 W	0501	2.0
	1043	0.3		1126	0.2
	1646	1.9		1738	1.8
	2254	0.4		2335	0.4
6 W	0500	2.0	21 TH	0542	2.0
	1119	0.3		1216	0.3
	1722	1.8		1825	1.7
	2331	0.4			
7 TH	0534	2.0	22 F	0021	0.5
	1201	0.4		0628	2.0
	1804	1.8		1309	0.4
				1921	1.6
8 F	0013	0.5	23 SA ☾	0111	0.6
	0616	2.0		0723	2.0
	1249	0.4		1410	0.4
	1855	1.7		2029	1.6
9 SA ☽	0102	0.5	24 SU	0210	0.6
	0708	2.0		0829	1.9
	1348	0.4		1515	0.5
	1959	1.7		2140	1.6
10 SU	0201	0.6	25 M	0318	0.6
	0811	2.0		0943	1.9
	1458	0.4		1619	0.5
	2118	1.7		2244	1.7
11 M	0312	0.6	26 TU	0427	0.6
	0924	2.0		1051	1.9
	1611	0.3		1717	0.4
	2238	1.7		2341	1.8
12 TU	0426	0.5	27 W	0529	0.5
	1040	2.0		1152	1.9
	1718	0.3		1809	0.4
	2345	1.8			
13 W	0533	0.4	28 TH	0033	1.8
	1151	2.1		0624	0.5
	1816	0.2		1245	2.0
				1855	0.3
14 TH	0044	1.9	29 F	0120	1.9
	0633	0.3		0713	0.4
	1254	2.1		1333	2.0
	1909	0.1		1936	0.3
15 F O	0136	2.0	30 SA	0203	2.0
	0727	0.2		0757	0.4
	1351	2.1		1416	2.0
	1959	0.1		2015	0.3

DECEMBER

Day	Time	m	Day	Time	m
1 SU ●	0241	2.0	16 M	0250	2.0
	0837	0.3		0854	0.2
	1456	2.0		1524	1.9
	2052	0.3		2111	0.3
2 M	0315	2.0	17 TU	0333	2.0
	0916	0.3		0943	0.2
	1532	1.9		1609	1.9
	2127	0.3		2154	0.3
3 TU	0347	2.0	18 W	0412	2.1
	0953	0.3		1030	0.2
	1607	1.9		1650	1.8
	2203	0.3		2236	0.4
4 W	0417	2.0	19 TH	0449	2.1
	1031	0.3		1115	0.2
	1642	1.8		1728	1.7
	2240	0.4		2318	0.4
5 TH	0449	2.0	20 F	0527	2.1
	1112	0.3		1200	0.3
	1720	1.8		1807	1.7
	2319	0.4			
6 F	0525	2.0	21 SA	0000	0.4
	1155	0.3		0608	2.1
	1802	1.7		1246	0.3
				1849	1.7
7 SA	0003	0.4	22 SU ☾	0044	0.4
	0607	2.0		0653	2.1
	1244	0.3		1334	0.4
	1851	1.7		1938	1.7
8 SU ☽	0051	0.4	23 M	0133	0.5
	0657	2.1		0744	2.0
	1338	0.3		1425	0.4
	1949	1.7		2035	1.7
9 M	0146	0.5	24 TU	0226	0.5
	0756	2.1		0842	1.9
	1438	0.3		1520	0.5
	2055	1.7		2136	1.7
10 TU	0248	0.5	25 W	0326	0.6
	0902	2.1		0945	1.9
	1541	0.3		1618	0.5
	2203	1.8		2239	1.7
11 W	0354	0.4	26 TH	0431	0.6
	1012	2.1		1052	1.9
	1644	0.3		1715	0.5
	2309	1.8		2340	1.8
12 TH	0501	0.4	27 F	0536	0.6
	1123	2.1		1156	1.9
	1745	0.2		1809	0.4
13 F	0011	1.9	28 SA	0036	1.9
	0605	0.3		0635	0.5
	1231	2.1		1256	1.9
	1842	0.2		1859	0.4
14 SA	0109	1.9	29 SU	0127	1.9
	0706	0.3		0728	0.4
	1335	2.0		1349	1.9
	1935	0.3		1945	0.4
15 SU O	0202	2.0	30 M ●	0213	2.0
	0802	0.2		0815	0.4
	1433	2.0		1438	1.9
	2025	0.3		2028	0.3
			31 TU	0255	2.0
				0859	0.3
				1522	1.9
				2109	0.3

HELGOLAND

LAT 54°11′N
LONG 7°53′E

TIMES AND HEIGHTS OF HIGH AND LOW WATER (Heights in Metres)

TIME ZONE
European Standard Time (UT+0100)
For Summer Time (area enclosed in shaded box) add 1 hour

2024

SUNRISE AND SUNSET TIMES

HELGOLAND
At 54°11′N 7°53′E
European Standard Time (UT+0100)

		Sunrise	Sunset
Jan	01	0848	1616
	15	0840	1637
Feb	01	0816	1709
	15	0749	1737
Mar	01	0717	1805
	15	0643	1833
European Summer Time (UT+0200)			
Apr	01	0701	2005
	15	0627	2031
May	01	0551	2101
	15	0525	2126
Jun	01	0502	2151
	15	0455	2204
Jul	01	0500	2205
	15	0515	2153
Aug	01	0541	2127
	15	0606	2059
Sep	01	0636	2020
	15	0702	1945
Oct	01	0731	1905
	15	0757	1831
European Standard Time (UT+0100)			
Nov	01	0730	1654
	15	0757	1629
Dec	01	0825	1610

JANUARY

Date	Day	Time	m	Time	m	Time	m	Time	m
1	M	0246	3.2	0936	0.7	1514	2.9	2138	0.8
2	TU	0320	3.2	1011	0.8	1552	2.8	2215	0.8
3	W	0359	3.1	1049	0.8	1632	2.8	2255	0.9
4	TH ☽	0441	3.1	1129	0.8	1714	2.8	2340	0.9
5	F	0527	3.0	1214	0.9	1803	2.8		
6	SA	0034	1.0	0624	2.9	1312	0.9	1904	2.8
7	SU	0141	1.0	0731	2.9	1420	0.9	2011	2.8
8	M	0253	1.0	0841	2.9	1528	0.8	2116	2.9
9	TU	0402	0.9	0946	3.0	1632	0.8	2215	3.0
10	W	0504	0.7	1045	3.0	1728	0.7	2308	3.1
11	TH ●	0558	0.6	1137	3.0	1818	0.6	2355	3.1
12	F	0647	0.5	1225	3.1	1906	0.6		
13	SA	0041	3.2	0737	0.4	1313	3.1	1954	0.5
14	SU	0128	3.3	0827	0.3	1402	3.0	2040	0.5
15	M	0215	3.3	0915	0.3	1449	2.9	2123	0.4
16	TU	0300	3.3	1000	0.3	1534	2.9	2207	0.4
17	W	0347	3.2	1047	0.4	1622	2.8	2254	0.5
18	TH ☾	0437	3.2	1133	0.5	1710	2.8	2343	0.6
19	F	0529	3.1	1221	0.6	1802	2.8		
20	SA	0040	0.7	0629	3.0	1321	0.8	1906	2.8
21	SU	0152	0.8	0742	3.0	1433	0.9	2020	2.8
22	M	0312	0.8	0900	2.9	1548	0.9	2132	2.9
23	TU	0427	0.8	1010	2.9	1653	0.9	2234	3.0
24	W	0529	0.6	1108	2.9	1747	0.8	2325	3.1
25	TH ○	0620	0.5	1157	2.9	1832	0.6		
26	F	0009	3.1	0702	0.5	1239	2.9	1911	0.6
27	SA	0048	3.2	0740	0.5	1316	2.9	1947	0.6
28	SU	0124	3.2	0815	0.5	1349	2.9	2018	0.6
29	M	0156	3.2	0846	0.5	1418	2.9	2047	0.6
30	TU	0226	3.2	0914	0.6	1448	2.9	2116	0.6
31	W	0256	3.2	0945	0.6	1520	2.9	2149	0.6

FEBRUARY

Date	Day	Time	m	Time	m	Time	m	Time	m
1	TH	0328	3.1	1016	0.6	1553	2.9	2220	0.6
2	F	0400	3.1	1041	0.7	1621	2.8	2248	0.7
3	SA ☽	0431	3.0	1109	0.8	1655	2.8	2328	0.8
4	SU	0516	2.8	1157	0.9	1750	2.7		
5	M	0034	0.9	0625	2.7	1313	0.9	1908	2.7
6	TU	0200	0.9	0751	2.7	1441	0.9	2032	2.7
7	W	0329	0.8	0915	2.8	1604	0.7	2148	2.9
8	TH	0446	0.6	1027	2.8	1712	0.6	2251	3.0
9	F ●	0549	0.4	1127	2.9	1809	0.5	2343	3.1
10	SA	0641	0.3	1217	3.0	1858	0.4		
11	SU	0030	3.2	0731	0.2	1303	3.0	1946	0.4
12	M	0117	3.3	0819	0.2	1349	3.0	2031	0.3
13	TU	0203	3.3	0904	0.1	1434	2.9	2113	0.2
14	W	0246	3.3	0945	0.2	1514	2.9	2152	0.2
15	TH	0329	3.2	1024	0.3	1554	2.8	2232	0.3
16	F ☾	0412	3.1	1100	0.4	1635	2.8	2312	0.4
17	SA	0457	3.0	1140	0.6	1720	2.8		
18	SU	0002	0.6	0552	2.9	1234	0.8	1821	2.7
19	M	0113	0.7	0706	2.8	1352	1.0	1942	2.8
20	TU	0244	0.8	0835	2.7	1521	1.0	2109	2.8
21	W	0414	0.7	0957	2.7	1639	0.9	2222	2.9
22	TH	0522	0.6	1100	2.8	1736	0.7	2314	3.0
23	F	0610	0.5	1146	2.8	1819	0.6	2355	3.1
24	SA ○	0648	0.4	1224	2.9	1856	0.5		
25	SU	0031	3.1	0722	0.4	1256	2.9	1929	0.5
26	M	0104	3.2	0753	0.4	1325	3.0	1959	0.4
27	TU	0133	3.2	0821	0.4	1352	3.0	2025	0.4
28	W	0201	3.1	0847	0.4	1419	2.9	2053	0.4
29	TH	0229	3.1	0915	0.5	1448	2.9	2122	0.4

MARCH

Date	Day	Time	m	Time	m	Time	m	Time	m
1	F	0258	3.1	0942	0.5	1516	2.9	2150	0.4
2	SA	0326	3.0	1003	0.5	1540	2.9	2213	0.5
3	SU ☽	0352	2.9	1024	0.6	1608	2.8	2245	0.7
4	M	0431	2.7	1107	0.8	1659	2.7	2349	0.8
5	TU	0541	2.6	1226	0.9	1821	2.6		
6	W	0123	0.7	0715	2.5	1407	0.8	1958	2.6
7	TH	0304	0.6	0852	2.6	1542	0.7	2125	2.8
8	F	0430	0.4	1012	2.7	1657	0.5	2234	3.0
9	SA	0537	0.3	1113	2.8	1756	0.4	2328	3.1
10	SU ●	0629	0.2	1203	2.9	1844	0.3		
11	M	0014	3.2	0715	0.1	1246	3.0	1929	0.3
12	TU	0058	3.3	0759	0.1	1328	3.0	2012	0.2
13	W	0142	3.3	0842	0.1	1409	3.0	2054	0.1
14	TH	0225	3.2	0920	0.2	1448	2.9	2131	0.1
15	F	0306	3.1	0954	0.3	1525	2.9	2208	0.2
16	SA	0346	3.0	1027	0.5	1601	2.9	2245	0.4
17	SU ☾	0428	2.9	1102	0.7	1644	2.8	2331	0.5
18	M	0521	2.7	1155	0.8	1744	2.8		
19	TU	0041	0.7	0635	2.6	1315	1.0	1908	2.7
20	W	0215	0.8	0808	2.5	1452	0.9	2043	2.8
21	TH	0352	0.7	0937	2.6	1618	0.8	2201	2.9
22	F	0504	0.5	1042	2.7	1717	0.6	2254	3.0
23	SA	0548	0.4	1124	2.8	1756	0.5	2331	3.0
24	SU	0620	0.3	1156	2.8	1830	0.4		
25	M ○	0004	3.0	0652	0.3	1227	2.9	1903	0.4
26	TU	0036	3.1	0723	0.3	1256	3.0	1934	0.3
27	W	0105	3.1	0751	0.3	1323	3.0	2001	0.3
28	TH	0133	3.1	0817	0.4	1349	3.0	2027	0.3
29	F	0200	3.0	0843	0.4	1416	3.0	2056	0.3
30	SA	0229	3.0	0910	0.4	1444	2.9	2125	0.3
31	SU	0259	2.9	0935	0.5	1512	2.9	2153	0.4

APRIL

Date	Day	Time	m	Time	m	Time	m	Time	m
1	M	0331	2.8	1001	0.6	1544	2.8	2229	0.5
2	TU ☽	0414	2.7	1046	0.8	1636	2.7	2331	0.6
3	W	0522	2.5	1203	0.9	1756	2.7		
4	TH	0103	0.6	0655	2.5	1343	0.8	1932	2.7
5	F	0244	0.5	0832	2.5	1519	0.6	2101	2.8
6	SA	0410	0.3	0951	2.7	1634	0.5	2210	3.0
7	SU	0514	0.2	1051	2.8	1732	0.4	2304	3.1
8	M ●	0606	0.2	1140	2.9	1822	0.3	2351	3.3
9	TU	0650	0.2	1222	3.0	1906	0.3		
10	W	0035	3.3	0731	0.2	1301	3.1	1948	0.2
11	TH	0118	3.2	0812	0.2	1341	3.0	2030	0.1
12	F	0201	3.1	0851	0.3	1421	3.0	2109	0.1
13	SA	0243	3.0	0926	0.4	1458	3.0	2146	0.2
14	SU	0323	2.9	0958	0.5	1535	3.0	2224	0.3
15	M ☾	0406	2.8	1035	0.7	1618	2.9	2309	0.5
16	TU	0458	2.6	1127	0.8	1716	2.8		
17	W	0014	0.7	0608	2.5	1241	0.9	1834	2.8
18	TH	0140	0.7	0734	2.5	1414	0.9	2003	2.8
19	F	0312	0.6	0859	2.5	1539	0.8	2122	2.8
20	SA	0424	0.5	1004	2.7	1638	0.6	2216	2.9
21	SU	0508	0.4	1045	2.8	1717	0.5	2253	3.0
22	M	0540	0.3	1117	2.9	1753	0.4	2328	3.0
23	TU	0613	0.3	1151	2.9	1830	0.4		
24	W ○	0003	3.0	0647	0.3	1223	3.0	1903	0.4
25	TH	0035	3.1	0718	0.3	1252	3.0	1933	0.4
26	F	0104	3.1	0746	0.4	1319	3.0	2002	0.4
27	SA	0134	3.0	0814	0.4	1348	3.0	2033	0.3
28	SU	0207	3.0	0845	0.5	1421	3.0	2108	0.4
29	M	0244	2.9	0919	0.5	1457	3.0	2146	0.4
30	TU	0326	2.8	0956	0.6	1539	2.9	2231	0.5

MAY

Date	Day	Time	m	Time	m	Time	m	Time	m
1	W ☾	0416	2.7	1046	0.7	1633	2.9	2332	0.5
2	TH	0521	2.6	1156	0.8	1745	2.8		
3	F	0053	0.5	0642	2.5	1325	0.8	1911	2.9
4	SA	0222	0.4	0808	2.6	1452	0.6	2033	3.0
5	SU	0340	0.3	0922	2.7	1603	0.5	2140	3.1
6	M	0442	0.3	1020	2.9	1701	0.4	2235	3.2
7	TU	0534	0.3	1109	3.0	1753	0.4	2326	3.2
8	W ●	0621	0.3	1154	3.1	1841	0.3		
9	TH	0012	3.2	0703	0.3	1234	3.1	1925	0.2
10	F	0056	3.2	0744	0.3	1315	3.1	2007	0.2
11	SA	0140	3.1	0824	0.4	1356	3.1	2050	0.2
12	SU	0224	2.9	0902	0.4	1437	3.1	2129	0.3
13	M	0306	2.8	0938	0.5	1516	3.0	2208	0.4
14	TU	0349	2.7	1016	0.7	1559	3.0	2252	0.5
15	W ☽	0439	2.6	1104	0.8	1651	2.9	2348	0.7
16	TH	0539	2.6	1206	0.9	1756	2.8		
17	F	0057	0.7	0648	2.6	1322	0.9	1910	2.8
18	SA	0214	0.6	0801	2.6	1438	0.8	2023	2.8
19	SU	0321	0.5	0905	2.7	1539	0.7	2120	2.9
20	M	0410	0.5	0952	2.8	1625	0.6	2205	3.0
21	TU	0449	0.5	1031	2.9	1708	0.6	2246	3.0
22	W	0529	0.4	1110	3.0	1751	0.5	2327	3.0
23	TH ○	0610	0.4	1148	3.0	1831	0.5		
24	F	0004	3.1	0646	0.4	1222	3.1	1906	0.5
25	SA	0038	3.1	0719	0.5	1255	3.1	1941	0.4
26	SU	0114	3.0	0754	0.5	1330	3.1	2019	0.4
27	M	0154	3.0	0832	0.5	1408	3.1	2101	0.4
28	TU	0238	2.9	0912	0.6	1451	3.1	2147	0.4
29	W	0326	2.8	0958	0.6	1540	3.1	2239	0.4
30	TH ☾	0420	2.7	1051	0.7	1635	3.1	2336	0.4
31	F	0520	2.6	1152	0.7	1738	3.0		

JUNE

Date	Day	Time	m	Time	m	Time	m	Time	m
1	SA	0043	0.4	0627	2.6	1304	0.7	1849	3.0
2	SU	0155	0.4	0739	2.6	1420	0.6	2002	3.1
3	M	0305	0.4	0847	2.8	1529	0.6	2108	3.1
4	TU	0407	0.4	0946	2.9	1630	0.5	2207	3.2
5	W	0502	0.5	1039	3.0	1727	0.5	2302	3.2
6	TH ●	0553	0.4	1128	3.1	1820	0.4	2354	3.1
7	F	0639	0.4	1214	3.1	1908	0.3		
8	SA	0041	3.1	0722	0.5	1256	3.2	1952	0.3
9	SU	0126	3.0	0804	0.5	1340	3.2	2035	0.3
10	M	0210	2.9	0844	0.5	1421	3.2	2115	0.4
11	TU	0251	2.8	0920	0.6	1500	3.1	2153	0.5
12	W	0331	2.8	0957	0.7	1539	3.1	2233	0.6
13	TH	0415	2.7	1039	0.8	1624	3.0	2318	0.7
14	F ☽	0504	2.7	1128	0.8	1714	3.0		
15	SA	0008	0.7	0556	2.7	1223	0.8	1810	3.0
16	SU	0103	0.7	0652	2.7	1324	0.8	1911	2.9
17	M	0203	0.7	0751	2.8	1426	0.8	2013	2.9
18	TU	0300	0.7	0848	2.8	1525	0.8	2109	3.0
19	W	0354	0.7	0940	2.9	1621	0.8	2202	3.0
20	TH	0446	0.6	1029	3.0	1714	0.7	2252	3.0
21	F	0535	0.6	1115	3.1	1802	0.6	2338	3.1
22	SA ○	0619	0.5	1157	3.1	1845	0.5		
23	SU	0019	3.1	0701	0.5	1237	3.2	1929	0.4
24	M	0102	3.1	0743	0.5	1318	3.2	2014	0.4
25	TU	0147	3.0	0826	0.5	1401	3.3	2059	0.3
26	W	0233	2.9	0909	0.5	1446	3.3	2147	0.3
27	TH	0322	2.8	0956	0.5	1535	3.2	2237	0.3
28	F ☾	0414	2.8	1047	0.6	1628	3.2	2329	0.4
29	SA	0507	2.7	1140	0.6	1724	3.1		
30	SU	0023	0.4	0603	2.7	1239	0.6	1824	3.1

HELGOLAND
LAT 54°11′N
LONG 7°53′E

TIMES AND HEIGHTS OF HIGH AND LOW WATER (Heights in Metres)

TIME ZONE
European Standard Time (UT+0100)
For Summer Time (area enclosed in shaded box) add 1 hour

2024

JULY

Day	Time	m	Time	m	Time	m	Time	m
1 M	0122	0.5	0705	2.7	1347	0.7	1931	3.1
2 TU	0229	0.6	0812	2.8	1459	0.7	2042	3.1
3 W	0335	0.7	0917	2.9	1608	0.7	2148	3.1
4 TH	0437	0.7	1017	3.1	1711	0.6	2248	3.1
5 F ●	0534	0.6	1111	3.1	1808	0.5	2343	3.0
6 SA	0624	0.6	1201	3.1	1858	0.4		
7 SU	0032	3.0	0709	0.5	1246	3.2	1942	0.4
8 M	0116	3.0	0750	0.6	1327	3.3	2022	0.4
9 TU	0156	3.0	0828	0.6	1406	3.3	2059	0.5
10 W	0232	2.9	0901	0.6	1440	3.3	2131	0.5
11 TH	0306	2.9	0933	0.6	1514	3.2	2206	0.6
12 F	0344	2.9	1010	0.7	1552	3.1	2242	0.7
13 SA ☽	0423	2.8	1048	0.8	1631	3.1	2317	0.7
14 SU	0501	2.8	1126	0.8	1711	3.0	2353	0.8
15 M	0542	2.8	1211	0.9	1759	2.9		
16 TU	0042	0.8	0634	2.8	1312	0.9	1902	2.9
17 W	0147	0.9	0740	2.8	1424	1.0	2013	2.9
18 TH	0259	0.8	0850	2.9	1538	0.9	2122	2.9
19 F	0408	0.8	0953	3.0	1645	0.7	2225	3.0
20 SA	0509	0.7	1049	3.1	1742	0.6	2319	3.0
21 SU ○	0601	0.6	1138	3.1	1832	0.5		
22 M	0007	3.1	0648	0.6	1223	3.3	1919	0.4
23 TU	0052	3.1	0734	0.5	1308	3.3	2007	0.3
24 W	0138	3.0	0819	0.5	1352	3.3	2053	0.3
25 TH	0223	3.0	0902	0.4	1436	3.3	2137	0.3
26 F	0308	2.9	0944	0.4	1522	3.3	2222	0.3
27 SA	0354	2.9	1030	0.5	1611	3.2	2307	0.4
28 SU ☾	0442	2.8	1118	0.6	1701	3.2	2352	0.5
29 M	0531	2.8	1209	0.6	1756	3.1		
30 TU	0044	0.7	0628	2.8	1314	0.8	1903	3.0
31 W	0153	0.9	0740	2.9	1435	0.8	2022	3.0

AUGUST

Day	Time	m	Time	m	Time	m	Time	m
1 TH	0310	0.9	0857	3.0	1556	0.8	2139	3.0
2 F	0423	0.9	1006	3.1	1706	0.7	2244	3.0
3 SA	0524	0.8	1104	3.1	1803	0.5	2338	3.0
4 SU ●	0615	0.6	1153	3.2	1850	0.4		
5 M	0024	3.0	0658	0.6	1235	3.2	1930	0.4
6 TU	0103	3.0	0736	0.6	1312	3.3	2005	0.4
7 W	0137	3.0	0809	0.6	1345	3.3	2035	0.5
8 TH	0207	3.0	0837	0.6	1415	3.3	2103	0.6
9 F	0235	3.0	0906	0.6	1444	3.2	2132	0.6
10 SA	0307	3.0	0938	0.6	1517	3.1	2202	0.6
11 SU	0340	2.9	1010	0.7	1550	3.1	2229	0.7
12 M ☽	0410	2.9	1037	0.8	1620	3.0	2253	0.8
13 TU	0440	2.9	1110	0.9	1658	2.9	2332	0.9
14 W	0527	2.8	1207	1.0	1800	2.8		
15 TH	0041	1.0	0639	2.8	1331	1.0	1923	2.7
16 F	0210	1.0	0805	2.8	1502	0.9	2050	2.8
17 SA	0337	0.9	0925	2.9	1623	0.8	2205	2.9
18 SU	0449	0.7	1029	3.0	1727	0.6	2305	3.0
19 M ○	0546	0.6	1122	3.2	1819	0.5	2355	3.0
20 TU	0635	0.6	1208	3.3	1906	0.4		
21 W	0039	3.1	0721	0.5	1252	3.4	1953	0.3
22 TH	0122	3.1	0805	0.4	1336	3.4	2037	0.3
23 F	0205	3.0	0847	0.4	1419	3.4	2117	0.3
24 SA	0246	3.0	0926	0.4	1501	3.3	2156	0.4
25 SU	0326	3.0	1007	0.5	1546	3.3	2235	0.6
26 M ☾	0409	3.0	1049	0.6	1633	3.1	2315	0.7
27 TU	0455	2.9	1138	0.8	1727	3.0		
28 W	0006	0.9	0553	2.9	1245	0.9	1838	2.9
29 TH	0120	1.1	0711	2.9	1414	1.0	2005	2.8
30 F	0251	1.1	0841	2.9	1548	0.9	2133	2.8
31 SA	0415	1.0	1000	3.1	1704	0.7	2241	2.9

SEPTEMBER

Day	Time	m	Time	m	Time	m	Time	m
1 SU	0518	0.8	1057	3.1	1755	0.6	2329	2.9
2 M	0603	0.7	1140	3.2	1834	0.5		
3 TU ●	0007	2.9	0640	0.6	1216	3.2	1907	0.4
4 W	0040	3.0	0714	0.6	1249	3.2	1938	0.4
5 TH	0110	3.0	0744	0.6	1319	3.2	2006	0.5
6 F	0136	3.0	0811	0.6	1346	3.2	2030	0.5
7 SA	0202	3.0	0837	0.6	1413	3.2	2055	0.6
8 SU	0230	3.0	0905	0.6	1442	3.1	2122	0.6
9 M	0259	3.0	0934	0.6	1511	3.0	2146	0.7
10 TU	0326	3.0	0959	0.7	1540	2.9	2208	0.8
11 W ☽	0354	2.9	1029	0.9	1616	2.8	2244	1.0
12 TH	0440	2.8	1124	1.0	1718	2.7	2355	1.1
13 F	0555	2.7	1252	1.0	1847	2.6		
14 SA	0134	1.1	0730	2.8	1434	0.9	2024	2.7
15 SU	0311	1.0	0859	2.9	1602	0.8	2146	2.8
16 M	0429	0.8	1008	3.1	1709	0.6	2247	2.9
17 TU	0527	0.7	1101	3.3	1800	0.5	2336	3.0
18 W ○	0616	0.6	1147	3.4	1845	0.4		
19 TH	0019	3.1	0700	0.5	1230	3.4	1928	0.4
20 F	0059	3.1	0743	0.5	1314	3.4	2011	0.4
21 SA	0140	3.1	0825	0.4	1357	3.4	2050	0.4
22 SU	0220	3.1	0904	0.4	1439	3.3	2126	0.5
23 M	0258	3.1	0942	0.5	1520	3.2	2202	0.7
24 TU ☾	0337	3.1	1022	0.6	1606	3.0	2241	0.9
25 W	0423	3.0	1112	0.8	1701	2.9	2333	1.1
26 TH	0523	2.9	1219	1.0	1814	2.7		
27 F	0050	1.2	0644	2.9	1351	1.0	1945	2.7
28 SA	0226	1.2	0819	2.9	1530	0.9	2117	2.7
29 SU	0357	1.0	0943	3.0	1648	0.8	2226	2.8
30 M	0501	0.9	1039	3.1	1735	0.6	2309	2.9

OCTOBER

Day	Time	m	Time	m	Time	m	Time	m
1 TU	0540	0.7	1115	3.1	1805	0.5	2339	3.0
2 W ●	0612	0.6	1147	3.1	1834	0.5		
3 TH	0008	3.0	0644	0.6	1220	3.2	1905	0.5
4 F	0038	3.0	0715	0.6	1250	3.2	1932	0.5
5 SA	0105	3.1	0742	0.6	1317	3.2	1957	0.6
6 SU	0130	3.1	0808	0.6	1343	3.1	2021	0.6
7 M	0156	3.1	0834	0.6	1411	3.1	2046	0.7
8 TU	0224	3.1	0904	0.7	1441	3.0	2113	0.8
9 W	0253	3.0	0933	0.8	1515	2.9	2141	0.9
10 TH ☽	0327	3.0	1009	0.9	1556	2.8	2222	1.1
11 F	0415	2.9	1104	1.0	1658	2.7	2331	1.2
12 SA	0528	2.8	1228	1.0	1824	2.6		
13 SU	0106	1.1	0701	2.8	1408	0.9	1959	2.6
14 M	0243	1.0	0830	3.0	1536	0.7	2120	2.8
15 TU	0401	0.8	0940	3.1	1642	0.6	2221	2.9
16 W	0459	0.7	1034	3.3	1732	0.5	2309	3.1
17 TH ○	0548	0.7	1121	3.4	1817	0.5	2352	3.1
18 F	0634	0.6	1205	3.4	1859	0.5		
19 SA	0032	3.2	0718	0.5	1249	3.4	1941	0.5
20 SU	0112	3.2	0801	0.5	1334	3.3	2022	0.6
21 M	0154	3.2	0843	0.5	1418	3.2	2100	0.6
22 TU	0234	3.2	0922	0.5	1501	3.1	2136	0.8
23 W	0313	3.1	1003	0.7	1546	2.9	2216	0.9
24 TH ☾	0359	3.1	1052	0.9	1641	2.8	2307	1.1
25 F	0457	3.0	1155	1.0	1749	2.7		
26 SA	0019	1.2	0613	2.9	1318	1.1	1912	2.6
27 SU	0148	1.2	0741	2.9	1450	1.0	2038	2.7
28 M	0315	1.1	0903	3.0	1606	0.8	2147	2.8
29 TU	0420	0.9	1001	3.1	1654	0.7	2231	2.9
30 W	0501	0.8	1039	3.1	1724	0.7	2301	3.0
31 TH	0534	0.8	1111	3.1	1754	0.6	2331	3.0

NOVEMBER

Day	Time	m	Time	m	Time	m	Time	m
1 F ●	0609	0.7	1146	3.1	1828	0.6		
2 SA	0004	3.1	0643	0.7	1219	3.1	1859	0.6
3 SU	0034	3.1	0713	0.7	1249	3.1	1926	0.6
4 M	0101	3.1	0742	0.7	1318	3.1	1953	0.7
5 TU	0130	3.1	0811	0.7	1349	3.0	2022	0.7
6 W	0200	3.1	0844	0.7	1424	3.0	2053	0.8
7 TH	0235	3.1	0922	0.7	1503	2.9	2130	0.9
8 F	0316	3.1	1005	0.8	1551	2.8	2216	1.0
9 SA ☽	0406	3.0	1100	0.8	1650	2.7	2319	1.1
10 SU	0512	3.0	1213	0.9	1804	2.6		
11 M	0041	1.0	0632	3.0	1339	0.8	1928	2.6
12 TU	0208	1.0	0755	3.0	1500	0.7	2045	2.8
13 W	0324	0.8	0906	3.2	1605	0.7	2146	2.9
14 TH	0425	0.8	1003	3.3	1659	0.6	2237	3.1
15 F ○	0518	0.7	1054	3.4	1747	0.6	2323	3.1
16 SA	0609	0.6	1143	3.3	1832	0.6		
17 SU	0007	3.2	0655	0.6	1230	3.3	1915	0.6
18 M	0049	3.2	0741	0.5	1317	3.2	1958	0.7
19 TU	0133	3.3	0827	0.5	1403	3.1	2040	0.7
20 W	0218	3.3	0910	0.6	1448	3.0	2119	0.8
21 TH	0259	3.2	0951	0.7	1532	2.9	2158	0.9
22 F	0342	3.2	1036	0.9	1621	2.8	2245	1.0
23 SA ☾	0433	3.1	1130	1.0	1719	2.7	2344	1.1
24 SU	0535	3.1	1235	1.1	1826	2.7		
25 M	0054	1.1	0646	3.0	1348	1.0	1936	2.7
26 TU	0210	1.1	0759	3.0	1457	0.9	2042	2.8
27 W	0315	1.0	0902	3.0	1552	0.9	2134	2.9
28 TH	0406	0.9	0950	3.1	1633	0.8	2215	3.0
29 F	0450	0.9	1031	3.1	1712	0.8	2253	3.0
30 SA	0532	0.8	1112	3.1	1751	0.7	2330	3.1

DECEMBER

Day	Time	m	Time	m	Time	m	Time	m
1 SU ●	0613	0.7	1150	3.1	1828	0.7		
2 M	0005	3.1	0648	0.7	1225	3.1	1901	0.7
3 TU	0038	3.2	0723	0.6	1259	3.1	1935	0.7
4 W	0112	3.2	0759	0.6	1337	3.0	2010	0.7
5 TH	0148	3.2	0837	0.6	1416	3.0	2046	0.7
6 F	0227	3.2	0919	0.6	1459	2.9	2127	0.7
7 SA	0311	3.1	1006	0.6	1547	2.8	2215	0.8
8 SU ☽	0401	3.1	1058	0.6	1641	2.7	2310	0.8
9 M	0457	3.1	1157	0.6	1742	2.7		
10 TU	0015	0.8	0603	3.0	1306	0.7	1851	2.7
11 W	0130	0.8	0717	3.1	1418	0.7	2002	2.8
12 TH	0244	0.8	0829	3.1	1526	0.8	2108	2.9
13 F	0352	0.8	0934	3.2	1626	0.8	2206	3.1
14 SA	0453	0.8	1033	3.2	1722	0.8	2259	3.1
15 SU ○	0551	0.7	1128	3.2	1812	0.7	2349	3.2
16 M	0642	0.6	1219	3.1	1858	0.7		
17 TU	0035	3.3	0730	0.6	1307	3.1	1943	0.7
18 W	0121	3.3	0817	0.6	1354	3.0	2027	0.7
19 TH	0206	3.3	0901	0.6	1437	3.0	2105	0.8
20 F	0247	3.3	0940	0.7	1517	2.9	2142	0.8
21 SA	0324	3.3	1018	0.8	1558	2.9	2221	0.9
22 SU ☾	0406	3.2	1059	0.9	1643	2.8	2305	1.0
23 M	0452	3.1	1145	1.0	1730	2.8	2355	1.0
24 TU	0544	3.1	1235	1.0	1823	2.8		
25 W	0052	1.0	0643	3.0	1332	1.0	1921	2.8
26 TH	0157	1.0	0747	3.0	1434	1.0	2023	2.8
27 F	0302	1.0	0850	2.9	1534	0.9	2122	2.9
28 SA	0403	1.0	0948	3.0	1629	0.8	2214	3.0
29 SU	0459	0.8	1040	3.0	1719	0.8	2301	3.0
30 M ●	0548	0.7	1126	3.0	1803	0.7	2342	3.1
31 TU	0630	0.6	1207	3.0	1844	0.6		

CUXHAVEN
LAT 53°52′N
LONG 8°43′E

TIMES AND HEIGHTS OF HIGH AND LOW WATER (Heights in Metres)

TIME ZONE
European Standard Time (UT+0100)
For Summer Time (area enclosed in shaded box) add 1 hour

2024

JANUARY

Day		Time	m
1	M	0359 1055 1629 2256	3.8 0.6 3.4 0.7
2	TU	0433 1129 1705 2331	3.7 0.7 3.3 0.8
3	W	0511 1204 1743	3.6 0.7 3.3
4	TH ☽	0009 0551 1241 1824	0.8 3.6 0.8 3.3
5	F	0051 0636 1324 1912	0.9 3.5 0.8 3.2
6	SA	0143 0732 1420 2012	0.9 3.4 0.9 3.2
7	SU	0250 0838 1529 2120	1.0 3.4 0.9 3.3
8	M	0404 0948 1640 2226	0.9 3.4 0.8 3.4
9	TU	0516 1056 1747 2326	0.8 3.5 0.7 3.5
10	W	0621 1157 1846	0.7 3.5 0.6
11	TH ●	0020 0716 1250 1938	3.6 0.5 3.6 0.6
12	F	0108 0806 1340 2027	3.7 0.5 3.6 0.5
13	SA	0155 0857 1429 2116	3.8 0.4 3.6 0.5
14	SU	0243 0949 1519 2203	3.9 0.3 3.6 0.4
15	M	0329 1037 1605 2246	3.9 0.3 3.5 0.4
16	TU	0414 1122 1650 2328	3.9 0.3 3.4 0.4
17	W	0500 1207 1735	3.8 0.4 3.4
18	TH ☾	0012 0548 1250 1822	0.5 3.7 0.4 3.3
19	F	0058 0640 1336 1913	0.5 3.7 0.6 3.3
20	SA	0151 0739 1432 2015	0.6 3.6 0.7 3.3
21	SU	0300 0851 1544 2129	0.7 3.5 0.9 3.3
22	M	0421 1009 1700 2241	0.8 3.5 0.9 3.5
23	TU	0538 1120 1808 2344	0.7 3.5 0.8 3.6
24	W	0643 1220 1905	0.6 3.5 0.7
25	TH ○	0036 0736 1310 1951	3.6 0.5 3.5 0.6
26	F	0121 0821 1353 2031	3.7 0.4 3.4 0.5
27	SA	0200 0901 1430 2107	3.7 0.4 3.5 0.5
28	SU	0235 0936 1503 2139	3.8 0.5 3.5 0.5
29	M	0307 1007 1533 2207	3.8 0.5 3.5 0.5
30	TU	0337 1035 1602 2236	3.8 0.5 3.5 0.6
31	W	0407 1104 1633	3.8 0.6 3.4

FEBRUARY

Day		Time	m
1	TH	0440 1134 1704 2337	3.7 0.6 3.4 0.6
2	F	0510 1157 1731	3.6 0.6 3.4
3	SA ☽	0001 0539 1220 1804	0.7 3.5 0.7 3.3
4	SU	0036 0623 1303 1857	0.8 3.4 0.8 3.2
5	M	0138 0731 1416 2014	0.9 3.3 0.9 3.2
6	TU	0305 0857 1547 2139	0.8 3.2 0.8 3.3
7	W	0437 1023 1715 2257	0.7 3.3 0.7 3.4
8	TH	0559 1138 1828	0.5 3.4 0.5
9	F ●	0002 0705 1240 1928	3.5 0.4 3.5 0.5
10	SA	0056 0800 1332 2020	3.7 0.3 3.5 0.4
11	SU	0143 0851 1420 2109	3.8 0.2 3.6 0.3
12	M	0230 0941 1506 2154	3.9 0.1 3.6 0.2
13	TU	0315 1027 1550 2235	3.9 0.1 3.5 0.2
14	W	0359 1107 1630 2313	3.9 0.2 3.5 0.2
15	TH	0442 1145 1708 2350	3.8 0.3 3.4 0.3
16	F ☾	0524 1219 1747	3.7 0.4 3.4
17	SA	0026 0608 1253 1830	0.4 3.6 0.6 3.3
18	SU	0110 0702 1342 1929	0.5 3.4 0.8 3.3
19	M	0216 0814 1457 2049	0.7 3.3 0.9 3.3
20	TU	0346 0942 1627 2216	0.8 3.2 0.9 3.4
21	W	0519 1106 1750 2329	0.7 3.3 0.8 3.5
22	TH	0634 1210 1852	0.5 3.3 0.7
23	F	0023 0726 1258 1937	3.6 0.4 3.4 0.5
24	SA ○	0105 0807 1336 2015	3.6 0.3 3.4 0.4
25	SU	0141 0843 1410 2049	3.7 0.3 3.5 0.4
26	M	0214 0915 1439 2120	3.7 0.3 3.5 0.4
27	TU	0244 0942 1506 2146	3.8 0.4 3.5 0.4
28	W	0312 1008 1532 2213	3.8 0.4 3.5 0.4
29	TH	0340 1035 1600 2242	3.7 0.4 3.5 0.4

MARCH

Day		Time	m
1	F	0409 1101 1628 2308	3.7 0.4 3.5 0.4
2	SA	0436 1119 1650 2327	3.6 0.5 3.4 0.5
3	SU ☽	0501 1135 1717 2353	3.4 0.6 3.3 0.6
4	M	0539 1211 1806	3.3 0.8 3.2
5	TU	0050 0647 1326 1927	0.7 3.1 0.9 3.1
6	W	0223 0822 1509 2104	0.7 3.0 0.8 3.2
7	TH	0409 0959 1650 2234	0.5 3.1 0.6 3.3
8	F	0542 1122 1813 2345	0.4 3.2 0.5 3.5
9	SA	0653 1227 1916	0.2 3.4 0.4
10	SU ●	0040 0749 1318 2007	3.7 0.1 3.5 0.3
11	M	0127 0837 1402 2052	3.8 0.1 3.6 0.3
12	TU	0211 0921 1444 2135	3.9 0.1 3.6 0.2
13	W	0255 1004 1525 2215	3.9 0.1 3.5 0.1
14	TH	0338 1041 1603 2252	3.8 0.1 3.5 0.1
15	F	0420 1115 1638 2326	3.7 0.3 3.5 0.2
16	SA	0459 1145 1713 2358	3.6 0.4 3.4 0.3
17	SU ☾	0540 1215 1754	3.4 0.6 3.4
18	M	0038 0631 1300 1852	0.5 3.2 0.8 3.3
19	TU	0141 0744 1416 2014	0.7 3.1 0.9 3.3
20	W	0314 0915 1553 2147	0.7 3.0 0.9 3.3
21	TH	0455 1045 1725 2307	0.6 3.1 0.8 3.4
22	F	0615 1151 1830	0.4 3.2 0.6
23	SA	0001 0704 1235 1913	3.5 0.3 3.3 0.5
24	SU	0039 0739 1308 1949	3.6 0.2 3.4 0.4
25	M ○	0114 0812 1340 2023	3.6 0.2 3.4 0.3
26	TU	0147 0844 1410 2054	3.6 0.2 3.5 0.3
27	W	0217 0912 1437 2122	3.7 0.3 3.6 0.3
28	TH	0244 0937 1502 2148	3.7 0.3 3.5 0.3
29	F	0312 1002 1528 2216	3.6 0.4 3.5 0.3
30	SA	0341 1028 1556 2243	3.6 0.4 3.5 0.3
31	SU	0411 1051 1623 [illegible]	3.5 0.4 3.5 [illegible]

APRIL

Day		Time	m
1	M	0442 1112 1654 2337	3.3 0.5 3.4 0.5
2	TU ☽	0524 1151 1745	3.2 0.7 3.3
3	W	0033 0631 1304 1904	0.6 3.1 0.8 3.2
4	TH	0204 0804 1446 2040	0.5 3.0 0.8 3.2
5	F	0350 0941 1628 2211	0.4 3.0 0.6 3.4
6	SA	0522 1102 1750 2322	0.3 3.2 0.5 3.6
7	SU	0631 1205 1852	0.2 3.4 0.4
8	M ●	0017 0726 1255 1944	3.7 0.2 3.5 0.3
9	TU	0104 0812 1338 2029	3.9 0.1 3.6 0.3
10	W	0148 0854 1417 2111	3.9 0.2 3.7 0.2
11	TH	0231 0933 1456 2151	3.8 0.2 3.6 0.1
12	F	0315 1010 1534 2229	3.7 0.2 3.6 0.1
13	SA	0358 1044 1611 2304	3.6 0.3 3.6 0.2
14	SU	0438 1115 1647 2337	3.5 0.5 3.5 0.3
15	M ☾	0520 1147 1729	3.3 0.6 3.4
16	TU	0017 0610 1232 1825	0.5 3.1 0.8 3.3
17	W	0115 0718 1342 1941	0.6 3.0 0.9 3.3
18	TH	0240 0842 1514 2110	0.7 3.0 0.8 3.3
19	F	0416 1008 1644 2229	0.6 3.0 0.7 3.4
20	SA	0534 1114 1750 2323	0.4 3.2 0.6 3.5
21	SU	0623 1157 1834	0.3 3.3 0.5
22	M	0002 0657 1230 1911	3.5 0.2 3.4 0.4
23	TU	0038 0731 1304 1949	3.6 0.3 3.5 0.3
24	W ○	0114 0807 1337 2024	3.6 0.3 3.5 0.3
25	TH	0146 0838 1406 2054	3.6 0.3 3.6 0.4
26	F	0216 0905 1433 2122	3.6 0.4 3.6 0.3
27	SA	0247 0933 1501 2152	3.6 0.4 3.6 0.3
28	SU	0320 1002 1533 2226	3.5 0.4 3.6 0.3
29	M	0357 1034 1609 2301	3.4 0.5 3.6 0.4
30	TU	0439 1109 1651 2342	3.3 0.6 3.5 0.4

MAY

Day		Time	m
1	W ☾	0527 1155 1744	3.2 0.7 3.4
2	TH	0039 0632 1303 1856	0.5 3.1 0.8 3.4
3	F	0159 0754 1432 2021	0.4 3.0 0.7 3.4
4	SA	0331 0920 1603 2144	0.4 3.1 0.6 3.5
5	SU	0454 1036 1719 2252	0.3 3.2 0.5 3.7
6	M	0559 1135 1820 2349	0.3 3.4 0.5 3.8
7	TU	0653 1226 1914	0.3 3.6 0.4
8	W ●	0039 0742 1310 2003	3.8 0.3 3.6 0.3
9	TH	0126 0825 1350 2046	3.8 0.3 3.7 0.2
10	F	0211 0904 1430 2127	3.7 0.3 3.7 0.2
11	SA	0255 0942 1510 2208	3.6 0.3 3.7 0.2
12	SU	0339 1018 1550 2246	3.5 0.4 3.6 0.3
13	M	0422 1053 1629 2323	3.4 0.5 3.6 0.4
14	TU	0505 1128 1711	3.2 0.6 3.5
15	W ☽	0003 0552 1212 1802	0.5 3.1 0.8 3.4
16	TH	0055 0650 1310 1906	0.6 3.0 0.8 3.4
17	F	0202 0800 1425 2020	0.6 3.0 0.8 3.4
18	SA	0320 0913 1544 2132	0.6 3.1 0.7 3.4
19	SU	0431 1017 1650 2230	0.5 3.2 0.6 3.5
20	M	0524 1104 1740 2314	0.4 3.3 0.6 3.5
21	TU	0605 1144 1825 2356	0.4 3.4 0.5 3.6
22	W	0646 1223 1910	0.4 3.5 0.5
23	TH ○	0037 0727 1302 1951	3.6 0.4 3.6 0.5
24	F	0116 0804 1337 2027	3.6 0.4 3.7 0.5
25	SA	0152 0838 1409 2101	3.6 0.4 3.7 0.4
26	SU	0229 0912 1443 2138	3.6 0.5 3.7 0.4
27	M	0309 0949 1521 2219	3.5 0.5 3.7 0.4
28	TU	0353 1028 1604 2304	3.4 0.5 3.7 0.4
29	W	0441 1113 1653 2353	3.4 0.6 3.7 0.4
30	TH ☾	0534 1204 1748	3.2 0.6 3.6
31	F	0049 0633 1304 1851	0.4 3.2 0.7 3.6

JUNE

Day		Time	m
1	SA	0155 0741 1415 2002	0.4 3.1 0.6 3.6
2	SU	0308 0854 1532 2115	0.4 3.2 0.6 3.7
3	M	0419 1003 1643 2222	0.4 3.3 0.6 3.7
4	TU	0522 1103 1747 2321	0.4 3.5 0.6 3.8
5	W	0619 1156 1846	0.4 3.6 0.5
6	TH ●	0017 0713 1245 1940	3.8 0.4 3.7 0.4
7	F	0109 0800 1330 2027	3.7 0.4 3.7 0.3
8	SA	0157 0842 1411 2111	3.6 0.4 3.7 0.3
9	SU	0242 0922 1453 2153	3.6 0.4 3.8 0.3
10	M	0326 1000 1534 2233	3.5 0.5 3.8 0.4
11	TU	0407 1035 1612 2309	3.4 0.5 3.7 0.5
12	W	0447 1111 1652 2348	3.3 0.6 3.7 0.5
13	TH	0530 1151 1736	3.2 0.7 3.6
14	F ☽	0030 0617 1238 1826	0.6 3.2 0.8 3.5
15	SA	0119 0709 1331 1922	0.6 3.2 0.8 3.5
16	SU	0213 0806 1432 2023	0.6 3.2 0.8 3.5
17	M	0312 0905 1536 2123	0.6 3.3 0.8 3.5
18	TU	0412 1001 1637 2219	0.6 3.4 0.8 3.5
19	W	0507 1053 1736 2312	0.6 3.5 0.7 3.6
20	TH	0601 1142 1832	0.6 3.6 0.6
21	F	0003 0651 1229 1921	3.6 0.5 3.6 0.5
22	SA ○	0050 0737 1311 2005	3.6 0.5 3.7 0.5
23	SU	0134 0819 1351 2048	3.7 0.5 3.8 0.5
24	M	0218 0901 1432 2133	3.6 0.5 3.9 0.4
25	TU	0304 0944 1515 2219	3.6 0.5 3.9 0.3
26	W	0350 1027 1600 2306	3.5 0.5 3.9 0.3
27	TH	0438 1113 1649 2356	3.4 0.5 3.8 0.3
28	F ☾	0530 1202 1741	3.3 0.5 3.8
29	SA	0046 0623 1254 1837	0.3 3.3 0.6 3.7
30	SU	0138 0719 1352 1938	0.4 3.2 0.6 3.7

SUNRISE AND SUNSET TIMES

CUXHAVEN
At 53°52′N 8°43′E
European Standard Time (UT+0100)

		Sunrise	Sunset
Jan	01	0843	1614
	15	0835	1635
Feb	01	0811	1707
	15	0745	1735
Mar	01	0713	1802
	15	0640	1829
European Summer Time (UT+0200)			
Apr	01	0658	2001
	15	0625	2027
May	01	0549	2056
	15	0523	2121
Jun	01	0501	2146
	15	0453	2158
Jul	01	0458	2159
	15	0513	2148
Aug	01	0539	2123
	15	0603	2055
Sep	01	0634	2015
	15	0658	1941
Oct	01	0727	1901
	15	0753	1828
European Standard Time (UT+0100)			
Nov	01	0725	1651
	15	0752	1626
Dec	01	0820	1608
	15	[illegible]	[illegible]

CUXHAVEN
LAT 53°52′N
LONG 8°43′E

TIMES AND HEIGHTS OF HIGH AND LOW WATER (Heights in Metres)

TIME ZONE
European Standard Time (UT+0100)
For Summer Time (area enclosed in shaded box) add 1 hour

2024

JULY

Date	Day	Time	m
1	M	0237 0822 1458 2046	0.5 3.2 0.6 3.7
2	TU	0342 0929 1610 2156	0.6 3.3 0.7 3.7
3	W	0449 1034 1721 2302	0.6 3.5 0.7 3.7
4	TH	0553 1134 1826	0.7 3.6 0.6
5	F ●	0003 0651 1228 1925	3.7 0.6 3.7 0.5
6	SA	0059 0743 1316 2016	3.6 0.5 3.7 0.4
7	SU	0149 0828 1400 2101	3.5 0.5 3.8 0.3
8	M	0233 0908 1440 2142	3.5 0.5 3.9 0.4
9	TU	0312 0945 1518 2218	3.5 0.5 3.9 0.5
10	W	0348 1017 1552 2250	3.5 0.5 3.9 0.5
11	TH	0422 1050 1627 2324	3.4 0.6 3.8 0.6
12	F	0459 1126 1705 2359	3.4 0.7 3.7 0.6
13	SA ☽	0537 1203 1744	3.4 0.7 3.7
14	SU	0033 0615 1239 1824	0.6 3.3 0.8 3.6
15	M	0106 0656 1321 1911	0.7 3.3 0.9 3.5
16	TU	0152 0748 1419 2012	0.8 3.3 0.9 3.4
17	W	0255 0853 1533 2122	0.8 3.3 0.9 3.4
18	TH	0408 1002 1649 2233	0.8 3.4 0.8 3.5
19	F	0519 1106 1800 2337	0.7 3.5 0.7 3.5
20	SA	0623 1203 1859	0.6 3.6 0.6
21	SU O	0033 0718 1253 1950	3.6 0.5 3.7 0.5
22	M	0122 0807 1338 2039	3.6 0.5 3.9 0.4
23	TU	0209 0854 1422 2128	3.7 0.5 4.0 0.3
24	W	0256 0940 1506 2215	3.6 0.4 4.0 0.3
25	TH	0342 1022 1550 2259	3.5 0.4 4.0 0.3
26	F	0426 1103 1636 2343	3.5 0.4 3.9 0.3
27	SA	0512 1148 1724	3.4 0.5 3.9
28	SU ☾	0027 0558 1233 1815	0.4 3.4 0.5 3.8
29	M	0109 0647 1322 1910	0.5 3.3 0.6 3.7
30	TU	0158 0744 1424 2018	0.7 3.3 0.8 3.6
31	W	0304 0856 1542 2135	0.9 3.4 0.8 3.6

AUGUST

Date	Day	Time	m
1	TH	0422 1013 1706 2252	0.9 3.5 0.8 3.6
2	F	0537 1122 1819 2359	0.9 3.6 0.7 3.6
3	SA	0640 1219 1919	0.7 3.7 0.5
4	SU ●	0053 0732 1307 2008	3.5 0.6 3.7 0.4
5	M	0140 0816 1348 2050	3.5 0.5 3.8 0.4
6	TU	0220 0854 1425 2126	3.5 0.5 3.9 0.4
7	W	0253 0927 1458 2157	3.6 0.5 3.9 0.5
8	TH	0323 0956 1528 2223	3.6 0.5 3.9 0.5
9	F	0351 1024 1558 2251	3.5 0.6 3.8 0.6
10	SA	0422 1056 1630 2322	3.5 0.6 3.7 0.6
11	SU	0455 1127 1702 2347	3.5 0.6 3.7 0.6
12	M ☽	0524 1153 1732	3.4 0.7 3.6
13	TU	0007 0554 1221 1809	0.7 3.4 0.9 3.4
14	W	0041 0641 1314 1910	0.9 3.3 1.0 3.3
15	TH	0146 0751 1436 2033	1.0 3.2 1.0 3.2
16	F	0316 0917 1610 2201	0.9 3.3 0.9 3.3
17	SA	0447 1038 1736 2318	0.8 3.4 0.7 3.4
18	SU	0603 1144 1844	0.6 3.6 0.6
19	M O	0020 0704 1237 1939	3.5 0.6 3.8 0.5
20	TU	0111 0756 1323 2028	3.6 0.5 3.9 0.4
21	W	0157 0843 1407 2116	3.7 0.5 4.0 0.4
22	TH	0241 0927 1451 2200	3.7 0.4 4.1 0.3
23	F	0324 1008 1534 2240	3.6 0.3 4.0 0.3
24	SA	0404 1046 1616 2318	3.6 0.4 4.0 0.4
25	SU	0444 1125 1700 2355	3.5 0.5 3.9 0.5
26	M ☾	0525 1205 1747	3.5 0.6 3.7
27	TU	0032 0610 1250 1841	0.7 3.4 0.7 3.6
28	W	0118 0707 1352 1951	0.9 3.4 0.9 3.4
29	TH	0228 0825 1518 2118	1.1 3.4 1.0 3.4
30	F	0358 0955 1655 2246	1.1 3.5 0.9 3.4
31	SA	0526 1114 1817 2356	1.0 3.6 0.7 3.4

SEPTEMBER

Date	Day	Time	m
1	SU	0633 1211 1913	0.8 3.7 0.6
2	M	0045 0721 1253 1953	3.5 0.6 3.7 0.4
3	TU ●	0123 0759 1329 2029	3.5 0.5 3.8 0.4
4	W	0157 0833 1403 2101	3.5 0.5 3.8 0.4
5	TH	0227 0904 1433 2128	3.6 0.5 3.8 0.5
6	F	0253 0931 1500 2152	3.6 0.5 3.8 0.5
7	SA	0318 0956 1527 2216	3.6 0.5 3.7 0.6
8	SU	0345 1024 1555 2242	3.5 0.6 3.7 0.6
9	M	0414 1053 1624 2304	3.5 0.6 3.6 0.6
10	TU	0440 1116 1652 2323	3.5 0.7 3.5 0.8
11	W ☽	0508 1140 1727 2353	3.4 0.9 3.3 1.0
12	TH	0553 1230 1828	3.3 1.0 3.2
13	F	0059 0707 1356 1958	1.1 3.2 1.0 3.1
14	SA	0238 0842 1541 2136	1.1 3.2 0.9 3.1
15	SU	0421 1013 1715 2300	0.9 3.4 0.7 3.3
16	M	0545 1124 1827	0.7 3.6 0.6
17	TU	0004 0648 1217 1922	3.5 0.6 3.8 0.5
18	W O	0054 0738 1302 2009	3.6 0.6 4.0 0.4
19	TH	0137 0824 1346 2053	3.7 0.5 4.1 0.4
20	F	0218 0907 1429 2135	3.7 0.4 4.1 0.4
21	SA	0258 0948 1512 2214	3.7 0.4 4.0 0.4
22	SU	0337 1026 1555 2248	3.7 0.4 3.9 0.5
23	M	0415 1102 1636 2322	3.6 0.5 3.8 0.6
24	TU ☾	0453 1139 1721 2357	3.6 0.6 3.6 0.8
25	W	0537 1222 1815	3.5 0.8 3.4
26	TH	0044 0635 1324 1926	1.0 3.4 1.0 3.2
27	F	0155 0756 1454 2057	1.2 3.4 1.0 3.2
28	SA	0331 0930 1636 2229	1.2 3.4 0.9 3.2
29	SU	0506 1055 1801 2340	1.0 3.5 0.8 3.3
30	M	0616 1152 1854	0.9 3.6 0.6

OCTOBER

Date	Day	Time	m
1	TU	0024 0658 1229 1926	3.4 0.7 3.7 0.5
2	W ●	0054 0731 1301 1956	3.5 0.6 3.7 0.5
3	TH	0124 0804 1333 2027	3.5 0.5 3.7 0.5
4	F	0155 0836 1404 2055	3.6 0.5 3.7 0.5
5	SA	0222 0904 1431 2119	3.6 0.5 3.7 0.5
6	SU	0247 0929 1457 2142	3.6 0.5 3.7 0.6
7	M	0312 0955 1525 2207	3.6 0.6 3.6 0.6
8	TU	0339 1023 1555 2231	3.5 0.6 3.5 0.7
9	W	0408 1050 1627 2256	3.5 0.7 3.4 0.8
10	TH ☽	0441 1121 1707 2332	3.5 0.8 3.3 1.0
11	F	0528 1211 1808	3.4 0.9 3.2
12	SA	0037 0640 1334 1934	1.1 3.3 0.9 3.1
13	SU	0213 0813 1517 2110	1.1 3.3 0.8 3.1
14	M	0355 0944 1651 2234	1.0 3.5 0.7 3.2
15	TU	0519 1057 1802 2338	0.8 3.7 0.6 3.5
16	W	0621 1150 1855	0.7 3.9 0.5
17	TH O	0028 0712 1237 1942	3.6 0.6 4.0 0.5
18	F	0111 0758 1321 2025	3.7 0.6 4.0 0.5
19	SA	0150 0842 1406 2106	3.8 0.5 4.0 0.5
20	SU	0230 0924 1451 2145	3.8 0.5 3.9 0.5
21	M	0310 1005 1535 2221	3.7 0.5 3.8 0.6
22	TU	0350 1043 1619 2255	3.7 0.5 3.6 0.7
23	W	0430 1120 1703 2331	3.7 0.6 3.5 0.9
24	TH ☾	0514 1203 1755	3.6 0.8 3.3
25	F	0018 0609 1302 1901	1.0 3.5 1.0 3.1
26	SA	0124 0723 1423 2023	1.2 3.4 1.0 3.1
27	SU	0252 0851 1557 2150	1.2 3.4 1.0 3.1
28	M	0424 1013 1720 2300	1.1 3.5 0.8 3.3
29	TU	0534 1113 1813 2345	0.9 3.6 0.6 3.4
30	W	0619 1152 1845	0.8 3.6 0.6
31	TH	0015 0653 1225 1915	3.5 0.7 3.7 0.6

NOVEMBER

Date	Day	Time	m
1	F ●	0046 0729 1300 1949	3.5 0.6 3.6 0.6
2	SA	0120 0804 1333 2021	3.6 0.6 3.7 0.6
3	SU	0151 0836 1403 2048	3.6 0.6 3.7 0.6
4	M	0218 0904 1432 2115	3.6 0.6 3.6 0.6
5	TU	0245 0932 1504 2142	3.6 0.6 3.5 0.7
6	W	0315 1004 1538 2212	3.6 0.6 3.5 0.7
7	TH	0350 1039 1617 2246	3.6 0.7 3.4 0.8
8	F	0429 1119 1702 2329	3.5 0.7 3.3 1.0
9	SA ☽	0519 1211 1800	3.5 0.8 3.2
10	SU	0030 0625 1323 1915	1.0 3.4 0.8 3.1
11	M	0152 0745 1451 2040	1.0 3.4 0.7 3.1
12	TU	0322 0909 1616 2159	0.9 3.5 0.7 3.2
13	W	0442 1021 1725 2302	0.8 3.7 0.6 3.4
14	TH	0546 1119 1821 2355	0.8 3.9 0.6 3.6
15	F O	0641 1210 1911	0.7 3.9 0.6
16	SA	0042 0732 1259 1957	3.7 0.6 3.9 0.6
17	SU	0125 0819 1347 2040	3.7 0.5 3.9 0.6
18	M	0206 0904 1434 2121	3.8 0.5 3.7 0.6
19	TU	0249 0948 1522 2201	3.8 0.5 3.6 0.7
20	W	0333 1030 1607 2238	3.8 0.5 3.5 0.7
21	TH	0414 1110 1650 2315	3.8 0.7 3.4 0.9
22	F	0456 1151 1737 2358	3.7 0.8 3.3 1.0
23	SA ☾	0545 1241 1831	3.6 0.9 3.2
24	SU	0053 0645 1344 1936	1.1 3.5 1.0 3.1
25	M	0202 0756 1457 2047	1.1 3.5 1.0 3.2
26	TU	0318 0909 1610 2153	1.1 3.5 0.9 3.2
27	W	0428 1012 1708 2246	1.0 3.5 0.8 3.4
28	TH	0522 1100 1752 2327	0.9 3.6 0.7 3.5
29	F	0608 1143 1831	0.8 3.6 0.7
30	SA	0005 0652 1224 1911	3.5 0.8 3.6 0.7

DECEMBER

Date	Day	Time	m
1	SU ●	0044 0733 1303 1949	3.6 0.7 3.6 0.6
2	M	0120 0810 1339 2022	3.6 0.6 3.6 0.6
3	TU	0154 0844 1414 2056	3.7 0.6 3.6 0.6
4	W	0227 0919 1452 2131	3.7 0.6 3.5 0.6
5	TH	0303 0957 1531 2207	3.7 0.5 3.5 0.6
6	F	0342 1038 1613 2246	3.7 0.5 3.4 0.7
7	SA	0425 1123 1700 2331	3.7 0.5 3.3 0.7
8	SU ☽	0514 1213 1753	3.6 0.6 3.2
9	M	0025 0610 1312 1853	0.8 3.6 0.6 3.2
10	TU	0129 0716 1420 2003	0.8 3.6 0.6 3.1
11	W	0243 0829 1534 2116	0.8 3.6 0.7 3.2
12	TH	0359 0942 1643 2223	0.8 3.7 0.7 3.4
13	F	0509 1048 1746 2322	0.8 3.8 0.8 3.6
14	SA	0613 1148 1844	0.8 3.8 0.7
15	SU O	0016 0712 1244 1936	3.7 0.6 3.8 0.7
16	M	0106 0804 1336 2022	3.7 0.5 3.7 0.7
17	TU	0151 0852 1425 2105	3.8 0.5 3.7 0.7
18	W	0236 0938 1512 2148	3.9 0.5 3.6 0.7
19	TH	0320 1022 1555 2226	3.9 0.6 3.5 0.7
20	F	0400 1100 1635 2301	3.9 0.6 3.5 0.8
21	SA	0438 1137 1713 2338	3.8 0.8 3.4 0.9
22	SU ☾	0518 1216 1754	3.7 0.8 3.3
23	M	0019 0603 1258 1840	0.9 3.7 0.9 3.3
24	TU	0106 0654 1346 1932	1.0 3.6 0.9 3.2
25	W	0202 0751 1443 2031	1.0 3.5 0.9 3.2
26	TH	0306 0855 1545 2132	1.0 3.5 0.9 3.3
27	F	0413 0957 1647 2231	1.0 3.4 0.9 3.4
28	SA	0517 1056 1745 2324	0.9 3.5 0.8 3.5
29	SU	0616 1150 1836	0.8 3.5 0.7
30	M ●	0012 0706 1238 1922	3.5 0.6 3.5 0.6
31	TU	0055 0749 1321 2004	3.6 0.6 3.5 0.6

HOEK VAN HOLLAND

LAT 51°51′N
LONG 4°03′E
TIMES AND HEIGHTS OF HIGH AND LOW WATER (Heights in Metres)

TIME ZONE
European Standard Time (UT+0100)
For Summer Time (area enclosed in shaded box) add 1 hour

2024

JANUARY

Date	Day	Time	m	Time	m	Time	m	Time	m
1	M	0151	0.7	0558	2.0	1117	0.2	1821	2.1
2	TU	0116	0.6	0636	1.9	1208	0.2	1905	2.0
3	W	0143	0.6	0719	1.9	1302	0.2	1955	2.0
4	TH ☽	0217	0.6	0811	1.8	1356	0.2	2051	1.9
5	F	0300	0.6	0912	1.8	1449	0.3	2149	1.9
6	SA	0356	0.6	1014	1.8	1545	0.3	2248	1.9
7	SU	0521	0.5	1118	1.8	1650	0.4	2348	2.0
8	M	0604	0.5	1217	1.9	1752	0.4		
9	TU	0045	2.0	0635	0.5	1309	2.0	1840	0.5
10	W	0135	2.1	0708	0.4	1355	2.1	1922	0.5
11	TH ●	0221	2.1	0742	0.4	1439	2.3	2001	0.5
12	F	0305	2.1	0818	0.3	1522	2.3	2318	0.5
13	SA	0349	2.1	0856	0.2	1606	2.4		
14	SU	0002	0.5	0433	2.1	0937	0.1	1650	2.4
15	M	0047	0.5	0518	2.1	1022	0.1	1737	2.4
16	TU	0133	0.6	0605	2.1	1111	0.1	1827	2.3
17	W	0219	0.6	0656	2.0	1209	0.1	1923	2.2
18	TH ☾	0301	0.6	0751	2.0	1319	0.1	2026	2.1
19	F	0250	0.6	0853	2.0	1433	0.2	2132	2.0
20	SA	0333	0.6	0959	1.9	1546	0.2	2245	1.9
21	SU	0441	0.6	1111	1.9	1701	0.3	2358	1.9
22	M	0543	0.5	1218	1.9	1948	0.4		
23	TU	0100	1.9	0900	0.5	1318	2.0	2136	0.4
24	W	0157	2.0	0957	0.4	1410	2.1	2231	0.5
25	TH ○	0247	2.0	1042	0.3	1454	2.1	2310	0.5
26	F	0328	2.0	0824	0.3	1532	2.2	2346	0.6
27	SA	0401	2.0	0855	0.3	1607	2.2		
28	SU	0024	0.6	0431	2.0	0926	0.2	1642	2.2
29	M	0100	0.6	0503	2.1	1001	0.2	1718	2.2
30	TU	0121	0.6	0535	2.1	1039	0.1	1752	2.2
31	W	0115	0.6	0608	2.0	1120	0.1	1825	2.1

FEBRUARY

Date	Day	Time	m	Time	m	Time	m	Time	m
1	TH	0000	0.5	0642	2.0	1205	0.1	1900	2.1
2	F	0118	0.5	0720	2.0	1258	0.2	1943	2.0
3	SA ☽	0201	0.5	0808	1.9	1403	0.2	2042	1.9
4	SU	0251	0.5	0918	1.8	1505	0.3	2154	1.9
5	M	0351	0.5	1033	1.8	1614	0.4	2305	1.8
6	TU	0513	0.5	1145	1.8	1731	0.4		
7	W	0018	1.8	0608	0.4	1248	1.9	1826	0.5
8	TH	0119	1.9	0644	0.4	1340	2.1	2149	0.5
9	F ●	0207	2.0	0719	0.3	1424	2.2	2233	0.5
10	SA	0251	2.1	0755	0.2	1507	2.4	2304	0.5
11	SU	0333	2.1	0833	0.1	1550	2.4	2345	0.5
12	M	0416	2.2	0914	0.0	1633	2.5		
13	TU	0029	0.5	0459	2.2	0958	0.0	1718	2.4
14	W	0115	0.5	0543	2.2	1046	0.0	1804	2.3
15	TH	0157	0.5	0629	2.2	1142	0.1	1855	2.2
16	F ☾	0209	0.5	0718	2.1	1306	0.1	1951	2.0
17	SA	0201	0.5	0815	2.0	1424	0.2	2055	1.9
18	SU	0257	0.4	0923	1.9	1533	0.3	2216	1.7
19	M	0415	0.4	1047	1.8	1647	0.4	2346	1.7
20	TU	0519	0.4	1209	1.9	1752	0.4		
21	W	0052	1.8	0609	0.4	1313	2.0	2134	0.4
22	TH	0148	1.9	0948	0.3	1404	2.1	2227	0.4
23	F	0233	1.9	1034	0.3	1442	2.1	2303	0.5
24	SA ○	0310	2.0	1111	0.3	1515	2.2	2333	0.5
25	SU	0339	2.0	0830	0.2	1546	2.2	2359	0.5
26	M	0407	2.1	0857	0.2	1618	2.2	2359	0.5
27	TU	0436	2.1	0928	0.2	1650	2.2	2359	0.5
28	W	0507	2.1	1003	0.2	1721	2.2	2224	0.5
29	TH	0537	2.1	1039	0.2	1751	2.2	2259	0.4

MARCH

Date	Day	Time	m	Time	m	Time	m	Time	m
1	F	0607	2.1	1117	0.1	1823	2.1	2336	0.3
2	SA	0641	2.1	1159	0.1	1901	2.1		
3	SU ☽	0019	0.3	0722	2.1	1256	0.2	1949	2.0
4	M	0155	0.3	0815	1.9	1442	0.3	2100	1.8
5	TU	0310	0.4	0950	1.8	1557	0.4	2231	1.6
6	W	0429	0.4	1120	1.8	1714	0.4	2358	1.6
7	TH	0534	0.3	1231	1.9	1806	0.5		
8	F	0102	1.8	0615	0.3	1322	2.1	2141	0.4
9	SA	0150	1.9	0652	0.2	1406	2.3	2221	0.5
10	SU ●	0231	2.0	0729	0.1	1447	2.4	1955	0.5
11	M	0312	2.1	0808	0.0	1529	2.4	2032	0.5
12	TU	0353	2.2	0849	0.0	1611	2.4	2111	0.5
13	W	0435	2.3	0933	0.0	1655	2.4	2200	0.5
14	TH	0517	2.3	1021	0.1	1739	2.3	2243	0.4
15	F	0600	2.3	1118	0.1	1826	2.1	2341	0.4
16	SA	0647	2.2	1325	0.2	1918	1.9		
17	SU ☾	0116	0.3	0741	2.0	1413	0.2	2020	1.7
18	M	0225	0.3	0851	1.9	1518	0.3	2151	1.5
19	TU	0352	0.3	1031	1.7	1630	0.4	2332	1.5
20	W	0457	0.3	1158	1.8	1732	0.5		
21	TH	0035	1.7	0547	0.3	1257	2.0	2110	0.4
22	F	0126	1.8	0924	0.3	1342	2.1	2201	0.4
23	SA	0208	1.9	1013	0.2	1418	2.1	2240	0.4
24	SU	0242	1.9	1047	0.2	1449	2.2	2311	0.4
25	M ○	0310	2.0	0805	0.2	1519	2.2	2338	0.4
26	TU	0337	2.1	0828	0.2	1549	2.2	2347	0.4
27	W	0407	2.1	0858	0.2	1620	2.2	2359	0.4
28	TH	0437	2.2	0931	0.2	1650	2.2	2153	0.4
29	F	0507	2.2	1005	0.2	1721	2.2	2226	0.3
30	SA	0538	2.2	1043	0.2	1754	2.2	2304	0.2
31	SU	0612	2.2	1126	0.2	1833	2.1	2349	0.2

APRIL

Date	Day	Time	m	Time	m	Time	m	Time	m
1	M	0653	2.1	1224	0.3	1920	1.9		
2	TU ☽	0052	0.2	0744	2.0	1440	0.3	2025	1.7
3	W	0241	0.3	0917	1.8	1547	0.4	2207	1.5
4	TH	0352	0.3	1100	1.8	1655	0.4	2337	1.5
5	F	0455	0.2	1210	2.0	2011	0.4		
6	SA	0039	1.7	0542	0.2	1300	2.1	2123	0.4
7	SU	0126	1.9	0623	0.1	1343	2.3	2154	0.4
8	M ●	0207	2.0	0703	0.0	1424	2.3	1930	0.4
9	TU	0248	2.1	0744	0.0	1506	2.4	2008	0.4
10	W	0329	2.2	0826	0.0	1549	2.3	2048	0.4
11	TH	0410	2.3	0910	0.1	1632	2.3	2132	0.3
12	F	0452	2.3	1319	0.2	1716	2.1	2220	0.3
13	SA	0535	2.3	1406	0.2	1801	2.0	2318	0.3
14	SU	0621	2.2	1321	0.3	1850	1.8		
15	M ☾	0043	0.2	0714	2.0	1401	0.3	1949	1.6
16	TU	0158	0.2	0827	1.8	1502	0.4	2115	1.4
17	W	0330	0.2	1009	1.7	1611	0.4	2306	1.4
18	TH	0433	0.2	1135	1.8	1711	0.5		
19	F	0006	1.6	0524	0.2	1228	1.9	2005	0.4
20	SA	0054	1.7	0611	0.2	1311	2.0	2114	0.4
21	SU	0134	1.8	0653	0.2	1346	2.1	2159	0.4
22	M	0207	1.9	0726	0.2	1417	2.1	2237	0.4
23	TU	0235	2.0	0950	0.3	1447	2.2	2308	0.4
24	W ○	0304	2.1	1032	0.3	1518	2.2	2310	0.4
25	TH	0335	2.1	1114	0.3	1550	2.2	2335	0.3
26	F	0408	2.2	1153	0.3	1623	2.2	2130	0.3
27	SA	0440	2.2	0941	0.3	1657	2.1	2205	0.2
28	SU	0514	2.2	1022	0.3	1733	2.0	2247	0.2
29	M	0552	2.2	1329	0.3	1814	1.9	2338	0.1
30	TU	0636	2.1	1400	0.3	1903	1.8		

MAY

Date	Day	Time	m	Time	m	Time	m	Time	m
1	W ☽	0050	0.1	0730	2.0	1443	0.4	2013	1.6
2	TH	0213	0.1	0905	1.8	1541	0.4	2147	1.5
3	F	0317	0.2	1035	1.9	1806	0.5	2308	1.6
4	SA	0418	0.2	1142	2.0	1944	0.4		
5	SU	0010	1.7	0510	0.1	1234	2.1	2045	0.4
6	M	0058	1.9	0556	0.1	1319	2.2	2116	0.4
7	TU	0142	2.0	0640	0.1	1402	2.3	1908	0.4
8	W ●	0224	2.1	0723	0.1	1446	2.3	1948	0.4
9	TH	0306	2.2	0808	0.2	1529	2.2	2030	0.3
10	F	0349	2.3	1200	0.2	1613	2.1		
11	SA	0029	0.3	0431	2.3	1301	0.3	1657	2.0
12	SU	0117	0.2	0515	2.2	1349	0.3	1742	1.9
13	M	0150	0.2	0601	2.1	1431	0.4	1829	1.7
14	TU	0015	0.1	0654	2.0	1350	0.4	1923	1.6
15	W ☾	0127	0.1	0803	1.8	1445	0.4	2027	1.5
16	TH	0302	0.1	0919	1.8	1547	0.4	2207	1.4
17	F	0406	0.1	1050	1.8	1643	0.4	2324	1.5
18	SA	0459	0.1	1148	1.9	1733	0.4		
19	SU	0012	1.6	0549	0.2	1231	1.9	2008	0.4
20	M	0052	1.7	0637	0.2	1308	2.0	2108	0.4
21	TU	0126	1.8	0821	0.3	1342	2.1	2157	0.3
22	W	0158	1.9	0917	0.3	1414	2.1	2236	0.3
23	TH ○	0232	2.0	1004	0.3	1448	2.1	2010	0.3
24	F	0306	2.1	1048	0.3	1524	2.1	2041	0.3
25	SA	0342	2.2	1129	0.4	1600	2.1	2114	0.3
26	SU	0419	2.2	1209	0.4	1639	2.0	2152	0.2
27	M	0457	2.2	1249	0.4	1720	2.0	2237	0.1
28	TU	0539	2.2	1332	0.4	1804	1.9	2329	0.1
29	W	0626	2.1	1419	0.4	1857	1.7		
30	TH ☽	0031	0.1	0725	2.0	1516	0.4	2005	1.6
31	F	0142	0.1	0848	2.0	1626	0.5	2123	1.6

JUNE

Date	Day	Time	m	Time	m	Time	m	Time	m
1	SA	0245	0.1	1004	2.0	1746	0.5	2234	1.7
2	SU	0345	0.1	1109	2.0	1903	0.5	2337	1.8
3	M	0442	0.1	1206	2.1	1959	0.4		
4	TU	0030	1.9	0536	0.1	1257	2.1	2043	0.4
5	W	0119	2.0	0627	0.2	1344	2.1	2127	0.4
6	TH ●	0204	2.1	0715	0.3	1431	2.1	1939	0.3
7	F	0249	2.2	1033	0.3	1516	2.0	2022	0.3
8	SA	0333	2.2	1146	0.4	1601	2.0		
9	SU	0012	0.2	0417	2.2	1244	0.4	1646	1.9
10	M	0059	0.2	0501	2.2	1332	0.4	1729	1.8
11	TU	0140	0.1	0546	2.1	1415	0.5	1812	1.8
12	W	0000	0.1	0636	2.0	1450	0.5	1857	1.7
13	TH	0043	0.1	0731	1.9	1422	0.5	1947	1.7
14	F ☾	0151	0.1	0829	1.9	1514	0.5	2043	1.6
15	SA	0332	0.1	0928	1.8	1608	0.5	2144	1.6
16	SU	0430	0.2	1031	1.8	1700	0.4	2253	1.6
17	M	0524	0.2	1132	1.9	1749	0.4	2353	1.7
18	TU	0620	0.3	1221	1.9	1833	0.4		
19	W	0041	1.8	0742	0.3	1303	2.0	1907	0.4
20	TH	0123	1.9	0847	0.4	1343	2.0	1925	0.4
21	F	0203	2.0	0941	0.4	1423	2.0	1952	0.3
22	SA ○	0242	2.1	1030	0.4	1503	2.1	2024	0.3
23	SU	0322	2.2	1114	0.5	1544	2.0	2059	0.2
24	M	0402	2.2	1158	0.5	1627	2.0	2137	0.2
25	TU	0444	2.3	1243	0.5	1710	2.0	2220	0.1
26	W	0529	2.2	1329	0.5	1757	1.9	2308	0.1
27	TH	0617	2.2	1416	0.5	1848	1.8		
28	F ☽	0003	0.0	0713	2.1	1506	0.5	1947	1.8
29	SA	0107	0.0	0821	2.1	1602	0.5	2052	1.8
30	SU	0216	0.1	0930	2.0	1709	0.5	2157	1.8

SUNRISE AND SUNSET TIMES

HOEK VAN HOLLAND

At 51°51′N 4°03′E

		Sunrise	Sunset
European Standard Time (UT+0100)			
Jan	01	0852	1643
	15	0845	1702
Feb	01	0824	1731
	15	0759	1757
Mar	01	0730	1823
	15	0659	1848
European Summer Time (UT+0200)			
Apr	01	0720	2017
	15	0648	2041
May	01	0615	2108
	15	0551	2131
Jun	01	0530	2154
	15	0523	2205
Jul	01	0528	2207
	15	0541	2157
Aug	01	0605	2134
	15	0627	2108
Sep	01	0655	2032
	15	0718	2000
Oct	01	0744	1922
	15	0808	1851
European Standard Time (UT+0100)			
Nov	01	0738	1716
	15	0803	1653
Dec	01	0829	1636

HOEK VAN HOLLAND
LAT 51°51′N
LONG 4°03′E

TIMES AND HEIGHTS OF HIGH AND LOW WATER (Heights in Metres)

TIME ZONE
European Standard Time (UT+0100)
For Summer Time (area enclosed in shaded box) add 1 hour

2024

Low waters - important note.
Double low waters often occur. Predictions are for the lower low water which is usually the first.

JULY

Day	Time	m	Day	Time	m
1 M	0321	0.1	16 TU	0327	0.3
	1036	2.0		1022	1.8
	1818	0.5		1719	0.5
	2303	1.8		2253	1.7
2 TU	0428	0.2	17 W	0550	0.4
	1141	2.0		1124	1.8
	1918	0.5		1808	0.4
				2357	1.8
3 W	0005	1.9	18 TH	0651	0.4
	0533	0.3		1225	1.9
	1240	2.0		1844	0.4
	2017	0.4			
4 TH	0101	2.0	19 F	0053	1.9
	0830	0.3		0640	0.4
	1334	2.0		1319	1.9
	2126	0.4		1903	0.4
5 F ●	0152	2.1	20 SA	0141	2.0
	0924	0.4		0712	0.5
	1425	2.0		1405	2.0
	1938	0.3		1930	0.3
6 SA	0239	2.1	21 SU ○	0225	2.1
	1049	0.5		0747	0.5
	1512	2.0		1448	2.0
	2017	0.3		2002	0.3
7 SU	0324	2.2	22 M	0306	2.2
	1141	0.5		1105	0.5
	1556	1.9		1531	2.1
	2055	0.2		2037	0.2
8 M	0406	2.2	23 TU	0348	2.3
	1229	0.5		1144	0.5
	1636	1.9		1613	2.1
	2133	0.2		2115	0.1
9 TU	0447	2.2	24 W	0430	2.4
	1314	0.5		1227	0.5
	1713	1.9		1657	2.1
	2215	0.1		2157	0.1
10 W	0528	2.1	25 TH	0514	2.3
	1357	0.5		1312	0.5
	1750	1.9		1741	2.0
	2300	0.1		2242	0.1
11 TH	0610	2.1	26 F	0601	2.3
	1432	0.6		1357	0.5
	1828	1.9		1827	2.0
	2350	0.1		2334	0.1
12 F	0654	2.0	27 SA	0652	2.2
	1401	0.6		1440	0.6
	1909	1.8		1918	2.0
13 SA ☾	0047	0.1	28 SU ☽	0035	0.1
	0740	2.0		0750	2.1
	1418	0.5		1514	0.6
	1956	1.8		2016	2.0
14 SU	0141	0.2	29 M	0159	0.1
	0832	1.9		0855	2.0
	1453	0.5		1511	0.5
	2050	1.8		2121	1.9
15 M	0232	0.2	30 TU	0311	0.2
	0925	1.9		1004	1.9
	1619	0.5		1608	0.5
	2150	1.7		2233	1.9
			31 W	0425	0.3
				1121	1.9
				1714	0.5
				2347	1.9

AUGUST

Day	Time	m	Day	Time	m
1 TH	0534	0.4	16 F	0543	0.5
	1232	1.9		1153	1.7
	1805	0.4		1818	0.4
2 F	0052	2.0	17 SA	0030	1.9
	0904	0.4		0620	0.5
	1331	1.9		1300	1.8
	2133	0.4		1834	0.4
3 SA	0148	2.1	18 SU	0124	2.0
	1016	0.5		0653	0.5
	1423	1.9		1350	1.9
	2223	0.3		1904	0.3
4 SU ●	0235	2.1	19 M ○	0208	2.2
	1100	0.5		0727	0.6
	1507	2.0		1432	2.0
	2001	0.3		1937	0.2
5 M	0315	2.2	20 TU	0248	2.3
	1134	0.6		0800	0.6
	1545	2.0		1513	2.1
	2034	0.2		2012	0.2
6 TU	0352	2.2	21 W	0329	2.4
	1213	0.6		0835	0.6
	1618	2.0		1554	2.2
	2107	0.2		2050	0.1
7 W	0428	2.2	22 TH	0411	2.5
	1254	0.6		1206	0.6
	1650	2.0		1635	2.2
	2142	0.2		2131	0.1
8 TH	0504	2.2	23 F	0454	2.4
	1333	0.6		1251	0.6
	1722	2.1		1717	2.2
	2220	0.2		2216	0.1
9 F	0539	2.2	24 SA	0538	2.4
	1402	0.6		1335	0.6
	1755	2.0		1801	2.2
	2301	0.2		2306	0.1
10 SA	0614	2.1	25 SU	0626	2.3
	1130	0.6		1413	0.6
	1829	2.0		1848	2.2
	2345	0.2			
11 SU	0647	2.1	26 M ☽	0009	0.2
	1238	0.5		0718	2.1
	1904	2.0		1401	0.6
				1941	2.1
12 M ☾	0037	0.2	27 TU	0159	0.2
	0724	2.0		0820	2.0
	1338	0.5		1429	0.5
	1946	1.9		2047	2.0
13 TU	0142	0.3	28 W	0303	0.3
	0813	1.9		0935	1.8
	1428	0.5		1541	0.5
	2048	1.8		2209	1.9
14 W	0243	0.3	29 TH	0415	0.4
	0924	1.8		1112	1.7
	1527	0.5		1654	0.5
	2207	1.8		2339	1.9
15 TH	0352	0.4	30 F	0714	0.5
	1035	1.8		1225	1.8
	1742	0.5		1746	0.4
	2321	1.8			
			31 SA	0049	2.0
				0912	0.5
				1323	1.9
				2124	0.4

SEPTEMBER

Day	Time	m	Day	Time	m
1 SU	0143	2.1	16 M	0104	2.1
	1015	0.5		0920	0.6
	1411	2.0		1329	1.9
	2217	0.3		1833	0.3
2 M	0224	2.2	17 TU	0146	2.3
	1106	0.5		1017	0.6
	1450	2.0		1409	2.1
	2258	0.3		1909	0.2
3 TU ●	0258	2.2	18 W ○	0226	2.4
	1124	0.6		0735	0.6
	1523	2.1		1449	2.2
	2011	0.3		1946	0.2
4 W	0331	2.3	19 TH	0306	2.5
	1153	0.6		0810	0.6
	1552	2.1		1529	2.3
	2039	0.3		2025	0.1
5 TH	0403	2.3	20 F	0348	2.5
	1228	0.6		0847	0.6
	1622	2.2		1610	2.3
	2110	0.3		2106	0.1
6 F	0435	2.3	21 SA	0430	2.5
	1300	0.6		0928	0.6
	1652	2.2		1652	2.4
	2144	0.3		2152	0.2
7 SA	0507	2.2	22 SU	0514	2.4
	1004	0.6		1013	0.6
	1722	2.2		1735	2.4
	2219	0.3		2242	0.3
8 SU	0536	2.2	23 M	0600	2.2
	1040	0.5		1104	0.5
	1752	2.2		1820	2.3
	2256	0.3			
9 M	0606	2.2	24 TU ☾	0116	0.4
	1117	0.5		0649	2.0
	1823	2.1		1213	0.5
	2336	0.3		1910	2.2
10 TU	0640	2.1	25 W	0150	0.4
	1158	0.4		0748	1.8
	1858	2.1		1351	0.5
				2017	2.0
11 W ☽	0024	0.4	26 TH	0248	0.5
	0721	2.0		0912	1.7
	1254	0.4		1515	0.5
	1944	2.0		2155	1.9
12 TH	0216	0.4	27 F	0400	0.6
	0817	1.8		1102	1.6
	1442	0.5		1633	0.5
	2101	1.8		2332	1.9
13 F	0332	0.5	28 SA	0655	0.6
	0955	1.7		1209	1.7
	1601	0.5		1726	0.4
	2253	1.8			
14 SA	0506	0.6	29 SU	0036	2.1
	1127	1.7		0851	0.5
	1730	0.5		1302	1.9
				2058	0.4
15 SU	0010	1.9	30 M	0123	2.2
	0557	0.6		0948	0.5
	1240	1.8		1347	2.0
	1759	0.4		2155	0.3

OCTOBER

Day	Time	m	Day	Time	m
1 TU	0201	2.3	16 W	0120	2.3
	1028	0.5		0950	0.6
	1424	2.1		1343	2.1
	2235	0.3		1841	0.2
2 W ●	0234	2.3	17 TH ○	0201	2.5
	1058	0.6		0709	0.6
	1455	2.1		1424	2.2
	1950	0.4		1921	0.2
3 TH	0304	2.3	18 F	0243	2.5
	1126	0.6		0746	0.6
	1523	2.2		1504	2.4
	2013	0.4		2002	0.2
4 F	0335	2.3	19 SA	0325	2.5
	1154	0.6		0825	0.5
	1551	2.2		1546	2.4
	2041	0.4		2045	0.2
5 SA	0405	2.3	20 SU	0408	2.4
	0902	0.6		0907	0.5
	1621	2.3		1628	2.4
	2113	0.4		2131	0.3
6 SU	0435	2.3	21 M	0452	2.3
	0935	0.5		0953	0.5
	1651	2.3		1711	2.4
	2146	0.4			
7 M	0505	2.2	22 TU	0145	0.4
	1009	0.5		0537	2.1
	1721	2.3		1045	0.4
	2222	0.4		1756	2.3
8 TU	0536	2.2	23 W	0107	0.5
	1045	0.4		0625	2.0
	1753	2.3		1153	0.4
	2302	0.4		1847	2.2
9 W	0611	2.2	24 TH ☾	0135	0.5
	1126	0.4		0723	1.8
	1830	2.2		1318	0.4
	2350	0.5		1956	2.0
10 TH ☽	0652	2.0	25 F	0230	0.6
	1219	0.4		0847	1.6
	1915	2.1		1444	0.4
				2135	1.9
11 F	0213	0.5	26 SA	0506	0.7
	0746	1.8		1035	1.6
	1404	0.4		1608	0.4
	2020	1.9		2310	1.9
12 SA	0320	0.6	27 SU	0621	0.6
	0923	1.6		1141	1.7
	1519	0.5		1703	0.4
	2227	1.9			
13 SU	0441	0.6	28 M	0008	2.1
	1059	1.6		0746	0.6
	1629	0.4		1232	1.9
	2343	2.0		1751	0.4
14 M	0729	0.6	29 TU	0053	2.2
	1212	1.8		0856	0.5
	1719	0.4		1315	2.0
				2046	0.4
15 TU	0037	2.2	30 W	0131	2.2
	0901	0.6		0942	0.5
	1301	1.9		1351	2.0
	1801	0.3		2118	0.4
			31 TH	0204	2.3
				1021	0.5
				1422	2.1
				2131	0.4

NOVEMBER

Day	Time	m	Day	Time	m
1 F ●	0235	2.3	16 SA	0222	2.4
	1055	0.6		0727	0.5
	1451	2.2		1442	2.4
	2207	0.4		1945	0.3
2 SA	0305	2.3	17 SU	0306	2.4
	1122	0.6		0809	0.5
	1521	2.2		1525	2.4
	2250	0.5		2031	0.4
3 SU	0336	2.3	18 M	0351	2.3
	0843	0.5		0853	0.4
	1552	2.3		1609	2.4
	2050	0.5			
4 M	0408	2.3	19 TU	0031	0.5
	0915	0.5		0436	2.2
	1624	2.3		0940	0.4
	2124	0.5		1653	2.4
5 TU	0440	2.2	20 W	0127	0.5
	0949	0.4		0521	2.0
	1657	2.3		1033	0.3
	2202	0.5		1739	2.3
6 W	0514	2.2	21 TH	0215	0.6
	1028	0.3		0610	1.9
	1732	2.3		1135	0.3
	2245	0.5		1831	2.2
7 TH	0552	2.1	22 F	0300	0.6
	1113	0.3		0704	1.8
	1812	2.3		1244	0.3
	2340	0.6		1936	2.0
8 F	0636	2.0	23 SA ☾	0209	0.7
	1210	0.3		0807	1.7
	1901	2.1		1359	0.3
				2051	1.9
9 SA ☽	0217	0.6	24 SU	0317	0.7
	0733	1.8		0926	1.6
	1329	0.3		1534	0.3
	2009	2.0		2218	1.9
10 SU	0311	0.7	25 M	0422	0.7
	0901	1.7		1055	1.7
	1441	0.3		1635	0.3
	2156	2.0		2327	2.0
11 M	0521	0.7	26 TU	0645	0.6
	1026	1.7		1150	1.8
	1544	0.3		1729	0.3
	2308	2.1			
12 TU	0707	0.7	27 W	0015	2.0
	1136	1.8		0750	0.6
	1640	0.3		1234	1.9
				1823	0.4
13 W	0005	2.2	28 TH	0055	2.1
	0826	0.6		0850	0.5
	1230	2.0		1312	2.0
	1730	0.3		2004	0.4
14 TH	0053	2.3	29 F	0131	2.1
	0907	0.6		0940	0.5
	1316	2.1		1346	2.0
	1816	0.3		2053	0.4
15 F ○	0138	2.4	30 SA	0204	2.2
	0647	0.6		1022	0.5
	1359	2.3		1419	2.1
	1901	0.3		2138	0.5

DECEMBER

Day	Time	m	Day	Time	m
1 SU ●	0236	2.2	16 M	0255	2.2
	1054	0.5		0802	0.4
	1453	2.2		1511	2.3
	2222	0.5		2313	0.5
2 M	0310	2.2	17 TU	0341	2.1
	0830	0.5		0846	0.4
	1528	2.3		1556	2.3
	2304	0.5			
3 TU	0346	2.2	18 W	0016	0.5
	0902	0.4		0427	2.1
	1603	2.3		0930	0.3
	2345	0.6		1641	2.3
4 W	0423	2.2	19 TH	0109	0.6
	0937	0.3		0511	2.0
	1640	2.3		1018	0.2
				1727	2.3
5 TH	0026	0.6	20 F	0156	0.6
	0501	2.1		0556	2.0
	1017	0.3		1110	0.2
	1719	2.3		1815	2.2
6 F	0108	0.6	21 SA	0240	0.6
	0543	2.0		0641	1.9
	1102	0.2		1208	0.2
	1802	2.3		1908	2.1
7 SA	0152	0.6	22 SU ☾	0137	0.7
	0629	1.9		0729	1.8
	1154	0.2		1310	0.2
	1853	2.2		2004	2.0
8 SU ☽	0239	0.6	23 M	0228	0.6
	0726	1.8		0821	1.8
	1255	0.2		1420	0.2
	1959	2.1		2101	1.9
9 M	0336	0.7	24 TU	0332	0.6
	0837	1.8		0918	1.7
	1403	0.2		1558	0.3
	2121	2.1		2203	1.9
10 TU	0454	0.7	25 W	0433	0.6
	0950	1.8		1024	1.7
	1506	0.2		1701	0.3
	2230	2.1		2311	1.9
11 W	0621	0.7	26 TH	0529	0.6
	1058	1.9		1132	1.8
	1608	0.3		1802	0.4
	2332	2.2			
12 TH	0732	0.6	27 F	0008	1.9
	1158	2.0		0619	0.5
	1707	0.3		1225	1.8
				1912	0.4
13 F	0028	2.2	28 SA	0054	2.0
	0823	0.6		0705	0.5
	1251	2.1		1310	1.9
	1802	0.3		2018	0.5
14 SA	0119	2.2	29 SU	0134	2.0
	0635	0.6		0740	0.5
	1339	2.2		1351	2.0
	1853	0.4		2113	0.5
15 SU ○	0208	2.2	30 M ●	0213	2.1
	0719	0.5		0751	0.4
	1426	2.3		1430	2.1
	2209	0.5		2203	0.5
			31 TU	0251	2.1
				0815	0.4
				1509	2.2
				2247	0.6

VLISSINGEN (FLUSHING)
LAT 51°27′N
LONG 3°36′E

TIMES AND HEIGHTS OF HIGH AND LOW WATER (Heights in Metres)

TIME ZONE
European Standard Time (UT+0100)
For Summer Time (area enclosed in shaded box) add 1 hour

2024

SUNRISE AND SUNSET TIMES

VLISSINGEN (FLUSHING)
At 51°27′N 3°36′E
European Standard Time (UT+0100)

		Sunrise	Sunset
Jan	01	0851	1648
	15	0844	1706
Feb	01	0824	1735
	15	0759	1801
Mar	01	0731	1826
	15	0700	1850
European Summer Time (UT+0200)			
Apr	01	0721	2020
	15	0650	2042
May	01	0618	2109
	15	0554	2131
Jun	01	0534	2153
	15	0528	2204
Jul	01	0533	2206
	15	0546	2156
Aug	01	0610	2133
	15	0631	2108
Sep	01	0658	2032
	15	0721	2000
Oct	01	0746	1923
	15	0810	1852
European Standard Time (UT+0100)			
Nov	01	0739	1719
	15	0804	1656

JANUARY

Day	Time	m	Time	m	Time	m	Time	m
1 M	0511	4.5	1135	0.7	1734	4.5	2335	1.2
2 TU	0549	4.4	1213	0.8	1815	4.4		
3 W	0013	1.2	0630	4.3	1252	0.9	1900	4.3
4 TH ☽	0056	1.3	0717	4.2	1339	1.0	1952	4.2
5 F	0149	1.4	0815	4.1	1437	1.1	2052	4.1
6 SA	0302	1.4	0920	4.0	1543	1.1	2157	4.1
7 SU	0414	1.4	1026	4.1	1649	1.1	2301	4.2
8 M	0517	1.2	1127	4.3	1748	1.0	2357	4.4
9 TU	0614	1.1	1220	4.5	1841	0.9		
10 W	0047	4.6	0706	0.9	1308	4.7	1929	0.8
11 TH ●	0133	4.7	0756	0.7	1353	4.9	2015	0.8
12 F	0217	4.8	0844	0.5	1437	5.0	2100	0.7
13 SA	0301	4.9	0932	0.4	1521	5.1	2145	0.7
14 SU	0345	4.9	1019	0.3	1607	5.1	2231	0.8
15 M	0430	4.9	1107	0.3	1654	5.1	2316	0.8
16 TU	0517	4.8	1154	0.3	1744	4.9		
17 W	0003	0.9	0607	4.8	1242	0.4	1839	4.8
18 TH ☾	0053	1.0	0702	4.6	1332	0.5	1939	4.6
19 F	0149	1.1	0802	4.5	1430	0.7	2045	4.4
20 SA	0255	1.2	0910	4.3	1541	0.9	2157	4.2
21 SU	0416	1.2	1024	4.2	1703	1.0	2310	4.2
22 M	0534	1.1	1135	4.3	1807	1.0		
23 TU	0015	4.3	0636	1.0	1240	4.5	1900	0.9
24 W	0111	4.4	0728	0.8	1335	4.6	1945	0.9
25 TH O	0158	4.5	0813	0.7	1419	4.7	2023	1.0
26 F	0237	4.6	0853	0.6	1455	4.8	2058	1.0
27 SA	0310	4.7	0928	0.6	1527	4.8	2131	1.0
28 SU	0342	4.7	1003	0.6	1559	4.8	2204	1.0
29 M	0413	4.7	1036	0.5	1632	4.8	2236	0.9
30 TU	0445	4.7	1108	0.6	1704	4.7	2306	0.9
31 W	0517	4.7	1138	0.6	1737	4.6		

FEBRUARY

Day	Time	m	Time	m	Time	m	Time	m
1 TH	0551	4.6	1208	0.6	1812	4.5		
2 F	0009	1.0	0628	4.5	1244	0.7	1854	4.4
3 SA ☽	0051	1.0	0713	4.3	1329	0.9	1950	4.2
4 SU	0144	1.1	0819	4.2	1431	1.0	2059	4.1
5 M	0259	1.3	0936	4.0	1555	1.2	2214	4.0
6 TU	0434	1.3	1052	4.1	1716	1.1	2329	4.1
7 W	0549	1.1	1200	4.3	1820	1.0		
8 TH	0029	4.4	0651	0.9	1254	4.6	1913	0.9
9 F ●	0119	4.6	0744	0.6	1341	4.9	2000	0.7
10 SA	0203	4.8	0832	0.4	1424	5.1	2045	0.7
11 SU	0245	5.0	0918	0.2	1507	5.2	2130	0.6
12 M	0327	5.1	1003	0.1	1550	5.3	2213	0.6
13 TU	0410	5.1	1047	0.1	1634	5.2	2256	0.6
14 W	0454	5.1	1130	0.1	1721	5.1	2339	0.7
15 TH	0540	5.0	1214	0.3	1810	4.9		
16 F ☾	0024	0.8	0630	4.8	1259	0.5	1905	4.6
17 SA	0115	0.9	0728	4.5	1353	0.7	2008	4.2
18 SU	0220	1.1	0837	4.2	1503	1.0	2127	4.0
19 M	0345	1.2	1002	4.0	1638	1.2	2252	3.9
20 TU	0516	1.2	1127	4.1	1753	1.1		
21 W	0003	4.1	0625	1.0	1235	4.4	1851	1.1
22 TH	0059	4.3	0719	0.8	1325	4.6	1935	1.0
23 F	0143	4.5	0801	0.7	1404	4.7	2008	1.0
24 SA O	0218	4.6	0835	0.6	1436	4.8	2039	0.9
25 SU	0248	4.7	0907	0.5	1505	4.8	2109	0.9
26 M	0316	4.8	0938	0.5	1534	4.9	2140	0.8
27 TU	0345	4.9	1010	0.4	1603	4.9	2210	0.8
28 W	0415	4.9	1039	0.4	1633	4.9	2237	0.7
29 TH	0445	4.9	1106	0.5	1702	4.8	2304	0.7

MARCH

Day	Time	m	Time	m	Time	m	Time	m
1 F	0515	4.8	1133	0.5	1733	4.7	2335	0.7
2 SA	0547	4.7	1206	0.6	1810	4.6		
3 SU ☽	0014	0.8	0627	4.6	1248	0.8	1858	4.4
4 M	0105	0.9	0722	4.3	1347	1.0	2009	4.0
5 TU	0216	1.1	0854	4.0	1514	1.2	2138	3.9
6 W	0402	1.2	1027	4.0	1651	1.2	2306	4.0
7 TH	0529	1.0	1144	4.3	1802	1.1		
8 F	0012	4.3	0636	0.8	1239	4.6	1856	0.9
9 SA	0101	4.6	0728	0.5	1324	4.9	1943	0.7
10 SU ●	0143	4.8	0814	0.2	1405	5.2	2027	0.6
11 M	0223	5.1	0858	0.1	1446	5.3	2109	0.5
12 TU	0304	5.2	0941	0.0	1528	5.3	2152	0.5
13 W	0346	5.3	1023	0.0	1611	5.2	2233	0.5
14 TH	0428	5.2	1104	0.1	1655	5.1	2315	0.5
15 F	0513	5.1	1145	0.3	1742	4.8	2358	0.6
16 SA	0601	4.8	1228	0.6	1833	4.5		
17 SU ☾	0047	0.8	0656	4.5	1320	0.9	1934	4.1
18 M	0153	1.0	0809	4.1	1433	1.2	2059	3.7
19 TU	0321	1.2	0946	3.9	1615	1.3	2234	3.7
20 W	0455	1.2	1113	4.0	1735	1.3	2344	3.9
21 TH	0606	1.0	1216	4.3	1833	1.1		
22 F	0037	4.2	0658	0.8	1302	4.5	1914	1.0
23 SA	0118	4.4	0737	0.6	1338	4.7	1945	0.9
24 SU	0150	4.6	0808	0.5	1408	4.8	2014	0.8
25 M O	0219	4.7	0838	0.5	1436	4.9	2044	0.7
26 TU	0246	4.8	0909	0.4	1504	4.9	2115	0.7
27 W	0315	4.9	0940	0.4	1533	4.9	2144	0.7
28 TH	0345	4.9	1010	0.5	1601	4.9	2212	0.6
29 F	0414	4.9	1037	0.5	1631	4.8	2240	0.6
30 SA	0445	4.9	1106	0.6	1703	4.8	2312	0.6
31 SU	0519	4.8	1139	0.6	1741	4.6	2352	0.7

APRIL

Day	Time	m	Time	m	Time	m	Time	m
1 M	0600	4.6	1223	0.8	1828	4.3		
2 TU ☽	0046	0.8	0655	4.3	1323	1.1	1938	4.0
3 W	0200	1.0	0830	4.0	1452	1.3	2114	3.8
4 TH	0342	1.1	1006	4.0	1630	1.3	2243	3.9
5 F	0509	0.9	1124	4.3	1742	1.1	2348	4.2
6 SA	0616	0.6	1218	4.7	1836	0.9		
7 SU	0036	4.6	0707	0.4	1301	5.0	1922	0.7
8 M ●	0118	4.8	0752	0.2	1342	5.1	2005	0.5
9 TU	0159	5.1	0834	0.1	1423	5.2	2047	0.5
10 W	0240	5.2	0917	0.1	1505	5.2	2130	0.4
11 TH	0322	5.2	0958	0.2	1548	5.1	2212	0.4
12 F	0405	5.2	1038	0.3	1632	4.9	2254	0.5
13 SA	0449	5.0	1118	0.5	1718	4.6	2338	0.6
14 SU	0537	4.7	1201	0.8	1807	4.3		
15 M ☾	0027	0.8	0633	4.4	1252	1.1	1905	4.0
16 TU	0134	1.0	0747	4.0	1407	1.3	2026	3.6
17 W	0254	1.1	0921	3.8	1538	1.4	2203	3.6
18 TH	0418	1.1	1044	4.0	1659	1.3	2312	3.8
19 F	0530	0.9	1143	4.2	1757	1.2		
20 SA	0003	4.1	0622	0.8	1228	4.5	1839	1.0
21 SU	0043	4.3	0702	0.6	1304	4.6	1912	0.9
22 M	0115	4.5	0734	0.6	1335	4.7	1943	0.8
23 TU	0145	4.7	0805	0.5	1403	4.8	2015	0.7
24 W O	0214	4.8	0837	0.5	1432	4.9	2047	0.6
25 TH	0244	4.9	0909	0.5	1503	4.9	2119	0.6
26 F	0316	4.9	0941	0.5	1534	4.9	2152	0.6
27 SA	0348	4.9	1013	0.6	1607	4.8	2225	0.6
28 SU	0422	4.9	1047	0.7	1643	4.7	2302	0.6
29 M	0500	4.8	1125	0.8	1724	4.5	2346	0.6
30 TU	0546	4.6	1212	0.9	1815	4.2		

MAY

Day	Time	m	Time	m	Time	m	Time	m
1 W ☾	0043	0.8	0647	4.3	1314	1.1	1928	4.0
2 TH	0158	0.9	0818	4.1	1437	1.3	2054	3.9
3 F	0324	0.9	0943	4.2	1604	1.2	2214	4.0
4 SA	0444	0.8	1056	4.4	1715	1.1	2318	4.3
5 SU	0551	0.6	1151	4.7	1811	0.9		
6 M	0008	4.6	0643	0.4	1237	4.9	1859	0.7
7 TU	0053	4.8	0728	0.3	1320	5.0	1944	0.6
8 W ●	0136	5.0	0811	0.2	1403	5.1	2028	0.5
9 TH	0219	5.1	0854	0.3	1446	5.0	2112	0.4
10 F	0302	5.1	0935	0.4	1530	4.9	2155	0.4
11 SA	0347	5.0	1016	0.5	1615	4.7	2239	0.5
12 SU	0433	4.8	1056	0.7	1700	4.5	2323	0.6
13 M	0522	4.6	1138	1.0	1748	4.2		
14 TU	0013	0.7	0618	4.3	1228	1.2	1840	4.0
15 W ☽	0113	0.9	0720	4.1	1335	1.3	1942	3.8
16 TH	0219	0.9	0834	3.9	1449	1.4	2106	3.7
17 F	0324	1.0	0956	3.9	1557	1.4	2222	3.8
18 SA	0432	0.9	1057	4.1	1700	1.2	2315	4.0
19 SU	0532	0.8	1144	4.3	1751	1.1	2358	4.2
20 M	0617	0.7	1223	4.5	1832	0.9		
21 TU	0035	4.4	0655	0.7	1257	4.6	1909	0.8
22 W	0108	4.6	0729	0.6	1329	4.7	1944	0.7
23 TH O	0142	4.7	0804	0.6	1402	4.8	2020	0.7
24 F	0216	4.8	0840	0.6	1437	4.8	2057	0.6
25 SA	0252	4.9	0917	0.6	1512	4.8	2136	0.6
26 SU	0329	4.9	0954	0.7	1550	4.7	2217	0.6
27 M	0408	4.8	1034	0.8	1631	4.6	2300	0.5
28 TU	0451	4.7	1117	0.9	1717	4.5	2349	0.6
29 W	0541	4.6	1207	1.0	1811	4.3		
30 TH ☾	0047	0.6	0646	4.4	1307	1.1	1918	4.1
31 F	0153	0.7	0802	4.3	1418	1.2	2030	4.1

JUNE

Day	Time	m	Time	m	Time	m	Time	m
1 SA	0301	0.7	0914	4.4	1531	1.2	2141	4.1
2 SU	0412	0.6	1023	4.5	1642	1.1	2245	4.3
3 M	0521	0.6	1122	4.6	1744	0.9	2340	4.5
4 TU	0617	0.5	1214	4.8	1838	0.8		
5 W	0031	4.7	0706	0.4	1302	4.8	1926	0.6
6 TH ●	0118	4.8	0751	0.4	1348	4.8	2012	0.5
7 F	0205	4.9	0835	0.5	1434	4.8	2058	0.5
8 SA	0251	4.9	0917	0.6	1519	4.7	2143	0.5
9 SU	0337	4.9	0957	0.8	1604	4.6	2227	0.5
10 M	0424	4.8	1037	0.9	1647	4.5	2310	0.6
11 TU	0510	4.6	1117	1.1	1729	4.4	2355	0.6
12 W	0556	4.4	1202	1.2	1813	4.2		
13 TH	0043	0.7	0645	4.3	1254	1.3	1900	4.1
14 F ☽	0136	0.8	0738	4.1	1357	1.3	1955	3.9
15 SA	0231	0.9	0838	4.0	1459	1.3	2059	3.9
16 SU	0329	0.9	0947	4.0	1559	1.3	2208	3.9
17 M	0428	0.9	1047	4.1	1656	1.2	2304	4.1
18 TU	0524	0.9	1135	4.3	1748	1.1	2351	4.3
19 W	0612	0.8	1218	4.4	1833	1.0		
20 TH	0034	4.4	0654	0.8	1258	4.6	1916	0.8
21 F	0115	4.6	0735	0.7	1337	4.7	1957	0.7
22 SA O	0155	4.7	0816	0.7	1417	4.8	2040	0.6
23 SU	0235	4.8	0857	0.7	1457	4.8	2125	0.5
24 M	0316	4.9	0940	0.8	1539	4.7	2211	0.5
25 TU	0359	4.9	1024	0.8	1623	4.7	2259	0.4
26 W	0445	4.8	1110	0.9	1710	4.6	2348	0.4
27 TH	0536	4.8	1159	1.0	1801	4.5		
28 F ☾	0040	0.4	0634	4.7	1252	1.0	1859	4.4
29 SA	0134	0.5	0737	4.6	1351	1.1	2001	4.4
30 SU	0232	0.5	0843	4.5	1455	1.1	2107	4.3

VLISSINGEN (FLUSHING)
LAT 51°27′N
LONG 3°36′E

TIMES AND HEIGHTS OF HIGH AND LOW WATER (Heights in Metres)

TIME ZONE
European Standard Time (UT+0100)
For Summer Time (area enclosed in shaded box) add 1 hour

2024

JULY

Date	Day	Time	m	Date	Day	Time	m
1	M	0337 0950 1606 2213	0.6 4.5 1.1 4.4	16	TU	0326 0932 1600 2203	1.0 4.1 1.3 4.0
2	TU	0450 1056 1719 2317	0.7 4.5 1.0 4.5	17	W	0431 1039 1703 2308	1.1 4.1 1.2 4.1
3	W	0554 1156 1820	0.7 4.5 0.9	18	TH	0532 1140 1801	1.0 4.2 1.1
4	TH	0016 0648 1251 1913	4.6 0.7 4.6 0.7	19	F	0005 0625 1233 1853	4.3 1.0 4.4 0.9
5	F ●	0111 0736 1342 2002	4.7 0.7 4.7 0.6	20	SA	0055 0712 1319 1941	4.5 0.9 4.6 0.7
6	SA	0202 0820 1429 2048	4.8 0.8 4.7 0.5	21	SU ○	0140 0757 1402 2027	4.7 0.8 4.7 0.6
7	SU	0248 0901 1511 2131	4.8 0.8 4.7 0.5	22	M	0222 0842 1444 2114	4.9 0.8 4.8 0.4
8	M	0330 0939 1550 2212	4.8 0.9 4.7 0.5	23	TU	0304 0926 1526 2200	5.0 0.8 4.9 0.3
9	TU	0410 1016 1627 2251	4.8 1.0 4.6 0.5	24	W	0347 1011 1609 2247	5.1 0.8 4.9 0.3
10	W	0449 1053 1704 2329	4.7 1.0 4.6 0.6	25	TH	0432 1056 1653 2333	5.1 0.8 4.9 0.3
11	TH	0527 1131 1741	4.6 1.1 4.5	26	F	0519 1141 1740	5.0 0.9 4.8
12	F	0008 0607 1210 1821	0.6 4.5 1.1 4.4	27	SA	0019 0610 1229 1831	0.3 4.9 0.9 4.7
13	SA ☽	0047 0649 1251 1905	0.7 4.4 1.2 4.3	28	SU ☾	0107 0707 1320 1929	0.4 4.7 1.0 4.6
14	SU	0131 0736 1341 1956	0.8 4.2 1.3 4.1	29	M	0159 0810 1422 2034	0.6 4.5 1.1 4.4
15	M	0223 0830 1450 2057	0.9 4.1 1.3 4.0	30	TU	0303 0919 1536 2147	0.8 4.3 1.2 4.3
				31	W	0422 1034 1659 2302	0.9 4.2 1.1 4.3

AUGUST

Date	Day	Time	m	Date	Day	Time	m
1	TH	0537 1145 1809	0.9 4.3 [illegible]	16	F	0458 1108 1733 2344	1.3 4.0 1.2 4.2
2	F	0013 0637 1246 1906	4.5 0.9 4.5 0.8	17	SA	0602 1213 1834	1.1 4.3 1.0
3	SA	0113 0727 1337 1956	4.3 0.9 4.3 0.7	18	SU	0040 0654 1303 1925	4.5 1.0 4.6 0.7
4	SU ●	0201 0809 1419 2038	4.3 0.9 4.7 0.5	19	M ○	0125 0740 1345 2012	4.8 0.9 4.8 0.5
5	M	0240 0846 1456 2116	4.3 1.0 4.7 0.5	20	TU	0206 0824 1425 2056	5.1 0.8 5.0 0.3
6	TU	0315 0920 1529 2151	4.3 1.0 4.3 0.5	21	W	0246 0908 1506 2141	5.2 0.7 5.1 0.2
7	W	0348 0953 1601 2226	4.3 1.0 4.3 0.5	22	TH	0328 0951 1547 2225	5.3 0.7 5.2 0.2
8	TH	0421 1026 1634 2259	4.3 1.0 4.3 0.5	23	F	0410 1034 1629 2308	5.3 0.7 5.1 0.2
9	F	0454 1058 1707 2330	4.3 1.0 4.7 0.5	24	SA	0455 1117 1713 2351	5.1 0.8 5.1 0.3
10	SA	0527 1128 1740 2359	4.7 1.0 4.5 0.7	25	SU	0542 1202 1801	4.9 0.8 4.9
11	SU	0601 1158 1815	4.5 1.0 4.5	26	M ☾	0035 0636 1251 1857	0.5 4.7 1.0 4.7
12	M ☽	0031 0639 1234 1856	0.8 4.4 1.1 4.4	27	TU	0126 0737 1351 2005	0.8 4.4 1.1 4.4
13	TU	0111 0728 1322 1954	0.9 4.2 1.2 4.1	28	W	0231 0851 1512 2127	1.0 4.1 1.2 4.2
14	W	0207 0832 1432 2110	1.1 4.1 1.4 4.0	29	TH	0404 1019 1646 2256	1.2 4.0 1.2 4.2
15	TH	0335 0946 1620 2230	1.3 4.0 1.4 4.0	30	F	0529 1136 1802	1.2 4.1 1.0
				31	SA	0010 0631 1237 1859	4.4 1.1 4.4 0.8

SEPTEMBER

Date	Day	Time	m	Date	Day	Time	m
1	SU	0106 0719 1324 1945	4.7 1.0 4.6 0.7	16	M	0021 0634 1241 1906	4.6 1.1 4.6 0.7
2	M	0147 0756 1401 2021	4.8 1.0 4.7 0.6	17	TU	0105 0720 1322 1951	4.9 0.9 4.9 0.4
3	TU ●	0222 0827 1433 2054	4.9 1.0 4.8 0.6	18	W ○	0144 0803 1401 2034	5.2 0.8 5.1 0.3
4	W	0252 0857 1502 2125	4.9 1.0 4.9 0.5	19	TH	0223 0845 1441 2116	5.3 0.7 5.3 0.2
5	TH	0321 0928 1532 2156	5.0 0.9 4.9 0.5	20	F	0304 0928 1521 2159	5.4 0.6 5.3 0.2
6	F	0350 0958 1602 2227	4.9 0.9 4.9 0.6	21	SA	0346 1010 1603 2241	5.3 0.6 5.3 0.3
7	SA	0420 1026 1632 2253	4.9 0.9 4.9 0.7	22	SU	0429 1053 1647 2322	5.2 0.7 5.2 0.5
8	SU	0449 1051 1701 2318	4.8 0.9 4.8 0.8	23	M	0516 1136 1734	4.9 0.8 5.0
9	M	0518 1119 1731 2347	4.7 0.9 4.7 0.8	24	TU ☾	0005 0606 1225 1828	0.7 4.6 0.9 4.6
10	TU	0551 1154 1806	4.6 1.0 4.6	25	W	0055 0707 1327 1941	1.0 4.2 1.1 4.3
11	W ☽	0025 0632 1240 1853	1.0 4.4 1.1 4.3	26	TH	0204 0827 1454 2113	1.3 3.9 1.3 4.0
12	TH	0117 0734 1343 2018	1.2 4.1 1.3 4.0	27	F	0352 1003 1632 2246	1.5 3.8 1.2 4.1
13	F	0240 0905 1540 2200	1.4 3.9 1.4 3.9	28	SA	0516 1120 1746 2355	1.4 4.0 1.0 4.4
14	SA	0430 1040 1708 2324	1.4 3.9 1.2 4.2	29	SU	0616 1217 1841	1.2 4.3 0.8
15	SU	0540 1152 1814	1.3 4.2 0.9	30	M	0045 0701 1300 1922	4.7 1.1 4.6 0.7

OCTOBER

Date	Day	Time	m	Date	Day	Time	m
1	TU	0123 0734 1335 1955	4.8 1.0 4.7 0.6	16	W	0038 0656 1254 1926	5.0 0.9 4.9 0.4
2	W ●	0155 0802 1405 2025	4.9 1.0 4.8 0.6	17	TH ○	0119 0739 1334 2009	5.2 0.8 5.1 0.3
3	TH	0223 0830 1432 2055	4.9 0.9 4.9 0.6	18	F	0159 0822 1415 2052	5.3 0.7 5.3 0.3
4	F	0251 0901 1501 2125	5.0 0.9 5.0 0.6	19	SA	0241 0906 1457 2134	5.3 0.6 5.3 0.3
5	SA	0319 0931 1530 2154	5.0 0.9 5.0 0.7	20	SU	0323 0949 1540 2215	5.2 0.6 5.3 0.5
6	SU	0347 0958 1559 2220	4.9 0.9 4.9 0.8	21	M	0407 1032 1625 2256	5.0 0.7 5.1 0.7
7	M	0416 1023 1628 2246	4.8 0.9 4.9 0.8	22	TU	0453 1117 1713 2339	4.8 0.8 4.9 0.9
8	TU	0446 1052 1700 2316	4.8 0.9 4.8 0.9	23	W	0544 1206 1808	4.5 0.9 4.6
9	W	0520 1128 1737 2355	4.6 0.9 4.7 1.0	24	TH ☾	0028 0643 1308 1922	1.2 4.1 1.1 4.2
10	TH ☽	0601 1216 1824	4.4 1.0 4.4	25	F	0137 0759 1430 2050	1.5 3.8 1.2 4.0
11	F	0049 0659 1323 1943	1.3 4.1 1.2 4.1	26	SA	0318 0932 1559 2218	1.6 3.8 1.2 4.1
12	SA	0209 0834 1509 2132	1.5 3.8 1.3 4.0	27	SU	0444 1048 1714 2323	1.5 3.9 1.1 4.3
13	SU	0400 1009 1639 2256	1.5 3.9 1.2 4.3	28	M	0545 1143 1808	1.3 4.2 0.9
14	M	0513 1122 1748 2354	1.3 4.2 0.9 4.7	29	TU	0012 0629 1226 1849	4.6 1.2 4.5 0.8
15	TU	0609 1212 1841	1.1 4.6 0.6	30	W	0050 0702 1301 1922	4.7 1.1 4.6 0.7
				31	TH	0123 0731 1332 1952	4.8 1.0 4.7 0.7

NOVEMBER

Date	Day	Time	m	Date	Day	Time	m
1	F ●	0152 0802 1400 2023	4.9 0.9 4.8 0.7	16	SA	0138 0803 1354 2029	5.1 0.7 5.2 0.4
2	SA	0220 0833 1430 2053	4.9 0.9 4.9 0.7	17	SU	0222 0848 1438 2112	5.1 0.6 5.2 0.5
3	SU	0248 0904 1501 2124	4.9 0.9 4.9 0.8	18	M	0306 0933 1523 2154	5.0 0.6 5.2 0.7
4	M	0319 0935 1532 2153	4.9 0.9 4.9 0.9	19	TU	0352 1017 1610 2235	4.9 0.6 5.0 0.9
5	TU	0350 1005 1605 2224	4.8 0.9 4.9 0.9	20	W	0439 1103 1700 2317	4.7 0.7 4.8 1.1
6	W	0424 1039 1640 2258	4.7 0.8 4.8 1.0	21	TH	0528 1151 1755	4.4 0.8 4.6
7	TH	0501 1119 1721 2340	4.6 0.9 4.7 1.1	22	F	0004 0621 1247 1856	1.3 4.2 1.0 4.3
8	F	0546 1210 1813	4.4 1.0 4.4	23	SA ☾	0103 0720 1352 2005	1.5 4.0 1.1 4.1
9	SA ☽	0036 0647 1316 1931	1.3 4.1 1.1 4.2	24	SU	0218 0834 1500 2127	1.6 3.8 1.1 4.0
10	SU	0149 0811 1443 2102	1.5 4.0 1.1 4.2	25	M	0333 0954 1613 2235	1.6 3.9 1.1 4.1
11	M	0320 0933 1603 2220	1.5 4.0 1.0 4.3	26	TU	0444 1054 1717 2327	1.5 4.0 1.0 4.3
12	TU	0436 1044 1715 2321	1.4 4.2 0.9 4.6	27	W	0539 1141 1804	1.3 4.2 0.9
13	W	0538 1139 1813	1.2 4.6 0.7	28	TH	0009 0621 1221 1842	4.5 1.2 4.4 0.9
14	TH	0010 0630 1226 1901	4.9 1.0 4.8 0.5	29	F	0046 0657 1256 1917	4.6 1.1 4.6 0.9
15	F ○	0054 0717 1310 1946	5.1 0.8 5.0 0.4	30	SA	0118 0732 1330 1950	4.7 1.0 4.7 0.8

DECEMBER

Date	Day	Time	m	Date	Day	Time	m
1	SU ●	0150 0807 1403 2024	4.8 0.9 4.8 0.8	16	M	0211 0836 1428 2055	4.9 0.6 5.0 0.7
2	M	0223 0842 1438 2059	4.8 0.8 4.9 0.9	17	TU	0257 0922 1516 2137	4.8 0.6 5.0 0.8
3	TU	0257 0918 1513 2134	4.8 0.8 4.9 0.9	18	W	0343 1007 1602 2217	4.8 0.6 4.9 1.0
4	W	0333 0956 1550 2210	4.8 0.8 4.9 0.9	19	TH	0427 1050 1649 2257	4.7 0.6 4.8 1.1
5	TH	0411 1036 1629 2250	4.7 0.7 4.8 1.0	20	F	0510 1134 1735 2339	4.6 0.7 4.7 1.2
6	F	0453 1121 1714 2335	4.6 0.7 4.7 1.1	21	SA	0554 1219 1823	4.4 0.8 4.5
7	SA	0540 1212 1808	4.5 0.8 4.6	22	SU ☾	0026 0639 1307 1913	1.3 4.3 0.9 4.3
8	SU ☽	0027 0637 1311 1915	1.2 4.3 0.8 4.4	23	M	0120 0730 1401 2008	1.4 4.1 1.0 4.1
9	M	0129 0745 1417 2029	1.3 4.2 0.9 4.4	24	TU	0224 0828 1500 2115	1.5 4.0 1.1 4.0
10	TU	0239 0857 1525 2140	1.4 4.2 0.9 4.4	25	W	0330 0938 1603 2224	1.5 3.9 1.1 4.0
11	W	0352 1005 1637 2246	1.3 4.3 0.8 4.5	26	TH	0433 1043 1705 2319	1.4 4.0 1.1 4.1
12	TH	0503 1107 1744 2343	1.2 4.5 0.7 4.7	27	F	0531 1136 1757	1.3 4.1 1.1
13	F	0605 1201 1838	1.0 4.7 0.7	28	SA	0006 0621 1221 1842	4.3 1.2 4.3 1.0
14	SA	0035 0659 1252 1926	4.8 0.9 4.9 0.6	29	SU	0047 0704 1303 1922	4.4 1.1 4.5 1.0
15	SU ○	0123 0748 1341 2012	4.9 0.7 5.0 0.6	30	M ●	0126 0745 1343 2001	4.6 0.9 4.7 0.9
				31	TU	0204 0825 1422 2040	4.7 0.8 4.8 0.9

ZEEBRUGGE
LAT 51°21'N
LONG 3°12'E

TIMES AND HEIGHTS OF HIGH AND LOW WATER (Heights in Metres)

TIME ZONE
European Standard Time (UT+0100)
For Summer Time (area enclosed in shaded box) add 1 hour

2024

JANUARY

Day	Time	m	Day	Time	m
1 M	0440 1100 1705 2300	4.3 0.8 4.4 1.2	16 TU	0445 1116 1717 2332	4.7 0.3 4.8 0.9
2 TU	0517 1140 1746 2340	4.2 0.9 4.3 1.3	17 W	0536 1207 1812	4.6 0.4 4.7
3 W	0558 1226 1832	4.1 1.0 4.2	18 TH ☽	0024 0631 1302 1912	1.0 4.5 0.5 4.4
4 TH ☾	0028 0647 1323 1928	1.4 4.0 1.1 4.1	19 F	0121 0733 1403 2018	1.2 4.3 0.7 4.2
5 F	0131 0748 1428 2031	1.5 3.9 1.2 4.0	20 SA	0229 0843 1514 2131	1.3 4.1 0.9 4.0
6 SA	0252 0854 1531 2136	1.5 3.9 1.2 4.0	21 SU	0352 1001 1632 2251	1.3 4.1 1.0 4.0
7 SU	0402 1000 1631 2239	1.4 3.9 1.1 4.1	22 M	0513 1120 1744 2359	1.2 4.2 1.0 4.1
8 M	0503 1101 1726 2337	1.3 4.1 1.1 4.2	23 TU	0617 1222 1840	1.0 4.3 1.0
9 TU	0557 1157 1815	1.1 4.2 1.0	24 W	0049 0706 1308 1924	4.3 0.9 4.4 1.0
10 W	0028 0645 1245 1901	4.3 1.0 4.4 0.9	25 TH O	0129 0746 1346 2000	4.3 0.8 4.5 1.1
11 TH ●	0111 0728 1329 1943	4.4 0.8 4.6 0.9	26 F	0203 0821 1420 2031	4.4 0.7 4.5 1.1
12 F	0151 0811 1411 2026	4.5 0.6 4.8 0.8	27 SA	0236 0855 1454 2100	4.4 0.6 4.6 1.0
13 SA	0232 0854 1454 2110	4.6 0.5 4.9 0.8	28 SU	0308 0927 1527 2129	4.5 0.5 4.6 1.0
14 SU	0314 0940 1539 2156	4.6 0.4 4.9 0.8	29 M	0340 1000 1601 2200	4.5 0.5 4.6 0.9
15 M	0358 1027 1626 2243	4.7 0.3 4.9 0.8	30 TU	0412 1032 1634 2233	4.5 0.6 4.6 0.9
			31 W	0444 1105 1707 [illegible]	4.5 0.6 4.5 [illegible]

FEBRUARY

Day	Time	m	Day	Time	m
1 TH	0518 1138 1744 2344	4.4 0.7 4.4 1.1	16 F ☽	0600 1230 1836	4.6 0.5 4.4
2 F	0557 1216 1826	4.3 0.9 4.3	17 SA	0044 0656 1329 1939	1.1 4.3 0.9 4.0
3 SA ☾	0026 0644 1304 1920	1.2 4.2 1.1 4.1	18 SU	0153 0807 1448 2101	1.3 4.0 1.2 3.7
4 SU	0122 0745 1420 2030	1.4 4.0 1.3 3.8	19 M	0330 0942 1613 2235	1.4 3.8 1.3 3.7
5 M	0308 0904 1551 2155	1.5 3.8 1.3 3.8	20 TU	0456 1111 1731 2345	1.3 3.9 1.3 3.9
6 TU	0432 1029 1658 2311	1.4 3.8 1.3 3.9	21 W	0602 1211 1830	1.0 4.2 1.2
7 W	0536 1137 1755	1.2 4.1 1.1	22 TH	0034 0652 1255 1911	4.1 0.8 4.4 1.1
8 TH	0009 0628 1230 1844	4.1 1.0 4.4 1.0	23 F	0111 0730 1329 1943	4.3 0.7 4.5 1.1
9 F ●	0054 0714 1314 1928	4.3 0.7 4.6 0.8	24 SA O	0143 0802 1400 2009	4.4 0.6 4.6 1.0
10 SA	0134 0756 1356 2011	4.5 0.5 4.9 0.7	25 SU	0212 0832 1430 2035	4.5 0.5 4.6 0.9
11 SU	0214 0840 1438 2055	4.7 0.3 5.0 0.6	26 M	0242 0901 1501 2103	4.6 0.4 4.7 0.8
12 M	0255 0924 1521 2139	4.9 0.1 5.1 0.6	27 TU	0312 0931 1532 2134	4.7 0.4 4.7 0.7
13 TU	0338 1009 1607 2224	4.9 0.1 5.1 0.6	28 W	0341 1002 1602 2206	4.7 0.4 4.7 0.7
14 W	0424 1055 1654 2309	4.9 0.1 4.9 0.7	29 TH	0411 1032 1632 2238	4.7 0.5 4.7 0.7
15 TH	0510 1141 1743 2354	4.8 0.3 4.7 0.8			

MARCH

Day	Time	m	Day	Time	m
1 F	0444 1103 1706 2311	4.6 0.6 4.5 0.8	16 SA	0532 1200 1803	4.6 0.7 4.2
2 SA	0520 1136 1744 2348	4.5 0.8 4.4 1.0	17 SU ☽	0013 0625 1256 1902	1.0 4.2 1.1 3.8
3 SU ☾	0603 1216 1831	4.3 1.0 4.1	18 M	0123 0737 1425 2030	1.3 3.8 1.4 3.5
4 M	0034 0657 1315 1934	1.2 4.0 1.3 3.8	19 TU	0306 0920 1547 2206	1.4 3.7 1.5 3.5
5 TU	0156 0818 1516 2117	1.5 3.8 1.5 3.5	20 W	0424 1048 1703 2317	1.3 3.8 1.4 3.8
6 W	0403 1003 1633 2246	1.4 3.8 1.4 3.7	21 TH	0533 1147 1805	1.0 4.1 1.3
7 TH	0511 1117 1734 2345	1.2 4.1 1.2 4.0	22 F	0006 0625 1229 1846	4.0 0.8 4.3 1.1
8 F	0606 1210 1824	0.9 4.4 1.0	23 SA	0043 0704 1302 1916	4.2 0.7 4.5 1.0
9 SA	0031 0653 1254 1909	4.3 0.6 4.7 0.8	24 SU	0115 0734 1333 1941	4.4 0.6 4.6 0.9
10 SU ●	0111 0736 1335 1952	4.6 0.3 5.0 0.6	25 M O	0144 0802 1402 2006	4.5 0.5 4.7 0.7
11 M	0151 0819 1417 2034	4.9 0.1 5.1 0.5	26 TU	0213 0830 1432 2036	4.7 0.4 4.8 0.6
12 TU	0233 0903 1500 2118	5.0 0.0 5.2 0.4	27 W	0242 0900 1501 2108	4.7 0.4 4.8 0.6
13 W	0316 0947 1544 2201	5.1 0.0 5.1 0.4	28 TH	0311 0931 1531 2140	4.7 0.4 4.7 0.6
14 TH	0400 1031 1629 2244	5.0 0.1 4.9 0.5	29 F	0342 1002 1601 2213	4.7 0.5 4.6 0.7
15 F	0445 1114 1714 2326	4.9 0.4 4.6 0.7	30 SA	0415 1033 1635 2245	4.7 0.6 4.5 0.8
			31 SU	0451 1107 1713 2321	4.6 0.8 4.3 0.9

APRIL

Day	Time	m	Day	Time	m
1 M	0534 1147 1758	4.4 1.0 4.1	16 TU	0105 0713 1357 1956	1.2 3.8 1.5 3.5
2 TU ☾	0008 0629 1247 1901	1.1 4.1 1.3 3.7	17 W	0235 0845 1511 2123	1.3 3.6 1.6 3.5
3 W	0133 0755 1448 2052	1.4 3.8 1.5 3.5	18 TH	0344 1006 1618 2233	1.2 3.8 1.5 3.7
4 TH	0334 0941 1606 2217	1.3 3.8 1.4 3.7	19 F	0448 1106 1720 2326	1.0 4.0 1.3 4.0
5 F	0440 1052 1707 2316	1.0 4.2 1.1 4.0	20 SA	0544 1151 1807	0.8 4.3 1.1
6 SA	0537 1145 1800	0.7 4.5 0.9	21 SU	0006 0626 1228 1840	4.2 0.7 4.4 1.0
7 SU	0003 0627 1230 1846	4.4 0.4 4.8 0.7	22 M	0040 0659 1301 1908	4.4 0.6 4.6 0.8
8 M ●	0046 0712 1312 1930	4.7 0.2 5.0 0.5	23 TU	0112 0728 1332 1937	4.5 0.5 4.7 0.7
9 TU	0128 0756 1354 2013	4.9 0.1 5.1 0.4	24 W O	0142 0758 1402 2009	4.6 0.5 4.7 0.6
10 W	0210 0840 1437 2056	5.1 0.0 5.1 0.4	25 TH	0212 0830 1432 2043	4.7 0.5 4.7 0.6
11 TH	0254 0923 1521 2138	5.1 0.1 4.9 0.4	26 F	0243 0903 1503 2117	4.7 0.5 4.6 0.6
12 F	0338 1006 1605 2220	5.0 0.3 4.7 0.5	27 SA	0316 0936 1536 2152	4.6 0.6 4.5 0.7
13 SA	0422 1048 1649 2302	4.8 0.6 4.4 0.7	28 SU	0352 1010 1612 2227	4.6 0.8 4.4 0.8
14 SU	0509 1132 1736 2349	4.5 0.9 4.1 1.0	29 M	0432 1047 1652 2307	4.5 0.9 4.2 0.9
15 M ☽	0601 1226 1833	4.1 1.3 3.7	30 TU	0518 1132 1741 2359	4.3 1.1 4.0 1.0

MAY

Day	Time	m	Day	Time	m
1 W ☾	0619 1239 1850	4.1 1.3 3.7	16 TH	0158 0801 1426 2031	1.1 3.8 1.6 3.6
2 TH	0136 0747 1421 2028	1.1 4.0 1.4 3.7	17 F	0300 0912 1527 2138	1.1 3.8 1.5 3.7
3 F	0303 0915 1534 2144	1.0 4.1 1.3 3.9	18 SA	0358 1013 1625 2234	1.0 3.9 1.4 3.9
4 SA	0407 1022 1635 2244	0.8 4.3 1.1 4.2	19 SU	0452 1104 1717 2321	0.9 4.1 1.2 4.1
5 SU	0506 1117 1732 2335	0.6 4.6 0.9 4.4	20 M	0539 1148 1759 2359	0.8 4.3 1.0 4.2
6 M	0600 1205 1822	0.4 4.8 0.7	21 TU	0618 1226 1835	0.7 4.4 0.9
7 TU	0022 0648 1250 1908	4.7 0.3 4.9 0.6	22 W	0038 0653 1302 1909	4.4 0.7 4.5 0.8
8 W ●	0106 0734 1334 1953	4.8 0.2 4.9 0.5	23 TH O	0113 0727 1335 1945	4.5 0.6 4.5 0.7
9 TH	0151 0818 1418 2036	4.9 0.3 4.8 0.5	24 F	0147 0802 1408 2021	4.5 0.7 4.5 0.7
10 F	0235 0901 1502 2119	4.9 0.4 4.7 0.5	25 SA	0221 0839 1442 2059	4.6 0.7 4.5 0.7
11 SA	0320 0943 1545 2201	4.8 0.6 4.5 0.6	26 SU	0258 0916 1518 2137	4.6 0.8 4.4 0.7
12 SU	0405 1025 1629 2245	4.6 0.8 4.3 0.7	27 M	0338 0954 1558 2218	4.5 0.9 4.3 0.7
13 M	0451 1107 1714 2334	4.4 1.1 4.0 0.9	28 TU	0422 1037 1642 2305	4.5 1.0 4.2 0.8
14 TU	0543 1157 1807	4.1 1.3 3.8	29 W	0513 1128 1736	4.4 1.1 4.1
15 W ☽	0044 0646 1316 1916	1.0 3.9 1.5 3.6	30 TH ☾	0006 0615 1234 1843	0.8 4.3 1.2 4.0
			31 F	0121 0731 1350 2000	0.8 4.2 1.2 4.0

JUNE

Day	Time	m	Day	Time	m
1 SA	0230 0844 1458 2109	0.7 4.3 1.2 4.1	16 SU	0305 0912 1528 2134	1.0 3.9 1.4 3.8
2 SU	0333 0949 1602 2212	0.6 4.4 1.1 4.2	17 M	0359 1009 1625 2229	1.0 4.0 1.3 3.9
3 M	0435 1049 1704 2309	0.6 4.5 1.0 4.4	18 TU	0450 1102 1717 2320	1.0 4.1 1.2 4.1
4 TU	0534 1144 1801 2359	0.5 4.6 0.8 4.6	19 W	0538 1151 1803	0.9 4.2 1.0
5 W	0628 1234 1852	0.5 4.6 0.7	20 TH	0006 0620 1234 1845	4.2 0.9 4.3 0.9
6 TH ●	0051 0716 1321 1938	4.6 0.5 4.6 0.6	21 F	0048 0700 1313 1924	4.3 0.8 4.4 0.8
7 F	0138 0801 1405 2022	4.7 0.6 4.5 0.6	22 SA O	0127 0739 1349 2004	4.4 0.8 4.4 0.7
8 SA	0223 0843 1447 2104	4.7 0.7 4.4 0.6	23 SU	0206 0819 1427 2044	4.5 0.8 4.4 0.7
9 SU	0307 0923 1529 2147	4.6 0.9 4.4 0.6	24 M	0246 0900 1506 2127	4.6 0.8 4.4 0.6
10 M	0350 1003 1610 2230	4.5 1.0 4.3 0.6	25 TU	0329 0943 1548 2213	4.7 0.9 4.4 0.5
11 TU	0434 1043 1653 2317	4.4 1.1 4.2 0.7	26 W	0415 1030 1634 2303	4.7 0.9 4.4 0.5
12 W	0521 1126 1739	4.2 1.3 4.0	27 TH	0505 1121 1725 2357	4.6 1.0 4.4 0.5
13 TH	0011 0612 1219 1832	0.8 4.1 1.4 3.9	28 F ☾	0602 1217 1823	4.6 1.0 4.3
14 F ☽	0111 0710 1325 1932	0.9 4.0 1.4 3.8	29 SA	0056 0705 1317 1927	0.5 4.5 1.1 4.3
15 SA	0210 0812 1429 2035	1.0 3.9 1.4 3.8	30 SU	0157 0810 1421 2033	0.6 4.4 1.1 4.2

SUNRISE AND SUNSET TIMES

ZEEBRUGGE
At 51°21'N 3°12'E
European Standard Time (UT+0100)

		Sunrise	Sunset
Jan	01	0852	1655
	15	0845	1708
Feb	01	0825	1738
	15	0800	1803
Mar	01	0732	1828
		0701	1852
European Summer Time (UT+0200)			
Apr	01	0723	2021
	15	0652	2044
May	01	0619	2110
	15	0556	2132
Jun	01	0537	2154
	15	0530	2205
Jul	01	0535	2207
	15	0549	2157
Aug	01	0612	2134
	15	0633	2109
Sep	01	0700	2033
	15	0722	2001
Oct	01	0740	1825
	15	0811	1824
European Standard Time (UT+0100)			
Nov	01	0741	1720
	15	0805	1659
Dec	01	0830	1642

ZEEBRUGGE
LAT 51°21′N
LONG 3°12′E

TIMES AND HEIGHTS OF HIGH AND LOW WATER (Heights in Metres)

TIME ZONE
European Standard Time (UT+0100)
For Summer Time (area enclosed in shaded box) add 1 hour

2024

JULY

Date	Day	Time	m	Time	m	Time	m	Time	m
1	M	0300	0.7	0916	4.3	1529	1.1	2140	4.2
2	TU	0407	0.7	1023	4.3	1641	1.1	2248	4.3
3	W	0514	0.8	1129	4.3	1748	1.0	2351	4.4
4	TH	0614	0.8	1226	4.3	1843	0.9		
5	F ●	0046	4.5	0705	0.9	1313	4.4	1929	0.8
6	SA	0132	4.5	0748	0.9	1355	4.4	2012	0.7
7	SU	0213	4.6	0827	1.0	1433	4.4	2052	0.6
8	M	0253	4.6	0904	1.0	1511	4.4	2131	0.6
9	TU	0332	4.6	0940	1.0	1549	4.4	2210	0.5
10	W	0412	4.5	1016	1.0	1627	4.4	2250	0.6
11	TH	0452	4.5	1053	1.1	1706	4.4	2331	0.7
12	F	0533	4.4	1131	1.1	1746	4.3		
13	SA ☽	0013	0.8	0616	4.3	1212	1.2	1829	4.2
14	SU	0059	0.9	0704	4.1	1302	1.3	1920	4.0
15	M	0155	1.1	0800	4.0	1412	1.4	2021	3.9
16	TU	0301	1.2	0904	3.9	1532	1.4	2130	3.8
17	W	0404	1.2	1012	3.9	1638	1.3	2238	3.9
18	TH	0502	1.2	1116	4.0	1735	1.2	2338	4.1
19	F	0553	1.1	1209	4.1	1824	1.0		
20	SA	0028	4.3	0638	1.0	1253	4.3	1907	0.9
21	SU O	0111	4.5	0720	0.9	1332	4.4	1949	0.7
22	M	0151	4.7	0802	0.8	1411	4.5	2031	0.5
23	TU	0232	4.8	0845	0.8	1451	4.7	2115	0.4
24	W	0315	4.9	0930	0.7	1533	4.7	2201	0.3
25	TH	0400	5.0	1016	0.7	1618	4.8	2249	0.2
26	F	0448	4.9	1104	0.8	1706	4.7	2337	0.3
27	SA	0539	4.8	1152	0.9	1757	4.7		
28	SU ☾	0028	0.4	0634	4.6	1244	1.0	1853	4.5
29	M	0124	0.6	0734	4.4	1344	1.1	1957	4.3
30	TU	0230	0.8	0844	4.1	1501	1.3	2113	4.1
31	W	0346	1.0	1004	4.0	1625	1.2	2237	4.1

AUGUST

Date	Day	Time	m	Time	m	Time	m	Time	m
1	TH	0502	1.1	1121	4.0	1739	1.1	2349	4.3
2	F	0607	1.1	1220	4.2	1836	0.9		
3	SA	0041	4.4	0657	1.1	1303	4.3	1920	0.8
4	SU ●	0123	4.5	0736	1.1	1340	4.4	1959	0.6
5	M	0159	4.6	0810	1.0	1414	4.5	2034	0.5
6	TU	0234	4.7	0842	1.0	1448	4.6	2109	0.5
7	W	0309	4.7	0914	0.9	1523	4.7	2144	0.4
8	TH	0345	4.7	0947	0.8	1557	4.7	2218	0.5
9	F	0420	4.7	1020	0.8	1631	4.6	2252	0.6
10	SA	0453	4.6	1054	0.9	1703	4.6	2324	0.7
11	SU	0527	4.5	1127	1.0	1739	4.5	2357	0.9
12	M ☽	0604	4.4	1205	1.1	1820	4.3		
13	TU	0037	1.1	0650	4.1	1251	1.3	1912	4.1
14	W	0135	1.3	0750	3.9	1413	1.5	2025	3.8
15	TH	0320	1.4	0919	3.7	1604	1.5	2159	3.8
16	F	0431	1.4	1044	3.8	1709	1.3	2314	4.0
17	SA	0529	1.2	1145	4.0	1802	1.0		
18	SU	0008	4.3	0618	1.1	1231	4.3	1848	0.8
19	M O	0052	4.6	0702	0.9	1311	4.6	1930	0.5
20	TU	0132	4.9	0744	0.7	1350	4.8	2013	0.3
21	W	0213	5.1	0828	0.6	1430	5.0	2057	0.1
22	TH	0255	5.2	0912	0.5	1512	5.1	2142	0.1
23	F	0339	5.2	0957	0.5	1556	5.1	2227	0.1
24	SA	0425	5.1	1041	0.6	1641	5.0	2312	0.3
25	SU	0512	4.9	1126	0.8	1729	4.8	2359	0.5
26	M ☾	0602	4.6	1213	1.0	1822	4.6		
27	TU	0052	0.8	0659	4.2	1311	1.2	1926	4.2
28	W	0204	1.1	0814	3.9	1441	1.4	2054	4.0
29	TH	0330	1.3	0948	3.8	1611	1.3	2230	4.0
30	F	0449	1.3	1109	3.9	1724	1.1	2340	4.3
31	SA	0555	1.2	1204	4.2	1820	0.9		

SEPTEMBER

Date	Day	Time	m	Time	m	Time	m	Time	m
1	SU	0028	4.5	0642	1.1	1245	4.4	1903	0.7
2	M	0105	4.6	0718	1.1	1319	4.5	1939	0.6
3	TU ●	0138	4.7	0748	1.0	1351	4.7	2011	0.5
4	W	0210	4.8	0817	0.9	1423	4.8	2042	0.4
5	TH	0243	4.9	0847	0.8	1455	4.8	2114	0.4
6	F	0315	4.9	0918	0.7	1526	4.9	2145	0.4
7	SA	0346	4.8	0950	0.7	1556	4.8	2216	0.6
8	SU	0416	4.7	1021	0.8	1627	4.7	2245	0.7
9	M	0447	4.6	1053	0.9	1700	4.6	2316	0.9
10	TU	0521	4.5	1127	1.0	1739	4.5	2352	1.1
11	W ☽	0603	4.2	1208	1.2	1828	4.2		
12	TH	0041	1.3	0658	3.9	1311	1.5	1938	3.9
13	F	0234	1.6	0833	3.7	1533	1.5	2129	3.8
14	SA	0404	1.5	1015	3.8	1641	1.3	2249	4.1
15	SU	0504	1.3	1117	4.1	1736	0.9	2344	4.5
16	M	0555	1.0	1204	4.4	1824	0.6		
17	TU	0028	4.8	0640	0.8	1245	4.7	1908	0.4
18	W O	0109	5.1	0724	0.6	1326	5.0	1951	0.2
19	TH	0151	5.3	0807	0.5	1407	5.2	2035	0.0
20	F	0233	5.4	0851	0.4	1449	5.3	2119	0.0
21	SA	0316	5.3	0934	0.4	1533	5.2	2203	0.2
22	SU	0401	5.1	1018	0.6	1618	5.1	2247	0.4
23	M	0446	4.8	1101	0.7	1704	4.8	2332	0.7
24	TU ☾	0534	4.4	1146	1.0	1756	4.5		
25	W	0024	1.1	0629	4.1	1246	1.2	1902	4.1
26	TH	0143	1.4	0749	3.7	1426	1.4	2038	3.9
27	F	0310	1.6	0925	3.7	1547	1.3	2211	4.0
28	SA	0425	1.5	1044	3.9	1657	1.1	2317	4.3
29	SU	0531	1.3	1138	4.2	1754	0.9		
30	M	0004	4.5	0619	1.2	1219	4.4	1838	0.7

OCTOBER

Date	Day	Time	m	Time	m	Time	m	Time	m
1	TU	0041	4.7	0653	1.0	1253	4.6	1913	0.6
2	W ●	0113	4.8	0722	0.9	1325	4.8	1943	0.5
3	TH	0144	4.9	0750	0.8	1356	4.8	2013	0.5
4	F	0216	4.9	0819	0.7	1426	4.9	2043	0.5
5	SA	0246	4.9	0851	0.6	1456	4.9	2113	0.5
6	SU	0315	4.8	0923	0.7	1526	4.8	2144	0.7
7	M	0344	4.7	0954	0.8	1556	4.8	2214	0.8
8	TU	0415	4.6	1026	0.9	1631	4.7	2245	0.9
9	W	0450	4.5	1100	1.0	1711	4.5	2322	1.1
10	TH ☽	0532	4.2	1142	1.2	1801	4.3		
11	F	0013	1.4	0627	3.9	1248	1.4	1915	4.0
12	SA	0200	1.6	0805	3.7	1502	1.4	2104	4.0
13	SU	0334	1.5	0943	3.8	1609	1.1	2220	4.3
14	M	0435	1.3	1045	4.2	1706	0.8	2316	4.6
15	TU	0529	1.0	1135	4.5	1757	0.5	2359	4.9
16	W	0617	0.8	1219	4.8	1844	0.3		
17	TH O	0046	5.2	0702	0.6	1302	5.1	1929	0.2
18	F	0128	5.3	0746	0.5	1344	5.2	2013	0.1
19	SA	0211	5.3	0830	0.4	1428	5.3	2057	0.2
20	SU	0255	5.1	0914	0.5	1512	5.2	2140	0.4
21	M	0339	4.9	0957	0.6	1558	5.0	2224	0.7
22	TU	0424	4.6	1040	0.7	1645	4.7	2308	1.0
23	W	0511	4.3	1127	1.0	1737	4.4		
24	TH ☾	0000	1.3	0607	4.0	1233	1.2	1844	4.1
25	F	0120	1.6	0723	3.7	1402	1.3	2012	3.9
26	SA	0239	1.6	0849	3.7	1513	1.2	2135	4.0
27	SU	0347	1.6	1003	3.9	1618	1.1	2240	4.2
28	M	0452	1.4	1101	4.1	1717	0.9	2329	4.4
29	TU	0545	1.2	1146	4.4	1805	0.7		
30	W	0010	4.6	0624	1.0	1223	4.6	1842	0.7
31	TH	0045	4.7	0655	0.9	1257	4.7	1914	0.6

NOVEMBER

Date	Day	Time	m	Time	m	Time	m	Time	m
1	F ●	0118	4.8	0724	0.8	1329	4.8	1944	0.6
2	SA	0150	4.8	0755	0.7	1400	4.8	2014	0.6
3	SU	0220	4.8	0827	0.7	1430	4.8	2045	0.7
4	M	0249	4.7	0900	0.7	1501	4.7	2117	0.8
5	TU	0319	4.6	0933	0.8	1534	4.7	2150	0.9
6	W	0352	4.5	1007	0.9	1611	4.6	2224	1.0
7	TH	0430	4.4	1045	1.0	1655	4.5	2306	1.2
8	F	0515	4.2	1133	1.1	1749	4.3	2359	1.4
9	SA ☽	0615	4.0	1248	1.2	1906	4.1		
10	SU	0135	1.5	0744	3.9	1428	1.1	2036	4.2
11	M	0259	1.4	0907	4.0	1535	0.9	2147	4.4
12	TU	0403	1.2	1011	4.3	1634	0.7	2246	4.6
13	W	0500	1.0	1105	4.5	1729	0.5	2337	4.9
14	TH	0554	0.9	1155	4.8	1821	0.4		
15	F O	0024	5.0	0643	0.7	1241	5.0	1908	0.3
16	SA	0110	5.0	0729	0.6	1327	5.1	1954	0.4
17	SU	0154	5.0	0814	0.5	1412	5.1	2038	0.5
18	M	0239	4.8	0857	0.6	1458	5.0	2121	0.7
19	TU	0323	4.7	0941	0.6	1544	4.8	2204	0.9
20	W	0407	4.5	1026	0.7	1631	4.6	2248	1.1
21	TH	0454	4.3	1115	0.8	1722	4.4	2338	1.3
22	F	0546	4.1	1217	1.0	1822	4.2		
23	SA ☾	0044	1.5	0650	3.9	1328	1.1	1933	4.0
24	SU	0156	1.6	0802	3.8	1433	1.1	2045	4.0
25	M	0301	1.6	0911	3.9	1534	1.1	2149	4.1
26	TU	0403	1.5	1012	4.0	1632	1.0	2245	4.2
27	W	0501	1.3	1104	4.2	1724	0.9	2333	4.4
28	TH	0549	1.2	1150	4.3	1808	0.9		
29	F	0016	4.5	0628	1.0	1230	4.5	1844	0.8
30	SA	0054	4.6	0702	0.9	1306	4.5	1917	0.8

DECEMBER

Date	Day	Time	m	Time	m	Time	m	Time	m
1	SU ●	0128	4.6	0734	0.9	1339	4.6	1949	0.8
2	M	0159	4.6	0808	0.8	1411	4.6	2022	0.9
3	TU	0230	4.5	0843	0.8	1444	4.6	2057	0.9
4	W	0302	4.5	0919	0.8	1521	4.6	2133	1.0
5	TH	0339	4.4	0958	0.8	1602	4.6	2213	1.1
6	F	0420	4.4	1041	0.8	1648	4.6	2259	1.2
7	SA	0508	4.3	1134	0.9	1743	4.5	2357	1.3
8	SU ☽	0606	4.2	1241	0.9	1850	4.4		
9	M	0108	1.3	0717	4.1	1352	0.9	2004	4.4
10	TU	0220	1.3	0829	4.2	1458	0.8	2112	4.4
11	W	0327	1.2	0935	4.3	1602	0.7	2215	4.5
12	TH	0432	1.1	1037	4.4	1704	0.7	2315	4.6
13	F	0534	1.0	1135	4.6	1802	0.6		
14	SA	0010	4.6	0629	0.9	1228	4.7	1854	0.7
15	SU O	0059	4.6	0718	0.7	1318	4.8	1940	0.7
16	M	0145	4.6	0803	0.7	1404	4.8	2024	0.8
17	TU	0228	4.6	0847	0.6	1448	4.8	2105	0.9
18	W	0310	4.5	0930	0.6	1532	4.7	2146	1.0
19	TH	0352	4.5	1014	0.6	1616	4.6	2228	1.1
20	F	0435	4.4	1100	0.6	1702	4.5	2312	1.2
21	SA	0521	4.3	1150	0.7	1752	4.4	2359	1.3
22	SU ☾	0611	4.2	1246	0.9	1847	4.2		
23	M	0058	1.4	0708	4.0	1345	1.0	1947	4.1
24	TU	0203	1.5	0809	3.9	1444	1.1	2049	4.0
25	W	0308	1.5	0912	3.9	1542	1.2	2150	4.0
26	TH	0412	1.5	1014	3.9	1639	1.2	2250	4.0
27	F	0511	1.3	1112	4.0	1731	1.1	2345	4.1
28	SA	0602	1.2	1203	4.1	1816	1.1		
29	SU	0032	4.2	0643	1.1	1246	4.3	1853	1.0
30	M ●	0110	4.3	0719	1.0	1322	4.4	1928	1.0
31	TU	0143	4.4	0753	0.8	1357	4.5	2004	1.0

DUNKERQUE

LAT 51°03′N
LONG 2°22′E

TIMES AND HEIGHTS OF HIGH AND LOW WATER (Heights in Metres)

TIME ZONE
European Standard Time (UT+0100)
For Summer Time (area enclosed in shaded box) add 1 hour

2024

JANUARY

Date	Day	Time	m	Time	m	Time	m	Time	m
1	M	0346	5.4	1039	1.1	1610	5.4	2253	1.4
2	TU	0424	5.3	1115	1.2	1650	5.2	2330	1.5
3	W	0506	5.1	1154	1.3	1735	5.1		
4	TH ☾	0012	1.7	0554	5.0	1240	1.4	1827	4.9
5	F	0102	1.8	0650	4.9	1337	1.6	1926	4.8
6	SA	0207	1.9	0752	4.8	1448	1.6	2030	4.8
7	SU	0321	1.8	0859	4.9	1556	1.5	2136	4.9
8	M	0426	1.7	1004	5.0	1656	1.4	2235	5.1
9	TU	0524	1.5	1059	5.3	1751	1.2	2327	5.4
10	W	0617	1.2	1148	5.5	1842	1.0		
11	TH ●	0013	5.6	0707	1.0	1234	5.8	1931	0.9
12	F	0057	5.8	0755	0.8	1320	6.0	2018	0.8
13	SA	0141	5.9	0842	0.6	1406	6.1	2105	0.7
14	SU	0226	5.9	0929	0.5	1453	6.1	2151	0.8
15	M	0311	5.9	1016	0.5	1541	6.0	2237	0.8
16	TU	0357	5.8	1104	0.5	1630	5.8	2323	1.0
17	W	0444	5.7	1153	0.7	1722	5.6		
18	TH ☽	0012	1.2	0536	5.5	1246	0.9	1820	5.4
19	F	0108	1.4	0636	5.3	1347	1.1	1927	5.1
20	SA	0212	1.5	0748	5.1	1454	1.3	2041	5.0
21	SU	0322	1.6	0904	5.0	1608	1.4	2152	5.0
22	M	0439	1.6	1016	5.1	1722	1.4	2259	5.1
23	TU	0547	1.4	1120	5.3	1820	1.3	2354	5.3
24	W	0639	1.1	1211	5.5	1905	1.1		
25	TH ○	0038	5.4	0723	0.9	1254	5.6	1944	1.1
26	F	0115	5.6	0802	0.8	1332	5.7	2019	1.0
27	SA	0149	5.7	0838	0.7	1407	5.7	2053	1.0
28	SU	0220	5.7	0912	0.7	1439	5.7	2124	1.0
29	M	0250	5.7	0943	0.7	1509	5.7	2155	1.0
30	TU	0319	5.6	1013	0.8	1539	5.6	2224	1.1
31	W	0350	5.6	1043	0.9	1612	5.5	2254	1.2

FEBRUARY

Date	Day	Time	m	Time	m	Time	m	Time	m
1	TH	0422	5.4	1114	1.0	1646	5.3	2326	1.3
2	F	0457	5.3	1150	1.2	1725	5.1		
3	SA ☾	0005	1.5	0541	5.1	1235	1.4	1819	4.9
4	SU	0054	1.7	0644	4.8	1336	1.6	1928	4.7
5	M	0207	1.9	0801	4.7	1459	1.7	2047	4.7
6	TU	0337	1.9	0926	4.8	1620	1.6	2208	4.9
7	W	0456	1.6	1041	5.1	1732	1.3	2312	5.2
8	TH	0603	1.2	1137	5.5	1831	1.0		
9	F ●	0002	5.5	0657	0.9	1225	5.8	1921	0.8
10	SA	0046	5.8	0745	0.5	1309	6.1	2006	0.6
11	SU	0128	6.0	0830	0.3	1353	6.2	2050	0.5
12	M	0209	6.1	0915	0.2	1437	6.2	2133	0.5
13	TU	0250	6.1	0959	0.2	1521	6.1	2216	0.6
14	W	0332	6.0	1042	0.3	1605	6.0	2257	0.8
15	TH	0415	5.9	1126	0.5	1651	5.7	2340	1.0
16	F ☽	0503	5.7	1212	0.8	1742	5.4		
17	SA	0029	1.3	0559	5.4	1307	1.2	1845	5.0
18	SU	0130	1.6	0711	5.0	1416	1.6	2006	4.7
19	M	0247	1.8	0840	4.7	1544	1.7	2134	4.6
20	TU	0422	1.7	1007	4.8	1710	1.6	2250	4.8
21	W	0536	1.4	1116	5.1	1808	1.4	2345	5.1
22	TH	0628	1.1	1205	5.3	1851	1.1		
23	F	0025	5.4	0709	0.9	1242	5.6	1927	1.0
24	SA ○	0058	5.6	0744	0.7	1315	5.7	1959	0.9
25	SU	0129	5.7	0816	0.6	1346	5.8	2029	0.8
26	M	0157	5.8	0846	0.6	1414	5.8	2058	0.8
27	TU	0223	5.8	0916	0.6	1440	5.8	2127	0.8
28	W	0249	5.8	0944	0.6	1506	5.8	2154	0.9
29	TH	0315	5.7	1011	0.7	1532	5.7	2220	1.0

MARCH

Date	Day	Time	m	Time	m	Time	m	Time	m
1	F	0339	5.6	1039	0.8	1558	5.5	2249	1.1
2	SA	0407	5.5	1111	1.0	1629	5.3	2324	1.3
3	SU ☾	0444	5.3	1151	1.3	1715	5.0		
4	M	0010	1.5	0542	4.9	1248	1.6	1834	4.6
5	TU	0118	1.8	0717	4.6	1415	1.8	2012	4.5
6	W	0257	1.9	0902	4.7	1553	1.7	2149	4.7
7	TH	0433	1.6	1025	5.1	1716	1.3	2256	5.1
8	F	0547	1.1	1123	5.5	1816	1.0	2346	5.5
9	SA	0641	0.7	1209	5.9	1904	0.7		
10	SU ●	0028	5.8	0727	0.4	1252	6.1	1947	0.5
11	M	0106	6.0	0811	0.2	1333	6.2	2028	0.4
12	TU	0145	6.2	0853	0.1	1414	6.2	2109	0.4
13	W	0224	6.2	0935	0.1	1455	6.2	2150	0.5
14	TH	0305	6.2	1016	0.3	1537	6.0	2229	0.7
15	F	0347	6.0	1057	0.6	1621	5.7	2310	0.9
16	SA	0434	5.7	1140	1.0	1710	5.3	2356	1.2
17	SU ☽	0529	5.3	1231	1.4	1811	4.8		
18	M	0055	1.6	0642	4.8	1342	1.8	1935	4.5
19	TU	0217	1.8	0819	4.6	1520	1.9	2112	4.4
20	W	0359	1.7	0952	4.7	1648	1.7	2228	4.7
21	TH	0514	1.4	1058	5.0	1745	1.4	2320	5.0
22	F	0605	1.1	1143	5.3	1827	1.1	2358	5.3
23	SA	0645	0.8	1218	5.5	1901	1.0		
24	SU	0030	5.6	0717	0.7	1249	5.7	1930	0.9
25	M ○	0101	5.7	0746	0.6	1318	5.8	1958	0.8
26	TU	0128	5.8	0815	0.6	1343	5.8	2027	0.7
27	W	0152	5.8	0844	0.6	1407	5.8	2056	0.7
28	TH	0216	5.8	0913	0.6	1432	5.8	2124	0.8
29	F	0242	5.8	0941	0.7	1458	5.7	2152	0.9
30	SA	0307	5.7	1009	0.8	1525	5.6	2222	1.0
31	SU	0337	5.6	1043	1.0	1558	5.4	2259	1.2

APRIL

Date	Day	Time	m	Time	m	Time	m	Time	m
1	M	0417	5.3	1125	1.3	1645	5.0	2347	1.4
2	TU ☾	0518	5.0	1225	1.6	1810	4.6		
3	W	0058	1.7	0701	4.7	1353	1.8	1952	4.5
4	TH	0236	1.7	0844	4.8	1533	1.6	2127	4.7
5	F	0411	1.4	1005	5.2	1653	1.3	2233	5.1
6	SA	0523	0.9	1101	5.6	1752	0.9	2321	5.5
7	SU	0617	0.5	1147	5.9	1839	0.7		
8	M ●	0001	5.8	0703	0.3	1228	6.1	1922	0.5
9	TU	0039	6.0	0746	0.2	1307	6.2	2003	0.5
10	W	0118	6.2	0828	0.2	1347	6.2	2043	0.5
11	TH	0158	6.2	0909	0.3	1429	6.1	2124	0.5
12	F	0241	6.1	0950	0.5	1512	5.9	2204	0.6
13	SA	0326	5.9	1030	0.8	1556	5.6	2246	0.9
14	SU	0414	5.6	1113	1.1	1645	5.2	2332	1.2
15	M ☽	0509	5.2	1203	1.5	1744	4.8		
16	TU	0028	1.5	0618	4.8	1310	1.9	1902	4.5
17	W	0146	1.7	0750	4.5	1444	2.0	2037	4.4
18	TH	0321	1.7	0919	4.6	1607	1.8	2148	4.7
19	F	0435	1.4	1020	4.9	1706	1.5	2239	5.0
20	SA	0527	1.1	1105	5.2	1750	1.2	2320	5.3
21	SU	0607	0.9	1142	5.5	1825	1.0	2355	5.5
22	M	0640	0.8	1215	5.6	1854	0.9		
23	TU	0027	5.6	0709	0.7	1244	5.7	1924	0.8
24	W ○	0055	5.7	0740	0.7	1310	5.7	1956	0.8
25	TH	0120	5.8	0813	0.7	1335	5.8	2028	0.8
26	F	0147	5.8	0845	0.7	1404	5.8	2100	0.8
27	SA	0217	5.8	0917	0.8	1435	5.7	2132	0.8
28	SU	0250	5.7	0950	0.9	1509	5.5	2208	1.0
29	M	0327	5.5	1028	1.1	1550	5.3	2250	1.1
30	TU	0416	5.3	1116	1.3	1649	5.0	2343	1.3

MAY

Date	Day	Time	m	Time	m	Time	m	Time	m
1	W ☽	0532	5.0	1220	1.6	1811	4.7		
2	TH	0055	1.5	0654	4.9	1343	1.6	1932	4.7
3	F	0222	1.4	0822	5.0	1510	1.5	2057	4.9
4	SA	0346	1.2	0938	5.3	1623	1.2	2201	5.2
5	SU	0453	0.8	1033	5.6	1722	0.9	2250	5.6
6	M	0549	0.6	1120	5.8	1811	0.8	2332	5.8
7	TU	0637	0.4	1201	6.0	1855	0.7		
8	W ●	0012	6.0	0721	0.4	1242	6.0	1938	0.6
9	TH	0054	6.1	0804	0.4	1324	6.0	2021	0.6
10	F	0138	6.1	0846	0.5	1409	5.9	2103	0.6
11	SA	0224	6.0	0928	0.7	1454	5.7	2145	0.7
12	SU	0312	5.8	1009	1.0	1541	5.5	2229	0.9
13	M	0402	5.5	1052	1.3	1628	5.2	2314	1.1
14	TU	0454	5.2	1140	1.5	1720	4.9		
15	W ☾	0006	1.4	0552	4.9	1237	1.8	1822	4.6
16	TH	0109	1.5	0704	4.7	1352	1.9	1941	4.5
17	F	0226	1.6	0826	4.7	1508	1.8	2054	4.7
18	SA	0336	1.4	0929	4.8	1609	1.6	2149	4.9
19	SU	0432	1.2	1018	5.1	1659	1.4	2234	5.1
20	M	0517	1.1	1059	5.3	1740	1.2	2315	5.3
21	TU	0556	1.0	1136	5.4	1816	1.1	2350	5.5
22	W	0632	0.9	1209	5.5	1851	1.0		
23	TH ○	0022	5.6	0708	0.8	1239	5.6	1927	0.9
24	F	0053	5.6	0745	0.8	1311	5.7	2005	0.8
25	SA	0127	5.7	0823	0.8	1347	5.7	2043	0.8
26	SU	0206	5.7	0902	0.9	1427	5.6	2123	0.8
27	M	0249	5.7	0943	1.0	1512	5.5	2206	0.9
28	TU	0337	5.5	1028	1.1	1602	5.3	2253	1.0
29	W	0432	5.4	1119	1.3	1659	5.1	2347	1.1
30	TH ☽	0533	5.3	1219	1.4	1800	5.0		
31	F	0051	1.1	0638	5.2	1329	1.4	1906	5.0

JUNE

Date	Day	Time	m	Time	m	Time	m	Time	m
1	SA	0204	1.1	0753	5.2	1442	1.4	2019	5.1
2	SU	0316	1.0	0904	5.3	1549	1.2	2125	5.3
3	M	0421	0.8	1003	5.5	1649	1.1	2219	5.5
4	TU	0520	0.7	1054	5.6	1744	1.0	2307	5.7
5	W	0613	0.7	1141	5.7	1834	0.9	2354	5.8
6	TH ●	0701	0.7	1227	5.7	1921	0.8		
7	F	0041	5.8	0747	0.7	1313	5.7	2006	0.7
8	SA	0129	5.9	0830	0.8	1359	5.7	2050	0.7
9	SU	0217	5.8	0913	0.9	1445	5.6	2133	0.7
10	M	0305	5.7	0954	1.1	1529	5.5	2215	0.8
11	TU	0350	5.5	1035	1.2	1610	5.3	2257	1.0
12	W	0434	5.3	1116	1.4	1652	5.1	2340	1.1
13	TH	0520	5.1	1201	1.6	1739	5.0		
14	F ☾	0028	1.3	0610	4.9	1254	1.7	1833	4.8
15	SA	0125	1.4	0709	4.8	1358	1.7	1936	4.8
16	SU	0228	1.4	0815	4.8	1503	1.7	2042	4.8
17	M	0329	1.4	0916	4.9	1600	1.6	2140	4.9
18	TU	0423	1.3	1008	5.0	1652	1.4	2230	5.1
19	W	0513	1.2	1055	5.2	1739	1.3	2315	5.3
20	TH	0558	1.1	1137	5.3	1823	1.2	2355	5.4
21	F	0642	1.0	1216	5.5	1906	1.0		
22	SA ○	0035	5.6	0725	1.0	1255	5.6	1949	0.9
23	SU	0116	5.7	0810	0.9	1338	5.7	2034	0.8
24	M	0200	5.8	0855	0.9	1423	5.7	2119	0.7
25	TU	0247	5.8	0940	0.9	1509	5.6	2205	0.7
26	W	0336	5.8	1027	1.0	1556	5.6	2252	0.7
27	TH	0425	5.7	1114	1.0	1645	5.5	2342	0.8
28	F ☽	0518	5.6	1206	1.2	1737	5.4		
29	SA	0037	0.8	0615	5.4	1304	1.3	1835	5.3
30	SU	0139	0.9	0719	5.3	1408	1.3	1941	5.2

SUNRISE AND SUNSET TIMES

DUNKERQUE
At 51°03′N 2°22′E

		Sunrise	Sunset
European Standard Time (UT+0100)			
Jan	01	0854	1655
	15	0847	1713
Feb	01	0827	1742
	15	0803	1807
Mar	01	0735	1832
	15	0704	1855
European Summer Time (UT+0200)			
Apr	01	0726	2023
	15	0656	2046
May	01	0624	2112
	15	0601	2134
Jun	01	0541	2156
	15	0535	2207
Jul	01	0540	2208
	15	0553	2159
Aug	01	0616	2137
	15	0637	2111
Sep	01	0704	2036
	15	0726	2005
Oct	01	0751	1928
	15	0814	1858
European Standard Time (UT+0100)			
Nov	01	0743	1725
	15	0807	1703
Dec	01	0832	1647
	15	0848	1644

DUNKERQUE
LAT 51°03′N
LONG 2°22′E

TIMES AND HEIGHTS OF HIGH AND LOW WATER (Heights in Metres)

TIME ZONE
European Standard Time (UT+0100)
For Summer Time (area enclosed in shaded box) add 1 hour

2024

JULY

Date	Day	Time	m	Time	m	Time	m	Time	m
1	M	0245	1.0	0828	5.3	1514	1.3	2050	5.3
2	TU	0351	1.0	0935	5.3	1621	1.3	2155	5.3
3	W	0457	1.0	1036	5.3	1725	1.2	2255	5.4
4	TH	0559	1.0	1133	5.4	1823	1.0	2350	5.5
5	F ●	0652	1.0	1225	5.5	1913	0.9		
6	SA	0041	5.7	0738	1.0	1311	5.6	1958	0.7
7	SU	0127	5.7	0820	1.0	1353	5.6	2040	0.7
8	M	0211	5.7	0900	1.0	1433	5.6	2120	0.7
9	TU	0252	5.7	0937	1.1	1510	5.6	2158	0.7
10	W	0330	5.6	1013	1.1	1544	5.5	2234	0.8
11	TH	0406	5.5	1048	1.2	1619	5.4	2309	0.9
12	F	0442	5.3	1123	1.3	1657	5.3	2345	1.1
13	SA ☾	0522	5.2	1201	1.5	1740	5.1		
14	SU	0026	1.2	0608	5.0	1247	1.6	1830	5.0
15	M	0117	1.4	0701	4.9	1345	1.7	1929	4.8
16	TU	0221	1.5	0803	4.8	1457	1.8	2036	4.8
17	W	0329	1.6	0911	4.8	1604	1.7	2145	4.9
18	TH	0432	1.5	1017	4.9	1706	1.5	2246	5.1
19	F	0531	1.4	1113	5.1	1802	1.3	2337	5.3
20	SA	0625	1.2	1200	5.4	1852	1.0		
21	SU ○	0023	5.6	0713	1.0	1244	5.6	1938	0.8
22	M	0106	5.8	0759	0.9	1326	5.7	2024	0.6
23	TU	0150	5.9	0844	0.8	1409	5.8	2109	0.5
24	W	0234	6.0	0929	0.7	1452	5.9	2154	0.4
25	TH	0320	6.0	1013	0.8	1535	5.8	2239	0.4
26	F	0405	5.9	1057	0.9	1618	5.8	2324	0.5
27	SA	0453	5.8	1142	1.0	1707	5.7		
28	SU ☽	0013	0.7	0545	5.6	1233	1.2	1802	5.5
29	M	0109	0.9	0645	5.3	1334	1.4	1907	5.3
30	TU	0214	1.2	0756	5.1	1444	1.5	2024	5.1
31	W	0327	1.4	0915	5.0	1601	1.5	2144	5.1

AUGUST

Date	Day	Time	m	Time	m	Time	m	Time	m
1	TH	0447	1.4	1030	5.0	1719	1.3	2255	5.2
2	F	0554	1.3	1134	5.2	1818	1.1	2354	5.4
3	SA	0645	1.1	1223	5.4	1905	0.9		
4	SU ●	0040	5.6	0728	1.1	1303	5.6	1947	0.7
5	M	0119	5.7	0806	1.0	1338	5.7	2025	0.6
6	TU	0156	5.8	0841	1.0	1412	5.7	2100	0.6
7	W	0230	5.8	0914	1.0	1443	5.7	2133	0.7
8	TH	0301	5.7	0945	1.0	1512	5.7	2204	0.7
9	F	0331	5.7	1015	1.1	1541	5.6	2234	0.8
10	SA	0401	5.6	1044	1.2	1613	5.5	2303	1.0
11	SU	0434	5.4	1114	1.3	1647	5.3	2336	1.2
12	M ☾	0511	5.2	1150	1.5	1729	5.1		
13	TU	0017	1.4	0600	4.9	1235	1.7	1827	4.8
14	W	0112	1.7	0705	4.7	1343	1.9	1942	4.6
15	TH	0232	1.8	0823	4.6	1514	2.0	2108	4.7
16	F	0356	1.8	0948	4.7	1636	1.7	2225	5.0
17	SA	0511	1.5	1054	5.1	1745	1.3	2322	5.4
18	SU	0611	1.2	1145	5.4	1838	1.0		
19	M ○	0008	5.7	0700	0.9	1228	5.7	1924	0.7
20	TU	0050	6.0	0744	0.8	1307	5.9	2008	0.4
21	W	0131	6.1	0826	0.7	1346	6.0	2051	0.3
22	TH	0212	6.2	0908	0.6	1425	6.1	2134	0.2
23	F	0255	6.2	0950	0.7	1506	6.1	2216	0.3
24	SA	0337	6.0	1031	0.8	1548	6.0	2259	0.5
25	SU	0423	5.8	1113	1.0	1636	5.8	2344	0.8
26	M ☽	0514	5.5	1200	1.2	1731	5.5		
27	TU	0037	1.2	0614	5.2	1300	1.5	1839	5.2
28	W	0145	1.5	0730	4.8	1418	1.7	2007	4.9
29	TH	0311	1.7	0903	4.7	1551	1.7	2141	4.9
30	F	0442	1.7	1026	4.9	1712	1.4	2256	5.2
31	SA	0546	1.4	1127	5.2	1807	1.1	2349	5.5

SEPTEMBER

Date	Day	Time	m	Time	m	Time	m	Time	m
1	SU	0632	1.2	1210	5.5	1851	0.8		
2	M	0028	5.7	0710	1.1	1243	5.7	1928	0.7
3	TU ●	0101	5.8	0744	1.0	1314	5.8	2002	0.6
4	W	0132	5.9	0814	0.9	1343	5.8	2033	0.6
5	TH	0201	5.9	0844	0.9	1410	5.9	2102	0.6
6	F	0227	5.9	0913	0.9	1435	5.8	2131	0.7
7	SA	0252	5.8	0940	1.0	1501	5.8	2157	0.8
8	SU	0318	5.7	1006	1.1	1528	5.7	2224	1.0
9	M	0345	5.5	1034	1.2	1554	5.5	2254	1.2
10	TU	0413	5.3	1106	1.4	1626	5.2	2332	1.5
11	W ☾	0451	5.0	1149	1.7	1716	4.9		
12	TH	0024	1.8	0604	4.7	1253	2.0	1859	4.6
13	F	0145	2.0	0748	4.5	1431	2.0	2040	4.6
14	SA	0325	1.9	0923	4.6	1610	1.8	2204	5.0
15	SU	0451	1.6	1034	5.1	1724	1.3	2302	5.5
16	M	0552	1.2	1124	5.5	1818	0.8	2348	5.9
17	TU	0639	0.9	1204	5.8	1903	0.5		
18	W ○	0028	6.1	0721	0.7	1240	6.0	1945	0.3
19	TH	0106	6.3	0802	0.6	1317	6.2	2027	0.2
20	F	0145	6.3	0842	0.6	1355	6.3	2108	0.3
21	SA	0226	6.2	0923	0.6	1437	6.3	2149	0.4
22	SU	0308	6.1	1004	0.8	1521	6.1	2231	0.7
23	M	0353	5.8	1046	1.0	1609	5.9	2315	1.0
24	TU ☽	0444	5.5	1133	1.3	1706	5.5		
25	W	0008	1.5	0546	5.0	1233	1.6	1819	5.0
26	TH	0120	1.9	0707	4.7	1357	1.8	1953	4.8
27	F	0257	2.0	0847	4.6	1536	1.8	2131	4.8
28	SA	0425	1.8	1008	4.8	1653	1.4	2239	5.2
29	SU	0525	1.5	1103	5.2	1746	1.1	2327	5.5
30	M	0609	1.2	1142	5.5	1827	0.8		

OCTOBER

Date	Day	Time	m	Time	m	Time	m	Time	m
1	TU	0002	5.7	0645	1.1	1214	5.7	1902	0.7
2	W ●	0033	5.8	0715	1.0	1243	5.8	1931	0.7
3	TH	0101	5.9	0743	1.0	1311	5.9	1959	0.7
4	F	0127	5.9	0811	0.9	1336	5.9	2028	0.7
5	SA	0151	5.9	0840	1.0	1400	5.9	2057	0.8
6	SU	0215	5.9	0908	1.0	1426	5.8	2124	0.9
7	M	0241	5.8	0935	1.1	1452	5.7	2152	1.1
8	TU	0308	5.6	1004	1.2	1520	5.6	2223	1.3
9	W	0338	5.4	1038	1.4	1555	5.3	2302	1.5
10	TH ☾	0418	5.1	1123	1.7	1646	5.0	2358	1.8
11	F	0528	4.7	1229	1.9	1836	4.7		
12	SA	0119	2.0	0720	4.5	1402	2.0	2013	4.7
13	SU	0258	1.9	0853	4.7	1541	1.7	2138	5.1
14	M	0423	1.6	1004	5.1	1655	1.2	2236	5.6
15	TU	0523	1.2	1054	5.5	1750	0.8	2321	5.9
16	W	0611	0.9	1134	5.9	1836	0.5		
17	TH ○	0000	6.2	0654	0.8	1210	6.1	1919	0.4
18	F	0038	6.3	0735	0.7	1249	6.3	2001	0.3
19	SA	0117	6.3	0816	0.7	1329	6.3	2043	0.4
20	SU	0159	6.2	0858	0.7	1413	6.3	2125	0.6
21	M	0243	6.0	0940	0.8	1500	6.1	2207	0.9
22	TU	0331	5.7	1024	1.0	1551	5.8	2252	1.3
23	W	0422	5.4	1112	1.3	1649	5.4	2344	1.7
24	TH ☽	0523	5.0	1211	1.6	1759	5.0		
25	F	0053	2.0	0639	4.7	1331	1.8	1929	4.7
26	SA	0225	2.1	0814	4.6	1503	1.8	2059	4.8
27	SU	0347	1.9	0928	4.8	1616	1.5	2202	5.1
28	M	0448	1.6	1021	5.1	1711	1.2	2248	5.4
29	TU	0534	1.4	1102	5.4	1753	1.0	2326	5.6
30	W	0610	1.2	1138	5.6	1827	0.9	2359	5.7
31	TH	0641	1.1	1210	5.7	1856	0.9		

NOVEMBER

Date	Day	Time	m	Time	m	Time	m	Time	m
1	F ●	0028	5.8	0709	1.0	1239	5.8	1925	0.9
2	SA	0054	5.8	0739	1.0	1305	5.8	1956	0.9
3	SU	0119	5.8	0811	1.0	1331	5.9	2028	0.9
4	M	0147	5.8	0842	1.0	1401	5.8	2059	1.0
5	TU	0217	5.8	0914	1.1	1433	5.7	2131	1.2
6	W	0250	5.6	0947	1.2	1508	5.6	2206	1.3
7	TH	0326	5.4	1026	1.3	1550	5.3	2251	1.6
8	F	0414	5.1	1116	1.5	1654	5.1	2348	1.8
9	SA ☾	0530	4.8	1221	1.7	1819	4.9		
10	SU	0101	1.9	0652	4.7	1341	1.7	1941	5.0
11	M	0227	1.8	0812	4.9	1507	1.5	2101	5.2
12	TU	0345	1.5	0924	5.2	1620	1.1	2202	5.6
13	W	0448	1.2	1018	5.5	1718	0.8	2250	5.9
14	TH	0540	1.0	1102	5.8	1808	0.6	2333	6.0
15	F ○	0627	0.9	1144	6.1	1854	0.5		
16	SA	0014	6.1	0712	0.8	1227	6.2	1939	0.6
17	SU	0057	6.1	0756	0.7	1312	6.2	2022	0.7
18	M	0142	6.0	0840	0.7	1359	6.2	2106	0.8
19	TU	0228	5.9	0925	0.8	1449	6.0	2151	1.1
20	W	0317	5.6	1010	1.0	1541	5.7	2236	1.4
21	TH	0407	5.4	1058	1.2	1635	5.4	2324	1.6
22	F	0459	5.1	1150	1.4	1733	5.1		
23	SA ☽	0019	1.9	0558	4.8	1252	1.6	1844	4.8
24	SU	0130	2.0	0715	4.7	1406	1.7	2004	4.8
25	M	0244	2.0	0830	4.8	1516	1.6	2108	4.9
26	TU	0347	1.8	0928	4.9	1614	1.4	2159	5.1
27	W	0441	1.6	1016	5.2	1703	1.3	2243	5.3
28	TH	0525	1.4	1058	5.4	1744	1.1	2321	5.5
29	F	0603	1.3	1136	5.5	1820	1.1	2355	5.6
30	SA	0638	1.2	1210	5.6	1855	1.1		

DECEMBER

Date	Day	Time	m	Time	m	Time	m	Time	m
1	SU ●	0026	5.6	0713	1.1	1241	5.7	1930	1.0
2	M	0057	5.7	0749	1.1	1313	5.8	2007	1.0
3	TU	0130	5.8	0826	1.0	1349	5.8	2045	1.1
4	W	0207	5.7	0904	1.0	1429	5.8	2123	1.1
5	TH	0247	5.6	0944	1.1	1512	5.6	2204	1.3
6	F	0331	5.5	1027	1.1	1559	5.5	2250	1.4
7	SA	0419	5.3	1116	1.2	1655	5.3	2341	1.5
8	SU ☾	0516	5.1	1212	1.3	1757	5.2		
9	M	0041	1.6	0619	5.1	1317	1.3	1904	5.2
10	TU	0151	1.6	0727	5.1	1431	1.3	2017	5.3
11	W	0304	1.5	0838	5.2	1542	1.1	2124	5.4
12	TH	0410	1.4	0941	5.4	1646	1.0	2222	5.6
13	F	0511	1.2	1037	5.6	1744	0.9	2313	5.7
14	SA	0606	1.0	1128	5.8	1837	0.8		
15	SU ○	0002	5.8	0657	0.9	1217	5.9	1926	0.8
16	M	0049	5.8	0745	0.8	1307	6.0	2012	0.9
17	TU	0136	5.8	0831	0.7	1356	6.0	2056	0.9
18	W	0222	5.8	0916	0.8	1444	5.9	2138	1.1
19	TH	0306	5.7	0959	0.8	1530	5.7	2219	1.3
20	F	0348	5.5	1041	1.0	1614	5.5	2300	1.4
21	SA	0429	5.3	1123	1.2	1658	5.3	2342	1.6
22	SU ☽	0513	5.1	1208	1.3	1746	5.1		
23	M	0029	1.7	0603	5.0	1300	1.5	1842	4.9
24	TU	0126	1.9	0704	4.8	1401	1.6	1948	4.8
25	W	0232	1.9	0813	4.8	1504	1.6	2053	4.8
26	TH	0335	1.8	0918	4.9	1603	1.6	2151	4.9
27	F	0433	1.7	1014	5.0	1658	1.5	2242	5.1
28	SA	0525	1.5	1104	5.2	1747	1.3	2326	5.3
29	SU	0611	1.4	1147	5.4	1831	1.2		
30	M ●	0006	5.4	0654	1.2	1225	5.5	1913	1.1
31	TU	0043	5.6	0735	1.0	1303	5.7	1954	1.0

CALAIS
LAT 50°58′N
LONG 1°51′E

TIMES AND HEIGHTS OF HIGH AND LOW WATER (Heights in Metres)

TIME ZONE
European Standard Time (UT+0100)
For Summer Time (area enclosed in shaded box) add 1 hour

2024

SUNRISE AND SUNSET TIMES
CALAIS
At 50°58′N 1°51′E
European Standard Time (UT+0100)

		Sunrise	Sunset
Jan	01	0856	1657
	15	0849	1715
Feb	01	0829	1744
	15	0805	1809
Mar	01	0737	1834
	15	0706	1857
European Summer Time (UT+0200)			
Apr	01	0728	2026
	15	0658	2048
May	01	0626	2114
	15	0603	2136
Jun	01	0544	2158
	15	0538	2209
Jul	01	0543	2210
	15	0556	2201
Aug	01	0618	2138
	15	0640	2113
Sep	01	0706	2038
	15	0728	2007
Oct	01	0753	1930
	15	0816	1900
European Standard Time (UT+0100)			
Nov	01	0745	1727
	15	0809	1705
Dec	01	0834	1649

JANUARY

Date	Day	Time	m	Time	m	Time	m	Time	m
1	M	0324	6.6	1021	1.6	1541	6.5	2240	1.8
2	TU	0400	6.5	1056	1.7	1620	6.3	2315	2.0
3	W	0440	6.3	1135	1.9	1705	6.1	2357	2.2
4	TH ☾	0526	6.1	1223	2.1	1756	5.9		
5	F	0049	2.3	0622	5.9	1324	2.2	1856	5.8
6	SA	0155	2.4	0725	5.9	1431	2.2	2003	5.8
7	SU	0303	2.3	0833	6.0	1537	2.1	2108	6.0
8	M	0408	2.1	0935	6.2	1640	1.9	2205	6.2
9	TU	0510	1.9	1028	6.4	1739	1.6	2255	6.5
10	W	0606	1.5	1115	6.7	1832	1.3	2341	6.8
11	TH ●	0656	1.3	1201	7.0	1922	1.1		
12	F	0026	7.0	0744	1.0	1247	7.2	2010	0.9
13	SA	0113	7.2	0831	0.9	1335	7.3	2058	0.8
14	SU	0201	7.3	0918	0.8	1425	7.4	2145	0.8
15	M	0249	7.2	1005	0.8	1515	7.3	2230	0.9
16	TU	0336	7.1	1052	0.9	1605	7.1	2315	1.1
17	W	0424	7.0	1139	1.1	1657	6.8		
18	TH ☽	0001	1.4	0515	6.7	1230	1.3	1753	6.5
19	F	0052	1.7	0614	6.5	1327	1.6	1859	6.2
20	SA	0151	1.9	0724	6.2	1435	1.8	2014	6.0
21	SU	0305	2.1	0842	6.1	1554	1.9	2129	6.0
22	M	0425	2.0	0955	6.2	1706	1.8	2234	6.2
23	TU	0531	1.8	1055	6.4	1804	1.6	2328	6.5
24	W	0623	1.5	1144	6.6	1851	1.4		
25	TH ○	0011	6.7	0708	1.3	1225	6.8	1933	1.3
26	F	0048	6.8	0749	1.1	1302	6.9	2012	1.2
27	SA	0123	6.9	0827	1.1	1337	7.0	2048	1.2
28	SU	0157	7.0	0901	1.1	1410	7.0	2120	1.2
29	M	0228	7.0	0932	1.1	1442	6.9	2149	1.3
30	TU	0257	6.9	1001	1.2	1512	6.8	2216	1.4
31	W	0327	6.8	1029	1.3	1544	6.6	[illegible]	[illegible]

FEBRUARY

Date	Day	Time	m	Time	m	Time	m	Time	m
1	TH	0359	6.6	1059	1.5	1618	6.4	2313	1.8
2	F	0434	6.4	1134	1.7	1658	6.2	2351	2.0
3	SA ☾	0519	6.1	1219	2.0	1751	5.9		
4	SU	0042	2.3	0618	5.9	1324	2.3	1857	5.7
5	M	0158	2.5	0733	5.7	1444	2.3	2018	5.7
6	TU	0321	2.4	0859	5.8	1604	2.1	2138	5.9
7	W	0442	2.1	1009	6.2	1720	1.7	2240	6.3
8	TH	0551	1.6	1105	6.6	1821	1.3	2332	6.7
9	F ●	0646	1.2	1154	7.0	1913	1.0		
10	SA	0020	7.0	0736	0.8	1240	7.3	2002	0.7
11	SU	0105	7.3	0823	0.6	1328	7.5	2049	0.6
12	M	0151	7.4	0909	0.4	1416	7.5	2133	0.5
13	TU	0235	7.5	0953	0.4	1502	7.4	2213	0.6
14	W	0316	7.4	1035	0.5	1545	7.2	2252	0.8
15	TH	0357	7.2	1115	0.8	1627	6.9	2331	1.2
16	F ☽	0441	6.9	1158	1.2	1716	6.5		
17	SA	0014	1.6	0535	6.4	1248	1.7	1818	6.0
18	SU	0110	2.0	0646	6.0	1356	2.1	1942	5.6
19	M	0228	2.4	0818	5.7	1527	2.3	2112	5.6
20	TU	0405	2.3	0945	5.9	1653	2.1	2226	5.9
21	W	0520	1.9	1050	6.2	1755	1.7	2320	6.3
22	TH	0615	1.5	1137	6.5	1843	1.4	2359	6.6
23	F	0658	1.3	1213	6.8	1922	1.2		
24	SA ○	0032	6.8	0736	1.1	1245	6.9	1957	1.1
25	SU	0103	7.0	0811	1.0	1317	7.0	2029	1.0
26	M	0133	7.1	0842	0.9	1346	7.0	2057	1.0
27	TU	0201	7.1	0910	0.9	1414	7.0	2124	1.1
28	W	0227	7.0	0936	1.0	1441	6.9	2148	1.2
29	TH	0253	6.9	1001	1.1	1508	6.8	2213	1.3

MARCH

Date	Day	Time	m	Time	m	Time	m	Time	m
1	F	0318	6.8	1027	1.3	1533	6.6	2238	1.5
2	SA	0343	6.6	1056	1.6	1603	6.3	2309	1.8
3	SU ☾	0419	6.3	1135	1.9	1649	6.0	2353	2.1
4	M	0518	5.9	1235	2.2	1805	5.6		
5	TU	0108	2.5	0649	5.6	1403	2.4	1944	5.4
6	W	0244	2.5	0834	5.6	1538	2.2	2119	5.7
7	TH	0422	2.1	0955	6.1	1705	1.7	2228	6.2
8	F	0536	1.5	1054	6.6	1807	1.2	2321	6.7
9	SA	0632	1.0	1143	7.1	1859	0.8		
10	SU ●	0006	7.1	0722	0.6	1228	7.4	1946	0.6
11	M	0048	7.4	0808	0.4	1313	7.5	2030	0.5
12	TU	0130	7.5	0852	0.3	1358	7.6	2110	0.4
13	W	0211	7.5	0932	0.3	1441	7.4	2148	0.6
14	TH	0250	7.4	1011	0.5	1519	7.2	2224	0.8
15	F	0328	7.2	1048	0.8	1558	6.8	2300	1.2
16	SA	0411	6.8	1127	1.3	1644	6.4	2340	1.7
17	SU ☽	0503	6.3	1214	1.9	1745	5.8		
18	M	0035	2.2	0616	5.8	1323	2.3	1913	5.4
19	TU	0200	2.5	0756	5.5	1501	2.5	2052	5.4
20	W	0342	2.4	0928	5.7	1632	2.2	2207	5.8
21	TH	0500	2.0	1032	6.0	1736	1.8	2258	6.2
22	F	0555	1.5	1116	6.4	1821	1.4	2334	6.5
23	SA	0637	1.2	1149	6.7	1858	1.2		
24	SU	0005	6.8	0712	1.1	1220	6.9	1930	1.1
25	M ○	0034	7.0	0744	1.0	1250	7.0	1959	1.0
26	TU	0103	7.0	0813	0.9	1317	7.0	2027	1.0
27	W	0129	7.1	0841	0.9	1342	7.0	2054	1.0
28	TH	0154	7.0	0908	0.9	1408	6.9	2120	1.1
29	F	0218	7.0	0935	1.0	1433	6.8	2145	1.2
30	SA	0242	6.8	1001	1.2	1457	6.6	2211	1.4
31	SU	0308	6.6	1030	1.5	1528	6.4	2243	1.7

APRIL

Date	Day	Time	m	Time	m	Time	m	Time	m
1	M	0346	6.3	1110	1.9	1616	6.0	2330	2.1
2	TU ☾	0448	5.9	1213	2.2	1739	5.6		
3	W	0046	2.4	0629	5.6	1339	2.4	1924	5.4
4	TH	0221	2.4	0816	5.7	1518	2.2	2100	5.7
5	F	0402	2.0	0937	6.1	1645	1.6	2208	6.3
6	SA	0515	1.4	1035	6.7	1745	1.1	2259	6.8
7	SU	0610	0.9	1123	7.1	1835	0.8	2341	7.1
8	M ●	0659	0.6	1207	7.3	1921	0.6		
9	TU	0021	7.3	0745	0.5	1249	7.4	2003	0.6
10	W	0100	7.5	0827	0.4	1333	7.4	2042	0.6
11	TH	0141	7.4	0907	0.5	1415	7.3	2120	0.7
12	F	0223	7.3	0945	0.7	1455	7.0	2156	0.9
13	SA	0304	7.0	1021	1.0	1535	6.7	2233	1.3
14	SU	0349	6.7	1100	1.5	1621	6.2	2314	1.7
15	M ☽	0443	6.2	1146	2.0	1720	5.7		
16	TU	0008	2.2	0551	5.7	1255	2.4	1840	5.4
17	W	0133	2.5	0724	5.4	1427	2.6	2015	5.4
18	TH	0305	2.4	0851	5.6	1550	2.3	2124	5.7
19	F	0418	2.0	0952	5.9	1653	1.9	2214	6.1
20	SA	0514	1.6	1036	6.3	1740	1.6	2253	6.4
21	SU	0557	1.4	1113	6.5	1818	1.4	2327	6.7
22	M	0634	1.2	1146	6.7	1852	1.2	2359	6.8
23	TU	0707	1.1	1216	6.8	1922	1.2		
24	W ○	0028	6.9	0738	1.0	1243	6.9	1952	1.1
25	TH	0053	6.9	0808	1.0	1309	6.9	2023	1.1
26	F	0120	6.9	0840	1.0	1337	6.9	2054	1.1
27	SA	0149	6.9	0912	1.1	1407	6.8	2125	1.2
28	SU	0219	6.8	0944	1.3	1439	6.6	2157	1.4
29	M	0255	6.6	1020	1.5	1519	6.3	2236	1.7
30	TU	0343	6.3	1106	1.8	1617	6.0	2329	2.0

MAY

Date	Day	Time	m	Time	m	Time	m	Time	m
1	W ☾	0454	6.0	1208	2.1	1737	5.7		
2	TH	0039	2.2	0621	5.8	1325	2.2	1905	5.7
3	F	0204	2.1	0753	5.9	1456	2.0	2032	5.9
4	SA	0335	1.8	0910	6.3	1615	1.6	2137	6.4
5	SU	0445	1.3	1007	6.7	1714	1.2	2227	6.8
6	M	0541	1.0	1056	7.0	1805	1.0	2311	7.0
7	TU	0632	0.8	1140	7.1	1852	0.9	2352	7.2
8	W ●	0718	0.7	1224	7.2	1935	0.8		
9	TH	0034	7.2	0801	0.7	1309	7.1	2016	0.8
10	F	0118	7.2	0843	0.8	1354	7.0	2056	0.9
11	SA	0204	7.1	0922	0.9	1437	6.8	2134	1.1
12	SU	0250	6.8	1000	1.2	1520	6.6	2213	1.4
13	M	0336	6.5	1039	1.6	1604	6.2	2255	1.7
14	TU	0425	6.2	1124	2.0	1655	5.9	2346	2.1
15	W ☽	0522	5.8	1224	2.3	1758	5.6		
16	TH	0057	2.3	0635	5.6	1340	2.5	1918	5.5
17	F	0213	2.3	0756	5.6	1450	2.4	2027	5.7
18	SA	0319	2.1	0857	5.8	1551	2.1	2120	5.9
19	SU	0416	1.8	0946	6.0	1643	1.9	2205	6.2
20	M	0504	1.6	1028	6.3	1728	1.6	2244	6.5
21	TU	0547	1.4	1105	6.5	1807	1.5	2319	6.6
22	W	0625	1.3	1138	6.6	1843	1.4	2351	6.7
23	TH ○	0701	1.2	1208	6.7	1919	1.3		
24	F	0021	6.8	0738	1.2	1240	6.8	1955	1.2
25	SA	0054	6.9	0816	1.1	1315	6.8	2033	1.2
26	SU	0131	6.9	0855	1.2	1354	6.8	2112	1.2
27	M	0213	6.8	0935	1.3	1438	6.6	2152	1.4
28	TU	0259	6.6	1018	1.4	1527	6.4	2237	1.5
29	W	0353	6.4	1107	1.6	1624	6.2	2330	1.7
30	TH ☾	0456	6.2	1203	1.8	1728	6.1		
31	F	0032	1.8	0606	6.1	1309	1.9	1839	6.0

JUNE

Date	Day	Time	m	Time	m	Time	m	Time	m
1	SA	0144	1.7	0722	6.2	1423	1.8	1953	6.2
2	SU	0300	1.6	0834	6.4	1536	1.6	2058	6.4
3	M	0410	1.4	0934	6.6	1639	1.4	2154	6.6
4	TU	0510	1.2	1028	6.7	1735	1.3	2244	6.8
5	W	0604	1.1	1119	6.8	1825	1.2	2332	6.9
6	TH ●	0654	1.0	1207	6.9	1911	1.1		
7	F	0019	7.0	0740	1.0	1254	6.9	1956	1.1
8	SA	0106	7.0	0824	1.1	1339	6.8	2038	1.1
9	SU	0153	6.9	0905	1.2	1423	6.8	2119	1.2
10	M	0237	6.8	0945	1.3	1504	6.6	2159	1.4
11	TU	0320	6.6	1023	1.6	1544	6.4	2238	1.6
12	W	0402	6.3	1102	1.8	1624	6.2	2320	1.8
13	TH	0446	6.1	1146	2.1	1709	6.0		
14	F ☽	0010	2.0	0536	5.9	1240	2.2	1802	5.8
15	SA	0109	2.1	0635	5.7	1341	2.3	1906	5.7
16	SU	0211	2.1	0742	5.7	1442	2.3	2011	5.8
17	M	0309	2.1	0843	5.8	1539	2.2	2108	6.0
18	TU	0404	1.9	0935	6.0	1632	2.0	2156	6.2
19	W	0456	1.8	1021	6.2	1722	1.8	2240	6.3
20	TH	0544	1.6	1102	6.4	1808	1.6	2319	6.5
21	F	0629	1.5	1141	6.5	1851	1.4	2358	6.7
22	SA ○	0714	1.3	1220	6.7	1935	1.3		
23	SU	0038	6.8	0759	1.2	1302	6.8	2019	1.2
24	M	0122	6.9	0844	1.1	1348	6.9	2103	1.1
25	TU	0209	6.9	0929	1.1	1435	6.8	2149	1.1
26	W	0258	6.9	1015	1.2	1524	6.7	2235	1.2
27	TH	0350	6.8	1102	1.3	1614	6.6	2324	1.3
28	F ☾	0444	6.6	1151	1.4	1708	6.5		
29	SA	0017	1.4	0543	6.5	1245	1.6	1807	6.4
30	SU	0117	1.5	0646	6.4	1346	1.7	1912	6.4

CALAIS
LAT 50°58′N
LONG 1°51′E

TIMES AND HEIGHTS OF HIGH AND LOW WATER (Heights in Metres)

TIME ZONE
European Standard Time (UT+0100)
For Summer Time (area enclosed in shaded box) add 1 hour

2024

JULY

Date	Time	m	Date	Time	m
1 M	0223 0755 1454 2021	1.6 6.3 1.8 6.3	**16** TU	0158 0726 1430 1959	2.2 5.7 2.4 5.8
2 TU	0334 0904 1605 2128	1.6 6.3 1.8 6.4	**17** W	0304 0835 1537 2108	2.2 5.8 2.3 5.9
3 W	0443 1009 1711 2230	1.5 6.4 1.6 6.5	**18** TH	0409 0940 1642 2207	2.1 5.9 2.1 6.1
4 TH	0545 1107 1807 2324	1.5 6.5 1.5 6.7	**19** F	0511 1035 1741 2257	1.8 6.2 1.8 6.4
5 F ●	0638 1158 1856	1.4 6.6 1.3	**20** SA	0607 1122 1833 2342	1.6 6.5 1.5 6.7
6 SA	0013 0725 1243 1942	6.8 1.3 6.7 1.2	**21** SU ○	0658 1207 1921	1.3 6.7 1.2
7 SU	0057 0809 1325 2025	6.9 1.2 6.8 1.1	**22** M	0027 0746 1252 2007	7.0 1.1 7.0 1.0
8 M	0139 0851 1404 2106	6.9 1.3 6.8 1.2	**23** TU	0112 0833 1337 2054	7.1 1.0 7.1 0.9
9 TU	0219 0929 1442 2143	6.8 1.3 6.8 1.3	**24** W	0159 0920 1424 2140	7.2 0.9 7.1 0.8
10 W	0257 1003 1516 2216	6.7 1.5 6.7 1.4	**25** TH	0248 1004 1509 2225	7.2 0.9 7.1 0.8
11 TH	0332 1035 1550 2249	6.6 1.6 6.5 1.5	**26** F	0336 1046 1554 2309	7.1 1.0 7.0 0.9
12 F	0407 1107 1625 2324	6.4 1.8 6.4 1.7	**27** SA	0423 1129 1641 2354	7.0 1.2 6.9 1.1
13 SA ☽	0446 1142 1706	6.2 2.0 6.2	**28** SU ☾	0513 1215 1733	6.7 1.5 6.7
14 SU	0004 0531 1226 1754	1.9 6.0 2.2 6.0	**29** M	0046 0611 1309 1835	1.4 6.4 1.8 6.4
15 M	0055 0623 1323 1851	2.1 5.9 2.3 5.9	**30** TU	0147 0721 1416 1951	1.7 6.1 2.0 6.1
			31 W	0304 0843 1540 2114	1.9 6.0 2.1 6.1

AUGUST

Date	Time	m	Date	Time	m
1 TH	0427 0959 1657 2224	1.9 6.[illegible] 1.9 6.3	**16** F	0330 0909 1610 2144	2.3 5.7 2.3 6.0
2 F	0534 1101 1757 2320	1.7 6.3 1.5 6.5	**17** SA	0448 1015 1722 2241	2.0 6.1 1.8 6.5
3 SA	0628 1149 1846	1.5 6.5 1.4	**18** SU	0552 1108 1818 2329	1.6 6.5 1.4 6.9
4 SU ●	0004 0714 1230 1930	6.3 1.4 6.3 1.2	**19** M ○	0644 1153 1907	1.2 6.9 1.1
5 M	0043 0755 1306 2010	6.9 1.3 6.9 1.1	**20** TU	0013 0732 1236 1954	7.2 1.0 7.2 0.8
6 TU	0119 0833 1341 2047	7.0 1.2 7.0 1.1	**21** W	0058 0818 1319 2039	7.4 0.8 7.4 0.6
7 W	0155 0907 1414 2120	7.0 1.2 7.0 1.1	**22** TH	0143 0901 1403 2123	7.5 0.7 7.5 0.6
8 TH	0228 0936 1444 2148	7.0 1.3 6.9 1.2	**23** F	0229 0943 1445 2204	7.5 0.7 7.4 0.6
9 F	0258 1003 1513 2215	6.9 1.4 6.9 1.3	**24** SA	0313 1022 1526 2245	7.4 0.9 7.3 0.8
10 SA	0329 1028 1543 2243	6.7 1.5 6.7 1.5	**25** SU	0356 1101 1611 2327	7.1 1.1 7.1 1.1
11 SU	0401 1055 1617 2314	6.5 1.7 6.5 1.7	**26** M ☾	0443 1143 1702	6.7 1.5 6.7
12 M ☽	0439 1128 1658 2353	6.3 2.0 6.2 2.0	**27** TU	0014 0540 1235 1807	1.6 6.3 1.9 6.3
13 TU	0526 1212 1753	6.0 2.3 5.9	**28** W	0116 0655 1349 1933	2.0 5.9 2.3 5.9
14 W	0049 0628 1320 1904	2.3 5.7 2.5 5.7	**29** TH	0245 0829 1527 2106	2.3 5.7 2.3 5.9
15 TH	0208 0746 1447 2030	2.4 5.6 2.6 5.7	**30** F	0417 0951 1648 2219	2.2 5.9 2.0 6.2
			31 SA	0526 1052 1748 2311	1.8 6.3 1.6 6.6

SEPTEMBER

Date	Time	m	Date	Time	m
1 SU	0618 1135 1834 2350	1.5 6.7 1.3 6.9	**16** M	0535 1050 1800 2312	1.5 6.7 1.2 7.1
2 M	0659 1209 1913	1.3 6.9 1.1	**17** TU	0626 1133 1848 2355	1.1 7.1 0.9 7.4
3 TU ●	0023 0734 1241 1949	7.0 1.2 7.1 1.1	**18** W ○	0711 1213 1933	0.8 7.4 0.6
4 W	0055 0807 1312 2021	7.1 1.2 7.2 1.0	**19** TH	0037 0755 1253 2017	7.6 0.7 7.6 0.5
5 TH	0126 0837 1341 2050	7.2 1.2 7.2 1.0	**20** F	0119 0836 1334 2059	7.7 0.6 7.7 0.5
6 F	0155 0904 1409 2117	7.1 1.2 7.1 1.1	**21** SA	0203 0916 1415 2139	7.6 0.7 7.6 0.6
7 SA	0223 0929 1435 2142	7.1 1.3 7.0 1.2	**22** SU	0246 0954 1458 2219	7.4 0.9 7.4 0.9
8 SU	0250 0953 1501 2207	6.9 1.4 6.9 1.4	**23** M	0329 1032 1544 2259	7.1 1.2 7.1 1.3
9 M	0317 1018 1528 2235	6.7 1.6 6.7 1.6	**24** TU ☾	0417 1114 1638 2346	6.7 1.6 6.6 1.8
10 TU	0345 1047 1600 2310	6.5 1.9 6.4 1.9	**25** W	0517 1208 1748	6.2 2.1 6.1
11 W ☽	0426 1127 1654	6.1 2.2 6.0	**26** TH	0052 0636 1331 1919	2.3 5.7 2.5 5.8
12 TH	0002 0538 1231 1825	2.3 5.7 2.6 5.6	**27** F	0230 0814 1512 2053	2.5 5.6 2.4 5.9
13 F	0125 0713 1408 2003	2.6 5.5 2.7 5.6	**28** SA	0400 0933 1631 2201	2.3 5.9 2.0 6.2
14 SA	0300 0846 1546 2125	2.5 5.7 2.3 6.1	**29** SU	0507 1029 1727 2249	1.9 6.4 1.6 6.6
15 SU	0430 0957 1704 2225	2.0 6.2 1.8 6.6	**30** M	0554 1108 1811 2325	1.5 6.7 1.3 6.9

OCTOBER

Date	Time	m	Date	Time	m
1 TU	0632 1140 1847 2356	1.3 7.0 1.1 7.1	**16** W	0600 1106 1824 2331	1.0 7.3 0.8 7.5
2 W ●	0705 1210 1919	1.2 7.2 1.0	**17** TH ○	0646 1145 1909	0.8 7.5 0.6
3 TH	0027 0735 1240 1949	7.2 1.2 7.2 1.0	**18** F	0012 0728 1225 1953	7.7 0.7 7.7 0.5
4 F	0056 0803 1307 2018	7.2 1.1 7.2 1.0	**19** SA	0054 0809 1306 2035	7.7 0.7 7.7 0.6
5 SA	0122 0831 1332 2046	7.2 1.2 7.2 1.1	**20** SU	0138 0850 1350 2116	7.6 0.8 7.6 0.7
6 SU	0147 0858 1358 2113	7.1 1.2 7.1 1.2	**21** M	0223 0930 1436 2156	7.3 1.0 7.3 1.0
7 M	0214 0925 1424 2140	7.0 1.4 7.0 1.4	**22** TU	0310 1010 1527 2238	7.0 1.3 7.0 1.5
8 TU	0240 0951 1451 2209	6.8 1.6 6.7 1.6	**23** W	0400 1054 1624 2325	6.6 1.7 6.5 2.0
9 W	0309 1022 1525 2246	6.6 1.9 6.4 2.0	**24** TH ☾	0459 1149 1731	6.1 2.2 6.0
10 TH ☽	0351 1104 1620 2341	6.2 2.2 6.0 2.3	**25** F	0032 0613 1311 1856	2.4 5.7 2.5 5.8
11 F	0509 1212 1803	5.8 2.5 5.7	**26** SA	0202 0743 1440 2022	2.6 5.7 2.4 5.9
12 SA	0101 0650 1342 1941	2.5 5.6 2.6 5.8	**27** SU	0323 0855 1553 2125	2.4 5.9 2.1 6.2
13 SU	0235 0822 1522 2103	2.4 5.8 2.2 6.2	**28** M	0426 0948 1649 2212	2.0 6.3 1.7 6.5
14 M	0407 0933 1640 2202	1.9 6.3 1.6 6.8	**29** TU	0515 1029 1734 2250	1.7 6.7 1.4 6.8
15 TU	0510 1024 1736 2249	1.4 6.9 1.1 7.2	**30** W	0555 1105 1811 2325	1.5 6.9 1.2 7.0
			31 TH	0629 1138 1845 2356	1.3 7.1 1.2 7.1

NOVEMBER

Date	Time	m	Date	Time	m
1 F ●	0701 1208 1917	1.3 7.1 1.1	**16** SA	0705 1203 1932	0.9 7.5 0.7
2 SA	0024 0731 1235 1948	7.1 1.2 7.1 1.1	**17** SU	0036 0748 1249 2016	7.5 0.9 7.5 0.8
3 SU	0051 0802 1302 2019	7.1 1.2 7.1 1.1	**18** M	0124 0831 1338 2059	7.4 0.9 7.4 0.9
4 M	0119 0833 1331 2051	7.1 1.3 7.1 1.2	**19** TU	0212 0914 1428 2141	7.2 1.1 7.2 1.2
5 TU	0150 0905 1403 2124	7.0 1.4 6.9 1.4	**20** W	0300 0956 1518 2224	6.9 1.3 6.9 1.5
6 W	0222 0937 1437 2159	6.8 1.6 6.7 1.6	**21** TH	0347 1041 1610 2310	6.6 1.7 6.5 1.9
7 TH	0300 1014 1520 2241	6.6 1.8 6.4 1.9	**22** F	0437 1133 1706	6.3 2.0 6.2
8 F	0350 1102 1624 2335	6.2 2.1 6.1 2.2	**23** SA ☾	0007 0537 1238 1815	2.3 6.0 2.2 5.9
9 SA ☽	0504 1205 1749	5.9 2.3 5.9	**24** SU	0116 0651 1350 1932	2.5 5.8 2.3 5.8
10 SU	0045 0627 1322 1914	2.3 5.8 2.3 6.0	**25** M	0225 0801 1456 2035	2.4 5.9 2.2 6.0
11 M	0208 0749 1450 2031	2.2 6.0 2.0 6.4	**26** TU	0327 0857 1554 2126	2.3 6.1 1.9 6.2
12 TU	0332 0858 1606 2132	1.9 6.5 1.5 6.8	**27** W	0422 0945 1646 2210	2.0 6.4 1.7 6.4
13 W	0438 0952 1706 2222	1.5 6.9 1.1 7.1	**28** TH	0510 1026 1731 2249	1.8 6.6 1.5 6.6
14 TH	0531 1037 1758 2307	1.2 7.2 0.9 7.3	**29** F	0551 1104 1810 2325	1.6 6.8 1.4 6.8
15 F ○	0620 1120 1846 2351	1.0 7.4 0.7 7.4	**30** SA	0629 1138 1846 2357	1.5 6.9 1.3 6.9

DECEMBER

Date	Time	m	Date	Time	m
1 SU ●	0704 1210 1922	1.4 6.9 1.3	**16** M	0031 0736 1246 2004	7.1 1.0 7.3 1.0
2 M	0028 0739 1242 1959	7.0 1.3 7.0 1.2	**17** TU	0118 0821 1334 2049	7.2 1.0 7.2 1.0
3 TU	0101 0816 1317 2037	7.0 1.3 7.0 1.3	**18** W	0204 0905 1420 2131	7.1 1.0 7.1 1.2
4 W	0139 0854 1356 2116	7.0 1.3 6.9 1.3	**19** TH	0247 0947 1505 2212	7.0 1.2 6.9 1.4
5 TH	0219 0933 1439 2156	6.9 1.4 6.8 1.5	**20** F	0328 1028 1548 2252	6.8 1.4 6.7 1.7
6 F	0303 1015 1527 2240	6.7 1.6 6.6 1.7	**21** SA	0409 1110 1631 2333	6.5 1.7 6.4 1.9
7 SA	0353 1102 1624 2330	6.5 1.7 6.4 1.8	**22** SU ☾	0451 1155 1719	6.3 1.9 6.1
8 SU ☽	0451 1157 1729	6.3 1.8 6.3	**23** M	0020 0541 1248 1815	2.2 6.0 2.1 5.9
9 M	0028 0557 1300 1840	1.9 6.2 1.9 6.3	**24** TU	0115 0641 1346 1922	2.3 5.9 2.2 5.8
10 TU	0135 0707 1413 1951	2.0 6.3 1.8 6.4	**25** W	0214 0750 1446 2026	2.4 5.9 2.2 5.8
11 W	0248 0817 1527 2058	1.9 6.4 1.6 6.6	**26** TH	0315 0851 1546 2122	2.4 6.0 2.1 6.0
12 TH	0359 0919 1635 2157	1.7 6.7 1.4 6.8	**27** F	0415 0945 1644 2212	2.2 6.1 2.0 6.2
13 F	0503 1015 1735 2251	1.5 6.9 1.2 7.0	**28** SA	0511 1033 1736 2257	2.0 6.3 1.8 6.4
14 SA	0558 1107 1829 2342	1.3 7.1 1.0 7.1	**29** SU	0600 1115 1821 2336	1.7 6.5 1.6 6.6
15 SU ○	0649 1157 1918	1.1 7.2 1.0	**30** M ●	0643 1153 1904	1.5 6.7 1.4
			31 TU	0014 0723 1230 1945	6.8 1.3 6.9 1.3

DIEPPE
LAT 49°56′N
LONG 1°05′E

TIMES AND HEIGHTS OF HIGH AND LOW WATER (Heights in Metres)

TIME ZONE
European Standard Time (UT+0100)
For Summer Time (area enclosed in shaded box) add 1 hour

2024

SUNRISE AND SUNSET TIMES

DIEPPE
At 49°56′N 1°05′E

	Sunrise	Sunset
European Standard Time (UT+0100)		
Jan 01	0854	1705
15	0848	1723
Feb 01	0829	1750
15	0806	1814
Mar 01	0739	1838
15	0709	1901
European Summer Time (UT+0200)		
Apr 01	0732	2028
15	0703	2049
May 01	0632	2114
15	0610	2135
Jun 01	0552	2156
15	0546	2206
Jul 01	0551	2208
15	0504	2159
Aug 01	0625	2138
15	0646	2114
Sep 01	0711	2039
15	0732	2010
Oct 01	0756	1934
15	0818	1905
European Standard Time (UT+0100)		
Nov 01	0745	1733
15	0808	1712
Dec 01	0832	1657
15	0847	1654

JANUARY

Date	Day	Time	m	Time	m	Time	m	Time	m
1	M	0238	8.4	0919	2.2	1450	8.3	2140	2.1
2	TU	0314	8.1	0953	2.4	1525	8.0	2214	2.3
3	W	0351	7.8	1032	2.6	1605	7.6	2254	2.6
4	TH ☽	0435	7.5	1118	2.9	1655	7.4	2342	2.8
5	F	0532	7.3	1212	3.0	1800	7.2		
6	SA	0039	3.0	0639	7.3	1317	3.1	1910	7.2
7	SU	0149	3.0	0746	7.4	1431	2.9	2016	7.4
8	M	0303	2.8	0849	7.8	1539	2.5	2119	7.8
9	TU	0407	2.4	0947	8.2	1636	2.1	2216	8.3
10	W	0501	2.0	1039	8.6	1728	1.7	2307	8.7
11	TH ●	0551	1.7	1128	9.0	1820	1.3	2356	9.1
12	F	0642	1.4	1216	9.3	1913	1.1		
13	SA	0043	9.3	0734	1.3	1303	9.5	2005	0.9
14	SU	0129	9.5	0825	1.2	1349	9.6	2054	0.8
15	M	0215	9.4	0914	1.2	1434	9.5	2140	0.9
16	TU	0300	9.3	0959	1.3	1520	9.2	2223	1.1
17	W	0346	9.0	1044	1.6	1607	8.8	2306	1.5
18	TH ☾	0433	8.6	1131	1.9	1658	8.3	2353	2.0
19	F	0528	8.1	1224	2.3	1801	7.8		
20	SA	0049	2.4	0637	7.7	1329	2.6	1919	7.5
21	SU	0201	2.7	0757	7.6	1449	2.6	2036	7.6
22	M	0320	2.6	0907	7.8	1601	2.4	2141	7.9
23	TU	0426	2.4	1006	8.1	1700	2.0	2236	8.2
24	W	0519	2.1	1055	8.4	1748	1.8	2321	8.5
25	TH ○	0603	1.9	1137	8.7	1830	1.5		
26	F	0001	8.7	0644	1.7	1214	8.8	1908	1.4
27	SA	0037	8.9	0721	1.5	1248	8.9	1944	1.3
28	SU	0110	8.9	0756	1.5	1322	9.0	2017	1.3
29	M	0143	8.9	0827	1.6	1354	8.9	2047	1.4
30	TU	0214	8.8	0856	1.7	1424	8.7	2114	1.6
31	W	0242	8.6	0924	1.9	1453	8.5	2141	1.8

FEBRUARY

Date	Day	Time	m	Time	m	Time	m	Time	m
1	TH	0311	8.3	0955	2.1	1523	8.2	2212	2.1
2	F	0343	8.0	1030	2.4	1559	7.8	2249	2.5
3	SA ☽	0423	7.7	1114	2.7	1647	7.4	2336	2.9
4	SU	0519	7.3	1212	3.0	1757	7.0		
5	M	0042	3.2	0642	7.1	1331	3.1	1926	7.0
6	TU	0212	3.2	0808	7.3	1502	2.8	2050	7.4
7	W	0338	2.7	0924	7.8	1613	2.2	2200	8.0
8	TH	0442	2.1	1026	8.4	1714	1.6	2256	8.7
9	F ●	0541	1.6	1118	9.0	1814	1.1	2345	9.2
10	SA	0639	1.2	1205	9.5	1911	0.7		
11	SU	0031	9.6	0733	0.9	1250	9.9	2001	0.4
12	M	0115	9.8	0821	0.7	1334	10.0	2045	0.3
13	TU	0158	9.9	0904	0.7	1416	9.9	2125	0.5
14	W	0239	9.7	0942	0.9	1458	9.6	2200	0.8
15	TH	0319	9.3	1019	1.2	1539	9.0	2236	1.4
16	F ☾	0400	8.7	1058	1.8	1624	8.3	2315	2.0
17	SA	0446	8.0	1145	2.3	1719	7.6		
18	SU	0006	2.7	0551	7.4	1248	2.9	1846	7.0
19	M	0121	3.1	0730	7.0	1420	3.0	2022	7.1
20	TU	0300	3.1	0856	7.3	1548	2.7	2135	7.5
21	W	0418	2.7	0959	7.8	1652	2.2	2229	8.0
22	TH	0513	2.2	1047	8.3	1740	1.8	2311	8.5
23	F	0556	1.8	1126	8.6	1819	1.4	2346	8.8
24	SA ○	0632	1.5	1159	8.9	1853	1.2		
25	SU	0018	9.0	0705	1.4	1230	9.0	1925	1.1
26	M	0048	9.1	0735	1.3	1300	9.1	1954	1.1
27	TU	0117	9.1	0803	1.3	1329	9.1	2020	1.1
28	W	0145	9.0	0830	1.3	1356	9.0	2045	1.3
29	TH	0211	8.9	0856	1.5	1423	8.8	2110	1.5

MARCH

Date	Day	Time	m	Time	m	Time	m	Time	m
1	F	0238	8.7	0923	1.7	1452	8.5	2137	1.9
2	SA	0307	8.3	0954	2.1	1524	8.1	2209	2.3
3	SU ☽	0340	7.9	1032	2.5	1606	7.5	2252	2.8
4	M	0428	7.3	1127	3.0	1709	7.0	2357	3.3
5	TU	0552	6.9	1249	3.2	1848	6.8		
6	W	0138	3.4	0738	7.0	1435	2.9	2032	7.2
7	TH	0317	2.8	0909	7.6	1554	2.2	2146	8.0
8	F	0427	2.1	1011	8.4	1700	1.5	2240	8.8
9	SA	0529	1.4	1102	9.2	1802	0.9	2328	9.4
10	SU ●	0628	0.9	1148	9.7	1857	0.5		
11	M	0012	9.8	0719	0.6	1231	10.0	1943	0.2
12	TU	0054	10.0	0803	0.4	1313	10.1	2024	0.2
13	W	0134	10.0	0843	0.5	1353	10.0	2100	0.4
14	TH	0213	9.8	0918	0.7	1433	9.6	2133	0.9
15	F	0251	9.3	0952	1.2	1512	9.0	2205	1.5
16	SA	0329	8.7	1028	1.8	1553	8.2	2243	2.2
17	SU ☾	0410	7.9	1112	2.5	1645	7.4	2333	2.9
18	M	0511	7.1	1214	3.0	1818	6.7		
19	TU	0050	3.4	0705	6.7	1352	3.3	2005	6.8
20	W	0242	3.3	0840	7.0	1529	2.8	2119	7.4
21	TH	0400	2.7	0941	7.6	1631	2.2	2208	8.0
22	F	0452	2.1	1025	8.1	1716	1.8	2246	8.5
23	SA	0532	1.7	1102	8.6	1753	1.4	2320	8.8
24	SU	0607	1.4	1133	8.8	1826	1.2	2350	9.0
25	M ○	0638	1.3	1203	9.0	1856	1.1		
26	TU	0019	9.1	0708	1.2	1232	9.1	1924	1.1
27	W	0047	9.1	0735	1.2	1301	9.1	1951	1.1
28	TH	0114	9.1	0802	1.2	1328	9.0	2017	1.3
29	F	0141	9.0	0829	1.4	1357	8.8	2043	1.5
30	SA	0210	8.8	0857	1.6	1427	8.5	2110	1.9
31	SU	0241	8.4	0929	2.0	1502	8.1	2143	2.3

APRIL

Date	Day	Time	m	Time	m	Time	m	Time	m
1	M	0316	7.9	1008	2.4	1545	7.6	2228	2.8
2	TU ☽	0406	7.3	1103	2.9	1651	7.0	2336	3.2
3	W	0531	6.9	1229	3.1	1831	6.8		
4	TH	0122	3.3	0719	7.0	1415	2.8	2015	7.3
5	F	0257	2.7	0848	7.7	1533	2.1	2124	8.1
6	SA	0406	1.9	0949	8.5	1640	1.4	2217	8.9
7	SU	0509	1.3	1039	9.2	1740	0.9	2304	9.5
8	M ●	0605	0.8	1124	9.7	1832	0.5	2347	9.8
9	TU	0655	0.6	1207	9.9	1917	0.4		
10	W	0028	9.9	0738	0.5	1249	9.9	1956	0.5
11	TH	0108	9.8	0817	0.6	1329	9.7	2032	0.7
12	F	0146	9.6	0852	0.9	1408	9.3	2105	1.2
13	SA	0224	9.1	0927	1.3	1447	8.7	2138	1.8
14	SU	0301	8.5	1003	1.9	1528	8.0	2217	2.4
15	M ☾	0343	7.7	1047	2.5	1621	7.2	2309	3.0
16	TU	0443	7.0	1147	3.1	1750	6.7		
17	W	0023	3.4	0628	6.6	1314	3.3	1925	6.8
18	TH	0202	3.3	0758	6.8	1446	2.9	2039	7.2
19	F	0318	2.8	0903	7.3	1547	2.4	2130	7.8
20	SA	0410	2.3	0948	7.9	1634	1.9	2209	8.3
21	SU	0452	1.9	1025	8.3	1713	1.6	2243	8.6
22	M	0529	1.6	1059	8.6	1748	1.4	2315	8.8
23	TU	0603	1.5	1131	8.8	1821	1.3	2346	8.9
24	W ○	0635	1.4	1202	8.9	1851	1.3		
25	TH	0016	9.0	0706	1.3	1232	8.9	1921	1.3
26	F	0046	9.0	0736	1.3	1303	8.9	1950	1.4
27	SA	0116	8.9	0807	1.4	1336	8.7	2020	1.6
28	SU	0149	8.7	0839	1.6	1412	8.5	2053	1.9
29	M	0226	8.4	0915	1.9	1452	8.1	2131	2.3
30	TU	0309	7.9	0959	2.3	1542	7.6	2221	2.7

MAY

Date	Day	Time	m	Time	m	Time	m	Time	m
1	W ☾	0406	7.4	1058	2.7	1650	7.2	2334	3.0
2	TH	0525	7.1	1224	2.8	1818	7.2		
3	F	0110	2.9	0657	7.3	1353	2.5	1945	7.6
4	SA	0231	2.4	0817	7.9	1506	1.9	2053	8.2
5	SU	0338	1.8	0919	8.5	1610	1.4	2148	8.8
6	M	0440	1.4	1011	9.0	1708	1.1	2236	9.3
7	TU	0536	1.1	1058	9.3	1800	0.9	2320	9.5
8	W ●	0625	0.9	1142	9.5	1846	0.9		
9	TH	0002	9.5	0710	0.9	1225	9.5	1927	0.9
10	F	0042	9.5	0750	0.9	1306	9.3	2004	1.2
11	SA	0122	9.2	0828	1.1	1346	9.0	2040	1.5
12	SU	0201	8.9	0905	1.5	1427	8.5	2117	1.9
13	M	0241	8.3	0943	1.9	1511	8.0	2158	2.4
14	TU	0324	7.7	1026	2.4	1602	7.4	2246	2.9
15	W ☽	0420	7.2	1119	2.8	1711	7.0	2348	3.2
16	TH	0538	6.8	1225	3.1	1824	6.9		
17	F	0102	3.2	0651	6.8	1340	3.0	1930	7.1
18	SA	0214	2.9	0755	7.1	1446	2.7	2028	7.5
19	SU	0313	2.6	0850	7.5	1539	2.3	2116	7.9
20	M	0402	2.2	0937	7.9	1625	2.0	2158	8.2
21	TU	0444	1.9	1017	8.2	1705	1.8	2236	8.5
22	W	0524	1.8	1056	8.4	1743	1.7	2312	8.7
23	TH ○	0601	1.6	1132	8.6	1819	1.6	2347	8.8
24	F	0637	1.5	1208	8.7	1853	1.6		
25	SA	0022	8.8	0713	1.4	1244	8.7	1928	1.6
26	SU	0059	8.8	0749	1.5	1323	8.7	2005	1.7
27	M	0139	8.7	0828	1.6	1406	8.5	2045	1.9
28	TU	0222	8.4	0911	1.8	1452	8.3	2130	2.2
29	W	0311	8.1	1001	2.0	1545	8.0	2226	2.4
30	TH ☾	0408	7.8	1102	2.2	1646	7.7	2335	2.5
31	F	0514	7.7	1213	2.3	1755	7.7		

JUNE

Date	Day	Time	m	Time	m	Time	m	Time	m
1	SA	0048	2.5	0626	7.7	1323	2.1	1908	7.9
2	SU	0158	2.2	0740	8.0	1431	1.9	2017	8.2
3	M	0304	1.9	0846	8.3	1535	1.7	2116	8.6
4	TU	0408	1.7	0943	8.6	1635	1.5	2208	8.8
5	W	0505	1.5	1034	8.8	1729	1.4	2255	9.0
6	TH ●	0557	1.3	1121	8.9	1816	1.4	2339	9.1
7	F	0643	1.3	1205	9.0	1900	1.4		
8	SA	0022	9.0	0726	1.3	1248	8.9	1941	1.5
9	SU	0103	8.9	0807	1.4	1330	8.7	2021	1.7
10	M	0143	8.7	0847	1.6	1412	8.5	2100	1.9
11	TU	0224	8.4	0925	1.9	1454	8.1	2139	2.3
12	W	0306	8.0	1004	2.2	1538	7.8	2219	2.5
13	TH	0351	7.6	1045	2.5	1626	7.5	2304	2.8
14	F ☽	0443	7.3	1131	2.7	1722	7.3	2356	2.9
15	SA	0544	7.1	1225	2.9	1820	7.2		
16	SU	0055	3.0	0645	7.1	1325	2.9	1918	7.3
17	M	0159	2.9	0744	7.2	1431	2.8	2015	7.5
18	TU	0302	2.7	0841	7.5	1530	2.6	2108	7.8
19	W	0357	2.4	0934	7.8	1622	2.3	2157	8.1
20	TH	0445	2.1	1022	8.0	1707	2.1	2241	8.4
21	F	0529	1.9	1107	8.3	1750	1.9	2324	8.6
22	SA ○	0612	1.7	1150	8.5	1832	1.8		
23	SU	0006	8.8	0656	1.5	1233	8.7	1915	1.7
24	M	0050	8.9	0741	1.4	1318	8.8	1959	1.6
25	TU	0135	8.9	0828	1.4	1403	8.8	2046	1.6
26	W	0221	8.8	0917	1.4	1450	8.7	2136	1.7
27	TH	0309	8.7	1006	1.5	1538	8.6	2228	1.9
28	F ☾	0358	8.5	1057	1.7	1628	8.4	2322	2.0
29	SA	0451	8.2	1150	1.9	1724	8.2		
30	SU	0019	2.1	0551	8.0	1248	2.0	1828	8.0

DIEPPE
LAT 49°56′N
LONG 1°05′E

TIMES AND HEIGHTS OF HIGH AND LOW WATER
(Heights in Metres)

TIME ZONE
European Standard Time (UT+0100)
For Summer Time (area enclosed in shaded box) add 1 hour

2024

JULY

Date	Day	Time	m	Time	m	Time	m	Time	m
1	M	0121	2.2	0702	7.9	1352	2.2	1940	8.0
2	TU	0230	2.2	0816	7.9	1501	2.2	2048	8.1
3	W	0339	2.1	0921	8.1	1608	2.1	2147	8.3
4	TH	0442	1.9	1018	8.3	1705	2.0	2239	8.5
5	F ●	0536	1.7	1108	8.5	1755	1.8	2326	8.7
6	SA	0625	1.6	1154	8.6	1841	1.7		
7	SU	0009	8.8	0709	1.5	1237	8.7	1924	1.7
8	M	0050	8.8	0751	1.4	1317	8.7	2004	1.7
9	TU	0128	8.7	0829	1.5	1355	8.7	2041	1.8
10	W	0206	8.6	0904	1.6	1431	8.5	2114	1.9
11	TH	0242	8.4	0935	1.8	1506	8.3	2146	2.1
12	F	0316	8.1	1006	2.1	1540	8.0	2219	2.4
13	SA ☽	0351	7.8	1040	2.3	1617	7.7	2258	2.6
14	SU	0431	7.5	1120	2.6	1702	7.5	2345	2.9
15	M	0524	7.2	1210	2.9	1803	7.2		
16	TU	0042	3.0	0634	7.0	1312	3.1	1912	7.2
17	W	0152	3.0	0745	7.1	1429	3.1	2019	7.4
18	TH	0309	2.8	0853	7.4	1542	2.8	2122	7.7
19	F	0411	2.4	0955	7.8	1638	2.4	2218	8.1
20	SA	0504	2.0	1049	8.2	1729	2.0	2309	8.5
21	SU ○	0555	1.6	1138	8.6	1819	1.7	2356	8.9
22	M	0648	1.4	1224	9.0	1910	1.5		
23	TU	0041	9.2	0741	1.1	1309	9.2	2001	1.3
24	W	0126	9.4	0830	0.9	1352	9.3	2048	1.2
25	TH	0210	9.4	0915	0.9	1436	9.3	2132	1.2
26	F	0253	9.3	0956	1.0	1519	9.1	2214	1.4
27	SA	0337	9.0	1036	1.3	1602	8.8	2258	1.7
28	SU ☾	0423	8.6	1120	1.7	1650	8.4	2346	2.1
29	M	0517	8.1	1210	2.2	1748	7.9		
30	TU	0045	2.4	0627	7.6	1315	2.6	1906	7.6
31	W	0159	2.6	0754	7.4	1436	2.7	2029	7.6

AUGUST

Date	Day	Time	m	Time	m	Time	m	Time	m
1	TH	0321	2.5	0911	7.6	1553	2.6	2137	7.9
2	F	0431	2.2	1013	8.0	1655	2.3	2233	8.3
3	SA	0528	1.9	1103	8.4	1747	2.0	2319	8.5
4	SU ●	0615	1.5	1146	8.7	1830	1.7	2359	8.3
5	M	0656	1.5	1224	8.3	1909	1.5		
6	TU	0035	8.9	0733	1.4	1258	8.9	1944	1.5
7	W	0109	9.0	0806	1.3	1331	8.9	2016	1.5
8	TH	0141	8.9	0835	1.4	1402	8.8	2044	1.6
9	F	0211	8.8	0902	1.6	1431	8.7	2111	1.8
10	SA	0240	8.6	0927	1.8	1457	8.5	2138	2.0
11	SU	0307	8.3	0955	2.1	1526	8.2	2210	2.3
12	M ☽	0339	7.9	1027	2.5	1601	7.8	2250	2.7
13	TU	0420	7.4	1109	2.9	1649	7.3	2341	3.1
14	W	0520	7.0	1209	3.3	1804	7.0		
15	TH	0053	3.3	0651	6.8	1335	3.4	1936	7.0
16	F	0228	3.1	0821	7.1	1511	3.1	2057	7.5
17	SA	0345	2.5	0937	7.7	1617	2.5	2202	8.1
18	SU	0445	2.0	1034	8.4	1713	1.9	2254	8.7
19	M ○	0542	1.5	1123	8.9	1808	1.5	2341	9.3
20	TU	0640	1.0	1208	9.4	1902	1.1		
21	W	0025	9.6	0732	0.7	1251	9.7	1952	0.9
22	TH	0108	9.9	0817	0.6	1333	9.8	2036	0.8
23	F	0150	9.9	0858	0.6	1413	9.8	2115	0.9
24	SA	0231	9.7	0934	0.8	1453	9.5	2152	1.2
25	SU	0312	9.3	1009	1.3	1533	9.0	2230	1.6
26	M ☾	0355	8.6	1048	1.9	1617	8.4	2315	2.2
27	TU	0445	7.9	1137	2.5	1712	7.7		
28	W	0014	2.7	0559	7.2	1246	3.1	1843	7.2
29	TH	0137	3.0	0745	7.1	1422	3.2	2021	7.3
30	F	0314	2.8	0907	7.5	1549	2.8	2132	7.8
31	SA	0427	2.3	1006	8.0	1651	2.2	2224	8.3

SEPTEMBER

Date	Day	Time	m	Time	m	Time	m	Time	m
1	SU	0520	1.8	1051	8.5	1738	1.8	2306	8.7
2	M	0602	1.5	1129	8.9	1815	1.6	2342	8.9
3	TU ●	0636	1.3	1202	9.0	1847	1.4		
4	W	0013	9.1	0707	1.3	1232	9.1	1918	1.4
5	TH	0043	9.2	0736	1.2	1301	9.1	1946	1.4
6	F	0112	9.1	0803	1.3	1329	9.1	2013	1.4
7	SA	0139	9.0	0828	1.4	1355	9.0	2038	1.6
8	SU	0206	8.8	0852	1.7	1420	8.7	2104	1.8
9	M	0233	8.5	0917	2.0	1448	8.4	2133	2.1
10	TU	0304	8.1	0947	2.4	1520	8.0	2209	2.6
11	W ☽	0342	7.6	1026	2.9	1602	7.4	2257	3.0
12	TH	0438	7.0	1124	3.4	1717	6.9		
13	F	0011	3.4	0613	6.7	1259	3.6	1904	6.9
14	SA	0200	3.2	0800	7.1	1448	3.1	2037	7.5
15	SU	0324	2.5	0918	7.8	1557	2.3	2142	8.3
16	M	0426	1.8	1013	8.6	1655	1.7	2234	9.0
17	TU	0525	1.2	1101	9.3	1751	1.2	2320	9.6
18	W ○	0620	0.8	1145	9.7	1844	0.8		
19	TH	0003	10.0	0710	0.5	1227	10.0	1931	0.6
20	F	0045	10.1	0754	0.5	1308	10.1	2013	0.6
21	SA	0126	10.1	0832	0.6	1348	9.9	2051	0.8
22	SU	0207	9.8	0907	1.0	1427	9.6	2127	1.2
23	M	0247	9.2	0941	1.5	1506	9.0	2204	1.7
24	TU ☾	0329	8.5	1020	2.2	1548	8.2	2249	2.3
25	W	0420	7.7	1111	2.9	1645	7.4	2350	2.9
26	TH	0542	7.0	1225	3.4	1828	6.9		
27	F	0119	3.2	0732	7.0	1411	3.3	2007	7.1
28	SA	0301	2.9	0851	7.5	1535	2.8	2114	7.7
29	SU	0407	2.3	0944	8.1	1630	2.2	2202	8.3
30	M	0454	1.8	1026	8.6	1711	1.7	2241	8.7

OCTOBER

Date	Day	Time	m	Time	m	Time	m	Time	m
1	TU	0532	1.5	1101	8.9	1746	1.5	2314	9.0
2	W ●	0605	1.3	1132	9.1	1817	1.4	2344	9.1
3	TH	0635	1.3	1201	9.2	1847	1.3		
4	F	0013	9.2	0703	1.3	1229	9.2	1915	1.3
5	SA	0041	9.2	0730	1.3	1256	9.2	1943	1.4
6	SU	0109	9.1	0756	1.5	1323	9.0	2010	1.5
7	M	0137	8.9	0822	1.7	1350	8.8	2037	1.7
8	TU	0207	8.6	0849	2.0	1421	8.5	2108	2.1
9	W	0240	8.2	0921	2.5	1455	8.0	2144	2.5
10	TH ☽	0321	7.7	1002	2.9	1540	7.4	2234	2.9
11	F	0420	7.1	1103	3.4	1657	7.0	2349	3.3
12	SA	0554	6.8	1242	3.5	1842	7.0		
13	SU	0138	3.1	0736	7.3	1424	3.0	2011	7.6
14	M	0259	2.4	0850	8.0	1532	2.2	2115	8.4
15	TU	0402	1.6	0946	8.8	1631	1.5	2207	9.2
16	W	0459	1.1	1034	9.4	1726	1.0	2254	9.7
17	TH ○	0553	0.8	1118	9.8	1818	0.8	2338	10.0
18	F	0642	0.6	1201	10.0	1905	0.7		
19	SA	0021	10.1	0726	0.6	1242	10.0	1947	0.7
20	SU	0103	10.0	0805	0.8	1322	9.8	2026	0.9
21	M	0144	9.6	0841	1.2	1402	9.4	2104	1.3
22	TU	0225	9.1	0918	1.7	1443	8.8	2144	1.8
23	W	0309	8.4	1000	2.4	1527	8.1	2230	2.4
24	TH ☾	0402	7.6	1053	3.0	1626	7.4	2329	2.9
25	F	0523	7.1	1204	3.4	1800	7.0		
26	SA	0049	3.2	0656	7.0	1336	3.3	1928	7.1
27	SU	0220	2.9	0811	7.4	1455	2.8	2036	7.6
28	M	0324	2.5	0907	8.0	1548	2.3	2125	8.1
29	TU	0412	2.0	0949	8.4	1631	1.9	2205	8.5
30	W	0452	1.7	1025	8.8	1709	1.6	2240	8.8
31	TH	0527	1.5	1057	9.0	1743	1.5	2312	8.9

NOVEMBER

Date	Day	Time	m	Time	m	Time	m	Time	m
1	F ●	0600	1.5	1128	9.1	1816	1.4	2343	9.0
2	SA	0631	1.5	1158	9.1	1846	1.4		
3	SU	0014	9.0	0701	1.5	1228	9.1	1917	1.4
4	M	0044	9.0	0730	1.6	1258	9.0	1947	1.5
5	TU	0116	8.8	0800	1.8	1329	8.8	2019	1.7
6	W	0150	8.6	0832	2.1	1405	8.5	2053	2.0
7	TH	0229	8.2	0909	2.4	1446	8.1	2134	2.4
8	F	0315	7.8	0954	2.8	1538	7.6	2226	2.7
9	SA ☽	0417	7.4	1057	3.1	1650	7.3	2340	2.9
10	SU	0538	7.3	1227	3.1	1816	7.4		
11	M	0111	2.7	0702	7.6	1353	2.7	1935	7.8
12	TU	0227	2.2	0814	8.2	1501	2.1	2042	8.4
13	W	0330	1.7	0913	8.8	1601	1.6	2138	9.0
14	TH	0429	1.3	1004	9.3	1658	1.2	2228	9.4
15	F ○	0523	1.0	1051	9.6	1751	1.0	2314	9.7
16	SA	0613	0.9	1136	9.8	1839	0.9	2359	9.7
17	SU	0659	1.0	1219	9.7	1924	0.9		
18	M	0043	9.6	0741	1.2	1301	9.6	2006	1.1
19	TU	0126	9.3	0821	1.5	1343	9.2	2047	1.4
20	W	0209	8.9	0902	1.9	1426	8.7	2128	1.8
21	TH	0255	8.4	0945	2.3	1512	8.2	2213	2.3
22	F	0346	7.8	1033	2.8	1607	7.6	2303	2.7
23	SA ☾	0450	7.4	1131	3.1	1716	7.2		
24	SU	0003	3.0	0600	7.2	1238	3.2	1827	7.1
25	M	0113	3.0	0707	7.3	1351	3.0	1932	7.3
26	TU	0222	2.8	0807	7.6	1453	2.7	2030	7.6
27	W	0319	2.5	0858	8.0	1545	2.3	2119	8.0
28	TH	0407	2.2	0941	8.3	1629	2.0	2201	8.3
29	F	0449	2.0	1020	8.6	1709	1.8	2240	8.5
30	SA	0527	1.8	1057	8.8	1746	1.7	2316	8.7

DECEMBER

Date	Day	Time	m	Time	m	Time	m	Time	m
1	SU ●	0603	1.7	1132	8.9	1821	1.6	2352	8.8
2	M	0637	1.7	1207	8.9	1856	1.5		
3	TU	0028	8.8	0711	1.7	1242	8.9	1932	1.5
4	W	0105	8.8	0747	1.8	1320	8.8	2009	1.6
5	TH	0145	8.7	0825	2.0	1401	8.6	2049	1.8
6	F	0228	8.4	0906	2.2	1447	8.4	2133	2.0
7	SA	0317	8.2	0955	2.4	1539	8.1	2225	2.2
8	SU ☽	0412	7.9	1054	2.6	1637	7.9	2329	2.4
9	M	0514	7.8	1204	2.6	1743	7.8		
10	TU	0038	2.4	0622	7.9	1315	2.5	1854	7.9
11	W	0147	2.2	0734	8.1	1424	2.2	2006	8.2
12	TH	0255	2.0	0840	8.5	1530	1.9	2110	8.6
13	F	0359	1.7	0938	8.8	1632	1.6	2205	8.9
14	SA	0457	1.5	1029	9.1	1729	1.3	2256	9.1
15	SU ○	0550	1.4	1117	9.3	1820	1.2	2344	9.2
16	M	0638	1.4	1203	9.3	1907	1.1		
17	TU	0029	9.2	0724	1.4	1247	9.3	1951	1.2
18	W	0113	9.1	0807	1.5	1330	9.1	2033	1.3
19	TH	0157	8.9	0848	1.7	1412	8.8	2113	1.6
20	F	0240	8.6	0928	2.0	1455	8.4	2152	1.9
21	SA	0323	8.2	1007	2.4	1538	8.0	2230	2.3
22	SU ☾	0408	7.8	1049	2.6	1626	7.6	2311	2.6
23	M	0458	7.5	1135	2.9	1720	7.3	2359	2.9
24	TU	0555	7.3	1229	3.1	1821	7.2		
25	W	0056	3.0	0656	7.3	1334	3.1	1923	7.2
26	TH	0206	3.0	0756	7.4	1447	2.9	2025	7.4
27	F	0316	2.8	0854	7.7	1547	2.6	2121	7.7
28	SA	0411	2.5	0946	8.0	1636	2.3	2211	8.0
29	SU	0457	2.3	1031	8.3	1720	2.0	2256	8.3
30	M ●	0539	2.0	1113	8.6	1802	1.7	2338	8.6
31	TU	0620	1.8	1154	8.8	1843	1.5		

LE HAVRE
LAT 49°29'N
LONG 0°07'E

TIMES AND HEIGHTS OF HIGH AND LOW WATER (Heights in Metres)

TIME ZONE
European Standard Time (UT+0100)
For Summer Time (area enclosed in shaded box) add 1 hour

2024

SUNRISE AND SUNSET TIMES

LE HAVRE
At 49°29'N 0°07'E
European Standard Time (UT+0100)

		Sunrise	Sunset
Jan	01	0856	1711
	15	0850	1728
Feb	01	0831	1756
	15	0809	1819
Mar	01	0742	1842
	15	0713	1905
European Summer Time (UT+0200)			
Apr	01	0737	2031
	15	0708	2052
May	01	0637	2117
	15	0616	2137
Jun	01	0558	2158
	15	0552	2208
Jul	01	0557	2209
	15	0609	2201
Aug	01	0631	2140
	15	0651	2116
Sep	01	0715	2043
	15	0736	2013
Oct	01	0759	1938
	15	0821	1909
European Standard Time (UT+0100)			
Nov	01	0748	1738
	15	0811	1717
Dec	01	0834	1703

JANUARY

Date	Day	Time	m	Time	m	Time	m	Time	m
1	M	0144	7.2	0833	2.5	1347	7.3	2055	2.3
2	TU	0220	7.0	0907	2.7	1423	7.0	2128	2.6
3	W	0258	6.9	0944	2.9	1504	6.8	2205	2.8
4	TH ☽	0344	6.7	1027	3.1	1554	6.6	2251	3.0
5	F	0442	6.6	1119	3.2	1700	6.5	2346	3.2
6	SA	0549	6.6	1219	3.3	1813	6.5		
7	SU	0049	3.2	0654	6.7	1329	3.1	1922	6.6
8	M	0205	3.0	0755	6.9	1447	2.8	2026	6.9
9	TU	0317	2.7	0850	7.2	1549	2.3	2122	7.2
10	W	0414	2.3	0941	7.5	1643	1.9	2212	7.5
11	TH ●	0506	2.0	1028	7.7	1734	1.6	2259	7.7
12	F	0557	1.7	1114	7.9	1826	1.3	2345	7.9
13	SA	0648	1.5	1200	8.0	1916	1.1		
14	SU	0032	8.0	0737	1.4	1247	8.1	2004	1.1
15	M	0118	7.9	0824	1.5	1334	8.0	2048	1.2
16	TU	0205	7.8	0908	1.6	1420	7.8	2131	1.4
17	W	0252	7.6	0951	1.9	1509	7.6	2212	1.8
18	TH ☾	0342	7.3	1036	2.2	1602	7.2	2259	2.2
19	F	0438	7.1	1131	2.6	1706	6.9	2358	2.6
20	SA	0547	6.9	1239	2.8	1825	6.7		
21	SU	0111	2.9	0703	6.8	1356	2.8	1944	6.7
22	M	0225	2.9	0813	6.9	1507	2.6	2051	6.9
23	TU	0331	2.7	0911	7.1	1610	2.3	2144	7.2
24	W	0429	2.4	0958	7.3	1702	2.0	2229	7.4
25	TH ○	0517	2.2	1039	7.5	1745	1.8	2307	7.5
26	F	0558	2.0	1114	7.6	1823	1.7	2342	7.6
27	SA	0635	1.9	1147	7.7	1858	1.6		
28	SU	0014	7.6	0710	1.8	1219	7.7	1931	1.6
29	M	0046	7.6	0742	1.9	1251	7.7	2001	1.7
30	TU	0117	7.5	0811	2.0	1321	7.5	2029	1.9
31	W	0146	7.4	0839	2.2	1351	7.4	2055	2.1

FEBRUARY

Date	Day	Time	m	Time	m	Time	m	Time	m
1	TH	0215	7.2	0906	2.4	1423	7.2	2123	2.4
2	F	0247	7.0	0939	2.7	1500	6.9	2157	2.7
3	SA ☽	0330	6.8	1021	3.0	1549	6.6	2245	3.1
4	SU	0426	6.5	1118	3.2	1701	6.3	2348	3.3
5	M	0551	6.4	1231	3.3	1835	6.3		
6	TU	0113	3.3	0717	6.6	1409	3.0	2002	6.6
7	W	0250	2.9	0831	6.9	1526	2.5	2109	7.1
8	TH	0357	2.4	0928	7.4	1628	1.9	2202	7.5
9	F ●	0456	1.9	1017	7.7	1727	1.4	2248	7.8
10	SA	0553	1.4	1103	8.1	1822	1.0	2333	8.1
11	SU	0645	1.1	1148	8.3	1911	0.7		
12	M	0017	8.2	0731	0.9	1232	8.4	1954	0.6
13	TU	0101	8.2	0813	0.9	1316	8.3	2033	0.7
14	W	0143	8.1	0851	1.1	1358	8.1	2109	1.1
15	TH	0224	7.8	0928	1.5	1441	7.7	2144	1.7
16	F ☾	0306	7.4	1004	2.1	1526	7.2	2221	2.3
17	SA	0352	7.0	1050	2.6	1626	6.7	2312	2.9
18	SU	0500	6.6	1156	3.1	1758	6.4		
19	M	0031	3.3	0636	6.4	1325	3.2	1935	6.4
20	TU	0202	3.3	0803	6.5	1454	2.9	2048	6.7
21	W	0328	3.0	0905	6.8	1609	2.5	2138	7.0
22	TH	0432	2.5	0950	7.1	1658	2.1	2217	7.3
23	F	0514	2.1	1026	7.4	1736	1.7	2250	7.5
24	SA ○	0549	1.8	1057	7.6	1809	1.5	2320	7.6
25	SU	0621	1.6	1126	7.7	1840	1.4	2349	7.7
26	M	0651	1.6	1156	7.8	1909	1.4		
27	TU	0018	7.7	0719	1.6	1225	7.8	1935	1.4
28	W	0046	7.7	0745	1.6	1254	7.7	2000	1.6
29	TH	0114	7.6	0810	1.8	1322	7.5	2025	1.8

MARCH

Date	Day	Time	m	Time	m	Time	m	Time	m
1	F	0141	7.4	0837	2.0	1351	7.3	2051	2.2
2	SA	0211	7.2	0906	2.4	1424	7.0	2120	2.6
3	SU ☽	0245	6.9	0942	2.8	1507	6.6	2202	3.0
4	M	0336	6.5	1034	3.1	1617	6.2	2306	3.4
5	TU	0504	6.2	1150	3.4	1805	6.2		
6	W	0039	3.5	0651	6.4	1344	3.1	1949	6.5
7	TH	0233	3.0	0815	6.8	1508	2.5	2056	7.1
8	F	0342	2.3	0913	7.3	1614	1.8	2145	7.6
9	SA	0444	1.7	1000	7.8	1715	1.2	2230	8.0
10	SU ●	0540	1.1	1045	8.2	1807	0.7	2313	8.2
11	M	0629	0.8	1128	8.4	1853	0.4	2355	8.3
12	TU	0712	0.6	1211	8.4	1933	0.4		
13	W	0037	8.3	0751	0.7	1253	8.3	2010	0.7
14	TH	0117	8.1	0827	1.0	1334	8.0	2043	1.2
15	F	0155	7.8	0901	1.5	1414	7.6	2114	1.8
16	SA	0232	7.4	0934	2.1	1458	7.1	2147	2.5
17	SU ☾	0315	6.9	1015	2.7	1556	6.5	2237	3.2
18	M	0420	6.4	1121	3.2	1738	6.2		
19	TU	0000	3.6	0611	6.1	1255	3.4	1921	6.2
20	W	0141	3.5	0747	6.3	1437	3.1	2034	6.6
21	TH	0316	3.0	0849	6.7	1548	2.5	2119	7.0
22	F	0410	2.5	0930	7.0	1632	2.1	2153	7.3
23	SA	0450	2.0	1002	7.3	1709	1.7	2223	7.5
24	SU	0524	1.7	1031	7.6	1741	1.5	2250	7.7
25	M ○	0555	1.6	1059	7.7	1812	1.4	2319	7.7
26	TU	0624	1.5	1128	7.7	1840	1.4	2347	7.7
27	W	0651	1.5	1158	7.7	1905	1.4		
28	TH	0015	7.7	0717	1.5	1227	7.7	1931	1.6
29	F	0043	7.6	0744	1.6	1257	7.5	1959	1.8
30	SA	0113	7.4	0813	1.9	1329	7.3	2027	2.2
31	SU	0143	7.2	0843	2.2	1404	7.0	2058	2.6

APRIL

Date	Day	Time	m	Time	m	Time	m	Time	m
1	M	0219	6.9	0919	2.6	1451	6.6	2139	3.0
2	TU ☽	0314	6.5	1011	3.0	1605	6.3	2244	3.4
3	W	0443	6.2	1128	3.2	1754	6.2		
4	TH	0027	3.5	0633	6.4	1328	3.0	1931	6.6
5	F	0214	2.9	0753	6.9	1446	2.3	2033	7.2
6	SA	0321	2.2	0849	7.4	1551	1.6	2121	7.7
7	SU	0421	1.5	0937	7.8	1650	1.1	2205	8.0
8	M ●	0517	1.1	1022	8.1	1742	0.7	2248	8.2
9	TU	0605	0.8	1105	8.3	1827	0.6	2329	8.2
10	W	0648	0.7	1148	8.3	1906	0.7		
11	TH	0010	8.2	0726	0.8	1230	8.1	1943	1.0
12	F	0049	8.0	0802	1.1	1311	7.8	2015	1.5
13	SA	0127	7.7	0836	1.6	1352	7.4	2047	2.1
14	SU	0205	7.3	0910	2.1	1437	6.9	2121	2.7
15	M ☾	0248	6.8	0951	2.7	1536	6.4	2213	3.3
16	TU	0352	6.3	1055	3.2	1711	6.2	2334	3.6
17	W	0535	6.1	1219	3.4	1842	6.2		
18	TH	0103	3.5	0704	6.2	1345	3.1	1957	6.5
19	F	0222	3.1	0811	6.5	1453	2.7	2043	6.9
20	SA	0320	2.6	0854	6.9	1544	2.3	2117	7.2
21	SU	0406	2.2	0926	7.2	1626	1.9	2146	7.4
22	M	0445	1.9	0957	7.4	1703	1.7	2216	7.6
23	TU	0520	1.7	1028	7.5	1736	1.6	2246	7.6
24	W ○	0551	1.6	1059	7.6	1806	1.6	2316	7.7
25	TH	0620	1.6	1131	7.6	1835	1.6	2346	7.7
26	F	0650	1.6	1203	7.5	1905	1.7		
27	SA	0017	7.6	0722	1.6	1238	7.4	1937	1.9
28	SU	0051	7.4	0754	1.8	1316	7.2	2009	2.2
29	M	0128	7.2	0829	2.1	1359	7.0	2046	2.6
30	TU	0213	6.9	0909	2.5	1452	6.7	2132	3.0

MAY

Date	Day	Time	m	Time	m	Time	m	Time	m
1	W ☾	0311	6.6	1002	2.8	1604	6.5	2237	3.2
2	TH	0435	6.5	1121	2.9	1740	6.5		
3	F	0020	3.2	0607	6.6	1304	2.7	1901	6.9
4	SA	0146	2.7	0721	7.0	1416	2.1	2002	7.3
5	SU	0250	2.1	0819	7.4	1519	1.7	2052	7.6
6	M	0350	1.6	0910	7.7	1618	1.3	2138	7.9
7	TU	0446	1.3	0957	7.9	1711	1.1	2221	8.0
8	W ●	0536	1.1	1042	8.0	1757	1.1	2303	8.0
9	TH	0621	1.0	1126	8.0	1838	1.2	2345	7.9
10	F	0701	1.1	1210	7.8	1916	1.4		
11	SA	0025	7.8	0738	1.4	1253	7.6	1951	1.8
12	SU	0104	7.5	0814	1.7	1336	7.3	2026	2.3
13	M	0144	7.2	0851	2.2	1421	6.9	2105	2.7
14	TU	0228	6.8	0934	2.6	1517	6.6	2156	3.2
15	W ☽	0326	6.5	1029	3.0	1630	6.3	2302	3.4
16	TH	0446	6.2	1135	3.2	1741	6.3		
17	F	0010	3.4	0558	6.3	1242	3.1	1846	6.5
18	SA	0117	3.2	0702	6.4	1346	2.9	1942	6.7
19	SU	0218	2.8	0756	6.7	1444	2.6	2026	7.0
20	M	0312	2.5	0839	6.9	1535	2.3	2103	7.2
21	TU	0358	2.2	0918	7.1	1618	2.1	2138	7.4
22	W	0439	2.0	0955	7.3	1657	2.0	2213	7.5
23	TH ○	0515	1.9	1031	7.4	1732	1.9	2247	7.5
24	F	0550	1.7	1108	7.4	1807	1.9	2322	7.6
25	SA	0627	1.7	1145	7.4	1844	1.9	2358	7.6
26	SU	0704	1.7	1226	7.4	1921	2.0		
27	M	0039	7.5	0742	1.8	1310	7.3	2000	2.2
28	TU	0123	7.3	0823	2.0	1358	7.1	2042	2.4
29	W	0212	7.2	0907	2.2	1453	7.0	2132	2.7
30	TH ☾	0310	7.0	1002	2.4	1557	6.8	2237	2.8
31	F	0419	6.8	1114	2.5	1711	6.8	2358	2.8

JUNE

Date	Day	Time	m	Time	m	Time	m	Time	m
1	SA	0534	6.9	1232	2.4	1823	7.0		
2	SU	0111	2.5	0644	7.0	1341	2.2	1926	7.2
3	M	0215	2.2	0747	7.2	1444	1.9	2021	7.4
4	TU	0317	1.9	0844	7.4	1543	1.8	2111	7.6
5	W	0415	1.7	0935	7.5	1639	1.7	2158	7.7
6	TH ●	0508	1.5	1024	7.6	1728	1.7	2242	7.7
7	F	0555	1.5	1110	7.6	1812	1.7	2325	7.7
8	SA	0638	1.5	1155	7.6	1853	1.8		
9	SU	0006	7.6	0718	1.6	1238	7.5	1932	2.0
10	M	0046	7.5	0757	1.8	1320	7.3	2011	2.3
11	TU	0126	7.3	0835	2.1	1403	7.1	2050	2.6
12	W	0208	7.0	0915	2.4	1448	6.8	2133	2.8
13	TH	0253	6.8	0957	2.7	1539	6.6	2219	3.1
14	F ☽	0346	6.5	1044	2.9	1636	6.5	2311	3.2
15	SA	0449	6.4	1135	3.0	1734	6.5		
16	SU	0005	3.2	0550	6.4	1231	3.1	1830	6.6
17	M	0103	3.1	0648	6.5	1331	3.0	1924	6.7
18	TU	0206	2.9	0744	6.6	1434	2.8	2014	6.9
19	W	0305	2.7	0836	6.8	1530	2.6	2100	7.1
20	TH	0356	2.4	0924	7.0	1619	2.4	2143	7.3
21	F	0442	2.1	1009	7.2	1703	2.2	2224	7.5
22	SA ○	0526	1.9	1052	7.4	1746	2.0	2305	7.6
23	SU	0610	1.7	1135	7.5	1830	1.9	2348	7.6
24	M	0655	1.6	1220	7.5	1915	1.9		
25	TU	0033	7.7	0741	1.6	1306	7.5	2001	1.9
26	W	0120	7.6	0826	1.6	1354	7.4	2047	2.0
27	TH	0208	7.5	0912	1.7	1443	7.3	2135	2.2
28	F ☾	0259	7.4	1000	1.9	1536	7.2	2227	2.3
29	SA	0354	7.2	1053	2.1	1634	7.1	2326	2.5
30	SU	0456	7.0	1154	2.3	1740	7.0		

LE HAVRE
LAT 49°29′N
LONG 0°07′E

TIMES AND HEIGHTS OF HIGH AND LOW WATER (Heights in Metres)

TIME ZONE European Standard Time (UT+0100) **For Summer Time (area enclosed in shaded box) add 1 hour**

2024

JULY

Day	Time	m
1 M	0032 0606 1302 1849	2.5 6.9 2.4 7.0
2 TU	0142 0718 1411 1953	2.5 7.0 2.4 7.1
3 W	0248 0825 1514 2051	2.3 7.1 2.3 7.3
4 TH	0349 0923 1613 2142	2.1 7.2 2.2 7.4
5 F ●	0446 1014 1706 2229	1.9 7.4 2.1 7.5
6 SA	0537 1101 1754 2312	1.8 7.4 2.0 7.6
7 SU	0622 1144 1837 2351	1.7 7.5 2.0 7.6
8 M	0703 1223 1917	1.7 7.5 2.0
9 TU	0029 0741 1300 1954	7.6 1.7 7.4 2.1
10 W	0105 0816 1336 2029	7.5 1.9 7.3 2.2
11 TH	0140 0848 1412 2101	7.3 2.1 7.1 2.4
12 F	0215 0918 1446 2133	7.1 2.3 7.0 2.7
13 SA ☽	0250 0950 1524 2209	6.9 2.6 6.8 2.9
14 SU	0331 1026 1609 2253	6.7 2.9 6.6 3.1
15 M	0425 1115 1710 2348	6.5 3.1 6.5 3.2
16 TU	0534 1214 1818	6.3 3.3 6.5
17 W	0054 0647 1328 1925	3.2 6.4 3.2 6.6
18 TH	0213 0758 1449 2027	3.0 6.5 3.0 6.9
19 F	0321 0901 1550 2121	2.6 6.8 2.6 7.2
20 SA	0417 0953 1643 2209	2.2 7.2 2.3 7.5
21 SU ○	0509 1040 1734 2254	1.9 7.4 2.0 7.7
22 M	0602 1125 1825 2338	1.6 7.6 1.7 7.9
23 TU	0653 1209 1915	1.3 7.8 1.5
24 W	0023 0740 1254 2000	8.0 1.1 7.8 1.5
25 TH	0108 0823 1339 2043	8.0 1.1 7.8 1.5
26 F	0153 0903 1423 2123	7.9 1.3 7.7 1.7
27 SA	0238 0942 1508 2204	7.7 1.6 7.5 2.0
28 SU ☾	0325 1023 1556 2252	7.4 2.0 7.2 2.4
29 M	0420 1114 1656 2354	7.1 2.5 6.9 2.7
30 TU	0533 1224 1815	6.7 2.8 6.8
31 W	0112 0701 1344 1935	2.8 6.6 2.9 6.8

AUGUST

Day	Time	m
1 TH	0227 0818 1456 2042	2.7 6.8 2.8 7.0
2 F	0336 0920 1602 2136	2.4 7.0 2.6 7.2
3 SA	0439 1010 1702 2221	2.1 7.3 2.3 7.4
4 SU ●	0531 1051 1748 2259	1.9 7.4 2.1 7.6
5 M	0612 1128 1825 2334	1.7 7.5 1.9 7.7
6 TU	0647 1201 1900	1.6 7.6 1.8
7 W	0006 0719 1233 1931	7.7 1.6 7.6 1.8
8 TH	0038 0749 1304 2000	7.7 1.6 7.5 1.9
9 F	0108 0816 1333 2026	7.6 1.8 7.4 2.1
10 SA	0137 0839 1401 2051	7.4 2.1 7.3 2.3
11 SU	0207 0903 1429 2118	7.2 2.3 7.1 2.6
12 M ☽	0240 0932 1506 2155	6.9 2.7 6.9 2.9
13 TU	0324 1013 1556 2247	6.6 3.1 6.6 3.2
14 W	0427 1113 1712 2357	6.3 3.4 6.4 3.4
15 TH	0558 1234 1844	6.2 3.6 6.4
16 F	0132 0731 1421 2005	3.3 6.4 3.3 6.7
17 SA	0258 0846 1531 2105	2.8 6.8 2.7 7.2
18 SU	0359 0939 1628 2154	2.2 7.3 2.2 7.6
19 M ○	0456 1025 1724 2238	1.7 7.6 1.7 7.9
20 TU	0552 1108 1816 2322	1.2 7.9 1.4 8.2
21 W	0642 1151 1903	0.9 8.1 1.1
22 TH	0005 0726 1234 1945	8.3 0.8 8.2 1.0
23 F	0048 0806 1316 2024	8.3 0.8 8.1 1.1
24 SA	0131 0842 1357 2101	8.2 1.1 7.9 1.5
25 SU	0213 0916 1437 2137	7.8 1.6 7.6 1.9
26 M ☾	0257 0951 1521 2219	7.4 2.2 7.2 2.5
27 TU	0350 1037 1619 2320	6.9 2.8 6.8 3.0
28 W	0512 1153 1753	6.5 3.3 6.5
29 TH	0050 0655 1328 1928	3.2 6.4 3.4 6.6
30 F	0218 0818 1454 2038	3.0 6.7 3.1 6.8
31 SA	0338 0915 1609 2128	2.5 7.0 2.6 7.2

SEPTEMBER

Day	Time	m
1 SU	0437 0957 1658 2206	2.1 7.3 2.2 7.5
2 M	0519 1032 1733 2239	1.8 7.5 1.9 7.7
3 TU ●	0552 1103 1805 2309	1.6 7.7 1.8 7.8
4 W	0622 1132 1834 2338	1.5 7.7 1.7 7.9
5 TH	0651 1200 1902	1.5 7.7 1.7
6 F	0007 0717 1229 1928	7.8 1.6 7.7 1.8
7 SA	0036 0742 1255 1953	7.8 1.7 7.6 1.9
8 SU	0103 0805 1322 2017	7.6 1.9 7.5 2.1
9 M	0132 0828 1350 2044	7.4 2.3 7.2 2.4
10 TU	0204 0855 1423 2117	7.0 2.7 6.9 2.8
11 W ☽	0245 0932 1511 2206	6.6 3.1 6.6 3.2
12 TH	0349 1031 1627 2317	6.3 3.5 6.3 3.5
13 F	0528 1158 1817	6.2 3.7 6.3
14 SA	0106 0716 1404 1946	3.4 6.4 3.3 6.7
15 SU	0239 0827 1513 2046	2.7 7.0 2.6 7.3
16 M	0340 0918 1610 2133	2.0 7.5 2.0 7.8
17 TU	0438 1002 1705 2217	1.4 7.9 1.4 8.1
18 W ○	0532 1045 1756 2300	1.0 8.2 1.1 8.4
19 TH	0620 1127 1842 2343	0.7 8.3 0.9 8.5
20 F	0702 1208 1923	0.6 8.3 0.8
21 SA	0025 0741 1249 2001	8.4 0.8 8.2 1.0
22 SU	0107 0816 1329 2036	8.2 1.2 8.0 1.4
23 M	0149 0849 1408 2111	7.8 1.8 7.6 2.0
24 TU ☾	0234 0923 1451 2152	7.3 2.4 7.2 2.6
25 W	0329 1010 1552 2255	6.8 3.1 6.6 3.2
26 TH	0503 1133 1738	6.3 3.6 6.3
27 F	0031 0645 1317 1914	3.4 6.3 3.6 6.4
28 SA	0208 0806 1446 2023	3.1 6.7 3.1 6.8
29 SU	0319 0856 1546 2108	2.6 7.1 2.5 7.2
30 M	0408 0933 1628 2142	2.1 7.4 2.1 7.5

OCTOBER

Day	Time	m
1 TU	0446 1003 1702 2212	1.8 7.6 1.9 7.7
2 W ●	0519 1032 1734 2240	1.6 7.8 1.7 7.9
3 TH	0550 1059 1804 2309	1.5 7.8 1.6 7.9
4 F	0618 1127 1832 2338	1.5 7.8 1.6 7.9
5 SA	0645 1155 1857	1.6 7.8 1.7
6 SU	0006 0710 1222 1924	7.8 1.8 7.7 1.8
7 M	0035 0736 1249 1952	7.6 2.0 7.6 2.0
8 TU	0106 0804 1320 2021	7.4 2.3 7.3 2.4
9 W	0142 0834 1357 2056	7.0 2.7 7.0 2.8
10 TH ☽	0228 0913 1449 2144	6.7 3.2 6.6 3.1
11 F	0336 1011 1609 2253	6.4 3.6 6.3 3.4
12 SA	0513 1139 1755	6.3 3.7 6.4
13 SU	0046 0654 1341 1920	3.2 6.6 3.2 6.8
14 M	0214 0800 1448 2018	2.6 7.2 2.5 7.4
15 TU	0314 0850 1545 2107	1.9 7.7 1.8 7.9
16 W	0411 0935 1639 2152	1.4 8.0 1.3 8.2
17 TH ○	0504 1018 1729 2236	1.0 8.2 1.0 8.4
18 F	0552 1100 1816 2320	0.8 8.3 0.9 8.4
19 SA	0635 1142 1858	0.8 8.3 0.9
20 SU	0003 0714 1223 1937	8.3 1.1 8.2 1.1
21 M	0047 0751 1304 2014	8.1 1.5 7.9 1.5
22 TU	0130 0826 1345 2051	7.7 2.0 7.5 2.1
23 W	0217 0903 1430 2134	7.2 2.7 7.1 2.7
24 TH ☾	0316 0954 1533 2236	6.7 3.3 6.6 3.2
25 F	0445 1113 1710	6.4 3.6 6.3
26 SA	0001 0611 1243 1835	3.3 6.4 3.5 6.4
27 SU	0124 0727 1400 1945	3.1 6.7 3.1 6.7
28 M	0230 0820 1457 2033	2.7 7.0 2.7 7.1
29 TU	0320 0857 1543 2108	2.3 7.4 2.3 7.4
30 W	0402 0928 1623 2140	2.0 7.6 2.0 7.6
31 TH	0440 0957 1659 2210	1.8 7.7 1.8 7.7

NOVEMBER

Day	Time	m
1 F ●	0515 1026 1732 2241	1.8 7.8 1.8 7.7
2 SA	0545 1056 1801 2312	1.8 7.8 1.7 7.7
3 SU	0614 1125 1830 2343	1.8 7.8 1.7 7.7
4 M	0643 1156 1901	1.9 7.7 1.8
5 TU	0016 0715 1228 1933	7.5 2.1 7.6 2.0
6 W	0053 0747 1304 2008	7.4 2.4 7.4 2.3
7 TH	0135 0823 1349 2046	7.1 2.7 7.1 2.6
8 F	0226 0906 1443 2135	6.8 3.1 6.8 2.9
9 SA ☽	0331 1004 1557 2241	6.6 3.3 6.6 3.1
10 SU	0455 1127 1726	6.6 3.4 6.7
11 M	0018 0620 1306 1844	2.9 6.8 3.0 7.0
12 TU	0139 0725 1414 1945	2.5 7.2 2.4 7.4
13 W	0242 0819 1514 2038	1.9 7.6 1.9 7.8
14 TH	0339 0907 1610 2127	1.5 7.9 1.5 8.0
15 F ○	0434 0952 1702 2214	1.3 8.1 1.2 8.2
16 SA	0524 1036 1751 2300	1.2 8.2 1.1 8.2
17 SU	0609 1119 1835 2346	1.2 8.2 1.1 8.1
18 M	0651 1202 1917	1.4 8.0 1.3
19 TU	0031 0731 1245 1957	7.9 1.8 7.8 1.6
20 W	0117 0810 1328 2037	7.6 2.2 7.5 2.1
21 TH	0205 0851 1415 2121	7.2 2.6 7.2 2.5
22 F	0300 0941 1512 2214	6.9 3.1 6.8 2.9
23 SA ☾	0407 1042 1624 2315	6.6 3.3 6.5 3.1
24 SU	0515 1147 1735	6.6 3.4 6.5
25 M	0020 0620 1254 1839	3.1 6.6 3.3 6.6
26 TU	0124 0719 1358 1937	3.0 6.8 3.0 6.8
27 W	0224 0807 1454 2025	2.7 7.1 2.7 7.0
28 TH	0316 0846 1542 2105	2.5 7.3 2.4 7.2
29 F	0401 0922 1624 2142	2.3 7.5 2.2 7.4
30 SA	0440 0957 1701 2218	2.1 7.6 2.0 7.5

DECEMBER

Day	Time	m
1 SU ●	0515 1031 1735 2253	2.1 7.7 1.9 7.5
2 M	0549 1105 1809 2329	2.0 7.7 1.8 7.6
3 TU	0624 1140 1846	2.0 7.7 1.8
4 W	0007 0701 1218 1923	7.5 2.1 7.6 1.9
5 TH	0048 0740 1300 2003	7.4 2.2 7.5 2.0
6 F	0133 0820 1347 2045	7.3 2.5 7.3 2.2
7 SA	0224 0906 1439 2133	7.1 2.7 7.1 2.4
8 SU ☽	0321 1000 1540 2231	7.0 2.8 7.0 2.6
9 M	0426 1107 1649 2342	6.9 2.9 6.9 2.6
10 TU	0538 1223 1802	7.0 2.8 7.0
11 W	0056 0646 1336 1911	2.4 7.2 2.5 7.2
12 TH	0206 0747 1442 2012	2.2 7.4 2.2 7.5
13 F	0309 0841 1543 2108	1.9 7.6 1.8 7.7
14 SA	0407 0931 1639 2200	1.7 7.8 1.6 7.8
15 SU ○	0500 1019 1731 2249	1.6 7.9 1.4 7.9
16 M	0550 1105 1819 2336	1.6 7.9 1.4 7.9
17 TU	0635 1149 1903	1.7 7.9 1.4
18 W	0021 0718 1232 1944	7.8 1.9 7.8 1.6
19 TH	0105 0759 1314 2024	7.6 2.1 7.6 1.8
20 F	0148 0839 1356 2103	7.4 2.3 7.3 2.2
21 SA	0232 0919 1440 2143	7.1 2.6 7.1 2.5
22 SU ☾	0320 1001 1529 2224	6.9 2.9 6.8 2.8
23 M	0412 1047 1626 2311	6.7 3.2 6.6 3.0
24 TU	0509 1138 1728	6.6 3.3 6.5
25 W	0004 0607 1237 1830	3.2 6.6 3.3 6.4
26 TH	0106 0705 1348 1932	3.2 6.7 3.2 6.6
27 F	0220 0801 1456 2029	3.1 6.9 2.9 6.8
28 SA	0321 0850 1549 2118	2.8 7.1 2.6 7.0
29 SU	0409 0934 1633 2201	2.5 7.3 2.3 7.3
30 M ●	0452 1014 1715 2242	2.3 7.5 2.0 7.4
31 TU	0533 1053 1757 2321	2.1 7.6 1.8 7.6

CHERBOURG
LAT 49°39′N
LONG 1°38′W

TIMES AND HEIGHTS OF HIGH AND LOW WATER (Heights in Metres)

TIME ZONE
European Standard Time (UT+0100)
For Summer Time (area enclosed in shaded box) add 1 hour

2024

JANUARY

Day	Time	m	Time	m	Time	m	Time	m
1 M	0621	2.2	1153	5.7	1847	2.0		
2 TU	0024	5.4	0658	2.4	1229	5.5	1923	2.2
3 W	0102	5.3	0738	2.6	1309	5.3	2004	2.4
4 TH ☽	0146	5.1	0825	2.8	1356	5.1	2052	2.6
5 F	0239	5.0	0922	2.9	1455	5.0	2152	2.7
6 SA	0343	5.0	1030	2.9	1604	4.9	2303	2.7
7 SU	0453	5.1	1142	2.7	1719	5.1		
8 M	0011	2.5	0559	5.3	1245	2.4	1827	5.3
9 TU	0110	2.3	0655	5.6	1340	2.1	1923	5.6
10 W	0203	2.0	0744	5.9	1432	1.7	2013	5.9
11 TH ●	0254	1.8	0830	6.2	1522	1.4	2101	6.1
12 F	0343	1.5	0917	6.4	1611	1.1	2149	6.3
13 SA	0431	1.4	1003	6.6	1659	1.0	2236	6.4
14 SU	0518	1.3	1050	6.6	1745	0.9	2322	6.3
15 M	0604	1.3	1137	6.6	1831	1.0		
16 TU	0009	6.2	0651	1.5	1224	6.4	1917	1.2
17 W	0055	6.0	0738	1.7	1311	6.1	2004	1.6
18 TH ☾	0143	5.7	0829	2.1	1402	5.7	2056	2.0
19 F	0238	5.4	0928	2.3	1504	5.4	2158	2.3
20 SA	0346	5.2	1041	2.5	1621	5.1	2313	2.5
21 SU	0502	5.2	1200	2.5	1742	5.1		
22 M	0027	2.5	0612	5.3	1309	2.3	1853	5.3
23 TU	0131	2.3	0711	5.5	1407	2.0	1949	5.5
24 W	0224	2.1	0800	5.8	1455	1.8	2035	5.7
25 TH ○	0308	1.9	0842	6.0	1536	1.6	2113	5.9
26 F	0347	1.8	0918	6.1	1613	1.5	2148	6.0
27 SA	0423	1.7	0953	6.2	1647	1.4	2220	6.0
28 SU	0456	1.7	1026	6.2	1719	1.4	2251	6.0
29 M	0527	1.7	1057	6.1	1749	1.5	2322	5.9
30 TU	0557	1.8	1127	6.0	1818	1.6	2351	5.7
31 W	0627	1.9	1157	5.8	1847	1.8		

FEBRUARY

Day	Time	m	Time	m	Time	m	Time	m
1 TH	0020	5.6	0658	2.1	1227	5.6	1918	2.1
2 F	0052	5.4	0734	2.4	1302	5.3	1955	2.4
3 SA ☽	0132	5.2	0819	2.6	1348	5.0	2044	2.7
4 SU	0226	5.0	0921	2.8	1454	4.8	2154	2.9
5 M	0344	4.8	1045	2.9	1628	4.8	2327	2.8
6 TU	0521	5.0	1212	2.6	1805	5.0		
7 W	0047	2.5	0634	5.3	1321	2.2	1910	5.4
8 TH	0150	2.1	0730	5.8	1420	1.7	2004	5.8
9 F ●	0245	1.7	0820	6.2	1513	1.2	2054	6.2
10 SA	0336	1.3	0909	6.6	1602	0.8	2141	6.5
11 SU	0423	1.0	0956	6.8	1649	0.6	2226	6.6
12 M	0508	0.9	1041	6.9	1732	0.5	2309	6.6
13 TU	0550	0.9	1124	6.8	1813	0.6	2349	6.5
14 W	0632	1.1	1205	6.6	1853	1.0		
15 TH	0028	6.2	0713	1.4	1245	6.2	1934	1.5
16 F ☾	0106	5.8	0757	1.9	1327	5.7	2018	2.0
17 SA	0150	5.4	0849	2.3	1422	5.1	2114	2.5
18 SU	0254	5.0	1001	2.7	1546	4.8	2237	2.9
19 M	0429	4.8	1137	2.7	1736	4.8		
20 TU	0012	2.8	0601	5.0	1301	2.5	1854	5.0
21 W	0125	2.5	0707	5.3	1401	2.1	1946	5.4
22 TH	0218	2.2	0753	5.6	1446	1.8	2024	5.7
23 F	0259	1.9	0830	5.9	1522	1.5	2058	5.9
24 SA ○	0334	1.7	0904	6.1	1555	1.3	2128	6.0
25 SU	0405	1.5	0935	6.2	1625	1.2	2157	6.1
26 M	0434	1.4	1004	6.3	1654	1.2	2225	6.1
27 TU	0502	1.4	1032	6.3	1721	1.3	2252	6.1
28 W	0530	1.5	1059	6.2	1747	1.4	2318	6.0
29 TH	0557	1.6	1126	6.0	1813	1.6	2345	5.8

MARCH

Day	Time	m	Time	m	Time	m	Time	m
1 F	0625	1.8	1154	5.7	1840	1.9		
2 SA	0012	5.6	0657	2.1	1223	5.4	1913	2.3
3 SU ☽	0043	5.3	0736	2.4	1302	5.1	1956	2.6
4 M	0130	5.0	0833	2.7	1404	4.7	2105	3.0
5 TU	0250	4.7	1003	2.9	1559	4.6	2256	3.0
6 W	0455	4.8	1148	2.6	1754	4.9		
7 TH	0031	2.6	0618	5.2	1305	2.1	1858	5.4
8 F	0137	2.1	0715	5.8	1405	1.5	1950	5.9
9 SA	0232	1.5	0806	6.3	1457	1.0	2038	6.4
10 SU ●	0321	1.1	0853	6.7	1545	0.6	2123	6.7
11 M	0406	0.7	0939	7.0	1629	0.4	2206	6.8
12 TU	0448	0.6	1022	7.0	1710	0.4	2246	6.8
13 W	0529	0.7	1103	6.9	1749	0.6	2323	6.6
14 TH	0608	0.9	1141	6.5	1826	1.0	2358	6.2
15 F	0647	1.3	1218	6.1	1903	1.6		
16 SA	0032	5.8	0727	1.8	1258	5.5	1944	2.2
17 SU ☾	0112	5.3	0816	2.4	1350	4.9	2038	2.8
18 M	0212	4.9	0927	2.8	1522	4.5	2207	3.1
19 TU	0357	4.6	1115	2.8	1731	4.6	2356	3.0
20 W	0547	4.8	1242	2.5	1843	5.0		
21 TH	0109	2.6	0649	5.1	1339	2.1	1925	5.3
22 F	0158	2.2	0731	5.5	1420	1.8	1959	5.7
23 SA	0236	1.9	0806	5.8	1455	1.5	2030	5.9
24 SU	0308	1.6	0838	6.0	1526	1.3	2059	6.1
25 M ○	0338	1.5	0908	6.2	1555	1.2	2128	6.2
26 TU	0406	1.3	0937	6.3	1623	1.2	2155	6.2
27 W	0434	1.3	1004	6.3	1650	1.3	2221	6.2
28 TH	0502	1.4	1031	6.2	1716	1.4	2247	6.1
29 F	0529	1.5	1059	6.0	1743	1.6	2315	5.9
30 SA	0558	1.7	1129	5.8	1811	1.9	2343	5.7
31 SU	0631	2.0	1200	5.4	1845	2.3		

APRIL

Day	Time	m	Time	m	Time	m	Time	m
1 M	0016	5.4	0712	2.3	1242	5.1	1931	2.7
2 TU ☽	0105	5.0	0810	2.6	1349	4.7	2046	3.0
3 W	0229	4.7	0944	2.8	1556	4.6	2241	3.0
4 TH	0436	4.8	1128	2.5	1738	5.0		
5 F	0012	2.5	0556	5.3	1243	1.9	1838	5.5
6 SA	0116	2.0	0654	5.8	1342	1.4	1927	6.0
7 SU	0209	1.4	0743	6.3	1433	0.9	2014	6.4
8 M ●	0257	1.0	0830	6.7	1520	0.6	2058	6.7
9 TU	0342	0.7	0915	6.9	1603	0.5	2139	6.8
10 W	0425	0.6	0958	6.9	1644	0.6	2218	6.7
11 TH	0505	0.7	1039	6.7	1722	0.9	2255	6.5
12 F	0544	1.0	1117	6.3	1759	1.3	2329	6.2
13 SA	0623	1.4	1156	5.9	1836	1.8		
14 SU	0005	5.8	0703	1.9	1237	5.3	1918	2.4
15 M ☾	0046	5.3	0751	2.4	1331	4.9	2012	2.9
16 TU	0145	4.9	0859	2.7	1458	4.6	2138	3.1
17 W	0321	4.6	1037	2.8	1654	4.6	2319	3.0
18 TH	0502	4.7	1158	2.6	1802	4.9		
19 F	0028	2.7	0607	5.0	1255	2.3	1844	5.3
20 SA	0117	2.3	0651	5.4	1338	1.9	1919	5.6
21 SU	0157	2.0	0728	5.6	1415	1.7	1952	5.8
22 M	0232	1.8	0803	5.9	1449	1.5	2024	6.0
23 TU	0303	1.6	0836	6.0	1519	1.4	2054	6.1
24 W ○	0334	1.4	0906	6.1	1549	1.4	2123	6.2
25 TH	0404	1.4	0936	6.1	1619	1.4	2151	6.2
26 F	0436	1.4	1006	6.1	1649	1.5	2221	6.1
27 SA	0507	1.5	1039	5.9	1720	1.7	2253	6.0
28 SU	0540	1.7	1114	5.7	1753	2.0	2329	5.7
29 M	0618	1.9	1154	5.4	1833	2.3		
30 TU	0011	5.5	0705	2.2	1244	5.1	1928	2.6

MAY

Day	Time	m	Time	m	Time	m	Time	m
1 W ☾	0106	5.2	0809	2.4	1355	4.9	2047	2.8
2 TH	0227	5.0	0934	2.5	1543	4.9	2223	2.8
3 F	0410	5.1	1102	2.2	1708	5.2	2343	2.4
4 SA	0524	5.4	1213	1.8	1807	5.6		
5 SU	0046	1.9	0622	5.8	1311	1.4	1857	6.0
6 M	0140	1.5	0714	6.2	1404	1.1	1944	6.3
7 TU	0230	1.2	0803	6.4	1452	0.9	2029	6.5
8 W ●	0317	1.0	0850	6.5	1536	0.9	2111	6.5
9 TH	0401	0.9	0934	6.5	1618	1.0	2150	6.5
10 F	0443	1.0	1017	6.3	1658	1.3	2229	6.3
11 SA	0523	1.2	1058	6.0	1736	1.6	2306	6.1
12 SU	0603	1.5	1139	5.7	1815	2.0	2345	5.7
13 M	0645	1.9	1223	5.3	1859	2.4		
14 TU	0029	5.4	0731	2.3	1315	5.0	1951	2.8
15 W ☽	0124	5.0	0829	2.5	1422	4.7	2059	3.0
16 TH	0235	4.8	0941	2.7	1543	4.7	2219	3.0
17 F	0353	4.8	1055	2.6	1656	4.9	2327	2.8
18 SA	0502	4.9	1155	2.4	1749	5.1		
19 SU	0022	2.5	0556	5.1	1245	2.2	1830	5.4
20 M	0108	2.3	0641	5.4	1328	2.0	1909	5.6
21 TU	0148	2.0	0722	5.6	1406	1.8	1945	5.8
22 W	0225	1.8	0800	5.8	1442	1.7	2020	6.0
23 TH ○	0301	1.6	0836	5.9	1517	1.7	2053	6.0
24 F	0337	1.5	0912	5.9	1553	1.6	2126	6.1
25 SA	0414	1.5	0948	5.9	1629	1.7	2202	6.1
26 SU	0452	1.5	1026	5.9	1707	1.8	2241	6.0
27 M	0532	1.6	1108	5.7	1748	2.0	2324	5.9
28 TU	0617	1.7	1155	5.6	1836	2.2		
29 W	0012	5.7	0708	1.9	1248	5.3	1933	2.4
30 TH ☾	0108	5.5	0808	2.0	1354	5.2	2041	2.5
31 F	0217	5.3	0917	2.1	1513	5.2	2155	2.5

JUNE

Day	Time	m	Time	m	Time	m	Time	m
1 SA	0335	5.3	1029	2.0	1627	5.3	2307	2.3
2 SU	0446	5.5	1137	1.9	1729	5.5		
3 M	0012	2.0	0549	5.7	1238	1.7	1824	5.8
4 TU	0110	1.7	0646	5.9	1334	1.5	1915	6.0
5 W	0204	1.5	0739	6.0	1425	1.4	2002	6.2
6 TH ●	0255	1.4	0830	6.1	1513	1.4	2047	6.2
7 F	0341	1.3	0917	6.1	1557	1.5	2129	6.2
8 SA	0425	1.3	1001	6.0	1639	1.6	2209	6.1
9 SU	0507	1.4	1043	5.9	1719	1.8	2250	6.0
10 M	0547	1.6	1124	5.7	1759	2.0	2330	5.8
11 TU	0627	1.8	1206	5.5	1840	2.3		
12 W	0012	5.6	0708	2.0	1249	5.2	1924	2.5
13 TH	0056	5.3	0752	2.3	1336	5.0	2012	2.7
14 F ☽	0145	5.1	0841	2.5	1429	4.9	2109	2.8
15 SA	0240	4.9	0938	2.6	1528	4.9	2211	2.8
16 SU	0341	4.9	1040	2.6	1630	4.9	2315	2.7
17 M	0444	4.9	1141	2.5	1729	5.1		
18 TU	0012	2.5	0545	5.1	1235	2.4	1820	5.3
19 W	0102	2.3	0639	5.3	1323	2.2	1906	5.6
20 TH	0148	2.1	0727	5.5	1408	2.0	1949	5.8
21 F	0232	1.8	0812	5.7	1451	1.9	2029	5.9
22 SA ○	0316	1.6	0854	5.8	1534	1.8	2109	6.1
23 SU	0400	1.5	0937	5.9	1618	1.7	2151	6.2
24 M	0444	1.4	1020	5.9	1702	1.7	2234	6.2
25 TU	0529	1.4	1106	5.9	1748	1.7	2320	6.2
26 W	0616	1.4	1153	5.9	1836	1.8		
27 TH	0009	6.0	0704	1.5	1243	5.7	1927	1.9
28 F ☾	0100	5.9	0755	1.6	1336	5.6	2022	2.1
29 SA	0155	5.7	0850	1.8	1435	5.4	2123	2.2
30 SU	0257	5.5	0952	2.0	1541	5.4	2230	2.3

SUNRISE AND SUNSET TIMES

CHERBOURG
At 49°39′N 1°38′W
European Standard Time (UT+0100)

		Sunrise	Sunset
Jan	01	0903	1717
	15	0858	1735
Feb	01	0839	1802
	15	0816	1826
Mar	01	0749	1849
	15	0720	1912
European Summer Time (UT+0200)			
Apr	01	0744	2038
	15	0714	2100
May	01	0644	2124
	15	0622	2145
Jun	01	0604	2205
	15	0559	2216
Jul	01	0603	2217
	15	0616	2209
Aug	01	0637	2148
	15	0657	2124
Sep	01	0722	2050
	15	0743	2020
Oct	01	0806	1945
	15	0828	1916
European Standard Time (UT+0100)			
Nov	01	0755	1744
	15	0818	1724

CHERBOURG
LAT 49°39′N
LONG 1°38′W

TIMES AND HEIGHTS OF HIGH AND LOW WATER (Heights in Metres)

TIME ZONE
European Standard Time (UT+0100)
For Summer Time (area enclosed in shaded box) add 1 hour

2024

JULY

Day	Time	m	Time	m	Time	m	Time	m
1 M	0407	5.4	1100	2.1	1650	5.4	2340	2.2
2 TU	0518	5.4	1208	2.1	1755	5.5		
3 W	0046	2.1	0625	5.5	1311	2.0	1853	5.7
4 TH	0146	1.9	0726	5.6	1407	1.9	1946	5.8
5 F	0240	1.7	0820	5.7	1458	1.8	● 2033	6.0
6 SA	0329	1.5	0908	5.8	1544	1.8	2116	6.1
7 SU	0413	1.5	0950	5.9	1626	1.8	2156	6.1
8 M	0453	1.4	1029	5.9	1704	1.8	2234	6.1
9 TU	0530	1.5	1106	5.8	1741	1.9	2311	6.0
10 W	0605	1.6	1141	5.7	1815	2.0	2347	5.8
11 TH	0638	1.8	1216	5.5	1850	2.2		
12 F	0021	5.6	0712	2.0	1250	5.4	1926	2.4
13 SA	0056	5.4	0747	2.2	1326	5.2	☽ 2007	2.6
14 SU	0136	5.2	0828	2.5	1409	5.0	2056	2.7
15 M	0224	5.0	0919	2.7	1504	4.9	2157	2.8
16 TU	0326	4.8	1025	2.8	1612	4.9	2311	2.8
17 W	0441	4.8	1140	2.7	1729	5.1		
18 TH	0019	2.6	0600	5.0	1246	2.6	1833	5.3
19 F	0118	2.3	0702	5.3	1343	2.3	1925	5.6
20 SA	0211	1.9	0755	5.6	1434	2.0	2012	5.9
21 SU	0301	1.6	0842	5.8	1523	1.8	○ 2058	6.2
22 M	0349	1.3	0929	6.1	1610	1.5	2142	6.4
23 TU	0436	1.1	1014	6.2	1655	1.4	2227	6.5
24 W	0521	1.0	1058	6.3	1740	1.3	2312	6.5
25 TH	0605	1.0	1142	6.2	1824	1.4	2357	6.5
26 F	0648	1.1	1225	6.1	1908	1.6		
27 SA	0041	6.2	0732	1.4	1308	5.9	1956	1.8
28 SU	0127	5.9	0819	1.8	1356	5.6	☾ 2049	2.2
29 M	0220	5.5	0915	2.2	1455	5.3	2155	2.4
30 TU	0331	5.2	1025	2.5	1613	5.2	2315	2.5
31 W	0457	5.0	1146	2.6	1734	5.2		

AUGUST

Day	Time	m	Time	m	Time	m	Time	m
1 TH	0033	2.4	0620	5.1	1259	2.4	1843	5.4
2 F	0139	2.1	0725	5.4	1401	2.2	1940	5.7
3 SA	0234	1.8	0817	5.6	1451	2.0	2026	5.9
4 SU	0320	1.6	0900	5.8	1534	1.8	● 2105	6.1
5 M	0359	1.5	0935	5.9	1611	1.7	2140	6.2
6 TU	0434	1.4	1008	6.0	1644	1.6	2214	6.2
7 W	0506	1.4	1039	6.0	1716	1.7	2246	6.2
8 TH	0536	1.4	1110	5.9	1745	1.7	2316	6.1
9 F	0604	1.6	1138	5.8	1813	1.9	2344	5.9
10 SA	0631	1.8	1205	5.7	1843	2.1		
11 SU	0012	5.7	0659	2.1	1234	5.5	1915	2.3
12 M	0044	5.4	0732	2.4	1309	5.2	☽ 1956	2.6
13 TU	0125	5.1	0813	2.7	1356	5.0	2051	2.9
14 W	0223	4.8	0915	3.0	1506	4.8	2212	3.0
15 TH	0350	4.7	1051	3.0	1645	4.9	2345	2.8
16 F	0537	4.8	1221	2.8	1810	5.2		
17 SA	0057	2.4	0647	5.2	1326	2.4	1908	5.6
18 SU	0154	1.9	0740	5.7	1420	2.0	1957	6.0
19 M	0246	1.4	0828	6.1	1510	1.5	○ 2043	6.4
20 TU	0335	1.0	0914	6.4	1556	1.2	2129	6.7
21 W	0420	0.8	0958	6.6	1640	1.0	2213	6.9
22 TH	0503	0.6	1041	6.6	1722	1.0	2255	6.9
23 F	0544	0.7	1121	6.6	1803	1.1	2337	6.7
24 SA	0624	0.9	1200	6.3	1844	1.3		
25 SU	0017	6.4	0705	1.4	1238	6.0	1928	1.8
26 M	0059	5.9	0748	1.9	1320	5.6	☾ 2018	2.2
27 TU	0149	5.4	0840	2.5	1416	5.2	2125	2.6
28 W	0304	4.9	0957	2.9	1545	4.9	2300	2.8
29 TH	0453	4.8	1137	2.9	1726	5.0		
30 F	0029	2.5	0624	5.0	1258	2.7	1841	5.3
31 SA	0135	2.2	0723	5.4	1356	2.3	1933	5.7

SEPTEMBER

Day	Time	m	Time	m	Time	m	Time	m
1 SU	0223	1.8	0805	5.7	1440	2.0	2012	6.0
2 M	0303	1.6	0840	6.0	1516	1.7	2046	6.2
3 TU	0336	1.4	0911	6.1	1548	1.6	● 2117	6.3
4 W	0407	1.3	0940	6.2	1618	1.5	2147	6.4
5 TH	0436	1.3	1008	6.2	1646	1.5	2215	6.3
6 F	0503	1.4	1035	6.2	1712	1.6	2242	6.2
7 SA	0528	1.5	1100	6.1	1739	1.7	2308	6.1
8 SU	0553	1.7	1126	5.9	1806	1.9	2335	5.8
9 M	0619	2.0	1152	5.7	1835	2.2		
10 TU	0004	5.5	0648	2.4	1222	5.4	1912	2.5
11 W	0041	5.2	0727	2.7	1305	5.1	☽ 2003	2.8
12 TH	0139	4.8	0827	3.1	1418	4.8	2128	3.0
13 F	0322	4.6	1017	3.2	1619	4.8	2320	2.9
14 SA	0525	4.9	1203	2.9	1751	5.2		
15 SU	0037	2.4	0630	5.3	1309	2.3	1848	5.7
16 M	0135	1.8	0720	5.9	1401	1.8	1936	6.2
17 TU	0225	1.2	0807	6.3	1449	1.3	2022	6.7
18 W	0312	0.8	0851	6.6	1534	1.0	○ 2107	7.0
19 TH	0357	0.6	0934	6.8	1617	0.8	2151	7.1
20 F	0439	0.5	1015	6.8	1659	0.8	2233	7.0
21 SA	0519	0.7	1054	6.7	1740	1.0	2313	6.7
22 SU	0558	1.1	1131	6.4	1820	1.3	2353	6.3
23 M	0637	1.6	1208	6.1	1903	1.8		
24 TU	0035	5.8	0720	2.2	1249	5.6	☾ 1952	2.3
25 W	0127	5.2	0813	2.8	1347	5.1	2103	2.8
26 TH	0250	4.8	0938	3.1	1524	4.8	2248	2.9
27 F	0453	4.8	1129	3.1	1716	4.9		
28 SA	0016	2.6	0614	5.1	1243	2.7	1825	5.3
29 SU	0114	2.2	0701	5.5	1334	2.3	1909	5.7
30 M	0157	1.9	0736	5.8	1414	2.0	1945	6.0

OCTOBER

Day	Time	m	Time	m	Time	m	Time	m
1 TU	0233	1.6	0809	6.0	1447	1.7	2018	6.2
2 W	0305	1.5	0838	6.2	1518	1.6	● 2048	6.3
3 TH	0334	1.4	0907	6.3	1547	1.5	2117	6.4
4 F	0402	1.4	0934	6.3	1614	1.5	2145	6.4
5 SA	0429	1.4	1000	6.3	1642	1.5	2211	6.3
6 SU	0456	1.6	1026	6.2	1709	1.7	2238	6.1
7 M	0522	1.8	1053	6.0	1737	1.9	2307	5.9
8 TU	0549	2.1	1121	5.8	1808	2.1	2339	5.5
9 W	0620	2.4	1154	5.5	1846	2.5		
10 TH	0019	5.2	0702	2.8	1239	5.2	☽ 1940	2.8
11 F	0122	4.9	0808	3.1	1356	4.9	2107	2.9
12 SA	0312	4.7	0959	3.2	1557	4.9	2255	2.7
13 SU	0504	5.0	1139	2.8	1725	5.3		
14 M	0011	2.2	0605	5.5	1243	2.3	1821	5.8
15 TU	0108	1.7	0653	6.0	1335	1.7	1910	6.3
16 W	0158	1.2	0739	6.4	1423	1.3	1957	6.7
17 TH	0245	0.8	0823	6.7	1509	1.0	○ 2042	7.0
18 F	0330	0.7	0906	6.9	1553	0.8	2127	7.0
19 SA	0413	0.7	0947	6.9	1636	0.9	2210	6.9
20 SU	0454	1.0	1027	6.7	1718	1.1	2252	6.6
21 M	0534	1.4	1105	6.4	1759	1.4	2334	6.1
22 TU	0614	1.9	1144	6.0	1843	1.9		
23 W	0018	5.6	0658	2.4	1229	5.6	1934	2.4
24 TH	0114	5.1	0754	2.9	1328	5.1	☾ 2041	2.7
25 F	0235	4.8	0916	3.2	1457	4.9	2215	2.9
26 SA	0421	4.8	1055	3.1	1634	4.9	2336	2.7
27 SU	0533	5.1	1205	2.8	1743	5.2		
28 M	0032	2.4	0620	5.4	1255	2.4	1830	5.5
29 TU	0116	2.1	0657	5.7	1336	2.1	1908	5.8
30 W	0154	1.8	0731	6.0	1412	1.9	1944	6.0
31 TH	0228	1.7	0803	6.1	1444	1.7	2017	6.2

NOVEMBER

Day	Time	m	Time	m	Time	m	Time	m
1 F	0259	1.6	0834	6.2	1515	1.6	● 2048	6.2
2 SA	0329	1.6	0903	6.3	1546	1.6	2117	6.2
3 SU	0359	1.6	0930	6.3	1616	1.6	2146	6.2
4 M	0429	1.7	0959	6.2	1648	1.7	2218	6.0
5 TU	0459	1.9	1031	6.1	1720	1.8	2252	5.8
6 W	0532	2.2	1106	5.9	1756	2.1	2331	5.6
7 TH	0609	2.4	1146	5.6	1839	2.3		
8 F	0019	5.3	0658	2.7	1238	5.3	1937	2.5
9 SA	0123	5.0	0807	3.0	1350	5.1	☽ 2054	2.6
10 SU	0255	5.0	0938	3.0	1526	5.1	2221	2.5
11 M	0427	5.2	1103	2.7	1647	5.4	2335	2.1
12 TU	0530	5.6	1209	2.2	1748	5.8		
13 W	0035	1.7	0622	6.0	1305	1.8	1841	6.2
14 TH	0129	1.3	0710	6.4	1356	1.4	1931	6.5
15 F	0218	1.1	0756	6.6	1445	1.2	○ 2019	6.7
16 SA	0305	1.0	0840	6.7	1532	1.0	2106	6.7
17 SU	0350	1.1	0923	6.7	1617	1.1	2152	6.6
18 M	0433	1.3	1005	6.6	1701	1.2	2236	6.3
19 TU	0515	1.6	1046	6.3	1744	1.5	2321	6.0
20 W	0558	2.0	1129	6.0	1829	1.8		
21 TH	0007	5.6	0643	2.4	1215	5.7	1917	2.2
22 F	0100	5.3	0734	2.7	1309	5.3	2012	2.5
23 SA	0202	5.0	0837	3.0	1415	5.1	☾ 2119	2.7
24 SU	0314	4.9	0953	3.0	1529	5.0	2232	2.7
25 M	0426	5.0	1104	2.9	1639	5.1	2334	2.6
26 TU	0526	5.2	1202	2.7	1737	5.2		
27 W	0026	2.4	0610	5.5	1250	2.4	1825	5.5
28 TH	0110	2.2	0651	5.7	1333	2.2	1907	5.7
29 F	0150	2.0	0728	5.9	1411	2.0	1946	5.8
30 SA	0226	1.9	0804	6.1	1447	1.8	2023	6.0

DECEMBER

Day	Time	m	Time	m	Time	m	Time	m
1 SU	0301	1.8	0837	6.1	1522	1.7	● 2057	6.0
2 M	0336	1.8	0910	6.2	1558	1.6	2131	6.0
3 TU	0412	1.8	0943	6.2	1635	1.6	2208	6.0
4 W	0449	1.9	1020	6.1	1714	1.7	2247	5.9
5 TH	0527	2.1	1101	6.0	1755	1.8	2331	5.7
6 F	0610	2.2	1146	5.9	1840	2.0		
7 SA	0019	5.5	0701	2.4	1237	5.7	1934	2.1
8 SU	0116	5.4	0800	2.5	1337	5.5	☽ 2035	2.2
9 M	0225	5.3	0908	2.6	1448	5.4	2144	2.2
10 TU	0341	5.3	1021	2.5	1603	5.5	2255	2.1
11 W	0450	5.5	1132	2.3	1712	5.7		
12 TH	0001	1.9	0549	5.8	1235	2.0	1814	5.9
13 F	0101	1.7	0644	6.0	1334	1.7	1910	6.1
14 SA	0156	1.6	0734	6.3	1428	1.5	2004	6.2
15 SU	0247	1.5	0822	6.4	1518	1.3	○ 2055	6.3
16 M	0335	1.5	0908	6.4	1606	1.2	2142	6.2
17 TU	0421	1.6	0952	6.4	1651	1.3	2227	6.1
18 W	0504	1.7	1035	6.3	1734	1.4	2310	6.0
19 TH	0545	1.9	1117	6.1	1815	1.6	2352	5.8
20 F	0626	2.1	1159	5.9	1855	1.9		
21 SA	0035	5.5	0708	2.4	1242	5.6	1936	2.2
22 SU	0119	5.3	0752	2.6	1327	5.3	☾ 2021	2.4
23 M	0207	5.1	0843	2.8	1418	5.1	2112	2.6
24 TU	0302	5.0	0942	2.9	1516	4.9	2214	2.7
25 W	0405	5.0	1050	2.9	1624	4.9	2320	2.7
26 TH	0510	5.1	1155	2.8	1732	5.0		
27 F	0021	2.6	0607	5.3	1251	2.5	1831	5.2
28 SA	0113	2.4	0655	5.5	1339	2.3	1920	5.5
29 SU	0158	2.2	0739	5.8	1423	2.0	2004	5.7
30 M	0241	2.0	0819	6.0	1505	1.8	● 2044	5.8
31 TU	0322	1.9	0857	6.1	1547	1.6	2124	6.0

ST PETER PORT
LAT 49°27′N
LONG 2°31′W

TIMES AND HEIGHTS OF HIGH AND LOW WATER (Heights in Metres)

TIME ZONE UT
For Summer Time (area enclosed in shaded box) add 1 hour

2024

JANUARY

Date	Day	Time	m	Time	m	Time	m	Time	m
1	M	0330	2.8	0931	8.1	1557	2.8	2156	7.6
2	TU	0404	3.1	1006	7.7	1631	3.1	2232	7.3
3	W	0441	3.4	1045	7.4	1710	3.4	2314	7.1
4	TH ☽	0527	3.7	1132	7.1	1758	3.6		
5	F	0006	6.9	0627	3.9	1231	6.9	1901	3.8
6	SA	0114	6.8	0739	3.9	1342	6.9	2013	3.7
7	**SU**	0228	7.0	0852	3.7	1454	7.1	2122	3.5
8	M	0333	7.4	0956	3.3	1558	7.5	2223	3.1
9	TU	0430	7.8	1054	2.8	1655	7.9	2318	2.6
10	W	0521	8.3	1148	2.2	1748	8.3		
11	TH ●	0009	2.2	0611	8.8	1238	1.8	1838	8.7
12	F	0059	1.8	0658	9.2	1328	1.4	1927	9.0
13	SA	0146	1.5	0745	9.4	1415	1.1	2013	9.2
14	**SU**	0231	1.4	0830	9.5	1500	1.1	2057	9.2
15	M	0315	1.4	0915	9.4	1544	1.2	2141	9.0
16	TU	0359	1.7	1000	9.1	1628	1.5	2225	8.6
17	W	0444	2.1	1046	8.7	1713	2.0	2312	8.1
18	TH ☾	0532	2.6	1137	8.1	1803	2.6		
19	F	0004	7.6	0630	3.1	1236	7.6	1903	3.1
20	SA	0111	7.2	0742	3.4	1352	7.2	2018	3.4
21	**SU**	0233	7.1	0908	3.5	1514	7.1	2138	3.4
22	M	0348	7.3	1023	3.3	1623	7.3	2245	3.2
23	TU	0447	7.7	1121	2.9	1718	7.7	2338	2.8
24	W	0536	8.1	1209	2.5	1805	8.0		
25	TH ○	0023	2.5	0619	8.5	1251	2.2	1847	8.3
26	F	0103	2.2	0659	8.7	1330	1.9	1925	8.5
27	SA	0140	2.0	0735	8.8	1405	1.8	2000	8.6
28	**SU**	0213	2.0	0809	8.8	1437	1.9	2032	8.5
29	M	0243	2.0	0840	8.7	1505	2.0	2101	8.4
30	TU	0311	2.2	0909	8.5	1532	2.2	2129	8.1
31	W	0338	2.5	0938	8.2	1557	2.5	2156	7.8

FEBRUARY

Date	Day	Time	m	Time	m	Time	m	Time	m
1	TH	0406	2.8	1007	7.9	1625	2.9	2226	7.5
2	F ☽	0437	3.2	1041	7.5	1659	3.3	2303	7.2
3	SA	0519	3.5	1126	7.1	1745	3.6	2355	6.9
4	**SU**	0620	3.8	1230	6.8	1855	3.9		
5	M	0112	6.7	0752	3.9	1400	6.7	2032	3.8
6	TU	0250	6.9	0923	3.5	1530	7.0	2157	3.4
7	W	0407	7.5	1036	2.9	1641	7.6	2304	2.8
8	TH	0508	8.1	1137	2.2	1739	8.2		
9	F ●	0000	2.1	0601	8.8	1230	1.5	1831	8.8
10	SA	0051	1.5	0649	9.4	1319	0.9	1917	9.3
11	**SU**	0137	1.0	0735	9.9	1404	0.5	2001	9.7
12	M	0221	0.7	0818	10.1	1446	0.4	2042	9.7
13	TU	0302	0.7	0859	10.0	1526	0.6	2121	9.5
14	W	0340	1.0	0939	9.6	1604	1.0	2159	9.0
15	TH	0418	1.5	1018	8.9	1641	1.8	2237	8.4
16	F ☾	0457	2.3	1100	8.1	1722	2.6	2319	7.6
17	SA	0544	3.1	1150	7.3	1812	3.4		
18	**SU**	0015	7.0	0651	3.7	1309	6.6	1928	4.0
19	M	0153	6.6	0842	4.0	1502	6.5	2121	4.0
20	TU	0335	6.8	1018	3.6	1618	6.9	2238	3.6
21	W	0438	7.3	1114	3.1	1710	7.4	2329	3.0
22	TH	0524	7.9	1158	2.5	1752	7.9		
23	F	0010	2.5	0605	8.4	1236	2.1	1830	8.3
24	SA ○	0047	2.1	0641	8.7	1311	1.7	1905	8.7
25	**SU**	0121	1.7	0716	9.0	1343	1.5	1937	8.8
26	M	0152	1.6	0747	9.1	1412	1.5	2007	8.9
27	TU	0220	1.6	0817	9.0	1438	1.6	2035	8.7
28	W	0246	1.7	0843	8.8	1502	1.9	2059	8.5
29	TH	0310	2.0	0909	8.5	1525	2.2	2123	8.2

MARCH

Date	Day	Time	m	Time	m	Time	m	Time	m
1	F	0334	2.4	0934	8.1	1549	2.6	2148	7.9
2	SA	0401	2.8	1004	7.7	1618	3.0	2220	7.5
3	**SU** ☽	0436	3.2	1043	7.2	1659	3.5	2305	7.0
4	M	0530	3.7	1144	6.8	1803	3.9		
5	TU	0020	6.7	0705	3.9	1321	6.5	1955	4.0
6	W	0216	6.7	0902	3.6	1515	6.8	2140	3.6
7	TH	0351	7.3	1022	2.9	1630	7.6	2251	2.7
8	F	0454	8.2	1122	2.0	1726	8.4	2346	1.9
9	SA	0545	9.0	1214	1.2	1814	9.1		
10	**SU** ●	0034	1.1	0632	9.7	1300	0.5	1859	9.6
11	M	0119	0.6	0716	10.1	1343	0.1	1940	10.0
12	TU	0201	0.3	0758	10.3	1423	0.1	2019	10.0
13	W	0240	0.3	0837	10.1	1501	0.4	2056	9.7
14	TH	0316	0.7	0914	9.6	1536	1.0	2130	9.2
15	F	0351	1.4	0950	8.8	1610	1.8	2204	8.4
16	SA	0427	2.2	1028	7.9	1646	2.7	2240	7.6
17	**SU** ☾	0508	3.1	1112	7.0	1731	3.6	2328	6.8
18	M	0612	3.9	1231	6.3	1847	4.3		
19	TU	0110	6.3	0819	4.2	1448	6.2	2104	4.3
20	W	0316	6.5	1002	3.7	1601	6.7	2220	3.7
21	TH	0417	7.1	1052	3.1	1648	7.3	2306	3.1
22	F	0501	7.7	1132	2.5	1726	7.9	2345	2.5
23	SA	0538	8.3	1208	2.0	1802	8.4		
24	**SU**	0020	2.0	0614	8.7	1241	1.7	1836	8.7
25	M ○	0053	1.6	0648	9.0	1313	1.5	1908	8.9
26	TU	0123	1.5	0719	9.1	1341	1.4	1938	9.0
27	W	0151	1.4	0749	9.0	1407	1.5	2005	8.9
28	TH	0218	1.6	0815	8.9	1431	1.7	2029	8.7
29	F	0243	1.8	0841	8.6	1455	2.1	2053	8.4
30	SA	0308	2.2	0908	8.2	1521	2.5	2120	8.1
31	**SU**	0336	2.6	0939	7.8	1551	2.9	2154	7.6

APRIL

Date	Day	Time	m	Time	m	Time	m	Time	m
1	M	0413	3.1	1021	7.3	1633	3.4	2242	7.2
2	TU ☽	0509	3.5	1126	6.7	1741	3.9		
3	W	0000	6.8	0648	3.8	1306	6.5	1937	4.0
4	TH	0154	6.8	0844	3.4	1458	7.0	2122	3.4
5	F	0328	7.5	1001	2.6	1609	7.7	2229	2.6
6	SA	0429	8.3	1058	1.8	1702	8.5	2322	1.7
7	**SU**	0520	9.1	1148	1.0	1748	9.2		
8	M ●	0010	1.0	0608	9.7	1233	0.5	1833	9.7
9	TU	0054	0.5	0652	10.0	1316	0.3	1914	9.9
10	W	0136	0.3	0733	10.1	1356	0.3	1953	9.9
11	TH	0215	0.5	0813	9.8	1434	0.7	2029	9.6
12	F	0252	0.9	0850	9.3	1509	1.3	2104	9.0
13	SA	0328	1.6	0927	8.6	1543	2.1	2137	8.3
14	**SU**	0404	2.4	1004	7.7	1619	2.9	2214	7.6
15	M ☾	0446	3.2	1050	6.9	1704	3.7	2302	6.9
16	TU	0550	3.8	1206	6.3	1819	4.3		
17	W	0031	6.4	0736	4.1	1408	6.2	2016	4.3
18	TH	0230	6.5	0917	3.8	1521	6.7	2138	3.8
19	F	0336	7.0	1011	3.2	1609	7.2	2227	3.2
20	SA	0422	7.5	1052	2.7	1649	7.8	2307	2.6
21	**SU**	0501	8.0	1129	2.2	1725	8.2	2343	2.2
22	M	0538	8.4	1203	1.9	1759	8.6		
23	TU ○	0016	1.8	0613	8.7	1236	1.7	1833	8.8
24	W	0049	1.6	0647	8.8	1306	1.6	1905	8.9
25	TH	0120	1.6	0718	8.9	1335	1.6	1934	8.9
26	F	0150	1.6	0748	8.7	1404	1.8	2002	8.7
27	SA	0219	1.8	0818	8.5	1432	2.1	2031	8.5
28	**SU**	0249	2.1	0851	8.2	1503	2.5	2104	8.2
29	M	0324	2.5	0929	7.8	1539	2.9	2145	7.8
30	TU	0408	2.9	1018	7.3	1628	3.4	2240	7.4

MAY

Date	Day	Time	m	Time	m	Time	m	Time	m
1	W ☽	0511	3.3	1126	6.9	1741	3.7	2358	7.1
2	TH	0643	3.4	1256	6.9	1922	3.7		
3	F	0131	7.2	0818	3.0	1426	7.3	2052	3.2
4	SA	0254	7.7	0929	2.4	1535	7.9	2158	2.5
5	**SU**	0357	8.3	1027	1.8	1629	8.5	2252	1.8
6	M	0450	8.9	1118	1.3	1718	9.0	2342	1.3
7	TU	0539	9.3	1205	0.9	1803	9.4		
8	W ●	0028	0.9	0626	9.5	1249	0.8	1847	9.6
9	TH	0111	0.8	0710	9.5	1331	0.9	1927	9.5
10	F	0153	1.0	0752	9.3	1410	1.2	2006	9.2
11	SA	0232	1.3	0831	8.8	1448	1.8	2043	8.8
12	**SU**	0310	1.9	0910	8.3	1524	2.4	2119	8.2
13	M	0349	2.5	0950	7.6	1602	3.0	2159	7.7
14	TU	0433	3.1	1037	7.0	1647	3.6	2247	7.1
15	W ☾	0530	3.6	1139	6.6	1750	4.0	2354	6.7
16	TH	0644	3.8	1300	6.5	1909	4.1		
17	F	0117	6.7	0803	3.7	1415	6.7	2027	3.9
18	SA	0231	6.9	0908	3.4	1513	7.1	2128	3.5
19	**SU**	0327	7.3	0957	3.0	1559	7.5	2215	3.0
20	M	0413	7.6	1040	2.7	1640	7.9	2257	2.6
21	TU	0455	8.0	1119	2.3	1719	8.2	2336	2.2
22	W	0535	8.3	1156	2.1	1756	8.5		
23	TH ○	0014	2.0	0613	8.5	1232	1.9	1832	8.7
24	F	0051	1.8	0650	8.6	1308	1.9	1907	8.7
25	SA	0127	1.8	0727	8.6	1343	2.0	1942	8.7
26	**SU**	0204	1.8	0804	8.5	1419	2.1	2019	8.6
27	M	0242	2.0	0844	8.2	1458	2.4	2100	8.4
28	TU	0325	2.3	0929	8.0	1541	2.7	2147	8.1
29	W	0414	2.5	1022	7.7	1634	3.0	2243	7.8
30	TH ☽	0516	2.8	1124	7.4	1740	3.2	2349	7.6
31	F	0628	2.8	1235	7.4	1857	3.2		

JUNE

Date	Day	Time	m	Time	m	Time	m	Time	m
1	SA	0102	7.6	0743	2.7	1348	7.5	2015	3.0
2	**SU**	0216	7.8	0852	2.5	1456	7.9	2122	2.6
3	M	0322	8.1	0953	2.1	1555	8.2	2222	2.2
4	TU	0421	8.4	1048	1.9	1649	8.6	2315	1.8
5	W	0514	8.7	1139	1.7	1738	8.9		
6	TH ●	0005	1.6	0605	8.8	1226	1.6	1825	9.0
7	F	0052	1.5	0652	8.8	1311	1.6	1908	9.0
8	SA	0137	1.5	0737	8.7	1354	1.8	1950	8.9
9	**SU**	0219	1.7	0819	8.5	1433	2.1	2029	8.6
10	M	0259	2.0	0900	8.2	1511	2.4	2107	8.3
11	TU	0338	2.4	0939	7.8	1549	2.8	2146	7.9
12	W	0418	2.8	1020	7.4	1629	3.2	2227	7.5
13	TH	0502	3.2	1105	7.1	1714	3.5	2314	7.2
14	F ☾	0552	3.4	1157	6.9	1809	3.7		
15	SA	0010	6.9	0649	3.6	1256	6.8	1911	3.8
16	**SU**	0113	6.9	0750	3.6	1359	6.9	2015	3.7
17	M	0217	7.0	0849	3.4	1458	7.1	2114	3.4
18	TU	0316	7.2	0944	3.2	1550	7.5	2208	3.0
19	W	0409	7.5	1033	2.9	1638	7.8	2257	2.7
20	TH	0458	7.8	1120	2.6	1723	8.2	2343	2.3
21	F	0544	8.1	1205	2.3	1806	8.5		
22	SA ○	0028	2.0	0630	8.4	1248	2.1	1849	8.7
23	**SU**	0113	1.8	0714	8.5	1332	2.0	1932	8.8
24	M	0157	1.7	0759	8.6	1415	1.9	2015	8.9
25	TU	0242	1.6	0844	8.6	1459	2.0	2100	8.8
26	W	0328	1.7	0929	8.4	1544	2.1	2146	8.7
27	TH	0415	1.9	1017	8.3	1632	2.3	2236	8.4
28	F ☽	0506	2.1	1109	8.0	1725	2.6	2330	8.1
29	SA	0602	2.4	1205	7.8	1825	2.8		
30	**SU**	0030	7.9	0704	2.6	1308	7.6	1934	3.0

SUNRISE AND SUNSET TIMES

ST PETER PORT (GUERNSEY)
At 49°27′N 2°31′W

UT		Sunrise	Sunset
Jan	01	0806	1622
	15	0800	1639
Feb	01	0742	1706
	15	0719	1730
Mar	01	0653	1753
	15	0624	1815
BST (UT+1)			
Apr	01	0647	1942
	15	0618	2003
May	01	0548	2027
	15	0526	2048
Jun	01	0508	2108
	15	0503	2118
Jul	01	0508	2120
	15	0520	2111
Aug	01	0541	2051
	15	0601	2027
Sep	01	0626	1953
	15	0646	1923
Oct	01	0710	1849
	15	0731	1820
UT			
Nov	01	0659	1648
	15	0721	1628
Dec	01	0745	1613
	15	0800	1611

ST PETER PORT

LAT 49°27'N
LONG 2°31'W

TIMES AND HEIGHTS OF HIGH AND LOW WATER (Heights in Metres)

TIME ZONE UT
For Summer Time (area enclosed in shaded box) add 1 hour

2024

JULY

Date	Day	Time	m	Time	m	Time	m	Time	m
1	M	0139	7.7	0812	2.8	1418	7.6	2047	2.9
2	TU	0251	7.7	0921	2.8	1526	7.7	2156	2.8
3	W	0359	7.8	1024	2.6	1627	8.0	2258	2.5
4	TH	0459	8.0	1122	2.4	1721	8.3	2353	2.2
5	F ●	0553	8.2	1213	2.2	1811	8.5		
6	SA	0042	2.0	0643	8.4	1300	2.1	1856	8.7
7	SU	0127	1.8	0727	8.5	1343	2.0	1938	8.8
8	M	0209	1.8	0808	8.5	1422	2.1	2017	8.7
9	TU	0247	1.9	0845	8.4	1457	2.2	2052	8.5
10	W	0321	2.1	0920	8.1	1530	2.4	2126	8.3
11	TH	0354	2.4	0953	7.9	1602	2.7	2159	8.0
12	F	0425	2.7	1026	7.6	1634	3.0	2234	7.6
13	SA ☾	0459	3.1	1102	7.3	1712	3.4	2313	7.3
14	SU	0538	3.4	1145	7.0	1759	3.6		
15	M	0001	7.0	0631	3.6	1240	6.9	1902	3.8
16	TU	0103	6.8	0739	3.7	1349	6.8	2015	3.7
17	W	0218	6.9	0850	3.6	1501	7.1	2124	3.5
18	TH	0329	7.1	0955	3.3	1603	7.4	2226	3.0
19	F	0431	7.5	1054	2.9	1658	7.9	2322	2.5
20	SA	0526	7.9	1147	2.5	1749	8.4		
21	SU ○	0015	2.0	0618	8.4	1237	2.0	1838	8.8
22	M	0104	1.6	0706	8.7	1325	1.7	1924	9.2
23	TU	0152	1.2	0752	9.0	1410	1.4	2008	9.4
24	W	0236	1.0	0836	9.1	1454	1.3	2051	9.5
25	TH	0319	1.0	0918	9.1	1535	1.4	2134	9.3
26	F	0401	1.3	1000	8.9	1617	1.7	2217	8.9
27	SA	0444	1.7	1043	8.5	1701	2.2	2303	8.4
28	SU ☽	0529	2.3	1131	8.0	1750	2.7	2356	7.8
29	M	0623	2.8	1228	7.5	1853	3.2		
30	TU	0103	7.3	0733	3.3	1343	7.2	2017	3.5
31	W	0231	7.0	0858	3.5	1509	7.2	2147	3.4

AUGUST

Date	Day	Time	m	Time	m	Time	m	Time	m
1	TH	0353	7.2	1016	3.3	1619	7.5	2255	3.0
2	F	0457	7.6	1117	2.9	1715	8.0	2349	2.5
3	SA	0548	8.0	1207	2.5	1802	8.4		
4	SU ●	0035	2.1	0633	8.3	1250	2.2	1844	8.7
5	M	0116	1.8	0713	8.6	1329	1.9	1923	8.9
6	TU	0153	1.7	0749	8.7	1404	1.8	1958	8.9
7	W	0226	1.7	0822	8.7	1436	1.9	2029	8.9
8	TH	0256	1.8	0852	8.5	1504	2.0	2059	8.6
9	F	0322	2.1	0920	8.3	1530	2.3	2126	8.3
10	SA	0346	2.4	0946	8.0	1555	2.7	2154	8.0
11	SU	0410	2.8	1013	7.6	1623	3.1	2223	7.6
12	M ☾	0439	3.2	1045	7.3	1658	3.5	2301	7.2
13	TU	0519	3.6	1130	6.9	1749	3.8	2357	6.8
14	W	0622	4.0	1239	6.7	1915	4.0		
15	TH	0122	6.6	0802	4.1	1416	6.7	2052	3.8
16	F	0301	6.8	0929	3.7	1540	7.2	2208	3.2
17	SA	0416	7.3	1038	3.1	1643	7.9	2310	2.5
18	SU	0515	8.0	1135	2.4	1736	8.6		
19	M ○	0003	1.8	0606	8.6	1226	1.8	1825	9.2
20	TU	0052	1.2	0653	9.2	1313	1.2	1910	9.7
21	W	0137	0.7	0736	9.5	1356	0.9	1953	10.0
22	TH	0219	0.5	0818	9.7	1437	0.7	2034	10.0
23	F	0259	0.6	0857	9.6	1516	0.9	2113	9.7
24	SA	0338	0.9	0935	9.2	1554	1.4	2152	9.2
25	SU	0415	1.6	1013	8.7	1632	2.1	2233	8.4
26	M ☽	0455	2.4	1055	7.9	1716	2.8	2320	7.6
27	TU	0545	3.2	1148	7.2	1818	3.6		
28	W	0031	6.8	0659	3.9	1317	6.7	2002	4.0
29	TH	0230	6.6	0853	4.1	1506	6.8	2152	3.7
30	F	0356	6.9	1016	3.6	1615	7.3	2253	3.1
31	SA	0451	7.5	1110	3.1	1705	7.9	2339	2.6

SEPTEMBER

Date	Day	Time	m	Time	m	Time	m	Time	m
1	SU	0534	8.0	1153	2.5	1746	8.4		
2	M	0017	2.1	0613	8.4	1231	2.1	1824	8.8
3	TU ●	0054	1.7	0648	8.8	1306	1.8	1859	9.1
4	W	0127	1.6	0721	8.9	1338	1.6	1931	9.2
5	TH	0157	1.5	0752	9.0	1407	1.6	2001	9.1
6	F	0223	1.7	0820	8.8	1433	1.8	2028	8.9
7	SA	0246	1.9	0845	8.6	1456	2.1	2053	8.6
8	SU	0308	2.3	0908	8.3	1519	2.5	2117	8.2
9	M	0330	2.7	0932	7.9	1544	2.9	2144	7.8
10	TU	0356	3.2	1000	7.5	1615	3.4	2217	7.3
11	W ☽	0432	3.7	1041	7.0	1701	3.8	2312	6.8
12	TH	0530	4.1	1151	6.7	1826	4.2		
13	F	0043	6.5	0725	4.3	1344	6.6	2031	3.9
14	SA	0246	6.7	0913	3.9	1523	7.2	2154	3.2
15	SU	0404	7.4	1023	3.1	1626	8.0	2254	2.4
16	M	0458	8.2	1118	2.2	1717	8.8	2344	1.5
17	TU	0546	8.9	1207	1.5	1804	9.5		
18	W ○	0030	0.9	0631	9.5	1251	0.9	1848	10.0
19	TH	0114	0.4	0713	9.9	1334	0.5	1930	10.3
20	F	0155	0.3	0752	10.0	1414	0.5	2011	10.2
21	SA	0234	0.5	0831	9.8	1452	0.8	2049	9.8
22	SU	0311	1.0	0907	9.4	1529	1.4	2127	9.1
23	M	0347	1.8	0944	8.7	1606	2.2	2205	8.2
24	TU ☾	0425	2.7	1023	7.9	1650	3.1	2251	7.3
25	W	0513	3.6	1115	7.1	1753	3.9		
26	TH	0009	6.5	0635	4.3	1259	6.5	1959	4.2
27	F	0227	6.4	0848	4.3	1454	6.7	2141	3.8
28	SA	0343	6.9	1001	3.7	1557	7.3	2233	3.2
29	SU	0430	7.5	1048	3.1	1641	7.9	2313	2.6
30	M	0508	8.1	1127	2.5	1719	8.4	2349	2.1

OCTOBER

Date	Day	Time	m	Time	m	Time	m	Time	m
1	TU	0543	8.5	1202	2.1	1755	8.8		
2	W ●	0022	1.8	0617	8.9	1235	1.8	1829	9.1
3	TH	0054	1.6	0648	9.1	1306	1.6	1900	9.2
4	F	0123	1.6	0718	9.1	1335	1.6	1930	9.1
5	SA	0149	1.7	0746	9.0	1401	1.8	1957	8.9
6	SU	0212	1.9	0811	8.7	1426	2.1	2022	8.6
7	M	0235	2.3	0835	8.4	1450	2.4	2048	8.3
8	TU	0259	2.7	0900	8.1	1516	2.8	2116	7.8
9	W	0327	3.2	0931	7.7	1550	3.3	2153	7.3
10	TH ☽	0405	3.7	1015	7.2	1640	3.8	2251	6.8
11	F	0507	4.2	1130	6.8	1807	4.1		
12	SA	0026	6.5	0702	4.3	1320	6.8	2009	3.8
13	SU	0225	6.9	0851	3.8	1456	7.4	2130	3.1
14	M	0339	7.6	0959	3.0	1559	8.2	2228	2.2
15	TU	0432	8.4	1052	2.1	1650	9.0	2318	1.5
16	W	0518	9.1	1141	1.4	1737	9.6		
17	TH ○	0003	0.9	0603	9.7	1226	0.9	1823	10.0
18	F	0047	0.6	0645	10.0	1309	0.6	1906	10.1
19	SA	0129	0.6	0726	10.0	1350	0.7	1947	10.0
20	SU	0209	0.8	0805	9.8	1430	1.0	2027	9.5
21	M	0247	1.4	0843	9.3	1509	1.6	2106	8.8
22	TU	0324	2.1	0921	8.6	1548	2.4	2146	8.0
23	W	0403	3.0	1001	7.8	1634	3.2	2235	7.2
24	TH ☾	0453	3.8	1055	7.1	1739	3.9	2353	6.5
25	F	0612	4.3	1229	6.7	1924	4.1		
26	SA	0151	6.5	0809	4.3	1414	6.8	2059	3.8
27	SU	0305	6.9	0923	3.9	1518	7.2	2154	3.4
28	M	0353	7.4	1011	3.3	1604	7.7	2235	2.9
29	TU	0432	7.9	1051	2.8	1643	8.2	2312	2.4
30	W	0507	8.4	1126	2.4	1719	8.5	2346	2.1
31	TH	0540	8.7	1200	2.1	1754	8.8		

NOVEMBER

Date	Day	Time	m	Time	m	Time	m	Time	m
1	F ●	0017	1.9	0614	8.9	1232	1.9	1828	8.9
2	SA	0047	1.9	0645	9.0	1303	1.8	1859	8.9
3	SU	0116	1.9	0715	8.9	1333	1.9	1930	8.8
4	M	0144	2.1	0743	8.8	1402	2.1	1959	8.6
5	TU	0212	2.4	0811	8.5	1431	2.4	2029	8.3
6	W	0241	2.7	0843	8.2	1504	2.8	2104	7.9
7	TH	0315	3.1	0921	7.8	1544	3.1	2149	7.4
8	F	0359	3.6	1012	7.4	1639	3.5	2250	7.1
9	SA ☽	0504	3.9	1123	7.2	1800	3.7		
10	SU	0012	6.9	0640	4.0	1253	7.2	1936	3.5
11	M	0147	7.2	0815	3.6	1417	7.6	2053	2.9
12	TU	0301	7.7	0925	2.9	1524	8.2	2154	2.3
13	W	0358	8.4	1022	2.2	1619	8.8	2247	1.7
14	TH	0448	9.0	1113	1.7	1710	9.3	2336	1.3
15	F ○	0535	9.4	1201	1.3	1758	9.5		
16	SA	0022	1.1	0620	9.6	1247	1.1	1844	9.6
17	SU	0106	1.1	0703	9.7	1331	1.1	1929	9.4
18	M	0148	1.3	0745	9.5	1414	1.4	2011	9.1
19	TU	0229	1.8	0826	9.1	1456	1.8	2053	8.6
20	W	0309	2.3	0906	8.6	1538	2.4	2136	8.0
21	TH	0350	3.0	0949	8.0	1624	3.0	2224	7.4
22	F	0438	3.6	1039	7.4	1719	3.5	2323	6.9
23	SA ☾	0539	4.0	1144	7.0	1827	3.8		
24	SU	0039	6.7	0656	4.2	1302	6.9	1943	3.9
25	M	0157	6.8	0814	4.0	1414	7.0	2050	3.7
26	TU	0257	7.1	0915	3.7	1511	7.3	2142	3.3
27	W	0344	7.5	1002	3.3	1558	7.7	2225	3.0
28	TH	0425	7.9	1044	2.9	1639	8.0	2304	2.7
29	F	0503	8.3	1122	2.5	1719	8.3	2340	2.4
30	SA	0540	8.6	1159	2.3	1757	8.5		

DECEMBER

Date	Day	Time	m	Time	m	Time	m	Time	m
1	SU ●	0015	2.2	0616	8.7	1235	2.1	1834	8.6
2	M	0050	2.2	0651	8.8	1312	2.1	1910	8.6
3	TU	0125	2.2	0725	8.8	1348	2.1	1946	8.5
4	W	0200	2.3	0800	8.6	1425	2.2	2023	8.3
5	TH	0236	2.5	0839	8.5	1504	2.4	2104	8.1
6	F	0317	2.8	0922	8.2	1549	2.7	2151	7.8
7	SA	0403	3.1	1013	8.0	1641	2.9	2246	7.6
8	SU ☽	0501	3.3	1112	7.7	1744	3.0	2350	7.4
9	M	0611	3.4	1221	7.7	1855	3.1		
10	TU	0102	7.4	0730	3.3	1335	7.7	2008	2.9
11	W	0216	7.7	0845	3.0	1446	8.0	2116	2.6
12	TH	0322	8.1	0950	2.6	1549	8.3	2217	2.3
13	F	0420	8.5	1048	2.2	1647	8.6	2312	2.0
14	SA	0513	8.8	1142	1.9	1740	8.8		
15	SU ○	0003	1.8	0602	9.1	1232	1.6	1831	8.9
16	M	0051	1.7	0649	9.2	1320	1.5	1918	8.9
17	TU	0137	1.8	0733	9.2	1405	1.6	2003	8.8
18	W	0219	1.9	0816	9.0	1448	1.8	2045	8.5
19	TH	0300	2.2	0856	8.7	1529	2.1	2125	8.2
20	F	0338	2.6	0936	8.3	1609	2.6	2205	7.8
21	SA	0417	3.0	1016	7.9	1649	3.0	2245	7.4
22	SU ☾	0458	3.4	1059	7.5	1732	3.4	2332	7.1
23	M	0547	3.7	1149	7.1	1822	3.7		
24	TU	0027	6.9	0646	3.9	1249	6.9	1921	3.8
25	W	0133	6.8	0752	3.9	1356	6.9	2024	3.8
26	TH	0239	7.0	0857	3.8	1500	7.1	2126	3.6
27	F	0337	7.3	0955	3.4	1557	7.3	2219	3.2
28	SA	0427	7.7	1046	3.0	1647	7.7	2307	2.9
29	SU	0511	8.1	1132	2.7	1733	8.0	2352	2.6
30	M ●	0554	8.4	1217	2.3	1816	8.3		
31	TU	0034	2.3	0635	8.7	1300	2.0	1900	8.5

ST HELIER
LAT 49°11′N
LONG 2°07′W

TIMES AND HEIGHTS OF HIGH AND LOW WATER (Heights in Metres)

TIME ZONE UT
For Summer Time (area enclosed in shaded box) add 1 hour

2024

JANUARY

Date	Day	Time	m	Time	m	Time	m	Time	m
1	M	0334	3.0	0919	9.5	1558	3.0	2145	9.0
2	TU	0408	3.4	0953	9.1	1631	3.4	2221	8.6
3	W	0445	3.7	1031	8.7	1710	3.7	2302	8.2
4	TH ☽	0529	4.1	1117	8.3	1758	4.1	2356	7.9
5	F	0626	4.3	1217	8.0	1900	4.3		
6	SA	0105	7.8	0738	4.4	1330	7.9	2015	4.2
7	SU	0218	8.1	0854	4.1	1443	8.2	2128	3.9
8	M	0322	8.6	1001	3.6	1546	8.7	2231	3.3
9	TU	0418	9.2	1100	3.0	1643	9.3	2327	2.8
10	W	0510	9.8	1154	2.3	1737	9.9		
11	TH ●	0018	2.3	0601	10.4	1245	1.8	1828	10.4
12	F	0108	1.9	0649	10.8	1335	1.4	1917	10.7
13	SA	0156	1.6	0737	11.1	1423	1.2	2004	10.9
14	SU	0242	1.4	0823	11.3	1510	1.1	2050	10.9
15	M	0326	1.5	0908	11.1	1554	1.2	2134	10.6
16	TU	0410	1.7	0952	10.8	1637	1.6	2217	10.2
17	W	0453	2.1	1037	10.2	1720	2.1	2302	9.6
18	TH ☾	0539	2.7	1124	9.5	1807	2.8	2351	9.0
19	F	0632	3.3	1221	8.9	1904	3.4		
20	SA	0053	8.5	0739	3.7	1332	8.4	2016	3.7
21	SU	0211	8.3	0900	3.8	1456	8.3	2135	3.7
22	M	0330	8.5	1019	3.6	1611	8.6	2246	3.4
23	TU	0435	9.0	1124	3.1	1710	9.0	2343	3.0
24	W	0527	9.5	1215	2.7	1758	9.5		
25	TH O	0030	2.6	0611	9.9	1258	2.3	1840	9.8
26	F	0110	2.4	0650	10.2	1336	2.1	1916	10.0
27	SA	0146	2.2	0725	10.3	1410	2.0	1950	10.1
28	SU	0218	2.2	0758	10.4	1440	2.1	2020	10.0
29	M	0247	2.2	0828	10.3	1507	2.2	2049	9.9
30	TU	0315	2.3	0857	10.1	1534	2.4	2117	9.7
31	W	0343	2.6	0925	9.8	1601	2.7		

FEBRUARY

Date	Day	Time	m	Time	m	Time	m	Time	m
1	TH	0412	3.0	0953	9.3	1629	3.1	2212	8.9
2	F ☽	0443	3.5	1024	8.8	1700	3.6	2246	8.4
3	SA	0522	3.9	1105	8.3	1743	4.1	2337	8.0
4	SU	0620	4.3	1209	7.8	1853	4.4		
5	M	0058	7.7	0749	4.4	1342	7.8	2034	4.4
6	TU	0235	8.0	0923	4.0	1515	8.2	2201	3.8
7	W	0354	8.7	1037	3.2	1628	9.0	2309	3.0
8	TH	0456	9.6	1140	2.3	1728	9.8		
9	F ●	0007	2.2	0551	10.4	1236	1.5	1821	10.5
10	SA	0100	1.5	0641	11.1	1328	0.9	1908	11.1
11	SU	0148	1.0	0727	11.6	1415	0.5	1953	11.5
12	M	0233	0.7	0811	11.9	1458	0.4	2035	11.5
13	TU	0314	0.7	0852	11.8	1538	0.5	2114	11.2
14	W	0353	1.0	0932	11.3	1615	1.1	2151	10.7
15	TH	0430	1.6	1009	10.5	1650	1.9	2227	9.9
16	F ☾	0506	2.4	1048	9.5	1727	2.8	2307	9.0
17	SA	0548	3.3	1135	8.6	1813	3.7		
18	SU	0000	8.2	0650	4.1	1247	7.7	1930	4.4
19	M	0129	7.7	0831	4.4	1438	7.5	2115	4.4
20	TU	0316	7.9	1012	4.0	1607	8.1	2239	3.8
21	W	0428	8.6	1118	3.3	1704	8.8	2336	3.2
22	TH	0518	9.3	1206	2.7	1747	9.4		
23	F	0019	2.6	0559	9.8	1245	2.2	1825	9.9
24	SA O	0056	2.2	0635	10.2	1320	1.9	1858	10.2
25	SU	0129	1.9	0707	10.5	1350	1.8	1928	10.3
26	M	0159	1.8	0736	10.6	1418	1.7	1956	10.4
27	TU	0226	1.8	0804	10.6	1443	1.7	2022	10.4
28	W	0252	1.8	0830	10.5	1508	1.9	2047	10.2
29	TH	0318	2.1	0855	10.2	1532	2.3	2110	9.8

MARCH

Date	Day	Time	m	Time	m	Time	m	Time	m
1	F	0344	2.5	0920	9.7	1556	2.8	2133	9.3
2	SA	0410	3.0	0946	9.1	1621	3.3	2201	8.8
3	SU ☽	0441	3.6	1020	8.5	1656	3.9	2242	8.2
4	M	0530	4.2	1117	7.9	1758	4.5	2359	7.7
5	TU	0700	4.4	1301	7.5	1952	4.6		
6	W	0204	7.7	0854	4.1	1500	8.0	2141	3.9
7	TH	0339	8.6	1020	3.1	1617	8.9	2254	2.9
8	F	0443	9.6	1125	2.1	1715	9.9	2352	1.9
9	SA	0536	10.6	1221	1.2	1805	10.8		
10	SU ●	0044	1.1	0625	11.4	1311	0.5	1851	11.5
11	M	0131	0.6	0709	12.0	1356	0.1	1933	11.8
12	TU	0214	0.3	0751	12.1	1437	0.1	2012	11.8
13	W	0254	0.4	0830	11.9	1514	0.4	2048	11.4
14	TH	0330	0.8	0907	11.3	1548	1.1	2122	10.8
15	F	0403	1.5	0942	10.4	1619	2.0	2155	9.9
16	SA	0436	2.5	1017	9.3	1651	3.1	2229	8.9
17	SU ☾	0512	3.5	1059	8.2	1732	4.1	2318	8.0
18	M	0610	4.3	1215	7.4	1849	4.8		
19	TU	0056	7.4	0808	4.7	1428	7.3	2058	4.7
20	W	0300	7.7	0958	4.1	1552	7.9	2223	4.0
21	TH	0409	8.4	1058	3.3	1643	8.7	2314	3.2
22	F	0455	9.2	1141	2.7	1723	9.4	2354	2.6
23	SA	0534	9.8	1218	2.2	1758	9.9		
24	SU	0030	2.1	0608	10.2	1251	1.9	1830	10.3
25	M O	0102	1.8	0640	10.5	1321	1.7	1859	10.5
26	TU	0132	1.7	0708	10.6	1349	1.6	1926	10.6
27	W	0200	1.6	0736	10.7	1416	1.6	1952	10.6
28	TH	0227	1.6	0802	10.6	1441	1.8	2017	10.4
29	F	0253	1.9	0828	10.3	1506	2.1	2041	10.1
30	SA	0320	2.3	0853	9.8	1531	2.6	2105	9.6
31	SU	0348	2.8	0921	9.2	1558	3.2	2134	9.0

APRIL

Date	Day	Time	m	Time	m	Time	m	Time	m
1	M	0421	3.4	0958	8.6	1635	3.9	2218	8.4
2	TU ☽	0513	4.0	1059	7.9	1740	4.4	2340	7.8
3	W	0643	4.2	1252	7.6	1934	4.5		
4	TH	0149	7.9	0835	3.8	1446	8.1	2120	3.8
5	F	0319	8.7	0958	2.9	1558	9.1	2231	2.7
6	SA	0421	9.8	1101	1.9	1653	10.1	2328	1.8
7	SU	0514	10.7	1156	1.1	1741	10.9		
8	M ●	0019	1.1	0601	11.5	1245	0.6	1826	11.5
9	TU	0106	0.6	0645	11.8	1329	0.3	1907	11.7
10	W	0149	0.4	0727	11.9	1410	0.4	1945	11.7
11	TH	0228	0.6	0806	11.6	1447	0.8	2021	11.3
12	F	0304	1.1	0842	10.9	1520	1.5	2055	10.6
13	SA	0338	1.8	0918	10.0	1552	2.4	2127	9.7
14	SU	0412	2.7	0953	9.0	1624	3.3	2203	8.8
15	M ☾	0450	3.6	1038	8.0	1706	4.2	2253	8.0
16	TU	0548	4.3	1156	7.3	1821	4.8		
17	W	0028	7.4	0734	4.6	1355	7.3	2019	4.8
18	TH	0221	7.6	0915	4.2	1513	7.9	2141	4.1
19	F	0329	8.3	1015	3.5	1604	8.6	2233	3.4
20	SA	0417	9.0	1059	2.9	1645	9.3	2314	2.8
21	SU	0457	9.5	1137	2.4	1720	9.7	2352	2.3
22	M	0532	9.9	1212	2.1	1753	10.1		
23	TU O	0026	2.0	0605	10.2	1245	1.9	1824	10.3
24	W	0059	1.8	0636	10.4	1317	1.8	1854	10.5
25	TH	0131	1.7	0706	10.5	1347	1.8	1922	10.5
26	F	0202	1.7	0736	10.4	1416	1.9	1950	10.4
27	SA	0232	1.9	0806	10.2	1444	2.2	2019	10.1
28	SU	0302	2.2	0838	9.8	1514	2.6	2051	9.7
29	M	0336	2.7	0914	9.2	1549	3.2	2129	9.1
30	TU	0417	3.2	1000	8.6	1635	3.7	2223	8.5

MAY

Date	Day	Time	m	Time	m	Time	m	Time	m
1	W ☾	0516	3.6	1111	8.1	1745	4.1	2348	8.2
2	TH	0639	3.8	1248	8.0	1921	4.0		
3	F	0129	8.4	0811	3.4	1418	8.5	2050	3.4
4	SA	0249	9.0	0927	2.7	1526	9.3	2159	2.6
5	SU	0351	9.8	1029	2.0	1622	10.1	2257	1.9
6	M	0445	10.5	1124	1.4	1711	10.7	2349	1.4
7	TU	0533	11.0	1214	1.1	1756	11.1		
8	W ●	0038	1.1	0619	11.2	1300	1.0	1839	11.2
9	TH	0122	1.0	0702	11.2	1342	1.1	1919	11.2
10	F	0204	1.2	0743	10.9	1421	1.5	1957	10.8
11	SA	0242	1.5	0822	10.4	1457	2.0	2033	10.3
12	SU	0319	2.1	0901	9.7	1532	2.7	2109	9.6
13	M	0356	2.8	0940	8.9	1608	3.4	2149	8.9
14	TU	0437	3.5	1027	8.2	1651	4.0	2239	8.2
15	W ☽	0528	4.0	1130	7.7	1751	4.5	2350	7.8
16	TH	0640	4.3	1255	7.6	1913	4.6		
17	F	0118	7.8	0803	4.2	1410	7.9	2033	4.3
18	SA	0229	8.1	0909	3.8	1508	8.4	2133	3.8
19	SU	0324	8.6	1001	3.3	1555	8.9	2222	3.2
20	M	0409	9.1	1046	2.9	1635	9.3	2305	2.8
21	TU	0449	9.5	1127	2.6	1712	9.7	2346	2.4
22	W	0527	9.8	1207	2.3	1747	10.0		
23	TH O	0025	2.1	0603	10.0	1244	2.1	1822	10.3
24	F	0103	2.0	0639	10.2	1320	2.1	1856	10.4
25	SA	0140	1.9	0716	10.2	1355	2.1	1932	10.4
26	SU	0216	1.9	0754	10.1	1431	2.2	2010	10.2
27	M	0254	2.1	0835	9.8	1508	2.5	2051	9.9
28	TU	0335	2.4	0920	9.4	1551	2.8	2139	9.5
29	W	0423	2.7	1013	9.0	1643	3.2	2236	9.1
30	TH ☾	0520	3.0	1115	8.7	1746	3.4	2343	8.9
31	F	0627	3.1	1226	8.6	1859	3.4		

JUNE

Date	Day	Time	m	Time	m	Time	m	Time	m
1	SA	0058	8.9	0740	3.0	1340	8.8	2014	3.2
2	SU	0210	9.2	0849	2.7	1447	9.2	2122	2.8
3	M	0315	9.5	0952	2.4	1547	9.7	2223	2.4
4	TU	0414	9.9	1051	2.1	1640	10.1	2320	2.0
5	W	0507	10.2	1145	1.9	1730	10.4		
6	TH ●	0012	1.8	0557	10.4	1234	1.8	1816	10.6
7	F	0101	1.7	0643	10.4	1319	1.9	1859	10.6
8	SA	0146	1.8	0727	10.3	1401	2.0	1940	10.4
9	SU	0227	1.9	0809	10.0	1441	2.3	2019	10.1
10	M	0307	2.3	0849	9.6	1518	2.7	2057	9.7
11	TU	0344	2.7	0928	9.1	1554	3.1	2136	9.2
12	W	0421	3.1	1008	8.7	1632	3.6	2217	8.8
13	TH	0501	3.5	1053	8.3	1716	3.9	2306	8.4
14	F ☽	0547	3.8	1147	8.0	1808	4.1		
15	SA	0005	8.1	0643	4.0	1252	7.9	1912	4.2
16	SU	0113	8.0	0747	4.0	1358	8.1	2019	4.1
17	M	0218	8.2	0852	3.8	1455	8.4	2122	3.8
18	TU	0314	8.5	0950	3.5	1545	8.8	2217	3.3
19	W	0404	8.9	1042	3.1	1631	9.2	2307	2.9
20	TH	0450	9.3	1131	2.8	1714	9.7	2355	2.5
21	F	0535	9.7	1217	2.5	1756	10.0		
22	SA O	0040	2.2	0620	10.0	1300	2.2	1839	10.3
23	SU	0124	1.9	0704	10.2	1343	2.1	1923	10.5
24	M	0208	1.8	0750	10.2	1426	2.0	2008	10.5
25	TU	0252	1.7	0836	10.2	1509	2.1	2054	10.5
26	W	0337	1.8	0922	10.1	1554	2.2	2141	10.3
27	TH	0424	1.9	1010	9.8	1642	2.4	2230	9.9
28	F ☾	0513	2.2	1100	9.5	1733	2.7	2323	9.6
29	SA	0605	2.5	1155	9.2	1830	3.0		
30	SU	0021	9.2	0704	2.8	1256	8.9	1935	3.2

SUNRISE AND SUNSET TIMES

ST HELIER
At 49°N 2°W

Month	Day	Sunrise	Sunset
UT			
Jan	01	0803	1621
	15	0758	1639
Feb	01	0739	1705
	15	0717	1729
Mar	01	0651	1752
	15	0622	1814
BST (UT+1)			
Apr	01	0646	1940
	15	0617	2001
May	01	0547	2025
	15	0526	2045
Jun	01	0508	2105
	15	0503	2115
Jul	01	0508	2117
	15	0520	2109
Aug	01	0541	2048
	15	0600	2025
Sep	01	0625	1951
	15	0645	1921
Oct	01	0708	1847
	15	0729	1818
UT			
Nov	01	0656	1647
	15	0719	1627
Dec	01	0742	1613
	15	0757	1611

ST HELIER
LAT 49°11′N
LONG 2°07′W

TIMES AND HEIGHTS OF HIGH AND LOW WATER (Heights in Metres)

TIME ZONE UT
For Summer Time (area enclosed in shaded box) add 1 hour

2024

JULY

Date	Time	m	Date	Time	m
1	0128	9.0	16	0056	7.9
	0809	3.0		0736	4.2
M	1405	8.9	TU	1344	7.9
	2045	3.2		2018	4.2
2	0240	8.9	17	0213	7.9
	0918	3.0		0853	4.1
TU	1513	9.0	W	1455	8.2
	2154	3.0		2132	3.9
3	0348	9.1	18	0322	8.3
	1024	2.9		1003	3.7
W	1616	9.4	TH	1555	8.8
	2300	2.7		2235	3.3
4	0450	9.4	19	0422	8.9
	1125	2.7		1103	3.1
TH	1712	9.7	F	1649	9.4
	2358	2.4		2331	2.7
5	0544	9.7	20	0516	9.4
	1219	2.5		1157	2.6
F	1801	10.0	SA	1740	10.0
●					
6	0050	2.2	21	0024	2.1
	0633	9.9		0608	10.0
SA	1307	2.3	SU	1247	2.1
	1847	10.2	○	1829	10.5
7	0136	2.1	22	0114	1.7
	0717	10.0		0657	10.4
SU	1350	2.3	M	1335	1.8
	1928	10.3		1916	10.9
8	0217	2.1	23	0203	1.3
	0757	9.9		0743	10.7
M	1428	2.3	TU	1421	1.5
	2006	10.2		2001	11.2
9	0254	2.2	24	0248	1.1
	0833	9.8		0828	10.9
TU	1503	2.5	W	1505	1.4
	2041	10.0		2045	11.2
10	0326	2.4	25	0331	1.0
	0907	9.6		0911	10.8
W	1534	2.7	TH	1547	1.4
	2114	9.7		2128	11.0
11	0357	2.6	26	0413	1.3
	0939	9.3		0952	10.5
TH	1605	3.0	F	1629	1.8
	2147	9.4		2211	10.6
12	0427	3.0	27	0453	1.7
	1012	8.9		1034	10.0
F	1638	3.3	SA	1711	2.3
	2222	9.0		2255	9.9
13	0500	3.3	28	0536	2.4
	1049	8.6		1119	9.4
SA	1715	3.7	SU	1757	2.9
☽	2301	8.5	☾	2344	9.2
14	0539	3.7	29	0625	3.1
	1133	8.2		1213	8.8
SU	1802	4.0	M	1856	3.5
	2351	8.1			
15	0629	4.1	30	0048	8.5
	1231	7.9		0730	3.6
M	1903	4.3	TU	1324	8.4
				2014	3.8
			31	0212	8.2
				0852	3.8
			W	1450	8.4
				2140	3.7

AUGUST

Date	Time	m	Date	Time	m
1	0339	8.4	16	0253	7.9
	1013	3.6		0934	4.1
TH	1606	8.8	F	1532	8.4
	2256	3.2		2212	3.5
2	0447	8.8	17	0406	8.6
	1120	3.1		1043	3.3
F	1706	9.3	SA	1634	9.3
	2355	2.7		2314	2.7
3	0540	9.4	18	0505	9.5
	1213	2.7		1141	2.5
SA	1754	9.8	SU	1727	10.1
4	0044	2.3	19	0010	1.9
	0625	9.8		0556	10.3
SU	1258	2.4	M	1234	1.8
●	1836	10.2	○	1816	10.9
5	0126	2.0	20	0102	1.2
	0703	10.1		0643	10.9
M	1337	2.2	TU	1323	1.3
	1913	10.4		1902	11.5
6	0202	1.9	21	0149	0.7
	0738	10.2		0728	11.3
TU	1410	2.1	W	1408	0.9
	1947	10.5		1946	11.8
7	0233	1.9	22	0233	0.5
	0810	10.2		0810	11.5
W	1440	2.1	TH	1450	0.8
	2018	10.4		2027	11.8
8	0300	2.0	23	0314	0.6
	0839	10.1		0849	11.4
TH	1508	2.2	F	1529	1.0
	2046	10.2		2107	11.5
9	0326	2.2	24	0351	1.0
	0906	9.8		0927	10.9
F	1534	2.5	SA	1607	1.5
	2114	9.9		2146	10.8
10	0351	2.5	25	0427	1.7
	0932	9.5		1004	10.2
SA	1601	2.8	SU	1644	2.2
	2140	9.4		2224	9.9
11	0417	3.0	26	0504	2.6
	0958	9.0		1042	9.3
SU	1631	3.3	M	1725	3.1
	2209	8.9	☾	2308	8.8
12	0446	3.5	27	0548	3.6
	1028	8.5		1131	8.5
M	1706	3.9	TU	1822	3.9
☽	2244	8.3			
13	0524	4.1	28	0013	7.9
	1111	8.0		0657	4.3
TU	1757	4.4	W	1252	7.8
	2339	7.8		1956	4.4
14	0624	4.5	29	0205	7.6
	1225	7.7		0842	4.5
W	1918	4.6	TH	1446	7.9
				2143	4.1
15	0111	7.5	30	0344	8.0
	0800	4.6		1013	4.0
TH	1409	7.8	F	1605	8.6
	2054	4.3		2256	3.3
			31	0444	8.8
				1114	3.2
			SA	1658	9.3
				2347	2.7

SEPTEMBER

Date	Time	m	Date	Time	m
1	0529	9.5	16	0448	9.7
	1201	2.6		1122	2.3
SU	1740	9.9	M	1709	10.5
				2350	1.6
2	0028	2.2	17	0537	10.7
	0607	10.0		1214	1.5
M	1240	2.2	TU	1756	11.3
	1818	10.4			
3	0105	1.9	18	0040	0.9
	0641	10.3		0623	11.3
TU	1314	2.0	W	1301	0.9
●	1851	10.6	○	1841	11.9
4	0136	1.8	19	0127	0.5
	0712	10.5		0705	11.7
W	1344	1.9	TH	1346	0.6
	1921	10.7		1924	12.1
5	0204	1.7	20	0209	0.3
	0740	10.5		0745	11.8
TH	1411	1.8	F	1427	0.6
	1949	10.7		2004	12.0
6	0229	1.8	21	0248	0.6
	0807	10.4		0823	11.6
F	1437	1.9	SA	1505	0.9
	2015	10.5		2043	11.5
7	0253	2.0	22	0325	1.1
	0831	10.2		0859	11.0
SA	1503	2.2	SU	1542	1.5
	2040	10.2		2119	10.6
8	0317	2.3	23	0359	2.0
	0854	9.9		0933	10.2
SU	1528	2.6	M	1617	2.5
	2103	9.7		2156	9.6
9	0341	2.9	24	0434	3.0
	0916	9.4		1010	9.2
M	1555	3.2	TU	1657	3.4
	2127	9.1	☾	2240	8.4
10	0405	3.5	25	0517	4.0
	0941	8.8		1058	8.2
TU	1625	3.8	W	1758	4.3
	2157	8.5		2353	7.5
11	0437	4.1	26	0634	4.8
	1015	8.2		1232	7.5
W	1710	4.4	TH	1950	4.7
☽	2245	7.8			
12	0532	4.7	27	0208	7.4
	1122	7.6		0836	4.8
TH	1834	4.7	F	1441	7.8
				2137	4.2
13	0027	7.4	28	0334	8.0
	0721	4.9		1001	4.0
F	1338	7.6	SA	1550	8.6
	2027	4.4		2237	3.4
14	0238	7.8	29	0424	8.9
	0913	4.3		1054	3.2
SA	1516	8.4	SU	1637	9.3
	2153	3.5		2321	2.7
15	0353	8.7	30	0504	9.6
	1025	3.3		1135	2.6
SU	1618	9.4	M	1715	10.0
	2256	2.5		2359	2.2

OCTOBER

Date	Time	m	Date	Time	m
1	0539	10.1	16	0511	10.8
	1211	2.2		1146	1.4
TU	1750	10.4	W	1731	11.3
2	0032	1.9	17	0012	0.9
	0611	10.4		0556	11.4
W	1243	2.0	TH	1234	1.0
●	1822	10.6	○	1816	11.8
3	0102	1.8	18	0058	0.6
	0641	10.6		0638	11.7
TH	1312	1.8	F	1319	0.7
	1851	10.7		1859	11.9
4	0130	1.8	19	0141	0.7
	0708	10.6		0718	11.7
F	1340	1.8	SA	1401	0.8
	1918	10.7		1940	11.7
5	0156	1.8	20	0221	1.0
	0734	10.6		0757	11.4
SA	1407	1.9	SU	1441	1.2
	1944	10.6		2019	11.1
6	0222	2.0	21	0258	1.6
	0758	10.4		0833	10.8
SU	1434	2.1	M	1519	1.8
	2009	10.3		2058	10.3
7	0247	2.4	22	0335	2.4
	0822	10.1		0909	10.0
M	1501	2.5	TU	1557	2.7
	2034	9.8		2137	9.3
8	0312	2.9	23	0412	3.3
	0845	9.6		0948	9.1
TU	1528	3.1	W	1640	3.6
	2100	9.2		2224	8.3
9	0338	3.5	24	0458	4.2
	0912	9.0		1039	8.2
W	1600	3.7	TH	1743	4.4
	2132	8.6	☾	2339	7.5
10	0412	4.1	25	0614	4.8
	0949	8.4		1209	7.6
TH	1648	4.2	F	1924	4.6
☽	2225	7.9			
11	0511	4.6	26	0135	7.5
	1100	7.8		0804	4.8
F	1812	4.6	SA	1402	7.8
				2058	4.2
12	0013	7.5	27	0255	8.0
	0700	4.8		0923	4.2
SA	1316	7.7	SU	1511	8.4
	2003	4.2		2157	3.6
13	0217	7.9	28	0346	8.7
	0848	4.2		1015	3.5
SU	1451	8.5	M	1559	9.1
	2127	3.3		2241	3.0
14	0329	8.9	29	0427	9.4
	0959	3.2		1056	2.9
M	1552	9.6	TU	1639	9.7
	2229	2.3		2319	2.6
15	0423	9.9	30	0503	9.9
	1056	2.2		1133	2.5
TU	1644	10.6	W	1715	10.0
	2323	1.5		2353	2.3
			31	0536	10.2
				1207	2.2
			TH	1748	10.3

NOVEMBER

Date	Time	m	Date	Time	m
1	0025	2.1	16	0030	1.2
	0607	10.4		0612	11.3
F	1238	2.1	SA	1254	1.2
●	1819	10.4		1836	11.3
2	0056	2.0	17	0115	1.3
	0636	10.5		0655	11.3
SA	1310	2.0	SU	1339	1.3
	1848	10.5		1920	11.1
3	0126	2.0	18	0158	1.5
	0704	10.5		0736	11.1
SU	1341	2.0	M	1422	1.6
	1917	10.4		2003	10.6
4	0155	2.2	19	0239	2.0
	0731	10.4		0816	10.6
M	1411	2.2	TU	1504	2.1
	1946	10.2		2045	10.0
5	0223	2.5	20	0318	2.6
	0759	10.2		0855	10.0
TU	1441	2.5	W	1545	2.7
	2017	9.8		2127	9.2
6	0253	2.9	21	0359	3.3
	0829	9.7		0937	9.2
W	1514	2.9	TH	1630	3.4
	2050	9.3		2214	8.5
7	0325	3.4	22	0444	4.0
	0904	9.2		1025	8.6
TH	1553	3.4	F	1722	4.0
	2133	8.7		2312	8.0
8	0407	3.9	23	0541	4.4
	0952	8.7		1129	8.1
F	1646	3.8	SA	1829	4.3
	2234	8.2	☾		
9	0510	4.3	24	0028	7.7
	1106	8.2		0657	4.6
SA	1802	4.0	SU	1251	7.9
☽				1946	4.3
10	0003	8.0	25	0146	7.9
	0640	4.3		0814	4.4
SU	1246	8.2	M	1407	8.2
	1933	3.8		2052	4.0
11	0139	8.3	26	0248	8.3
	0812	3.9		0916	4.0
M	1412	8.8	TU	1506	8.6
	2051	3.2		2145	3.6
12	0252	9.0	27	0338	8.8
	0924	3.1		1006	3.5
TU	1518	9.6	W	1554	9.0
	2155	2.4		2230	3.2
13	0350	9.8	28	0420	9.3
	1023	2.4		1049	3.1
W	1613	10.3	TH	1635	9.4
	2250	1.8		2311	2.9
14	0440	10.5	29	0458	9.7
	1116	1.8		1129	2.7
TH	1703	10.9	F	1713	9.7
	2342	1.4		2349	2.6
15	0527	11.0	30	0533	10.0
	1206	1.4		1208	2.4
F	1751	11.2	SA	1748	9.9
○					

DECEMBER

Date	Time	m	Date	Time	m
1	0026	2.4	16	0058	1.9
	0607	10.2		0639	10.8
SU	1245	2.2	M	1327	1.7
●	1824	10.1		1909	10.5
2	0102	2.3	17	0144	1.9
	0640	10.3		0724	10.7
M	1321	2.2	TU	1413	1.8
	1859	10.1		1954	10.3
3	0136	2.3	18	0228	2.1
	0715	10.4		0806	10.5
TU	1356	2.2	W	1456	2.0
	1935	10.1		2036	10.0
4	0210	2.4	19	0308	2.5
	0750	10.2		0846	10.2
W	1432	2.3	TH	1536	2.4
	2014	9.9		2115	9.6
5	0246	2.6	20	0346	2.9
	0829	10.0		0924	9.7
TH	1511	2.5	F	1613	2.9
	2055	9.6		2154	9.1
6	0325	2.9	21	0422	3.3
	0912	9.7		1003	9.2
F	1555	2.8	SA	1650	3.4
	2142	9.2		2234	8.6
7	0411	3.2	22	0501	3.8
	1002	9.3		1045	8.7
SA	1646	3.1	SU	1730	3.8
	2237	8.9	☾	2321	8.2
8	0507	3.5	23	0547	4.1
	1101	9.0		1137	8.3
SU	1746	3.3	M	1819	4.1
☽	2341	8.7			
9	0614	3.7	24	0019	8.0
	1211	8.9		0645	4.3
M	1855	3.3	TU	1240	8.0
				1921	4.2
10	0052	8.7	25	0129	7.9
	0729	3.6		0754	4.4
TU	1325	8.9	W	1353	8.0
	2008	3.2		2030	4.2
11	0205	8.9	26	0236	8.1
	0842	3.3		0903	4.2
W	1436	9.2	TH	1458	8.2
	2115	2.8		2135	3.9
12	0311	9.3	27	0333	8.5
	0948	2.8		1003	3.8
TH	1540	9.6	F	1553	8.6
	2218	2.5		2230	3.5
13	0410	9.8	28	0421	9.0
	1048	2.4		1055	3.3
F	1638	10.0	SA	1641	9.0
	2315	2.2		2318	3.1
14	0503	10.3	29	0504	9.4
	1145	2.0		1142	2.8
SA	1732	10.3	SU	1724	9.4
15	0008	2.0	30	0002	2.7
	0553	10.6		0545	9.8
SU	1237	1.8	M	1226	2.4
○	1822	10.5	●	1807	9.8
			31	0045	2.4
				0626	10.2
			TU	1308	2.1
				1849	10.0

ST-MALO
LAT 48°38′N
LONG 2°02′W

TIMES AND HEIGHTS OF HIGH AND LOW WATER (Heights in Metres)

TIME ZONE
European Standard Time (UT+0100)
For Summer Time (area enclosed in shaded box) add 1 hour

2024

JANUARY

Date	Day	Time	m	Time	m	Time	m	Time	m
1	M	0434	3.3	1003	10.6	1657	3.3	2229	10.1
2	TU	0506	3.6	1038	10.2	1729	3.7	2304	9.7
3	W	0540	4.0	1115	9.8	1804	4.1	2344	9.3
4	TH ☽	0621	4.4	1159	9.3	1848	4.4		
5	F	0036	9.0	0713	4.7	1259	9.0	1944	4.6
6	SA	0145	8.8	0820	4.7	1414	8.9	2057	4.6
7	SU	0301	9.0	0938	4.5	1528	9.2	2214	4.3
8	M	0408	9.5	1049	4.0	1633	9.7	2320	3.7
9	TU	0505	10.1	1150	3.3	1731	10.3		
10	W	0018	3.1	0557	10.8	1246	2.7	1824	10.9
11	TH ●	0112	2.6	0647	11.4	1341	2.1	1914	11.4
12	F	0205	2.1	0734	11.9	1434	1.7	2002	11.8
13	SA	0256	1.8	0821	12.3	1525	1.4	2049	12.1
14	SU	0344	1.6	0907	12.4	1612	1.2	2134	12.1
15	M	0430	1.7	0952	12.3	1657	1.4	2218	11.8
16	TU	0513	1.9	1037	11.9	1740	1.8	2302	11.3
17	W	0556	2.4	1122	11.3	1822	2.4	2346	10.7
18	TH ☾	0640	3.1	1210	10.6	1908	3.1		
19	F	0037	10.0	0731	3.7	1308	9.9	2003	3.8
20	SA	0140	9.5	0837	4.1	1422	9.4	2112	4.1
21	SU	0300	9.3	0956	4.2	1545	9.3	2230	4.1
22	M	0419	9.6	1113	3.9	1658	9.7	2339	3.7
23	TU	0522	10.1	1216	3.4	1756	10.2		
24	W	0036	3.3	0613	10.6	1307	2.9	1844	10.6
25	TH O	0123	2.9	0656	11.1	1351	2.6	1925	11.0
26	F	0204	2.6	0735	11.4	1430	2.3	2002	11.2
27	SA	0241	2.4	0810	11.6	1505	2.2	2035	11.3
28	SU	0315	2.3	0842	11.6	1538	2.2	2105	11.3
29	M	0346	2.3	0912	11.5	1607	2.3	2134	11.1
30	TU	0414	2.5	0941	11.3	1634	2.6	2202	10.8
31	W	0440	2.8	1009	10.9	1658	3.0	[illegible]	[illegible]

FEBRUARY

Date	Day	Time	m	Time	m	Time	m	Time	m
1	TH	0506	3.2	1036	10.4	1724	3.4	2256	10.0
2	F	0537	3.7	1107	9.9	1756	3.9	2328	9.5
3	SA ☽	0616	4.2	1146	9.3	1839	4.4		
4	SU	0016	9.0	0710	4.7	1250	8.8	1941	4.8
5	M	0139	8.6	0832	4.9	1430	8.6	2117	4.9
6	TU	0325	8.8	1011	4.5	1606	9.0	2250	4.3
7	W	0444	9.6	1127	3.7	1717	9.9		
8	TH	0001	3.4	0546	10.5	1233	2.7	1816	10.8
9	F ●	0103	2.6	0638	11.5	1333	1.8	1907	11.6
10	SA	0159	1.8	0727	12.3	1428	1.1	1954	12.3
11	SU	0251	1.1	0813	12.9	1518	0.6	2039	12.7
12	M	0337	0.8	0857	13.1	1603	0.4	2121	12.8
13	TU	0420	0.8	0938	13.0	1643	0.6	2200	12.5
14	W	0458	1.2	1018	12.5	1720	1.3	2237	11.9
15	TH	0534	1.9	1056	11.7	1754	2.2	2314	11.0
16	F ☾	0609	2.8	1135	10.7	1830	3.2	2354	10.1
17	SA	0650	3.7	1223	9.6	1916	4.1		
18	SU	0049	9.2	0749	4.5	1339	8.7	2027	4.8
19	M	0222	8.7	0924	4.8	1531	8.6	2206	4.8
20	TU	0406	8.9	1101	4.4	1655	9.1	2328	4.2
21	W	0515	9.6	1207	3.7	1749	9.9		
22	TH	0026	3.5	0603	10.4	1256	3.0	1832	10.5
23	F	0111	2.9	0643	11.0	1338	2.5	1909	11.1
24	SA O	0150	2.4	0718	11.5	1414	2.1	1942	11.4
25	SU	0225	2.1	0751	11.7	1447	1.9	2013	11.6
26	M	0256	1.9	0820	11.9	1516	1.8	2041	11.7
27	TU	0324	1.9	0848	11.9	1543	1.9	2107	11.6
28	W	0350	2.0	0915	11.7	1606	2.1	2132	11.4
29	TH	0414	2.3	0940	11.3	1628	2.5	2155	11.0

MARCH

Date	Day	Time	m	Time	m	Time	m	Time	m
1	F	0437	2.7	1004	10.8	1651	3.0	2218	10.5
2	SA	0504	3.3	1029	10.2	1718	3.6	2245	9.9
3	SU ☽	0537	3.9	1103	9.5	1754	4.3	2323	9.2
4	M	0625	4.6	1155	8.8	1851	4.9		
5	TU	0032	8.5	0746	5.0	1345	8.3	2035	5.2
6	W	0256	8.5	0945	4.7	1552	8.8	2232	4.5
7	TH	0431	9.4	1112	3.7	1707	9.8	2348	3.4
8	F	0532	10.5	1221	2.5	1803	11.0		
9	SA	0051	2.3	0624	11.7	1320	1.5	1852	12.0
10	SU ●	0146	1.3	0711	12.6	1413	0.6	1937	12.7
11	M	0236	0.6	0756	13.3	1501	0.1	2019	13.1
12	TU	0320	0.3	0837	13.5	1542	0.1	2058	13.1
13	W	0400	0.4	0917	13.2	1620	0.5	2135	12.7
14	TH	0436	0.9	0953	12.6	1653	1.3	2209	12.0
15	F	0508	1.8	1028	11.6	1723	2.4	2242	11.1
16	SA	0539	2.8	1104	10.4	1754	3.5	2318	10.0
17	SU ☾	0615	3.9	1147	9.3	1836	4.5		
18	M	0008	9.0	0711	4.8	1306	8.3	1950	5.2
19	TU	0152	8.3	0857	5.1	1521	8.2	2147	5.2
20	W	0351	8.6	1045	4.6	1642	8.9	2311	4.4
21	TH	0456	9.4	1146	3.7	1729	9.8		
22	F	0004	3.6	0540	10.2	1231	3.0	1807	10.5
23	SA	0046	2.9	0617	10.9	1310	2.4	1841	11.1
24	SU	0123	2.4	0651	11.4	1346	2.1	1913	11.5
25	M O	0157	2.0	0723	11.7	1418	1.9	1943	11.7
26	TU	0228	1.8	0753	11.9	1447	1.8	2011	11.8
27	W	0257	1.8	0820	11.9	1513	1.8	2037	11.8
28	TH	0323	1.9	0847	11.8	1537	2.0	2102	11.6
29	F	0348	2.1	0912	11.4	1601	2.4	2126	11.2
30	SA	0413	2.6	0937	10.9	1625	2.9	2150	10.7
31	SU	0441	3.1	1005	10.3	1652	3.6	2219	10.1

APRIL

Date	Day	Time	m	Time	m	Time	m	Time	m
1	M	0515	3.8	1041	9.5	1730	4.3	2300	9.3
2	TU ☽	0605	4.5	1137	8.7	1830	5.0		
3	W	0015	8.6	0729	4.9	1338	8.3	2022	5.2
4	TH	0240	8.6	0928	4.5	1537	8.9	2215	4.4
5	F	0409	9.5	1054	3.5	1647	10.0	2328	3.2
6	SA	0510	10.7	1200	2.3	1740	11.1		
7	SU	0029	2.1	0601	11.8	1258	1.3	1828	12.1
8	M ●	0123	1.2	0648	12.6	1349	0.7	1912	12.7
9	TU	0212	0.7	0731	13.1	1435	0.4	1953	13.0
10	W	0256	0.5	0813	13.2	1516	0.5	2031	12.9
11	TH	0335	0.7	0852	12.8	1552	1.0	2107	12.5
12	F	0410	1.3	0928	12.1	1624	1.7	2141	11.8
13	SA	0442	2.1	1004	11.2	1654	2.7	2215	10.9
14	SU	0513	3.0	1040	10.1	1726	3.7	2252	9.9
15	M ☾	0550	4.0	1125	9.1	1808	4.6	2343	9.0
16	TU	0646	4.8	1243	8.3	1921	5.3		
17	W	0120	8.3	0822	5.1	1445	8.2	2110	5.2
18	TH	0311	8.5	1003	4.7	1604	8.8	2230	4.6
19	F	0417	9.2	1104	4.0	1652	9.6	2323	3.8
20	SA	0501	9.9	1150	3.3	1729	10.3		
21	SU	0006	3.1	0540	10.6	1230	2.8	1804	10.8
22	M	0045	2.7	0615	11.1	1307	2.4	1837	11.3
23	TU	0121	2.3	0649	11.4	1341	2.2	1909	11.5
24	W O	0154	2.1	0721	11.6	1413	2.1	1938	11.7
25	TH	0226	2.0	0751	11.6	1442	2.1	2007	11.7
26	F	0257	2.0	0820	11.5	1510	2.2	2035	11.5
27	SA	0326	2.2	0850	11.3	1538	2.6	2103	11.2
28	SU	0357	2.6	0921	10.9	1608	3.0	2135	10.8
29	M	0430	3.1	0957	10.3	1642	3.6	2213	10.1
30	TU	0511	3.7	1043	9.6	1727	4.2	2305	9.4

MAY

Date	Day	Time	m	Time	m	Time	m	Time	m
1	W ☾	0607	4.2	1151	8.9	1835	4.7		
2	TH	0031	9.0	0731	4.4	1334	8.8	2017	4.7
3	F	0216	9.1	0907	4.0	1506	9.3	2149	4.1
4	SA	0336	9.9	1025	3.2	1614	10.2	2258	3.1
5	SU	0438	10.8	1130	2.4	1709	11.1	2359	2.3
6	M	0531	11.6	1228	1.7	1757	11.8		
7	TU	0054	1.6	0619	12.1	1319	1.3	1842	12.2
8	W ●	0143	1.3	0705	12.4	1406	1.1	1925	12.4
9	TH	0228	1.2	0748	12.4	1447	1.3	2004	12.3
10	F	0308	1.4	0829	12.1	1523	1.7	2042	12.0
11	SA	0344	1.8	0907	11.5	1557	2.3	2118	11.5
12	SU	0419	2.4	0945	10.8	1630	3.0	2155	10.8
13	M	0454	3.1	1025	10.0	1706	3.8	2236	10.0
14	TU	0534	3.9	1111	9.2	1749	4.5	2326	9.3
15	W ☽	0624	4.5	1213	8.7	1849	5.0		
16	TH	0035	8.7	0732	4.8	1336	8.4	2009	5.1
17	F	0159	8.7	0853	4.7	1456	8.7	2125	4.7
18	SA	0312	9.0	1000	4.3	1553	9.2	2224	4.2
19	SU	0406	9.5	1053	3.8	1639	9.8	2313	3.7
20	M	0451	10.0	1139	3.4	1719	10.3	2357	3.2
21	TU	0532	10.5	1221	3.0	1757	10.8		
22	W	0039	2.8	0611	10.8	1301	2.7	1833	11.1
23	TH O	0118	2.5	0648	11.1	1338	2.5	1907	11.3
24	F	0157	2.4	0724	11.2	1414	2.5	1941	11.4
25	SA	0234	2.3	0759	11.2	1450	2.5	2016	11.4
26	SU	0311	2.3	0837	11.1	1526	2.7	2053	11.3
27	M	0350	2.5	0917	10.9	1604	3.0	2134	10.9
28	TU	0432	2.8	1002	10.5	1646	3.4	2222	10.5
29	W	0519	3.2	1055	10.0	1738	3.8	2319	10.1
30	TH ☾	0616	3.5	1157	9.6	1842	4.1		
31	F	0027	9.8	0724	3.7	1310	9.5	1957	4.1

JUNE

Date	Day	Time	m	Time	m	Time	m	Time	m
1	SA	0143	9.8	0837	3.6	1425	9.7	2113	3.8
2	SU	0255	10.1	0948	3.2	1533	10.1	2222	3.3
3	M	0401	10.5	1054	2.8	1633	10.7	2325	2.8
4	TU	0459	11.0	1154	2.4	1727	11.2		
5	W	0023	2.4	0552	11.3	1248	2.2	1816	11.5
6	TH ●	0115	2.1	0642	11.5	1337	2.1	1901	11.7
7	F	0203	2.0	0729	11.5	1420	2.2	1944	11.7
8	SA	0245	2.1	0812	11.3	1459	2.3	2024	11.5
9	SU	0324	2.2	0853	11.1	1536	2.6	2103	11.3
10	M	0402	2.6	0933	10.7	1613	3.0	2142	10.9
11	TU	0439	3.0	1012	10.2	1650	3.5	2221	10.4
12	W	0516	3.5	1052	9.8	1728	3.9	2302	9.8
13	TH	0556	3.9	1135	9.3	1811	4.4	2348	9.4
14	F ☽	0640	4.3	1226	9.0	1901	4.6		
15	SA	0044	9.1	0732	4.5	1326	8.8	2002	4.7
16	SU	0148	9.0	0834	4.6	1432	8.9	2108	4.6
17	M	0253	9.1	0940	4.4	1534	9.2	2211	4.3
18	TU	0353	9.4	1040	4.1	1628	9.7	2307	3.8
19	W	0446	9.8	1134	3.7	1716	10.2	2358	3.4
20	TH	0535	10.2	1223	3.3	1800	10.6		
21	F	0046	3.0	0621	10.6	1309	3.0	1843	11.0
22	SA O	0133	2.6	0705	10.9	1354	2.7	1925	11.3
23	SU	0219	2.4	0748	11.1	1439	2.6	2007	11.5
24	M	0305	2.2	0833	11.2	1523	2.5	2051	11.6
25	TU	0351	2.1	0918	11.2	1608	2.5	2136	11.5
26	W	0437	2.2	1004	11.1	1654	2.7	2223	11.3
27	TH	0524	2.4	1052	10.8	1742	2.9	2313	11.0
28	F ☾	0612	2.7	1142	10.5	1832	3.3		
29	SA	0006	10.6	0704	3.0	1237	10.1	1929	3.5
30	SU	0106	10.2	0802	3.3	1340	9.9	2033	3.7

SUNRISE AND SUNSET TIMES

ST MALO
At 48°38′N 2°02′W
European Standard Time (UT+0100)

Month	Day	Sunrise	Sunset
Jan	01	0901	1723
	15	0855	1740
Feb	01	0838	1807
	15	0816	1829
Mar	01	0750	1852
	15	0721	1913
European Summer Time (UT+0200)			
Apr	01	0746	2039
	15	0718	2100
May	01	0648	2123
	15	0627	2143
Jun	01	0610	2202
	15	0605	2212
Jul	01	0610	2214
	15	0622	2206
Aug	01	0642	2146
	15	0701	2123
Sep	01	0725	2050
	15	0745	2021
Oct	01	0808	1947
	15	0828	1919
European Standard Time (UT+0100)			
Nov	01	0755	1748
	15	0816	1728
Dec	01	0839	1715

ST-MALO
LAT 48°38′N
LONG 2°02′W

TIMES AND HEIGHTS OF HIGH AND LOW WATER (Heights in Metres)

TIME ZONE
European Standard Time (UT+0100)
For Summer Time (area enclosed in shaded box) add 1 hour

2024

JULY

Day	Time	m	Day	Time	m
1 M	0213 0907 1450 2144	10.0 3.5 9.9 3.7	16 TU	0135 0813 1420 2101	8.9 4.7 8.8 4.8
2 TU	0325 1017 1559 2254	10.0 3.5 10.1 3.4	17 W	0252 0935 1537 2220	8.9 4.7 9.1 4.4
3 W	0433 1124 1703 2358	10.2 3.3 10.4 3.1	18 TH	0405 1051 1642 2325	9.2 4.3 9.6 3.9
4 TH	0535 1224 1759	10.4 3.1 10.8	19 F	0508 1153 1738	9.7 3.8 10.2
5 F	0055 0630 1316 ● 1848	2.8 10.7 2.8 11.1	20 SA	0022 0603 1249 1828	3.2 10.3 3.2 10.9
6 SA	0145 0719 1402 1932	2.6 10.9 2.7 11.3	21 SU	0117 0654 1342 ○ 1915	2.6 10.9 2.7 11.5
7 SU	0230 0802 1444 2013	2.4 11.0 2.6 11.4	22 M	0211 0741 1434 2001	2.1 11.4 2.2 11.9
8 M	0310 0842 1522 2050	2.4 11.0 2.6 11.4	23 TU	0302 0827 1522 2045	1.7 11.8 1.9 12.3
9 TU	0347 0918 1557 2125	2.4 10.9 2.7 11.2	24 W	0349 0911 1607 2129	1.4 12.0 1.7 12.4
10 W	0421 0951 1630 2158	2.6 10.7 3.0 10.9	25 TH	0433 0954 1650 2212	1.3 11.9 1.8 12.2
11 TH	0453 1023 1700 2231	3.0 10.4 3.3 10.5	26 F	0514 1036 1730 2254	1.6 11.6 2.1 11.7
12 F	0521 1055 1730 2304	3.3 10.0 3.7 10.1	27 SA	0554 1117 1811 2338	2.1 11.1 2.7 11.0
13 SA	0551 1129 1804 ☽ 2342	3.8 9.6 4.1 9.6	28 SU ☾	0635 1202 1856	2.8 10.5 3.4
14 SU	0625 1210 1847	4.1 9.2 4.5	29 M	0028 0723 1256 1954	10.3 3.5 9.9 4.0
15 M	0029 0711 1306 1944	9.2 4.5 8.9 4.8	30 TU	0133 0826 1409 2111	9.6 4.1 9.4 4.3
			31 W	0257 0946 1537 2235	9.3 4.3 9.4 4.1

AUGUST

Day	Time	m	Day	Time	m
1 TH	0423 1106 1653 2347	9.4 4.0 9.3 3.3	16 F	0337 1019 1620 2301	8.7 4.8 9.2 4.1
2 F	0531 1212 1752	9.3 3.3 10.4	17 SA	0452 1134 1723	9.5 4.0 10.1
3 SA	0046 0625 1306 1840	3.1 10.4 3.1 11.0	18 SU	0006 0551 1235 1815	3.2 10.4 3.1 11.1
4 SU	0135 0709 1351 ● 1921	2.7 10.3 2.7 11.4	19 M	0105 0641 1332 ○ 1902	2.3 11.2 2.3 12.0
5 M	0217 0748 1430 1958	2.4 11.2 2.4 11.5	20 TU	0200 0728 1424 1947	1.6 12.0 1.6 12.6
6 TU	0254 0823 1505 2031	2.2 11.3 2.3 11.7	21 W	0250 0812 1511 2030	1.0 12.5 1.1 13.0
7 W	0327 0854 1536 2101	2.1 11.4 2.3 11.7	22 TH	0336 0854 1554 2112	0.7 12.7 0.9 13.1
8 TH	0357 0923 1604 2130	2.3 11.3 2.5 11.5	23 F	0416 0934 1633 2151	0.7 12.6 1.2 12.8
9 F	0422 0950 1628 2157	2.5 11.0 2.8 11.1	24 SA	0454 1011 1709 2229	1.2 12.2 1.7 12.1
10 SA	0444 1016 1652 2223	2.9 10.6 3.2 10.6	25 SU	0528 1048 1744 2308	2.0 11.4 2.6 11.1
11 SU	0507 1041 1718 2250	3.3 10.2 3.7 10.0	26 M	0603 1127 1823 ☾ 2353	2.9 10.6 3.5 10.0
12 M	0534 1109 1752 ☽ 2324	3.8 9.7 4.2 9.4	27 TU	0646 1217 1917	3.9 9.6 4.3
13 TU	0610 1148 1840	4.4 9.1 4.7	28 W	0059 0750 1338 2045	9.1 4.7 8.9 4.8
14 W	0017 0704 1258 1953	8.8 4.9 8.6 5.1	29 TH	0247 0928 1530 2229	8.6 4.9 8.9 4.5
15 TH	0153 0831 1452 2140	8.4 5.2 8.6 4.9	30 F	0424 1100 1649 2342	9.1 4.4 9.6 3.8
			31 SA	0526 1203 1742	9.8 3.6 10.4

SEPTEMBER

Day	Time	m	Day	Time	m
1 SU	0035 0611 1252 1824	3.0 10.6 3.0 11.1	16 M	0533 1218 1755	10.7 2.8 11.5
2 M	0118 0650 1333 1901	2.5 11.1 2.5 11.6	17 TU	0047 0621 1313 1842	1.9 11.7 1.8 12.5
3 TU	0156 0724 1408 ● 1934	2.2 11.5 2.2 11.9	18 W	0140 0707 1404 ○ 1926	1.1 12.5 1.1 13.1
4 W	0230 0756 1440 2004	2.0 11.7 2.0 12.0	19 TH	0229 0749 1450 2009	0.5 13.0 0.7 13.5
5 TH	0259 0824 1508 2032	1.9 11.7 2.0 12.0	20 F	0313 0830 1532 2049	0.4 13.2 0.6 13.4
6 F	0325 0851 1534 2058	2.0 11.7 2.2 11.8	21 SA	0352 0908 1610 2127	0.6 12.9 1.0 12.8
7 SA	0348 0915 1556 2123	2.3 11.4 2.5 11.4	22 SU	0428 0944 1645 2204	1.3 12.3 1.8 12.0
8 SU	0409 0938 1618 2146	2.6 11.1 2.9 10.9	23 M	0500 1019 1718 2241	2.2 11.4 2.7 10.8
9 M	0430 1000 1643 2210	3.1 10.6 3.4 10.3	24 TU	0533 1056 1755 ☾ 2325	3.3 10.4 3.7 9.7
10 TU	0454 1024 1713 2240	3.7 10.0 4.1 9.6	25 W	0614 1146 1850	4.3 9.4 4.7
11 W	0527 1057 1757 ☽ 2325	4.4 9.3 4.7 8.8	26 TH	0037 0722 1319 2028	8.7 5.1 8.6 5.1
12 TH	0618 1156 1909	5.0 8.6 5.2	27 F	0243 0916 1520 2217	8.4 5.2 8.8 4.6
13 F	0106 0748 1424 2111	8.2 5.5 8.4 5.1	28 SA	0413 1045 1631 2322	9.0 4.5 9.6 3.8
14 SA	0323 0959 1603 2244	8.6 5.0 9.2 4.1	29 SU	0505 1140 1718	9.9 3.6 10.5
15 SU	0438 1117 1705 2349	9.6 3.9 10.3 3.0	30 M	0009 0545 1224 1757	3.0 10.7 2.9 11.1

OCTOBER

Day	Time	m	Day	Time	m
1 TU	0049 0620 1303 1831	2.5 11.3 2.4 11.6	16 W	0021 0554 1247 1816	1.7 12.0 1.6 12.6
2 W	0124 0653 1337 ● 1904	2.2 11.6 2.2 11.9	17 TH	0114 0639 1338 ○ 1901	1.0 12.7 1.0 13.1
3 TH	0157 0723 1408 1934	2.0 11.8 2.0 12.0	18 F	0202 0722 1425 1944	0.6 13.1 0.7 13.3
4 F	0226 0751 1437 2001	2.0 11.9 2.0 12.0	19 SA	0246 0802 1507 2025	0.6 13.1 0.8 13.1
5 SA	0252 0817 1503 2027	2.1 11.8 2.1 11.8	20 SU	0325 0841 1546 2104	1.0 12.8 1.3 12.5
6 SU	0316 0841 1528 2052	2.3 11.6 2.4 11.5	21 M	0400 0918 1621 2142	1.7 12.1 2.0 11.6
7 M	0338 0905 1552 2117	2.6 11.3 2.8 11.0	22 TU	0434 0955 1657 2222	2.6 11.3 2.9 10.5
8 TU	0401 0929 1619 2144	3.1 10.8 3.3 10.4	23 W	0509 1035 1736 2309	3.6 10.3 3.8 9.5
9 W	0428 0957 1651 2217	3.7 10.2 4.0 9.7	24 TH ☾	0553 1128 1831	4.5 9.4 4.7
10 TH	0503 1033 1737 ☽ 2307	4.4 9.4 4.6 8.9	25 F	0022 0700 1256 1959	8.7 5.2 8.7 5.0
11 F	0557 1139 1852	5.1 8.7 5.1	26 SA	0212 0842 1443 2137	8.5 5.2 8.8 4.7
12 SA	0056 0733 1404 2050	8.3 5.4 8.6 4.9	27 SU	0336 1005 1553 2241	9.0 4.6 9.4 4.0
13 SU	0302 0937 1537 2219	8.8 4.8 9.4 3.9	28 M	0428 1100 1640 2328	9.7 3.9 10.1 3.4
14 M	0413 1053 1637 2324	9.8 3.7 10.6 2.7	29 TU	0508 1144 1720	10.4 3.2 10.8
15 TU	0507 1152 1728	11.0 2.6 11.7	30 W	0008 0543 1224 1756	2.8 11.0 2.8 11.2
			31 TH	0045 0617 1300 1830	2.5 11.4 2.5 11.5

NOVEMBER

Day	Time	m	Day	Time	m
1 F	0120 0649 1334 ● 1902	2.3 11.6 2.3 11.7	16 SA	0134 0656 1359 1921	1.2 12.6 1.3 12.6
2 SA	0151 0719 1406 1932	2.2 11.7 2.2 11.7	17 SU	0219 0739 1443 2005	1.3 12.6 1.3 12.4
3 SU	0221 0747 1436 2001	2.3 11.7 2.3 11.6	18 M	0300 0820 1524 2047	1.6 12.3 1.7 11.9
4 M	0249 0815 1506 2030	2.5 11.6 2.5 11.3	19 TU	0338 0900 1603 2129	2.1 11.9 2.2 11.2
5 TU	0316 0843 1536 2101	2.7 11.3 2.8 11.0	20 W	0415 0940 1642 2211	2.8 11.2 2.9 10.5
6 W	0345 0914 1608 2135	3.2 10.9 3.2 10.4	21 TH	0453 1023 1723 2258	3.5 10.4 3.6 9.7
7 TH	0418 0950 1647 2217	3.7 10.3 3.8 9.8	22 F	0537 1112 1812 2355	4.2 9.7 4.3 9.1
8 F	0500 1037 1738 2316	4.3 9.7 4.3 9.1	23 SA ☾	0632 1216 1913	4.7 9.1 4.7
9 SA ☽	0559 1150 1851	4.8 9.1 4.6	24 SU	0109 0742 1334 2027	8.7 5.0 8.9 4.7
10 SU	0049 0727 1333 2024	8.8 4.9 9.1 4.3	25 M	0228 0857 1449 2135	8.8 4.8 9.1 4.4
11 M	0224 0904 1458 2145	9.2 4.4 9.7 3.6	26 TU	0331 1001 1547 2232	9.3 4.4 9.5 4.0
12 TU	0336 1018 1602 2251	10.0 3.6 10.6 2.8	27 W	0419 1053 1634 2320	9.8 3.9 10.0 3.5
13 W	0433 1120 1657 2350	10.9 2.7 11.5 2.0	28 TH	0501 1139 1717	10.3 3.4 10.5
14 TH	0524 1217 1747	11.7 1.9 12.1	29 F	0003 0540 1222 1756	3.1 10.8 3.0 10.9
15 F	0044 0611 1310 ○ 1835	1.5 12.3 1.5 12.5	30 SA	0043 0617 1301 1833	2.9 11.1 2.7 11.1

DECEMBER

Day	Time	m	Day	Time	m
1 SU	0120 0651 1339 ● 1909	2.7 11.4 2.5 11.2	16 M	0158 0724 1426 1955	2.0 12.0 1.8 11.7
2 M	0156 0725 1416 1944	2.6 11.5 2.5 11.3	17 TU	0243 0808 1511 2039	2.0 11.9 1.9 11.5
3 TU	0231 0759 1453 2019	2.6 11.5 2.5 11.2	18 W	0324 0850 1552 2121	2.3 11.7 2.2 11.2
4 W	0306 0834 1531 2058	2.7 11.4 2.6 11.0	19 TH	0403 0930 1631 2200	2.6 11.4 2.6 10.8
5 TH	0343 0913 1610 2139	3.0 11.1 2.9 10.7	20 F	0441 1010 1708 2239	3.0 10.9 3.1 10.3
6 F	0423 0956 1654 2226	3.3 10.8 3.2 10.3	21 SA	0518 1049 1745 2319	3.5 10.3 3.6 9.7
7 SA	0509 1046 1745 2320	3.7 10.3 3.5 9.9	22 SU ☾	0556 1131 1824	4.0 9.8 4.1
8 SU ☽	0604 1146 1844	4.0 10.0 3.7	23 M	0003 0640 1219 1909	9.3 4.5 9.3 4.5
9 M	0025 0710 1257 1952	9.6 4.1 9.8 3.8	24 TU	0057 0733 1320 2006	8.9 4.7 9.0 4.7
10 TU	0138 0824 1412 2104	9.6 4.0 9.9 3.5	25 W	0205 0839 1430 2115	8.8 4.8 8.9 4.7
11 W	0250 0938 1522 2213	9.9 3.7 10.3 3.1	26 TH	0314 0950 1538 2223	9.0 4.6 9.2 4.4
12 TH	0356 1047 1625 2318	10.5 3.1 10.8 2.7	27 F	0414 1052 1636 2320	9.5 4.2 9.6 4.0
13 F	0454 1149 1723	11.0 2.6 11.3	28 SA	0505 1146 1726	10.0 3.7 10.0
14 SA	0017 0548 1246 1817	2.3 11.5 2.2 11.6	29 SU	0010 0550 1234 1812	3.5 10.5 3.2 10.5
15 SU	0110 0637 1339 ○ 1907	2.1 11.8 1.9 11.7	30 M	0056 0632 1320 ● 1854	3.1 10.9 2.8 10.8
			31 TU	0140 0712 1404 1936	2.8 11.3 2.5 11.1

BREST
LAT 48°23′N
LONG 4°30′W

TIMES AND HEIGHTS OF HIGH AND LOW WATER (Heights in Metres)

TIME ZONE
European Standard Time (UT+0100)
For Summer Time (area enclosed in shaded box) add 1 hour

2024

SUNRISE AND SUNSET TIMES

BREST
At 48°23′N 4°30′W
European Standard Time (UT+0100)

		Sunrise	Sunset
Jan	01	0910	1735
	15	0905	1752
Feb	01	0847	1818
	15	0826	1841
Mar	01	0800	1903
	15	0732	1924
European Summer Time (UT+0200)			
Apr	01	0757	2049
	15	0729	2110
May	01	0700	2133
	15	0639	2152
Jun	01	0622	2212
	15	0617	2222
Jul	01	0622	2223
	15	0633	2215
Aug	01	0654	2156
	15	0713	2133
Sep	01	0736	2100
	15	0756	2031
Oct	01	0818	1958
	15	0839	1930
European Standard Time (UT+0100)			
Nov	01	0805	1759
	15	0826	1740
Dec	01	0849	1726

JANUARY

	Time	m		Time	m
1 M	0204 0800 1431 2025	2.2 6.2 2.2 5.8	16 TU	0228 0830 1455 2056	1.4 7.0 1.4 6.5
2 TU	0241 0838 1509 2105	2.4 6.0 2.5 5.6	17 W	0317 0920 1546 2147	1.7 6.7 1.7 6.1
3 W	0322 0919 1552 2152	2.6 5.7 2.7 5.4	18 TH ☾	0410 1013 1641 2244	2.0 6.3 2.1 5.8
4 TH ☽	0409 1009 1644 2250	2.8 5.5 2.9 5.3	19 F	0510 1115 1744 2351	2.4 5.9 2.5 5.6
5 F	0506 1111 1745 2355	3.0 5.4 2.9 5.3	20 SA	0619 1229 1855	2.6 5.6 2.6
6 SA	0612 1221 1852	3.0 5.4 2.9	21 SU	0107 0735 1347 2007	5.6 2.6 5.6 2.6
7 SU	0102 0720 1329 1955	5.4 2.8 5.5 2.7	22 M	0220 0847 1454 2110	5.8 2.4 5.8 2.4
8 M	0204 0824 1430 2052	5.7 2.6 5.8 2.4	23 TU	0319 0946 1548 2202	6.0 2.2 6.0 2.2
9 TU	0259 0920 1525 2144	6.1 2.2 6.1 2.1	24 W	0408 1033 1632 2246	6.3 1.9 6.2 2.0
10 W	0350 1011 1614 2233	6.4 1.8 6.4 1.8	25 TH ○	0450 1114 1711 2325	6.5 1.7 6.4 1.8
11 TH ●	0438 1059 1702 2320	6.8 1.4 6.7 1.5	26 F	0527 1151 1746	6.7 1.6 6.5
12 F	0524 1146 1749	7.1 1.2 6.9	27 SA	0000 0600 1225 1819	1.7 6.7 1.5 6.5
13 SA	0007 0611 1233 1835	1.3 7.3 1.0 7.0	28 SU	0033 0632 1257 1850	1.7 6.7 1.6 6.5
14 SU	0053 0657 1319 1921	1.2 7.3 1.0 6.9	29 M	0105 0702 1328 1920	1.7 6.7 1.7 6.4
15 M	0140 0743 1407 2008	1.2 7.2 1.1 6.8	30 TU	0137 0732 1358 1950	1.8 6.5 1.8 6.2
			31 W	0208 0802 1429 2022	2.0 6.3 2.1 6.0

FEBRUARY

	Time	m		Time	m
1 TH	0241 0834 1502 2057	2.2 6.1 2.3 5.8	16 F ☾	0340 0937 1605 2202	1.9 6.2 2.2 5.8
2 F	0317 0912 1542 2141	2.5 5.8 2.6 5.5	17 SA	0434 1035 1704 2309	2.4 5.6 2.7 5.4
3 SA ☽	0402 1000 1634 2242	2.8 5.5 2.9 5.3	18 SU	0544 1155 1822	2.8 5.2 3.0
4 SU	0505 1110 1744	3.0 5.2 3.0	19 M	0039 0714 1334 1952	5.3 2.9 5.2 2.9
5 M	0000 0623 1237 1908	5.2 3.0 5.2 3.0	20 TU	0209 0840 1450 2102	5.5 2.7 5.5 2.6
6 TU	0123 0747 1403 2025	5.4 2.8 5.5 2.7	21 W	0312 0938 1541 2152	5.8 2.3 5.9 2.3
7 W	0236 0859 1510 2127	5.8 2.3 5.9 2.2	22 TH	0358 1022 1621 2233	6.2 2.0 6.2 1.9
8 TH	0335 0956 1604 2220	6.3 1.8 6.4 1.7	23 F	0436 1059 1655 2308	6.5 1.7 6.4 1.7
9 F ●	0426 1047 1652 2308	6.8 1.2 6.8 1.2	24 SA ○	0509 1132 1726 2340	6.7 1.5 6.6 1.5
10 SA	0513 1134 1737 2355	7.3 0.8 7.2 0.9	25 SU	0539 1202 1755	6.8 1.4 6.7
11 SU	0558 1220 1821	7.6 0.5 7.3	26 M	0010 0608 1230 1823	1.5 6.9 1.4 6.7
12 M	0039 0642 1304 1903	0.7 7.7 0.5 7.3	27 TU	0039 0635 1258 1850	1.4 6.8 1.4 6.6
13 TU	0124 0725 1347 1945	0.7 7.6 0.7 7.1	28 W	0108 0703 1325 1917	1.5 6.7 1.6 6.5
14 W	0207 0807 1430 2027	1.0 7.3 1.1 6.7	29 TH	0137 0730 1353 1945	1.7 6.5 1.8 6.3
15 TH	0252 0850 1515 2111	1.4 6.8 1.6 6.3			

MARCH

	Time	m		Time	m
1 F	0207 0759 1423 2017	1.9 6.3 2.1 6.0	16 SA	0311 0906 1531 2125	1.9 6.0 2.4 5.8
2 SA	0241 0832 1500 2056	2.2 5.9 2.5 5.7	17 SU ☾	0405 1002 1629 2234	2.5 5.4 2.9 5.3
3 SU ☽	0325 0916 1548 2151	2.6 5.5 2.8 5.4	18 M	0516 1128 1753	3.0 5.0 3.2
4 M	0421 1021 1656 2315	2.9 5.2 3.1 5.1	19 TU	0016 0655 1320 1934	5.1 3.1 5.0 3.1
5 TU	0542 1201 1832	3.0 5.0 3.1	20 W	0153 0823 1434 2043	5.3 2.8 5.4 2.7
6 W	0054 0720 1346 2005	5.3 2.8 5.3 2.8	21 TH	0252 0917 1520 2130	5.7 2.3 5.8 2.3
7 TH	0218 0841 1456 2111	5.7 2.3 5.9 2.1	22 F	0335 0958 1557 2208	6.1 2.0 6.1 2.0
8 F	0318 0940 1549 2203	6.4 1.6 6.5 1.5	23 SA	0410 1033 1629 2241	6.4 1.7 6.4 1.7
9 SA	0409 1030 1635 2251	7.0 1.0 7.0 1.0	24 SU	0442 1103 1658 2312	6.6 1.5 6.6 1.5
10 SU ●	0455 1116 1718 2336	7.5 0.6 7.4 0.6	25 M ○	0511 1132 1726 2341	6.8 1.4 6.8 1.4
11 M	0539 1159 1800	7.8 0.3 7.6	26 TU	0539 1200 1753	6.9 1.3 6.8
12 TU	0019 0621 1242 1839	0.5 7.9 0.4 7.5	27 W	0010 0606 1227 1820	1.4 6.9 1.4 6.8
13 W	0101 0701 1323 1918	0.5 7.7 0.6 7.3	28 TH	0039 0633 1255 1847	1.4 6.8 1.5 6.7
14 TH	0143 0741 1403 1957	0.8 7.3 1.1 6.8	29 F	0108 0701 1323 1916	1.6 6.6 1.8 6.5
15 F	0226 0822 1445 2038	1.3 6.7 1.7 6.3	30 SA	0141 0731 1355 1948	1.8 6.3 2.1 6.2
			31 SU	0216 0807 1433 2029	2.1 5.9 2.4 5.8

APRIL

	Time	m		Time	m
1 M	0302 0853 1523 2127	2.5 5.5 2.8 5.4	16 TU	0451 1101 1721 2342	2.9 5.0 3.2 5.1
2 TU ☽	0400 1003 1634 2255	2.8 5.2 3.1 5.2	17 W	0620 1241 1855	3.0 5.0 3.1
3 W	0523 1146 1812	2.9 5.1 3.1	18 TH	0111 0742 1355 2005	5.3 2.8 5.3 2.8
4 TH	0035 0701 1328 1945	5.4 2.7 5.4 2.7	19 F	0213 0838 1443 2053	5.6 2.5 5.7 2.4
5 F	0155 0819 1435 2049	5.9 2.1 6.0 2.0	20 SA	0257 0919 1520 2131	5.9 2.1 6.0 2.1
6 SA	0255 0917 1526 2140	6.5 1.5 6.6 1.4	21 SU	0333 0955 1553 2206	6.2 1.9 6.3 1.8
7 SU	0345 1006 1611 2228	7.0 1.0 7.1 0.9	22 M	0406 1027 1624 2238	6.4 1.7 6.5 1.6
8 M ●	0431 1052 1654 2312	7.5 0.6 7.4 0.6	23 TU	0437 1058 1653 2310	6.6 1.5 6.7 1.5
9 TU	0515 1135 1735 2356	7.7 0.5 7.5 0.5	24 W ○	0507 1128 1723 2341	6.7 1.5 6.7 1.5
10 W	0556 1217 1814	7.7 0.6 7.4	25 TH	0537 1158 1752	6.7 1.5 6.7
11 TH	0038 0637 1257 1852	0.7 7.4 0.9 7.2	26 F	0013 0608 1228 1823	1.5 6.6 1.6 6.7
12 F	0120 0717 1337 1930	1.0 7.0 1.4 6.7	27 SA	0046 0639 1301 1855	1.6 6.5 1.8 6.5
13 SA	0203 0758 1419 2011	1.5 6.4 1.9 6.2	28 SU	0123 0715 1338 1933	1.8 6.2 2.1 6.2
14 SU	0249 0842 1505 2100	2.0 5.8 2.5 5.7	29 M	0204 0756 1421 2021	2.1 5.9 2.4 5.9
15 M ☾	0342 0939 1602 2208	2.6 5.3 3.0 5.3	30 TU	0254 0850 1516 2124	2.4 5.5 2.7 5.6

MAY

	Time	m		Time	m
1 W ☽	0356 1004 1628 2247	2.6 5.3 2.9 5.5	16 TH	0529 1139 1755	2.9 5.1 3.1
2 TH	0514 1134 1756	2.6 5.3 2.8	17 F	0007 0638 1249 1903	5.3 2.8 5.2 2.9
3 F	0012 0638 1259 1917	5.6 2.4 5.6 2.5	18 SA	0111 0738 1346 1959	5.4 2.6 5.5 2.6
4 SA	0126 0749 1404 2020	6.0 2.0 6.1 2.0	19 SU	0202 0827 1431 2044	5.6 2.4 5.8 2.4
5 SU	0225 0847 1457 2113	6.5 1.5 6.5 1.5	20 M	0246 0909 1510 2125	5.9 2.2 6.0 2.1
6 M	0317 0939 1544 2202	6.9 1.2 6.9 1.1	21 TU	0325 0947 1546 2202	6.1 2.0 6.3 1.9
7 TU	0405 1026 1628 2248	7.2 0.9 7.1 0.9	22 W	0402 1023 1621 2239	6.3 1.8 6.5 1.7
8 W ●	0450 1110 1710 2333	7.3 0.9 7.2 0.9	23 TH ○	0437 1058 1656 2315	6.4 1.7 6.6 1.6
9 TH	0533 1153 1750	7.2 1.0 7.1	24 F	0513 1133 1730 2352	6.5 1.7 6.6 1.6
10 F	0017 0616 1234 1830	1.0 7.0 1.3 6.9	25 SA	0549 1209 1807	6.5 1.7 6.6
11 SA	0100 0657 1315 1911	1.3 6.6 1.6 6.6	26 SU	0031 0628 1248 1847	1.6 6.4 1.8 6.5
12 SU	0144 0740 1358 1953	1.7 6.2 2.1 6.2	27 M	0113 0710 1331 1932	1.7 6.2 2.0 6.3
13 M	0230 0825 1443 2042	2.1 5.8 2.5 5.8	28 TU	0200 0758 1419 2023	1.9 6.0 2.2 6.1
14 TU	0321 0919 1536 2141	2.5 5.4 2.8 5.5	29 W	0252 0854 1515 2124	2.0 5.8 2.4 5.9
15 W ☾	0420 1025 1641 2253	2.8 5.1 3.0 5.3	30 TH ☽	0351 0959 1620 2232	2.2 5.6 2.5 5.9
			31 F	0458 1111 1732 2343	2.2 5.6 2.5 5.9

JUNE

	Time	m		Time	m
1 SA	0609 1222 1843	2.2 5.7 2.3	16 SU	0628 1235 1853	2.8 5.3 2.8
2 SU	0051 0715 1327 1947	6.1 2.0 6.0 2.0	17 M	0057 0725 1332 1949	5.4 2.7 5.5 2.7
3 M	0153 0816 1425 2045	6.3 1.8 6.3 1.7	18 TU	0153 0818 1423 2041	5.6 2.5 5.7 2.4
4 TU	0250 0911 1517 2139	6.5 1.6 6.5 1.5	19 W	0243 0906 1509 2128	5.8 2.3 6.0 2.2
5 W	0342 1002 1605 2229	6.7 1.5 6.7 1.4	20 TH	0329 0950 1552 2212	6.0 2.1 6.2 1.9
6 TH ●	0430 1049 1650 2316	6.7 1.4 6.8 1.3	21 F	0413 1033 1634 2255	6.2 1.9 6.4 1.7
7 F	0516 1134 1734	6.7 1.5 6.8	22 SA ○	0455 1115 1716 2338	6.3 1.8 6.6 1.6
8 SA	0001 0600 1216 1816	1.4 6.6 1.6 6.7	23 SU	0538 1157 1759	6.4 1.7 6.7
9 SU	0045 0643 1258 1857	1.5 6.4 1.8 6.5	24 M	0022 0622 1241 1843	1.5 6.5 1.7 6.7
10 M	0128 0724 1340 1938	1.7 6.1 2.0 6.3	25 TU	0107 0708 1326 1930	1.4 6.4 1.7 6.7
11 TU	0210 0806 1422 2020	2.0 5.9 2.3 6.0	26 W	0154 0755 1414 2019	1.5 6.3 1.8 6.6
12 W	0254 0850 1506 2106	2.2 5.6 2.5 5.7	27 TH	0244 0846 1506 2111	1.6 6.2 1.9 6.4
13 TH	0341 0939 1555 2158	2.5 5.4 2.7 5.5	28 F ☽	0336 0940 1601 2208	1.8 6.0 2.1 6.2
14 F ☾	0432 1034 1651 2256	2.7 5.3 2.9 5.4	29 SA	0434 1039 1702 2309	1.9 5.9 2.2 6.0
15 SA	0529 1135 1752 2358	2.8 5.2 2.9 5.3	30 SU	0536 1143 1808	2.1 5.8 2.3

BREST
LAT 48°23′N
LONG 4°30′W

TIMES AND HEIGHTS OF HIGH AND LOW WATER (Heights in Metres)

TIME ZONE
European Standard Time (UT+0100)
For Summer Time (area enclosed in shaded box) add 1 hour

2024

JULY

Date	Day	Time	m
1	M	0015 0641 1251 1916	5.9 2.2 5.8 2.2
2	TU	0124 0747 1357 2023	5.9 2.2 5.9 2.1
3	W	0229 0849 1458 2123	6.0 2.1 6.1 1.9
4	TH	0328 0945 1551 2217	6.2 1.9 6.3 1.7
5	F ●	0419 1035 1639 2306	6.3 1.8 6.5 1.6
6	SA	0506 1121 1723 2350	6.4 1.7 6.6 1.5
7	SU	0548 1202 1803	6.4 1.7 6.6
8	M	0030 0627 1241 1841	1.5 6.4 1.7 6.6
9	TU	0109 0704 1319 1917	1.6 6.3 1.8 6.5
10	W	0145 0739 1355 1952	1.8 6.1 2.0 6.3
11	TH	0221 0814 1431 2027	2.0 5.9 2.2 6.0
12	F	0257 0851 1509 2105	2.2 5.7 2.4 5.8
13	SA ☾	0336 0932 1551 2148	2.5 5.5 2.6 5.5
14	SU	0420 1021 1641 2242	2.7 5.3 2.8 5.3
15	M	0514 1122 1742 2347	2.9 5.2 2.9 5.2
16	TU	0618 1230 1851	2.9 5.3 2.9
17	W	0058 0725 1336 1958	5.3 2.8 5.4 2.7
18	TH	0205 0828 1437 2059	5.4 2.6 5.7 2.4
19	F	0304 0924 1530 2151	5.7 2.3 6.1 2.1
20	SA	0355 1013 1618 2240	6.0 2.0 6.4 1.7
21	SU O	0443 1100 1704 2326	6.3 1.7 6.7 1.3
22	M	0528 1145 1749	6.6 1.4 7.0
23	TU	0011 0612 1230 1833	1.1 6.8 1.3 7.2
24	W	0055 0656 1315 1917	1.0 6.8 1.2 7.2
25	TH	0140 0740 1400 2002	1.0 6.8 1.3 7.1
26	F	0226 0825 1447 2048	1.2 6.6 1.5 6.8
27	SA	0313 0912 1536 2138	1.5 6.3 1.8 6.4
28	SU ☽	0404 1004 1631 2234	1.9 6.0 2.1 6.0
29	M	0502 1106 1736 2342	2.3 5.7 2.4 5.7
30	TU	0609 1220 1851	2.5 5.6 2.6
31	W	0103 0725 1341 2011	5.5 2.6 5.6 2.5

AUGUST

Date	Day	Time	m
1	TH	0221 0838 1451 2118	5.6 2.5 5.9 2.2
2	F	0324 0938 1546 2212	5.9 2.2 6.2 1.9
3	SA	0413 1027 1632 2257	6.1 2.0 6.4 1.7
4	SU ●	0456 1109 1711 2336	6.3 1.8 6.6 1.5
5	M	0533 1146 1747	6.4 1.6 6.7
6	TU	0011 0606 1220 1819	1.5 6.5 1.6 6.7
7	W	0044 0637 1252 1849	1.5 6.5 1.6 6.7
8	TH	0115 0707 1323 1918	1.6 6.4 1.7 6.5
9	F	0144 0736 1354 1947	1.7 6.3 1.9 6.3
10	SA	0214 0806 1425 2018	2.0 6.0 2.1 6.1
11	SU	0245 0838 1500 2052	2.3 5.8 2.4 5.8
12	M ☾	0321 0918 1540 2136	2.6 5.5 2.7 5.4
13	TU	0407 1012 1637 2239	2.9 5.3 3.0 5.1
14	W	0511 1129 1754	3.1 5.1 3.1
15	TH	0006 0636 1256 1921	5.0 3.1 5.2 2.9
16	F	0136 0759 1412 2036	5.2 2.9 5.6 2.5
17	SA	0246 0904 1512 2133	5.6 2.4 6.1 2.0
18	SU	0340 0956 1602 2223	6.1 1.9 6.6 1.5
19	M O	0428 1044 1648 2309	6.6 1.5 7.0 1.0
20	TU	0512 1129 1732 2353	7.0 1.1 7.4 0.7
21	W	0554 1212 1815	7.2 0.8 7.6
22	TH	0036 0636 1255 1857	0.6 7.3 0.8 7.6
23	F	0119 0717 1339 1939	0.7 7.2 0.9 7.4
24	SA	0202 0758 1423 2021	1.0 6.9 1.2 6.9
25	SU	0246 0841 1510 2108	1.4 6.5 1.7 6.4
26	M ☽	0333 0930 1603 2203	2.0 6.0 2.2 5.8
27	TU	0430 1033 1710 2317	2.5 5.6 2.7 5.3
28	W	0543 1200 1837	2.9 5.3 2.9
29	TH	0056 0714 1336 2008	5.2 3.0 5.5 2.7
30	F	0220 0833 1446 2112	5.4 2.7 5.8 2.3
31	SA	0317 0929 1536 2200	5.8 2.3 6.2 1.9

SEPTEMBER

Date	Day	Time	m
1	SU	0400 1012 1616 2240	6.2 2.0 6.5 1.6
2	M	0437 1050 1651 2314	6.4 1.7 6.7 1.5
3	TU ●	0509 1123 1722 2345	6.6 1.6 6.8 1.4
4	W	0538 1153 1750	6.7 1.5 6.9
5	TH	0014 0606 1222 1818	1.4 6.7 1.5 6.8
6	F	0041 0633 1250 1845	1.5 6.6 1.6 6.7
7	SA	0108 0700 1319 1911	1.6 6.5 1.8 6.5
8	SU	0135 0727 1348 1939	1.9 6.3 2.0 6.2
9	M	0204 0756 1420 2011	2.2 6.0 2.3 5.9
10	TU	0238 0832 1503 2051	2.5 5.7 2.7 5.5
11	W ☽	0322 0923 1556 2153	2.9 5.4 3.0 5.1
12	TH	0425 1045 1715 2331	3.2 5.1 3.2 5.0
13	F	0559 1227 1853	3.3 5.2 3.0
14	SA	0116 0737 1351 2015	5.2 2.9 5.6 2.5
15	SU	0229 0844 1451 2113	5.7 2.4 6.2 1.9
16	M	0321 0936 1540 2201	6.3 1.8 6.8 1.2
17	TU	0407 1022 1626 2247	6.9 1.2 7.3 0.8
18	W O	0449 1107 1709 2330	7.3 0.8 7.7 0.5
19	TH	0531 1150 1751	7.5 0.6 7.8
20	F	0013 0611 1232 1832	0.4 7.5 0.6 7.7
21	SA	0054 0651 1315 1914	0.6 7.4 0.8 7.4
22	SU	0136 0731 1359 1956	1.0 7.0 1.3 6.9
23	M	0219 0813 1446 2042	1.6 6.5 1.8 6.2
24	TU ☾	0306 0901 1540 2139	2.2 6.0 2.4 5.6
25	W	0404 1009 1651 2302	2.8 5.5 2.9 5.1
26	TH	0523 1147 1826	3.2 5.3 3.0
27	F	0047 0702 1324 1954	5.1 3.1 5.5 2.7
28	SA	0206 0816 1427 2052	5.4 2.7 5.8 2.3
29	SU	0256 0907 1512 2136	5.9 2.3 6.2 2.0
30	M	0335 0947 1550 2212	6.2 2.0 6.5 1.7

OCTOEER

Date	Day	Time	m
1	TU	0409 1022 1622 2244	6.5 1.7 6.7 1.5
2	W ●	0439 1053 1651 2314	6.7 1.6 6.8 1.4
3	TH	0507 1123 1719 2342	6.8 1.5 6.9 1.4
4	F	0535 1151 1747	6.8 1.5 6.9
5	SA	0009 0602 1220 1814	1.5 6.8 1.6 6.7
6	SU	0036 0628 1249 1841	1.7 6.7 1.8 6.5
7	M	0104 0656 1320 1910	1.9 6.5 2.0 6.3
8	TU	0134 0727 1354 1943	2.2 6.2 2.3 5.9
9	W	0210 0805 1438 2027	2.5 5.8 2.6 5.5
10	TH ☽	0257 0858 1534 2133	2.9 5.5 2.9 5.2
11	F	0403 1023 1654 2313	3.2 5.2 3.1 5.0
12	SA	0536 1203 1829	3.2 5.3 2.9
13	SU	0053 0711 1324 1948	5.3 2.9 5.8 2.4
14	M	0202 0817 1424 2045	5.9 2.3 6.4 1.7
15	TU	0254 0910 1514 2135	6.5 1.7 7.0 1.2
16	W	0340 0957 1600 2221	7.0 1.1 7.4 0.8
17	TH O	0424 1042 1644 2305	7.4 0.8 7.7 0.6
18	F	0506 1126 1727 2348	7.6 0.6 7.8 0.6
19	SA	0546 1210 1810	7.6 0.7 7.6
20	SU	0031 0627 1254 1852	0.9 7.4 1.0 7.2
21	M	0113 0708 1339 1935	1.3 7.0 1.4 6.7
22	TU	0157 0751 1427 2023	1.8 6.5 2.0 6.1
23	W	0245 0842 1522 2122	2.4 6.0 2.5 5.5
24	TH ☾	0342 0950 1632 2242	2.9 5.5 2.9 5.2
25	F	0458 1120 1758	3.2 5.3 3.0
26	SA	0014 0627 1247 1918	5.2 3.1 5.5 2.8
27	SU	0128 0739 1350 2015	5.4 2.8 5.7 2.5
28	M	0219 0831 1436 2059	5.8 2.5 6.1 2.2
29	TU	0259 0912 1514 2136	6.1 2.2 6.3 1.9
30	W	0334 0948 1548 2209	6.4 1.9 6.5 1.7
31	TH	0406 1021 1619 2240	6.6 1.7 6.7 1.7

NOVEMBER

Date	Day	Time	m
1	F ●	0436 1053 1649 2311	6.7 1.6 6.7 1.6
2	SA	0506 1124 1719 2341	6.8 1.6 6.7 1.7
3	SU	0535 1156 1749	6.8 1.7 6.6
4	M	0011 0605 1228 1820	1.8 6.7 1.8 6.5
5	TU	0042 0637 1303 1854	2.0 6.5 2.0 6.2
6	W	0117 0713 1342 1933	2.2 6.3 2.2 5.9
7	TH	0158 0756 1429 2022	2.5 6.0 2.5 5.6
8	F	0248 0853 1527 2130	2.8 5.7 2.7 5.4
9	SA ☽	0353 1010 1638 2255	3.0 5.5 2.8 5.3
10	SU	0514 1134 1800	3.0 5.6 2.6
11	M	0019 0637 1249 1913	5.5 2.7 6.0 2.2
12	TU	0127 0744 1351 2013	6.0 2.2 6.4 1.8
13	W	0223 0840 1445 2106	6.5 1.7 6.9 1.4
14	TH	0312 0931 1534 2155	6.9 1.3 7.2 1.1
15	F O	0359 1019 1622 2242	7.2 1.0 7.4 1.0
16	SA	0443 1106 1707 2327	7.4 0.9 7.4 1.0
17	SU	0527 1152 1752	7.3 1.0 7.2
18	M	0011 0610 1238 1836	1.2 7.2 1.2 6.9
19	TU	0055 0653 1324 1922	1.5 6.9 1.5 6.5
20	W	0140 0738 1412 2010	1.9 6.5 2.0 6.0
21	TH	0227 0827 1504 2103	2.3 6.1 2.4 5.6
22	F	0320 0924 1602 2206	2.7 5.7 2.7 5.4
23	SA ☾	0421 1032 1709 2317	3.0 5.5 2.9 5.3
24	SU	0531 1144 1817	3.0 5.4 2.9
25	M	0026 0639 1250 1919	5.3 3.0 5.5 2.7
26	TU	0124 0739 1345 2010	5.5 2.7 5.7 2.5
27	W	0213 0828 1431 2053	5.8 2.5 6.0 2.3
28	TH	0254 0910 1511 2132	6.1 2.3 6.2 2.1
29	F	0332 0949 1548 2209	6.3 2.1 6.3 2.0
30	SA	0408 1026 1624 2244	6.5 1.9 6.5 1.9

DECEMBER

Date	Day	Time	m
1	SU ●	0442 1102 1659 2319	6.6 1.8 6.5 1.8
2	M	0517 1138 1734 2354	6.7 1.7 6.5 1.9
3	TU	0552 1215 1810	6.7 1.8 6.4
4	W	0031 0630 1255 1850	1.9 6.6 1.8 6.3
5	TH	0111 0711 1337 1933	2.1 6.5 1.9 6.1
6	F	0155 0757 1424 2023	2.2 6.3 2.1 5.9
7	SA	0245 0850 1518 2122	2.4 6.1 2.3 5.7
8	SU ☽	0342 0952 1619 2228	2.5 6.0 2.4 5.7
9	M	0447 1100 1726 2338	2.6 5.9 2.4 5.7
10	TU	0558 1209 1835	2.5 6.0 2.2
11	W	0047 0707 1316 1940	5.9 2.3 6.2 2.0
12	TH	0150 0811 1418 2039	6.2 2.0 6.5 1.8
13	F	0247 0909 1514 2133	6.5 1.7 6.7 1.6
14	SA	0339 1003 1606 2224	6.8 1.4 6.9 1.4
15	SU O	0428 1053 1655 2312	7.0 1.3 6.9 1.4
16	M	0515 1141 1741 2358	7.1 1.3 6.9 1.5
17	TU	0600 1227 1826	7.0 1.3 6.7
18	W	0042 0643 1311 1909	1.6 6.9 1.5 6.5
19	TH	0125 0725 1355 1952	1.8 6.7 1.8 6.2
20	F	0208 0807 1438 2034	2.1 6.4 2.1 5.9
21	SA	0251 0850 1523 2120	2.3 6.1 2.4 5.7
22	SU ☾	0337 0936 1611 2211	2.6 5.8 2.7 5.4
23	M	0428 1030 1706 2309	2.8 5.5 2.8 5.3
24	TU	0526 1132 1806	3.0 5.4 2.9
25	W	0012 0629 1238 1908	5.3 3.0 5.4 2.9
26	TH	0115 0733 1340 2005	5.4 2.9 5.5 2.7
27	F	0211 0830 1434 2056	5.6 2.7 5.7 2.5
28	SA	0300 0919 1521 2141	5.9 2.4 5.9 2.3
29	SU	0344 1004 1604 2223	6.2 2.1 6.1 2.1
30	M ●	0425 1045 1645 2303	6.4 1.9 6.3 1.9
31	TU	0505 1126 1725 2343	6.6 1.7 6.5 1.8

POINTE DE GRAVE

LAT 45°34′N
LONG 1°04′W

TIMES AND HEIGHTS OF HIGH AND LOW WATER (Heights in Metres)

TIME ZONE
European Standard Time (UT+0100)
For Summer Time (area enclosed in shaded box) add 1 hour

2024

JANUARY

Date	Time	m	Time	m	Time	m	Time	m
1 M	0153	1.8	0810	4.8	1424	1.8	2034	4.5
2 TU	0233	2.0	0849	4.6	1504	2.0	2118	4.3
3 W	0315	2.1	0934	4.5	1548	2.1	2212	4.2
4 TH ☽	0404	2.2	1029	4.3	1641	2.2	2317	4.1
5 F	0502	2.3	1135	4.2	1742	2.3		
6 SA	0024	4.2	0604	2.3	1246	4.3	1845	2.3
7 SU	0126	4.3	0708	2.2	1352	4.4	1947	2.1
8 M	0222	4.5	0809	2.0	1450	4.6	2043	2.0
9 TU	0312	4.8	0906	1.8	1542	4.8	2135	1.7
10 W	0400	5.0	1000	1.6	1631	4.9	2223	1.5
11 TH ●	0447	5.2	1050	1.3	1718	5.1	2311	1.3
12 F	0534	5.4	1139	1.1	1805	5.2	2358	1.2
13 SA	0622	5.5	1225	1.0	1851	5.2		
14 SU	0043	1.2	0710	5.5	1311	1.0	1938	5.1
15 M	0129	1.2	0758	5.4	1356	1.1	2026	5.0
16 TU	0215	1.3	0848	5.3	1442	1.2	2116	4.8
17 W	0302	1.4	0940	5.1	1531	1.5	2211	4.6
18 TH ☾	0355	1.6	1037	4.8	1626	1.7	2314	4.4
19 F	0457	1.8	1144	4.6	1731	2.0		
20 SA	0030	4.4	0608	2.0	1303	4.4	1843	2.1
21 SU	0145	4.4	0723	2.0	1417	4.4	1955	2.1
22 M	0247	4.6	0834	1.9	1517	4.5	2058	1.9
23 TU	0338	4.7	0933	1.8	1606	4.7	2150	1.8
24 W	0422	4.9	1023	1.6	1647	4.8	2235	1.6
25 TH ○	0500	5.0	1106	1.5	1724	4.9	2314	1.5
26 F	0535	5.1	1144	1.4	1757	4.9	2350	1.5
27 SA	0608	5.1	1218	1.4	1827	4.9		
28 SU	0024	1.5	0638	5.1	1251	1.4	1857	4.9
29 M	0056	1.5	0708	5.0	1322	1.5	1926	4.8
30 TU	0127	1.5	0737	4.9	1352	1.6	1956	4.7
31 W	0158	1.7	0809	4.8	1422	1.7	2029	4.6

FEBRUARY

Date	Time	m	Time	m	Time	m	Time	m
1 TH	0230	1.8	0843	4.6	1454	1.9	2108	4.4
2 F	0307	2.0	0925	4.4	1534	2.1	2158	4.2
3 SA ☽	0356	2.1	1020	4.2	1628	2.3	2309	4.1
4 SU	0501	2.3	1139	4.1	1742	2.4		
5 M	0034	4.1	0619	2.3	1312	4.1	1904	2.3
6 TU	0151	4.3	0737	2.2	1429	4.3	2018	2.1
7 W	0253	4.6	0848	1.9	1530	4.6	2119	1.8
8 TH	0347	5.0	0948	1.5	1621	4.9	2212	1.5
9 F ●	0436	5.3	1040	1.2	1708	5.2	2300	1.2
10 SA	0523	5.5	1127	0.9	1752	5.3	2346	1.0
11 SU	0608	5.7	1212	0.7	1836	5.4		
12 M	0030	0.8	0653	5.7	1255	0.7	1918	5.4
13 TU	0113	0.8	0738	5.6	1337	0.8	2001	5.2
14 W	0155	1.0	0822	5.4	1418	1.1	2043	5.0
15 TH	0238	1.2	0908	5.1	1501	1.4	2130	4.7
16 F ☾	0325	1.5	0959	4.7	1550	1.8	2227	4.4
17 SA	0423	1.9	1106	4.3	1652	2.1	2353	4.2
18 SU	0539	2.1	1244	4.1	1813	2.3		
19 M	0130	4.2	0708	2.2	1410	4.2	1941	2.3
20 TU	0239	4.4	0828	2.0	1512	4.3	2049	2.1
21 W	0331	4.6	0925	1.8	1559	4.5	2140	1.8
22 TH	0412	4.8	1010	1.6	1635	4.7	2221	1.6
23 F	0445	4.9	1049	1.4	1706	4.8	2258	1.4
24 SA ○	0516	5.1	1123	1.3	1734	4.9	2331	1.3
25 SU	0544	5.1	1155	1.3	1801	5.0		
26 M	0002	1.3	0611	5.1	1224	1.3	1827	5.0
27 TU	0031	1.3	0638	5.1	1252	1.3	1854	5.0
28 W	0058	1.4	0705	5.0	1318	1.4	1921	4.9
29 TH	0125	1.5	0733	4.9	1344	1.6	1951	4.8

MARCH

Date	Time	m	Time	m	Time	m	Time	m
1 F	0153	1.6	0805	4.7	1413	1.7	2025	4.6
2 SA	0229	1.8	0842	4.5	1449	1.9	2108	4.4
3 SU ☽	0311	2.0	0933	4.3	1537	2.2	2213	4.2
4 M	0412	2.2	1053	4.0	1650	2.4	2349	4.1
5 TU	0540	2.3	1247	4.0	1829	2.4		
6 W	0125	4.3	0715	2.2	1413	4.3	1959	2.2
7 TH	0234	4.6	0834	1.8	1514	4.6	2103	1.8
8 F	0329	5.0	0932	1.4	1604	5.0	2155	1.4
9 SA	0418	5.4	1022	1.0	1649	5.3	2243	1.0
10 SU ●	0504	5.6	1108	0.7	1731	5.5	2327	0.8
11 M	0548	5.8	1151	0.6	1812	5.5		
12 TU	0010	0.7	0631	5.8	1232	0.7	1853	5.5
13 W	0051	0.7	0713	5.7	1311	0.8	1932	5.3
14 TH	0131	0.9	0755	5.4	1350	1.1	2012	5.0
15 F	0212	1.2	0839	5.0	1430	1.5	2054	4.7
16 SA	0257	1.5	0927	4.5	1516	1.9	2146	4.4
17 SU ☾	0352	1.9	1034	4.1	1616	2.3	2315	4.1
18 M	0512	2.3	1227	3.9	1745	2.5		
19 TU	0108	4.1	0651	2.3	1355	4.0	1921	2.4
20 W	0220	4.3	0810	2.1	1455	4.3	2029	2.1
21 TH	0311	4.5	0903	1.8	1537	4.5	2117	1.9
22 F	0349	4.7	0945	1.6	1609	4.7	2156	1.6
23 SA	0420	4.9	1021	1.4	1637	4.8	2231	1.4
24 SU	0448	5.0	1054	1.3	1704	5.0	2303	1.3
25 M ○	0515	5.1	1124	1.3	1730	5.0	2333	1.3
26 TU	0542	5.1	1152	1.3	1757	5.1		
27 W	0002	1.3	0609	5.1	1219	1.3	1824	5.1
28 TH	0029	1.3	0636	5.1	1246	1.4	1851	5.0
29 F	0058	1.4	0705	4.9	1313	1.5	1922	4.9
30 SA	0127	1.5	0737	4.8	1344	1.7	1957	4.7
31 SU	0204	1.7	0817	4.5	1421	1.9	2042	4.5

APRIL

Date	Time	m	Time	m	Time	m	Time	m
1 M	0247	1.9	0911	4.2	1510	2.2	2148	4.3
2 TU ☽	0349	2.2	1038	4.0	1624	2.4	2325	4.2
3 W	0518	2.3	1233	4.1	1805	2.4		
4 TH	0101	4.4	0655	2.1	1351	4.4	1935	2.1
5 F	0209	4.7	0811	1.7	1450	4.7	2039	1.7
6 SA	0305	5.1	0908	1.3	1539	5.1	2131	1.3
7 SU	0354	5.4	0957	1.0	1624	5.3	2218	1.0
8 M ●	0440	5.6	1042	0.8	1706	5.5	2303	0.8
9 TU	0524	5.7	1124	0.7	1747	5.5	2345	0.7
10 W	0607	5.7	1205	0.8	1827	5.5		
11 TH	0027	0.8	0650	5.5	1244	1.0	1907	5.3
12 F	0107	1.0	0732	5.2	1322	1.3	1946	5.0
13 SA	0148	1.3	0814	4.8	1402	1.6	2028	4.7
14 SU	0232	1.6	0902	4.4	1448	2.0	2119	4.4
15 M ☾	0327	2.0	1009	4.1	1547	2.3	2238	4.1
16 TU	0444	2.3	1154	3.9	1711	2.5		
17 W	0025	4.1	0614	2.3	1319	4.0	1840	2.4
18 TH	0139	4.2	0731	2.1	1416	4.2	1949	2.2
19 F	0232	4.4	0826	1.9	1458	4.4	2039	2.0
20 SA	0311	4.6	0908	1.7	1531	4.6	2120	1.7
21 SU	0344	4.8	0945	1.5	1600	4.8	2156	1.6
22 M	0414	4.9	1018	1.4	1629	4.9	2229	1.4
23 TU	0443	5.0	1048	1.4	1658	5.0	2300	1.4
24 W ○	0513	5.1	1118	1.4	1727	5.1	2332	1.3
25 TH	0542	5.1	1148	1.4	1757	5.1		
26 F	0003	1.3	0613	5.0	1218	1.4	1828	5.0
27 SA	0036	1.4	0646	4.9	1251	1.6	1903	4.9
28 SU	0112	1.5	0723	4.7	1327	1.7	1944	4.8
29 M	0150	1.6	0809	4.5	1409	1.9	2036	4.6
30 TU	0239	1.8	0910	4.3	1503	2.1	2145	4.4

MAY

Date	Time	m	Time	m	Time	m	Time	m
1 W ☽	0342	2.0	1038	4.1	1615	2.3	2312	4.4
2 TH	0503	2.1	1212	4.2	1743	2.2		
3 F	0033	4.5	0628	1.9	1322	4.5	1902	2.0
4 SA	0139	4.8	0739	1.6	1420	4.8	2006	1.7
5 SU	0237	5.1	0836	1.4	1510	5.0	2100	1.4
6 M	0329	5.3	0927	1.1	1556	5.2	2150	1.1
7 TU	0417	5.5	1013	1.0	1640	5.4	2237	1.0
8 W ●	0502	5.5	1057	1.0	1723	5.4	2321	1.0
9 TH	0547	5.4	1139	1.1	1805	5.3		
10 F	0004	1.0	0630	5.3	1219	1.3	1846	5.2
11 SA	0046	1.2	0713	5.0	1259	1.5	1928	5.0
12 SU	0129	1.4	0756	4.7	1340	1.7	2011	4.8
13 M	0214	1.7	0843	4.4	1426	2.0	2059	4.5
14 TU	0306	2.0	0940	4.1	1522	2.2	2201	4.3
15 W ☾	0409	2.2	1056	4.0	1630	2.4	2318	4.2
16 TH	0519	2.2	1213	4.0	1741	2.4		
17 F	0031	4.2	0628	2.2	1315	4.1	1847	2.3
18 SA	0131	4.3	0729	2.1	1403	4.3	1944	2.1
19 SU	0219	4.4	0819	1.9	1443	4.5	2032	1.9
20 M	0259	4.6	0900	1.8	1519	4.7	2113	1.8
21 TU	0336	4.7	0937	1.6	1553	4.8	2151	1.6
22 W	0412	4.8	1012	1.6	1627	5.0	2228	1.5
23 TH ○	0447	4.9	1046	1.5	1701	5.0	2305	1.4
24 F	0522	4.9	1122	1.5	1737	5.1	2343	1.4
25 SA	0558	4.9	1159	1.5	1815	5.1		
26 SU	0022	1.4	0638	4.8	1238	1.6	1856	5.0
27 M	0104	1.4	0722	4.7	1320	1.7	1944	4.9
28 TU	0149	1.5	0813	4.6	1407	1.8	2039	4.8
29 W	0239	1.7	0914	4.4	1501	1.9	2143	4.7
30 TH ☽	0336	1.8	1028	4.3	1604	2.0	2253	4.7
31 F	0443	1.8	1141	4.4	1716	2.0		

JUNE

Date	Time	m	Time	m	Time	m	Time	m
1 SA	0002	4.7	0554	1.8	1247	4.5	1827	1.9
2 SU	0107	4.8	0702	1.7	1347	4.7	1932	1.7
3 M	0208	4.9	0803	1.5	1442	4.9	2030	1.5
4 TU	0305	5.1	0857	1.4	1532	5.0	2124	1.4
5 W	0357	5.1	0947	1.3	1620	5.1	2215	1.3
6 TH ●	0446	5.2	1034	1.3	1705	5.2	2303	1.2
7 F	0532	5.1	1118	1.4	1749	5.2	2349	1.3
8 SA	0616	5.0	1200	1.5	1831	5.1		
9 SU	0033	1.4	0658	4.9	1242	1.6	1912	5.0
10 M	0115	1.5	0739	4.7	1323	1.7	1953	4.8
11 TU	0158	1.7	0819	4.5	1407	1.9	2034	4.7
12 W	0242	1.8	0903	4.3	1454	2.0	2120	4.5
13 TH	0331	2.0	0954	4.2	1546	2.1	2213	4.3
14 F ☾	0423	2.1	1054	4.1	1643	2.2	2314	4.2
15 SA	0520	2.2	1158	4.1	1741	2.2		
16 SU	0016	4.2	0619	2.2	1258	4.2	1839	2.2
17 M	0116	4.3	0716	2.1	1351	4.3	1935	2.1
18 TU	0210	4.4	0809	2.0	1437	4.5	2027	2.0
19 W	0259	4.5	0856	1.9	1520	4.7	2115	1.8
20 TH	0343	4.6	0939	1.7	1601	4.8	2200	1.6
21 F	0426	4.8	1022	1.6	1642	5.0	2245	1.5
22 SA ○	0509	4.8	1104	1.5	1724	5.1	2329	1.4
23 SU	0551	4.9	1147	1.5	1808	5.1		
24 M	0014	1.3	0636	4.9	1231	1.4	1854	5.1
25 TU	0059	1.3	0722	4.8	1316	1.4	1943	5.1
26 W	0144	1.3	0811	4.8	1402	1.5	2034	5.0
27 TH	0231	1.4	0904	4.6	1451	1.6	2129	5.0
28 F ☽	0321	1.5	1002	4.5	1545	1.7	2227	4.8
29 SA	0417	1.6	1105	4.5	1646	1.8	2329	4.7
30 SU	0520	1.7	1211	4.5	1754	1.8		

SUNRISE AND SUNSET TIMES

POINTE DE GRAVE
At 45°34′N 1°04′W
European Standard Time (UT+0100)

		Sunrise	Sunset
Jan	01	0845	1731
	15	0841	1747
Feb	01	0825	1811
	15	0806	1831
Mar	01	0743	1851
	15	0717	1910
European Summer Time (UT+0200)			
Apr	01	0745	2033
	15	0719	2051
May	01	0652	2111
	15	0634	2128
Jun	01	0619	2146
	15	0615	2155
Jul	01	0619	2157
	15	0630	2150
Aug	01	0648	2132
	15	0705	2112
Sep	01	0726	2042
	15	0743	2015
Oct	01	0803	1945
	15	0821	1919
European Standard Time (UT+0100)			
Nov	01	0744	1751
	15	0804	1734
Dec	01	0824	1722

POINTE DE GRAVE
LAT 45°34′N
LONG 1°04′W

TIMES AND HEIGHTS OF HIGH AND LOW WATER (Heights in Metres)

TIME ZONE
European Standard Time (UT+0100)
For Summer Time (area enclosed in shaded box) add 1 hour

2024

JULY

Date	Day	Time	m	Time	m	Time	m	Time	m
1	M	0036	4.7	0627	1.8	1318	4.5	1902	1.8
2	TU	0145	4.7	0734	1.8	1422	4.7	2008	1.7
3	W	0250	4.7	0835	1.7	1518	4.8	2109	1.6
4	TH	0346	4.8	0931	1.6	1608	4.9	2204	1.5
5	F	0436	4.8	1021	1.6	1654	5.0	● 2255	1.4
6	SA	0521	4.9	1107	1.5	1736	5.1	2340	1.4
7	SU	0602	4.9	1150	1.5	1816	5.1		
8	M	0022	1.4	0640	4.8	1229	1.5	1853	5.0
9	TU	0101	1.4	0715	4.7	1307	1.6	1927	4.9
10	W	0138	1.5	0748	4.6	1344	1.7	2001	4.8
11	TH	0214	1.6	0822	4.5	1421	1.8	2037	4.7
12	F	0250	1.8	0859	4.4	1500	1.9	2117	4.5
13	SA	0330	1.9	0944	4.2	1544	2.1	☾ 2203	4.3
14	SU	0415	2.1	1041	4.1	1637	2.2	2301	4.2
15	M	0511	2.2	1148	4.1	1738	2.3		
16	TU	0010	4.1	0614	2.3	1257	4.2	1842	2.2
17	W	0121	4.2	0719	2.2	1358	4.3	1946	2.1
18	TH	0226	4.3	0821	2.1	1452	4.5	2046	1.9
19	F	0322	4.5	0915	1.9	1541	4.8	2141	1.7
20	SA	0411	4.7	1005	1.7	1627	5.0	2231	1.4
21	SU	0458	4.9	1051	1.5	1713	5.2	O 2319	1.2
22	M	0543	5.0	1137	1.3	1758	5.3		
23	TU	0004	1.1	0627	5.1	1221	1.2	1844	5.4
24	W	0048	1.0	0711	5.1	1305	1.1	1930	5.4
25	TH	0131	1.0	0755	5.0	1348	1.2	2017	5.3
26	F	0214	1.1	0841	4.9	1433	1.3	2105	5.1
27	SA	0258	1.3	0931	4.7	1521	1.5	2158	4.9
28	SU	0348	1.5	1027	4.5	1617	1.7	☽ 2258	4.6
29	M	0446	1.8	1136	4.4	1725	1.9		
30	TU	0012	4.4	0557	2.0	1259	4.3	1842	2.0
31	W	0135	4.4	0714	2.1	1414	4.5	1959	1.9

AUGUST

Date	Day	Time	m	Time	m	Time	m	Time	m
1	TH	0246	4.4	0826	2.0	1513	4.6	2106	1.8
2	F	0343	4.6	0926	1.8	1602	4.8	2201	1.6
3	SA	0430	4.7	1015	1.6	1644	5.0	2247	1.4
4	SU	0509	4.8	1058	1.5	1721	5.1	● 2328	1.3
5	M	0544	4.9	1136	1.4	1755	5.1		
6	TU	0005	1.3	0615	4.9	1211	1.4	1826	5.1
7	W	0039	1.3	0644	4.9	1244	1.4	1855	5.0
8	TH	0110	1.4	0712	4.8	1315	1.5	1924	4.9
9	F	0140	1.5	0741	4.7	1345	1.6	1954	4.8
10	SA	0208	1.7	0812	4.6	1416	1.8	2027	4.6
11	SU	0238	1.8	0848	4.4	1448	1.9	2105	4.4
12	M	0313	2.0	0932	4.3	1532	2.1	☾ 2154	4.2
13	TU	0400	2.2	1035	4.1	1632	2.3	2306	4.0
14	W	0509	2.4	1202	4.1	1754	2.4		
15	TH	0040	4.0	0635	2.4	1325	4.2	1915	2.3
16	F	0202	4.2	0753	2.2	1430	4.5	2027	2.0
17	SA	0304	4.5	0857	1.9	1523	4.8	2126	1.6
18	SU	0356	4.7	0949	1.6	1610	5.1	2216	1.3
19	M	0442	5.0	1037	1.3	1656	5.4	O 2303	1.0
20	TU	0525	5.2	1121	1.1	1740	5.6	2347	0.8
21	W	0607	5.3	1205	0.9	1824	5.7		
22	TH	0029	0.8	0649	5.3	1247	0.9	1908	5.6
23	F	0110	0.8	0731	5.2	1328	0.9	1953	5.5
24	SA	0151	1.0	0813	5.1	1410	1.1	2039	5.2
25	SU	0232	1.3	0859	4.8	1455	1.4	2129	4.8
26	M	0318	1.6	0952	4.5	1549	1.8	☽ 2231	4.4
27	TU	0414	2.0	1108	4.3	1701	2.1		
28	W	0001	4.2	0532	2.3	1252	4.2	1833	2.2
29	TH	0135	4.2	0704	2.3	1410	4.4	1958	2.0
30	F	0244	4.3	0821	2.1	1508	4.6	2100	1.8
31	SA	0336	4.5	0916	1.8	1552	4.8	2148	1.6

SEPTEMBER

Date	Day	Time	m	Time	m	Time	m	Time	m
1	SU	0416	4.7	1000	1.6	1627	5.0	2229	1.4
2	M	0448	4.8	1039	1.4	1658	5.1	2305	1.3
3	TU	0517	4.9	1114	1.3	1727	5.2	● 2338	1.3
4	W	0544	5.0	1146	1.3	1754	5.2		
5	TH	0009	1.3	0611	5.0	1216	1.3	1821	5.1
6	F	0037	1.4	0637	5.0	1243	1.4	1848	5.0
7	SA	0103	1.5	0704	4.9	1310	1.5	1916	4.9
8	SU	0128	1.6	0733	4.8	1337	1.7	1946	4.7
9	M	0156	1.8	0805	4.6	1410	1.9	2021	4.5
10	TU	0229	2.0	0845	4.4	1448	2.1	2108	4.2
11	W	0312	2.2	0944	4.2	1544	2.3	☽ 2223	4.0
12	TH	0418	2.5	1118	4.1	1713	2.5		
13	F	0017	4.0	0558	2.5	1258	4.2	1851	2.3
14	SA	0144	4.2	0730	2.3	1407	4.5	2008	2.0
15	SU	0244	4.5	0836	1.9	1501	4.9	2106	1.6
16	M	0333	4.9	0928	1.5	1548	5.3	2154	1.2
17	TU	0418	5.2	1015	1.2	1633	5.6	2240	0.9
18	W	0500	5.4	1059	0.9	1717	5.8	O 2323	0.7
19	TH	0542	5.5	1142	0.8	1800	5.8		
20	F	0005	0.7	0623	5.5	1224	0.8	1844	5.7
21	SA	0045	0.8	0704	5.4	1305	0.9	1928	5.5
22	SU	0124	1.1	0746	5.2	1346	1.2	2014	5.1
23	M	0205	1.4	0831	4.9	1431	1.5	2105	4.7
24	TU	0250	1.8	0926	4.5	1525	1.9	☾ 2213	4.3
25	W	0348	2.2	1051	4.3	1643	2.2	2359	4.1
26	TH	0512	2.4	1242	4.2	1823	2.3		
27	F	0127	4.1	0649	2.4	1356	4.4	1944	2.1
28	SA	0230	4.3	0802	2.2	1450	4.6	2040	1.8
29	SU	0315	4.5	0853	1.9	1530	4.8	2123	1.6
30	M	0349	4.7	0935	1.6	1601	5.0	2201	1.4

OCTOBER

Date	Day	Time	m	Time	m	Time	m	Time	m
1	TU	0418	4.9	1012	1.5	1629	5.1	2235	1.3
2	W	0444	5.0	1045	1.4	1656	5.2	● 2306	1.3
3	TH	0511	5.1	1116	1.3	1723	5.2	2335	1.3
4	F	0538	5.1	1144	1.4	1750	5.2		
5	SA	0002	1.4	0605	5.1	1212	1.4	1817	5.1
6	SU	0029	1.5	0633	5.0	1240	1.5	1845	4.9
7	M	0056	1.6	0702	4.9	1309	1.7	1917	4.8
8	TU	0126	1.8	0736	4.7	1345	1.8	1954	4.5
9	W	0201	2.0	0819	4.5	1425	2.1	2045	4.3
10	TH	0247	2.3	0921	4.3	1522	2.3	☽ 2207	4.0
11	F	0354	2.5	1054	4.2	1647	2.4		
12	SA	0001	4.1	0530	2.5	1231	4.4	1824	2.2
13	SU	0119	4.3	0659	2.3	1339	4.7	1940	1.9
14	M	0217	4.7	0805	1.9	1434	5.1	2037	1.5
15	TU	0306	5.0	0859	1.5	1523	5.4	2126	1.2
16	W	0351	5.3	0947	1.2	1609	5.7	2212	0.9
17	TH	0434	5.5	1033	0.9	1654	5.8	O 2255	0.8
18	F	0516	5.6	1117	0.8	1738	5.8	2338	0.9
19	SA	0559	5.6	1200	0.9	1823	5.6		
20	SU	0019	1.0	0641	5.4	1242	1.0	1908	5.4
21	M	0059	1.3	0725	5.2	1325	1.3	1955	5.0
22	TU	0141	1.6	0812	4.9	1412	1.6	2049	4.6
23	W	0228	1.9	0908	4.6	1507	2.0	2159	4.2
24	TH	0326	2.3	1030	4.3	1621	2.3	☾ 2336	4.1
25	F	0446	2.5	1208	4.3	1751	2.3		
26	SA	0057	4.2	0612	2.4	1321	4.4	1908	2.2
27	SU	0155	4.3	0724	2.2	1415	4.6	2005	2.0
28	M	0238	4.5	0817	2.0	1455	4.7	2049	1.8
29	TU	0312	4.7	0901	1.8	1528	4.9	2127	1.6
30	W	0342	4.9	0938	1.6	1557	5.0	2200	1.5
31	TH	0411	5.0	1012	1.5	1627	5.1	2231	1.5

NOVEMBER

Date	Day	Time	m	Time	m	Time	m	Time	m
1	F	0440	5.1	1043	1.5	1656	5.1	● 2301	1.5
2	SA	0510	5.1	1115	1.5	1725	5.1	2331	1.5
3	SU	0539	5.1	1146	1.5	1755	5.0		
4	M	0001	1.6	0610	5.1	1219	1.5	1827	4.9
5	TU	0033	1.7	0644	5.0	1254	1.7	1902	4.7
6	W	0109	1.8	0723	4.8	1331	1.8	1945	4.5
7	TH	0149	2.0	0811	4.6	1416	2.0	2041	4.3
8	F	0239	2.2	0914	4.5	1514	2.1	2201	4.2
9	SA	0343	2.3	1036	4.4	1628	2.2	☽ 2335	4.2
10	SU	0503	2.3	1158	4.5	1749	2.1		
11	M	0046	4.4	0621	2.2	1305	4.8	1902	1.8
12	TU	0144	4.7	0728	1.9	1403	5.1	2002	1.6
13	W	0236	5.0	0826	1.6	1457	5.3	2054	1.3
14	TH	0324	5.3	0918	1.3	1546	5.5	2143	1.1
15	F	0410	5.4	1007	1.1	1634	5.6	O 2229	1.1
16	SA	0455	5.5	1055	1.0	1721	5.6	2314	1.1
17	SU	0540	5.5	1141	1.1	1808	5.4	2357	1.2
18	M	0626	5.4	1226	1.2	1854	5.2		
19	TU	0040	1.4	0712	5.2	1311	1.4	1942	4.9
20	W	0123	1.7	0759	5.0	1358	1.7	2032	4.6
21	TH	0210	1.9	0850	4.7	1450	1.9	2131	4.3
22	F	0305	2.2	0952	4.5	1550	2.1	2242	4.2
23	SA	0409	2.3	1105	4.3	1658	2.2	☾ 2356	4.1
24	SU	0518	2.4	1217	4.3	1807	2.2		
25	M	0058	4.2	0624	2.3	1318	4.4	1910	2.1
26	TU	0148	4.4	0724	2.2	1407	4.5	2002	2.0
27	W	0229	4.6	0815	2.0	1448	4.7	2045	1.9
28	TH	0305	4.7	0858	1.9	1525	4.8	2123	1.8
29	F	0340	4.9	0937	1.8	1600	4.9	2158	1.7
30	SA	0414	5.0	1014	1.7	1634	4.9	2232	1.6

DECEMBER

Date	Day	Time	m	Time	m	Time	m	Time	m
1	SU	0448	5.1	1050	1.6	1709	5.0	● 2307	1.6
2	M	0522	5.1	1128	1.5	1743	4.9	2343	1.6
3	TU	0558	5.1	1206	1.5	1820	4.9		
4	W	0021	1.6	0637	5.1	1246	1.6	1900	4.8
5	TH	0102	1.7	0720	5.0	1328	1.6	1946	4.6
6	F	0145	1.8	0810	4.9	1414	1.7	2040	4.5
7	SA	0234	1.9	0907	4.8	1506	1.8	2146	4.4
8	SU	0330	2.0	1013	4.7	1605	1.9	☽ 2258	4.4
9	M	0434	2.1	1122	4.7	1712	1.9		
10	TU	0007	4.5	0543	2.0	1229	4.8	1822	1.8
11	W	0110	4.7	0652	1.9	1334	4.9	1927	1.7
12	TH	0209	4.9	0755	1.7	1435	5.1	2026	1.6
13	F	0303	5.0	0854	1.5	1531	5.2	2120	1.5
14	SA	0354	5.2	0949	1.4	1623	5.3	2210	1.4
15	SU	0443	5.3	1041	1.3	1712	5.3	O 2258	1.4
16	M	0530	5.4	1130	1.2	1758	5.2	2343	1.4
17	TU	0615	5.3	1216	1.3	1843	5.1		
18	W	0027	1.5	0659	5.2	1301	1.4	1926	4.9
19	TH	0111	1.6	0741	5.1	1345	1.6	2008	4.7
20	F	0154	1.8	0823	4.9	1428	1.7	2050	4.5
21	SA	0239	1.9	0906	4.7	1514	1.9	2137	4.3
22	SU	0328	2.1	0954	4.5	1604	2.1	☾ 2232	4.2
23	M	0421	2.2	1052	4.3	1659	2.2	2336	4.1
24	TU	0519	2.3	1158	4.2	1759	2.3		
25	W	0041	4.2	0619	2.3	1304	4.3	1900	2.3
26	TH	0139	4.3	0719	2.3	1404	4.3	1958	2.2
27	F	0228	4.5	0816	2.1	1454	4.5	2047	2.0
28	SA	0312	4.6	0906	2.0	1538	4.6	2130	1.9
29	SU	0353	4.8	0951	1.8	1619	4.7	2211	1.7
30	M	0432	5.0	1034	1.6	1658	4.9	● 2252	1.6
31	TU	0512	5.1	1116	1.5	1738	4.9	2333	1.5

LISBON
LAT 38°42′N
LONG 9°08′W

TIMES AND HEIGHTS OF HIGH AND LOW WATER (Heights in Metres)

TIME ZONE UT (Portuguese Standard Time) **For Portuguese Summer Time (area enclosed in shaded box) add 1 hour**

2024

SUNRISE AND SUNSET TIMES

LISBON
At 38°42′N 9°08′W
Portuguese Standard Time UT

		Sunrise	Sunset
Jan	01	0755	1726
	15	0753	1739
Feb	01	0742	1758
	15	0727	1814
Mar	01	0709	1829
	15	0648	1844
Portuguese Summer Time (UT+0100)			
Apr	01	0721	2000
	15	0700	2013
May	01	0639	2029
	15	0624	2042
Jun	01	0614	2055
	15	0611	2103
Jul	01	0616	2105
	15	0624	2101
Aug	01	0638	2047
	15	0650	2031
Sep	01	0706	2007
	15	0718	1945
Oct	01	0732	1919
	15	0746	1858
Portuguese Standard Time (UT)			
Nov	01	0703	1736
	15	0719	1723
Dec	01	0736	1715
	15	[illegible]	[illegible]

JANUARY

Day	Time	m	Day	Time	m
1 M	0605 1213 1830	3.2 1.1 2.9	16 TU	0003 0638 1238 1908	0.7 3.7 0.7 3.3
2 TU	0017 0644 1254 1914	1.3 3.1 1.2 2.8	17 W	0053 0729 1328 2002	0.9 3.5 0.9 3.2
3 W	0102 0729 1343 2007	1.4 3.0 1.3 2.8	18 TH ☽	0148 0826 1427 2103	1.1 3.3 1.1 3.0
4 TH ☾	0157 0825 1441 2110	1.5 2.9 1.4 2.7	19 F	0254 0932 1535 2213	1.2 3.1 1.3 3.0
5 F	0304 0930 1548 2217	1.5 2.8 1.4 2.8	20 SA	0411 1046 1648 2325	1.3 3.0 1.3 3.0
6 SA	0416 1038 1652 2319	1.5 2.8 1.4 2.9	21 SU	0528 1159 1756	1.3 3.0 1.3
7 SU	0520 1142 1747	1.4 2.9 1.3	22 M	0031 0636 1303 1854	3.1 1.2 3.0 1.2
8 M	0015 0616 1240 1837	3.0 1.2 3.0 1.1	23 TU	0128 0731 1356 1943	3.3 1.1 3.1 1.1
9 TU	0106 0707 1332 1925	3.2 1.0 3.2 1.0	24 W	0215 0818 1440 2025	3.4 1.0 3.2 1.0
10 W	0155 0756 1422 2012	3.4 0.9 3.3 0.8	25 TH ○	0257 0858 1519 2102	3.5 0.9 3.3 0.9
11 TH ●	0243 0844 1511 2059	3.6 0.7 3.5 0.7	26 F	0333 0933 1553 2136	3.5 0.8 3.3 0.9
12 F	0330 0932 1558 2145	3.7 0.5 3.5 0.6	27 SA	0406 1006 1625 2208	3.5 0.8 3.3 0.9
13 SA	0417 1018 1645 2231	3.8 0.4 3.6 0.6	28 SU	0436 1037 1655 2240	3.5 0.8 3.3 0.9
14 SU	0503 1104 1731 2317	3.9 0.4 3.5 0.6	29 M	0506 1107 1725 2311	3.5 0.8 3.3 0.9
15 M	0550 1150 1819	3.8 0.5 3.5	30 TU	0537 1138 1757 2343	3.4 0.9 3.2 1.0
			31 W	0609 1210 1831	3.3 1.0 3.1

FEBRUARY

Day	Time	m	Day	Time	m
1 TH	0018 0645 1245 1911	1.2 3.2 1.2 3.0	16 F ☽	0115 0751 1345 2021	1.0 3.3 1.2 3.1
2 F ☾	0059 0727 1328 2000	1.3 3.0 1.4 2.8	17 SA	0219 0856 1454 2135	1.3 3.0 1.5 2.9
3 SA	0151 0821 1427 2104	1.5 2.8 1.5 2.8	18 SU	0344 1022 1621 2304	1.5 2.8 1.6 2.9
4 SU	0305 0934 1547 2222	1.6 2.7 1.5 2.8	19 M	0519 1152 1745	1.5 2.8 1.5
5 M	0433 1100 1707 2339	1.5 2.8 1.5 2.9	20 TU	0022 0635 1259 1848	3.0 1.4 2.9 1.4
6 TU	0549 1217 1813	1.4 2.9 1.3	21 W	0120 0728 1348 1935	3.2 1.2 3.1 1.2
7 W	0044 0651 1319 1910	3.2 1.1 3.1 1.1	22 TH	0204 0808 1427 2012	3.4 1.0 3.2 1.1
8 TH	0140 0745 1412 2001	3.4 0.9 3.4 0.8	23 F	0241 0842 1501 2045	3.5 0.9 3.3 1.0
9 F ●	0231 0834 1500 2048	3.7 0.6 3.6 0.6	24 SA ○	0313 0912 1531 2116	3.6 0.8 3.4 0.9
10 SA	0318 0920 1546 2133	3.9 0.4 3.8 0.5	25 SU	0343 0940 1600 2145	3.7 0.8 3.5 0.8
11 SU	0404 1004 1630 2217	4.1 0.3 3.8 0.4	26 M	0412 1008 1628 2214	3.7 0.7 3.5 0.8
12 M	0448 1046 1712 2259	4.1 0.3 3.8 0.4	27 TU	0440 1036 1656 2244	3.7 0.8 3.5 0.8
13 TU	0531 1127 1755 2341	4.0 0.4 3.7 0.6	28 W	0509 1104 1726 2313	3.6 0.9 3.4 0.9
14 W	0614 1209 1838	3.8 0.6 3.5	29 TH	0539 1132 1756 2344	3.4 1.0 3.3 1.1
15 TH	0026 0700 1253 1925	0.8 3.6 0.9 3.3			

MARCH

Day	Time	m	Day	Time	m
1 F	0611 1202 1830	3.3 1.1 3.2	16 SA	0049 0722 1310 1946	1.1 3.2 1.4 3.1
2 SA	0019 0647 1238 1911	1.2 3.1 1.3 3.0	17 SU ☽	0153 0827 1420 2103	1.4 2.9 1.6 2.9
3 SU ☾	0105 0735 1329 2009	1.4 2.9 1.5 2.9	18 M	0326 1006 1559 2244	1.6 2.7 1.8 2.9
4 M	0214 0848 1454 2136	1.6 2.7 1.7 2.8	19 TU	0508 1142 1730	1.6 2.8 1.7
5 TU	0359 1033 1637 2312	1.6 2.7 1.6 3.0	20 W	0005 0621 1245 1831	3.0 1.4 2.9 1.5
6 W	0529 1203 1755	1.4 2.9 1.4	21 TH	0059 0708 1328 1913	3.2 1.3 3.1 1.3
7 TH	0026 0636 1306 1855	3.2 1.1 3.2 1.1	22 F	0140 0743 1402 1948	3.4 1.1 3.3 1.1
8 F	0124 0730 1357 1946	3.6 0.8 3.5 0.8	23 SA	0214 0813 1433 2019	3.5 0.9 3.4 1.0
9 SA	0214 0817 1443 2031	3.9 0.5 3.8 0.6	24 SU	0245 0842 1502 2049	3.6 0.8 3.5 0.9
10 SU ●	0300 0900 1526 2114	4.1 0.3 3.9 0.4	25 M ○	0314 0910 1530 2118	3.7 0.8 3.6 0.8
11 M	0344 0942 1608 2156	4.2 0.3 4.0 0.3	26 TU	0343 0937 1559 2148	3.7 0.8 3.6 0.8
12 TU	0426 1021 1648 2237	4.2 0.3 4.0 0.4	27 W	0413 1005 1628 2217	3.7 0.8 3.6 0.8
13 W	0508 1100 1728 2317	4.1 0.5 3.8 0.6	28 TH	0442 1032 1657 2247	3.6 0.9 3.5 0.9
14 TH	0549 1140 1808	3.8 0.7 3.6	29 F	0513 1100 1728 2319	3.5 1.0 3.4 1.0
15 F	0000 0633 1221 1852	0.8 3.5 1.0 3.4	30 SA	0545 1131 1802 2355	3.3 1.2 3.3 1.2
			31 SU	0623 1209 1844	3.1 1.4 3.1

APRIL

Day	Time	m	Day	Time	m
1 M	0043 0713 1302 1944	1.4 2.9 1.5 3.0	16 TU	0303 0940 1526 2208	1.6 2.7 1.8 2.9
2 TU ☾	0157 0833 1431 2114	1.5 2.8 1.7 2.9	17 W	0433 1109 1651 2326	1.6 2.7 1.7 3.0
3 W	0341 1021 1617 2251	1.5 2.8 1.6 3.1	18 TH	0541 1209 1752	1.5 2.9 1.6
4 TH	0510 1145 1735	1.3 3.0 1.4	19 F	0020 0628 1251 1836	3.1 1.3 3.1 1.4
5 F	0004 0614 1245 1833	3.3 1.0 3.3 1.1	20 SA	0102 0704 1326 1913	3.3 1.1 3.3 1.2
6 SA	0101 0706 1334 1923	3.7 0.8 3.6 0.8	21 SU	0137 0736 1358 1946	3.4 1.0 3.4 1.0
7 SU	0151 0752 1419 2008	3.9 0.5 3.8 0.6	22 M	0210 0806 1428 2018	3.5 0.9 3.5 0.9
8 M ●	0236 0835 1501 2051	4.1 0.4 4.0 0.4	23 TU ○	0242 0836 1459 2049	3.6 0.8 3.6 0.9
9 TU	0320 0915 1542 2133	4.2 0.4 4.0 0.4	24 W	0314 0905 1530 2121	3.6 0.8 3.6 0.8
10 W	0403 0955 1623 2214	4.1 0.4 4.0 0.5	25 TH	0346 0935 1601 2153	3.6 0.9 3.6 0.9
11 TH	0445 1034 1703 2256	4.0 0.6 3.8 0.6	26 F	0418 1005 1634 2226	3.5 0.9 3.6 0.9
12 F	0526 1113 1743 2340	3.7 0.9 3.6 0.9	27 SA	0453 1037 1708 2303	3.4 1.0 3.5 1.0
13 SA	0610 1155 1827	3.4 1.2 3.4	28 SU	0530 1113 1747 2346	3.3 1.1 3.4 1.1
14 SU	0030 0659 1243 1919	1.2 3.1 1.5 3.1	29 M	0614 1158 1835	3.1 1.3 3.2
15 M ☽	0135 0805 1352 2034	1.4 2.8 1.7 2.9	30 TU	0041 0712 1258 1939	1.3 2.9 1.5 3.1

MAY

Day	Time	m	Day	Time	m
1 W ☾	0156 0832 1423 2102	1.4 2.8 1.6 3.1	16 TH	0335 1010 1551 2224	1.5 2.7 1.7 2.9
2 TH	0324 1004 1553 2226	1.4 2.9 1.5 3.2	17 F	0441 1112 1656 2323	1.4 2.8 1.6 3.0
3 F	0442 1118 1706 2335	1.2 3.1 1.3 3.4	18 SA	0533 1201 1747	1.3 3.0 1.4
4 SA	0545 1216 1805	1.0 3.4 1.0	19 SU	0012 0616 1241 1831	3.1 1.2 3.2 1.3
5 SU	0033 0637 1306 1856	3.6 0.8 3.6 0.8	20 M	0053 0654 1318 1909	3.2 1.1 3.3 1.1
6 M	0124 0724 1352 1943	3.8 0.6 3.8 0.6	21 TU	0132 0728 1353 1946	3.3 1.0 3.4 1.0
7 TU	0211 0807 1435 2028	3.9 0.5 3.9 0.5	22 W	0208 0802 1427 2021	3.4 0.9 3.5 0.9
8 W ●	0257 0849 1518 2112	3.9 0.5 3.9 0.5	23 TH ○	0245 0835 1503 2057	3.4 0.9 3.5 0.9
9 TH	0341 0930 1600 2156	3.8 0.6 3.8 0.6	24 F	0322 0909 1539 2135	3.4 0.9 3.6 0.8
10 F	0424 1011 1642 2240	3.7 0.8 3.7 0.7	25 SA	0400 0945 1617 2214	3.4 0.9 3.5 0.9
11 SA	0508 1051 1724 2326	3.5 1.0 3.5 0.9	26 SU	0440 1024 1658 2257	3.3 1.0 3.5 0.9
12 SU	0552 1134 1807	3.2 1.2 3.3	27 M	0524 1108 1743 2346	3.2 1.0 3.4 1.0
13 M	0016 0640 1222 1857	1.1 3.0 1.4 3.1	28 TU	0614 1158 1834	3.1 1.2 3.3
14 TU	0113 0738 1321 1957	1.4 2.8 1.6 3.0	29 W	0041 0713 1257 1934	1.0 3.0 1.3 3.3
15 W ☽	0222 0853 1435 2111	1.5 2.7 1.7 2.9	30 TH ☾	0146 0821 1407 2043	1.1 3.0 1.3 3.2
			31 F	0257 0935 1522 2155	1.1 3.0 1.3 3.3

JUNE

Day	Time	m	Day	Time	m
1 SA	0406 1043 1632 2302	1.1 3.1 1.2 3.3	16 SU	0430 1058 1651 2313	1.4 2.8 1.5 2.9
2 SU	0510 1143 1734	1.0 3.3 1.0	17 M	0523 1149 1745	1.3 3.0 1.4
3 M	0002 0605 1236 1830	3.4 0.9 3.4 0.9	18 TU	0005 0609 1235 1832	3.0 1.2 3.1 1.2
4 TU	0058 0656 1326 1921	3.5 0.8 3.5 0.8	19 W	0053 0651 1317 1916	3.1 1.1 3.2 1.1
5 W	0149 0743 1414 2010	3.6 0.7 3.6 0.7	20 TH	0138 0730 1359 1958	3.2 1.0 3.3 1.0
6 TH ●	0238 0827 1459 2057	3.5 0.8 3.7 0.7	21 F	0221 0810 1440 2040	3.2 0.9 3.5 0.9
7 F	0325 0911 1544 2143	3.5 0.8 3.7 0.7	22 SA ○	0304 0851 1522 2123	3.3 0.9 3.5 0.8
8 SA	0410 0953 1627 2228	3.4 0.9 3.6 0.8	23 SU	0348 0934 1606 2207	3.3 0.9 3.6 0.7
9 SU	0453 1035 1708 2312	3.3 1.0 3.5 0.9	24 M	0433 1018 1651 2253	3.4 0.8 3.7 0.7
10 M	0535 1116 1748 2356	3.1 1.1 3.3 1.0	25 TU	0520 1104 1738 2340	3.3 0.9 3.6 0.7
11 TU	0617 1158 1830	3.0 1.3 3.2	26 W	0608 1152 1827	3.3 0.9 3.6
12 W	0041 0702 1245 1915	1.2 2.9 1.4 3.1	27 TH	0030 0700 1244 1919	0.8 3.2 1.0 3.5
13 TH	0131 0754 1339 2008	1.3 2.8 1.5 3.0	28 F ☾	0124 0757 1342 2017	0.9 3.1 1.1 3.3
14 F ☽	0228 0855 1442 2109	1.4 2.7 1.5 2.9	29 SA	0223 0859 1447 2121	1.0 3.1 1.2 3.3
15 SA	0329 0959 1549 2213	1.4 2.8 1.5 2.9	30 SU	0328 1005 1557 2229	1.1 3.1 1.2 3.2

LISBON
LAT 38°42′N
LONG 9°08′W

TIMES AND HEIGHTS OF HIGH AND LOW WATER (Heights in Metres)

TIME ZONE UT (Portuguese Standard Time) **For Portuguese Summer Time (area enclosed in shaded box) add 1 hour**

2024

JULY

Date	Day	Time	m	Time	m	Time	m	Time	m
1	M	0434	1.1	1110	3.2	1706	1.1	2336	3.2
2	TU	0537	1.1	1212	3.3	1810	1.1		
3	W	0039	3.2	0634	1.0	1308	3.4	1909	1.0
4	TH	0137	3.3	0726	1.0	1401	3.5	2002	0.9
5	F ●	0228	3.3	0814	0.9	1449	3.5	2050	0.8
6	SA	0315	3.3	0859	0.9	1533	3.6	2134	0.8
7	SU	0358	3.3	0940	0.9	1613	3.6	2215	0.8
8	M	0437	3.3	1018	1.0	1650	3.5	2252	0.9
9	TU	0513	3.2	1054	1.0	1724	3.4	2327	0.9
10	W	0547	3.1	1130	1.1	1758	3.3		
11	TH	0003	1.0	0622	3.0	1206	1.2	1833	3.2
12	F	0040	1.1	0701	3.0	1247	1.3	1914	3.1
13	SA ☽	0123	1.3	0747	2.9	1336	1.4	2002	3.0
14	SU	0215	1.4	0843	2.8	1437	1.5	2100	2.8
15	M	0318	1.5	0947	2.8	1549	1.6	2208	2.8
16	TU	0424	1.5	1053	2.8	1658	1.5	2317	2.8
17	W	0525	1.4	1153	3.0	1758	1.4		
18	TH	0019	2.9	0617	1.3	1247	3.1	1851	1.2
19	F	0114	3.0	0706	1.1	1336	3.3	1940	1.0
20	SA	0204	3.2	0753	1.0	1423	3.5	2027	0.8
21	SU O	0252	3.3	0838	0.9	1509	3.7	2112	0.7
22	M	0337	3.5	0923	0.7	1555	3.8	2156	0.5
23	TU	0422	3.6	1008	0.6	1640	3.9	2240	0.5
24	W	0507	3.6	1052	0.6	1724	3.9	2324	0.5
25	TH	0551	3.5	1136	0.7	1809	3.8		
26	F	0008	0.6	0637	3.5	1222	0.8	1857	3.6
27	SA	0054	0.8	0727	3.3	1313	1.0	1949	3.4
28	SU ☾	0147	1.0	0823	3.2	1413	1.2	2049	3.2
29	M	0250	1.2	0929	3.1	1527	1.3	2202	3.0
30	TU	0405	1.3	1044	3.0	1649	1.3	2322	3.0
31	W	0520	1.4	1158	3.1	1805	1.3		

AUGUST

Date	Day	Time	m	Time	m	Time	m	Time	m
1	TH	0034	3.0	0626	1.3	1302	3.3	1909	1.1
2	F	0133	3.1	0721	1.2	1355	3.4	2000	1.0
3	SA	0222	3.2	0807	1.1	1440	3.5	2042	0.9
4	SU ●	0304	3.3	0847	1.0	1519	3.6	2120	0.8
5	M	0340	3.4	0923	0.9	1554	3.6	2153	0.8
6	TU	0413	3.4	0956	0.9	1625	3.6	2224	0.8
7	W	0444	3.4	1027	0.9	1655	3.6	2254	0.9
8	TH	0513	3.3	1058	1.0	1725	3.5	2324	0.9
9	F	0544	3.3	1130	1.0	1756	3.4	2355	1.1
10	SA	0617	3.2	1204	1.2	1830	3.2		
11	SU	0028	1.2	0654	3.0	1242	1.4	1909	3.0
12	M ☽	0108	1.4	0739	2.9	1331	1.5	1959	2.9
13	TU	0201	1.6	0839	2.8	1442	1.7	2108	2.7
14	W	0321	1.7	0957	2.8	1614	1.7	2235	2.7
15	TH	0445	1.6	1116	2.9	1731	1.5	2356	2.8
16	F	0552	1.5	1223	3.1	1833	1.3		
17	SA	0058	3.1	0648	1.2	1318	3.4	1925	1.0
18	SU	0150	3.3	0738	1.0	1407	3.7	2012	0.8
19	M O	0236	3.5	0824	0.8	1453	3.9	2056	0.5
20	TU	0321	3.7	0908	0.6	1538	4.1	2138	0.4
21	W	0403	3.8	0950	0.5	1621	4.2	2219	0.4
22	TH	0445	3.9	1032	0.5	1704	4.1	2300	0.4
23	F	0527	3.8	1114	0.6	1747	4.0	2341	0.6
24	SA	0610	3.7	1157	0.8	1831	3.7		
25	SU	0024	0.9	0656	3.5	1246	1.0	1921	3.4
26	M ☾	0113	1.2	0749	3.2	1346	1.3	2022	3.1
27	TU	0218	1.5	0900	3.0	1509	1.5	2146	2.9
28	W	0346	1.6	1030	3.0	1647	1.5	2320	2.9
29	TH	0515	1.6	1153	3.1	1809	1.4		
30	F	0034	3.0	0624	1.5	1256	3.3	1907	1.2
31	SA	0127	3.2	0714	1.3	1343	3.5	1949	1.1

SEPTEMBER

Date	Day	Time	m	Time	m	Time	m	Time	m
1	SU	0208	3.3	0753	1.1	1422	3.6	2024	0.9
2	M	0244	3.4	0828	1.0	1456	3.7	2055	0.9
3	TU ●	0315	3.5	0859	0.9	1527	3.7	2124	0.8
4	W	0344	3.6	0929	0.9	1556	3.8	2152	0.8
5	TH	0412	3.6	0958	0.9	1624	3.7	2220	0.8
6	F	0440	3.5	1027	0.9	1653	3.6	2247	0.9
7	SA	0509	3.5	1057	1.0	1722	3.5	2315	1.1
8	SU	0539	3.4	1128	1.2	1753	3.3	2344	1.2
9	M	0612	3.2	1202	1.3	1828	3.1		
10	TU	0018	1.4	0652	3.0	1244	1.5	1913	2.9
11	W ☾	0104	1.6	0747	2.9	1351	1.7	2023	2.7
12	TH	0225	1.8	0911	2.8	1538	1.7	2208	2.7
13	F	0414	1.8	1047	3.0	1709	1.6	2339	2.9
14	SA	0532	1.5	1201	3.2	1813	1.3		
15	SU	0041	3.2	0629	1.3	1257	3.5	1905	1.0
16	M	0130	3.5	0718	1.0	1346	3.8	1950	0.7
17	TU	0215	3.8	0803	0.7	1431	4.1	2032	0.5
18	W O	0258	4.0	0846	0.5	1515	4.2	2113	0.4
19	TH	0339	4.0	0928	0.4	1558	4.3	2153	0.4
20	F	0420	4.0	1009	0.4	1640	4.2	2233	0.5
21	SA	0501	3.9	1051	0.6	1723	4.0	2313	0.7
22	SU	0543	3.8	1134	0.8	1807	3.7	2355	1.0
23	M	0628	3.5	1224	1.1	1858	3.3		
24	TU ☽	0045	1.4	0723	3.3	1327	1.4	2003	3.0
25	W	0153	1.6	0839	3.0	1500	1.6	2138	2.8
26	TH	0332	1.8	1017	3.0	1643	1.6	2315	2.9
27	F	0505	1.7	1140	3.1	1759	1.4		
28	SA	0021	3.0	0609	1.5	1237	3.3	1848	1.3
29	SU	0107	3.2	0653	1.3	1320	3.5	1924	1.1
30	M	0143	3.4	0729	1.2	1355	3.6	1955	1.0

OCTOBER

Date	Day	Time	m	Time	m	Time	m	Time	m
1	TU	0215	3.5	0801	1.0	1427	3.7	2024	0.9
2	W ●	0244	3.6	0831	0.9	1456	3.8	2052	0.8
3	TH	0313	3.7	0900	0.9	1525	3.8	2119	0.8
4	F	0341	3.7	0930	0.9	1554	3.7	2147	0.9
5	SA	0409	3.7	0959	0.9	1623	3.6	2214	1.0
6	SU	0439	3.6	1029	1.0	1653	3.5	2242	1.1
7	M	0509	3.5	1100	1.1	1725	3.3	2311	1.3
8	TU	0542	3.3	1135	1.3	1801	3.1	2346	1.4
9	W	0622	3.2	1220	1.5	1849	2.9		
10	TH ☾	0034	1.6	0719	3.0	1329	1.6	2003	2.8
11	F	0157	1.8	0844	3.0	1512	1.7	2150	2.8
12	SA	0346	1.7	1020	3.1	1642	1.5	2316	3.0
13	SU	0505	1.5	1134	3.3	1746	1.2		
14	M	0015	3.3	0604	1.2	1231	3.6	1837	0.9
15	TU	0104	3.6	0653	0.9	1320	3.9	1923	0.6
16	W	0149	3.8	0739	0.7	1406	4.1	2005	0.5
17	TH O	0231	4.0	0822	0.5	1451	4.2	2047	0.4
18	F	0313	4.1	0905	0.4	1534	4.2	2127	0.5
19	SA	0355	4.0	0947	0.5	1618	4.0	2208	0.6
20	SU	0437	3.9	1031	0.6	1702	3.8	2249	0.8
21	M	0520	3.7	1117	0.8	1748	3.5	2333	1.1
22	TU	0607	3.5	1209	1.1	1840	3.2		
23	W	0024	1.4	0702	3.3	1314	1.4	1947	2.9
24	TH ☽	0131	1.7	0816	3.0	1441	1.6	2117	2.8
25	F	0303	1.8	0947	3.0	1611	1.6	2245	2.8
26	SA	0429	1.7	1104	3.1	1721	1.5	2347	3.0
27	SU	0532	1.6	1200	3.2	1810	1.3		
28	M	0032	3.2	0618	1.4	1243	3.4	1847	1.2
29	TU	0108	3.3	0655	1.2	1319	3.5	1919	1.0
30	W	0140	3.5	0729	1.1	1353	3.6	1949	0.9
31	TH	0211	3.6	0801	1.0	1424	3.6	2019	0.9

NOVEMBER

Date	Day	Time	m	Time	m	Time	m	Time	m
1	F ●	0241	3.6	0833	0.9	1456	3.6	2048	0.9
2	SA	0312	3.6	0904	0.9	1527	3.6	2117	0.9
3	SU	0343	3.6	0936	0.9	1559	3.5	2147	1.0
4	M	0414	3.6	1008	1.0	1632	3.4	2218	1.1
5	TU	0448	3.5	1043	1.1	1708	3.2	2252	1.2
6	W	0525	3.4	1124	1.2	1750	3.1	2333	1.3
7	TH	0610	3.2	1214	1.3	1842	2.9		
8	F	0027	1.5	0708	3.1	1321	1.4	1955	2.8
9	SA ☾	0143	1.6	0825	3.1	1445	1.4	2123	2.9
10	SU	0313	1.6	0948	3.2	1605	1.3	2241	3.0
11	M	0430	1.4	1059	3.3	1711	1.1	2342	3.3
12	TU	0532	1.1	1159	3.5	1805	0.9		
13	W	0034	3.5	0625	0.9	1252	3.7	1853	0.7
14	TH	0121	3.7	0713	0.7	1341	3.9	1939	0.6
15	F O	0206	3.8	0800	0.6	1428	3.9	2022	0.6
16	SA	0251	3.9	0846	0.5	1515	3.9	2105	0.6
17	SU	0335	3.9	0932	0.5	1601	3.8	2148	0.7
18	M	0420	3.8	1018	0.7	1647	3.6	2232	0.9
19	TU	0505	3.7	1106	0.8	1734	3.3	2317	1.1
20	W	0552	3.5	1157	1.1	1824	3.1		
21	TH	0006	1.3	0643	3.3	1254	1.3	1921	2.9
22	F	0103	1.5	0742	3.1	1359	1.4	2031	2.8
23	SA ☽	0212	1.6	0852	3.0	1511	1.5	2145	2.7
24	SU	0326	1.6	1003	3.0	1618	1.5	2250	2.8
25	M	0434	1.6	1104	3.0	1715	1.4	2342	3.0
26	TU	0529	1.4	1155	3.1	1800	1.2		
27	W	0024	3.1	0615	1.3	1238	3.2	1839	1.1
28	TH	0102	3.3	0655	1.1	1317	3.3	1914	1.0
29	F	0138	3.4	0732	1.0	1354	3.3	1948	1.0
30	SA	0212	3.5	0808	1.0	1430	3.4	2021	0.9

DECEMBER

Date	Day	Time	m	Time	m	Time	m	Time	m
1	SU ●	0247	3.5	0843	0.9	1506	3.3	2054	0.9
2	M	0322	3.5	0919	0.9	1542	3.3	2128	0.9
3	TU	0358	3.5	0957	0.9	1621	3.3	2205	1.0
4	W	0437	3.5	1037	0.9	1701	3.2	2245	1.0
5	TH	0519	3.5	1121	1.0	1747	3.1	2331	1.1
6	F	0606	3.4	1210	1.0	1838	3.0		
7	SA	0023	1.2	0700	3.3	1307	1.1	1939	3.0
8	SU ☾	0125	1.3	0802	3.2	1412	1.1	2049	3.0
9	M	0235	1.3	0911	3.2	1522	1.1	2159	3.0
10	TU	0348	1.3	1021	3.3	1630	1.1	2304	3.2
11	W	0456	1.1	1126	3.3	1731	1.0		
12	TH	0003	3.3	0557	1.0	1226	3.4	1826	0.9
13	F	0056	3.5	0653	0.8	1321	3.5	1916	0.8
14	SA	0147	3.6	0745	0.7	1413	3.6	2005	0.7
15	SU O	0236	3.7	0835	0.6	1503	3.5	2051	0.7
16	M	0324	3.7	0924	0.6	1551	3.5	2136	0.8
17	TU	0409	3.7	1011	0.7	1636	3.4	2220	0.9
18	W	0453	3.6	1056	0.8	1720	3.3	2302	1.0
19	TH	0535	3.5	1139	0.9	1802	3.1	2344	1.1
20	F	0617	3.3	1223	1.1	1845	3.0		
21	SA	0027	1.3	0700	3.2	1309	1.2	1932	2.8
22	SU ☽	0115	1.4	0748	3.0	1400	1.3	2027	2.8
23	M	0213	1.5	0844	2.9	1500	1.4	2131	2.7
24	TU	0321	1.5	0949	2.8	1605	1.4	2235	2.8
25	W	0429	1.5	1053	2.8	1705	1.4	2332	2.9
26	TH	0530	1.4	1152	2.9	1756	1.3		
27	F	0022	3.0	0621	1.3	1242	3.0	1840	1.2
28	SA	0107	3.1	0706	1.2	1328	3.1	1921	1.1
29	SU	0148	3.3	0748	1.0	1410	3.2	1959	1.0
30	M ●	0228	3.4	0829	0.9	1451	3.2	2038	0.9
31	TU	0308	3.5	0909	0.8	1532	3.3	2118	0.9

GIBRALTAR
LAT 36°08′N
LONG 5°21′W

TIMES AND HEIGHTS OF HIGH AND LOW WATER (Heights in Metres)

TIME ZONE
European Standard Time (UT+0100)
For Summer Time (area enclosed in shaded box) add 1 hour

2024

JANUARY

Date	Day	Time	m	Time	m	Time	m	Time	m
1	M	0624	0.8	1202	0.2	1841	0.7		
2	TU	0015	0.2	0706	0.8	1249	0.3	1924	0.7
3	W	0100	0.3	0752	0.7	1343	0.3	2011	0.7
4	TH ☽	0154	0.3	0843	0.7	1445	0.3	2106	0.7
5	F	0301	0.3	0941	0.7	1552	0.3	2211	0.7
6	SA	0416	0.3	1046	0.7	1702	0.3	2323	0.7
7	SU	0524	0.3	1148	0.8	1800	0.2		
8	M	0024	0.7	0615	0.3	1242	0.8	1848	0.2
9	TU	0116	0.8	0659	0.2	1331	0.9	1932	0.1
10	W	0204	0.8	0742	0.2	1420	0.9	2016	0.1
11	TH ●	0250	0.9	0826	0.1	1509	0.9	2100	0.0
12	F	0336	1.0	0912	0.1	1556	1.0	2144	0.0
13	SA	0421	1.0	0958	0.1	1642	1.0	2228	0.0
14	SU	0506	1.0	1045	0.1	1729	1.0	2311	0.0
15	M	0552	1.0	1133	0.1	1817	0.9	2357	0.1
16	TU	0641	0.9	1225	0.1	1908	0.9		
17	W	0047	0.1	0734	0.9	1323	0.2	2003	0.8
18	TH ☾	0144	0.2	0831	0.8	1427	0.2	2105	0.7
19	F	0251	0.2	0936	0.8	1543	0.2	2217	0.7
20	SA	0413	0.3	1048	0.8	1712	0.2	2339	0.7
21	SU	0535	0.3	1200	0.8	1823	0.2		
22	M	0049	0.7	0635	0.2	1300	0.8	1914	0.2
23	TU	0145	0.8	0722	0.2	1352	0.8	1957	0.1
24	W	0232	0.8	0804	0.1	1438	0.8	2035	0.1
25	TH ○	0313	0.8	0842	0.1	1519	0.8	2110	0.1
26	F	0349	0.8	0919	0.1	1557	0.8	2144	0.1
27	SA	0422	0.8	0954	0.1	1632	0.8	2215	0.1
28	SU	0452	0.8	1027	0.1	1704	0.8	2244	0.1
29	M	0522	0.8	1100	0.1	1736	0.8	2313	0.1
30	TU	0551	0.8	1132	0.1	1808	0.8	2341	0.1
31	W	0623	0.8	1205	0.2	1842	0.7		

FEBRUARY

Date	Day	Time	m	Time	m	Time	m	Time	m
1	TH	0011	0.2	0659	0.7	1243	0.2	1922	0.7
2	F	0046	0.2	0743	0.7	1330	0.2	2011	0.6
3	SA ☽	0132	0.3	0838	0.7	1436	0.3	2111	0.6
4	SU	0245	0.3	0946	0.7	1611	0.3	2230	0.6
5	M	0441	0.3	1109	0.7	1742	0.2	2356	0.6
6	TU	0600	0.3	1222	0.7	1840	0.2		
7	W	0101	0.7	0651	0.2	1320	0.8	1927	0.1
8	TH	0153	0.8	0737	0.1	1412	0.9	2011	0.0
9	F ●	0241	0.9	0822	0.1	1501	0.9	2054	0.0
10	SA	0326	1.0	0907	0.0	1547	1.0	2136	-0.1
11	SU	0409	1.0	0952	0.0	1632	1.0	2216	-0.1
12	M	0452	1.0	1035	0.0	1716	1.0	2256	0.0
13	TU	0535	1.0	1118	0.0	1801	0.9	2336	0.0
14	W	0620	1.0	1202	0.0	1848	0.9		
15	TH	0018	0.1	0707	0.9	1250	0.1	1939	0.8
16	F ☾	0105	0.2	0800	0.8	1346	0.2	2035	0.7
17	SA	0205	0.2	0901	0.7	1503	0.3	2146	0.7
18	SU	0337	0.3	1020	0.7	1707	0.3	2322	0.6
19	M	0532	0.3	1152	0.7	1826	0.2		
20	TU	0048	0.7	0636	0.3	1302	0.7	1914	0.2
21	W	0144	0.7	0720	0.2	1352	0.8	1951	0.1
22	TH	0225	0.8	0757	0.1	1432	0.8	2024	0.1
23	F	0300	0.8	0831	0.1	1508	0.8	2055	0.1
24	SA ○	0331	0.8	0903	0.1	1540	0.9	2124	0.1
25	SU	0359	0.9	0935	0.1	1611	0.9	2152	0.0
26	M	0426	0.9	1005	0.1	1640	0.9	2219	0.1
27	TU	0452	0.9	1033	0.1	1708	0.9	2244	0.1
28	W	0518	0.8	1101	0.1	1737	0.8	2309	0.1
29	TH	0547	0.8	1130	0.1	1809	0.8	2335	0.1

MARCH

Date	Day	Time	m	Time	m	Time	m	Time	m
1	F	0620	0.8	1201	0.2	1847	0.7		
2	SA	0005	0.2	0659	0.7	1240	0.2	1934	0.7
3	SU ☽	0044	0.3	0753	0.7	1339	0.3	2035	0.6
4	M	0147	0.3	0904	0.6	1532	0.3	2155	0.6
5	TU	0411	0.3	1040	0.6	1730	0.2	2333	0.6
6	W	0550	0.3	1208	0.7	1829	0.2		
7	TH	0045	0.7	0643	0.2	1310	0.8	1914	0.1
8	F	0138	0.8	0728	0.1	1400	0.9	1956	0.0
9	SA	0224	0.9	0812	0.0	1447	0.9	2037	0.0
10	SU ●	0307	1.0	0855	-0.1	1531	1.0	2117	-0.1
11	M	0350	1.0	0937	-0.1	1615	1.0	2156	-0.1
12	TU	0431	1.1	1017	-0.1	1658	1.0	2234	-0.1
13	W	0513	1.0	1057	0.0	1741	1.0	2311	0.0
14	TH	0556	1.0	1136	0.0	1826	0.9	2349	0.1
15	F	0641	0.9	1218	0.1	1916	0.8		
16	SA	0032	0.2	0731	0.8	1308	0.2	2011	0.7
17	SU ☾	0128	0.3	0832	0.7	1424	0.3	2120	0.6
18	M	0307	0.3	0954	0.6	1651	0.3	2300	0.6
19	TU	0524	0.3	1140	0.6	1810	0.3		
20	W	0030	0.7	0624	0.3	1251	0.7	1852	0.2
21	TH	0121	0.7	0703	0.2	1335	0.7	1925	0.2
22	F	0159	0.8	0735	0.2	1410	0.8	1955	0.1
23	SA	0230	0.8	0806	0.1	1442	0.8	2024	0.1
24	SU	0259	0.9	0837	0.1	1513	0.9	2053	0.1
25	M ○	0327	0.9	0907	0.1	1542	0.9	2121	0.1
26	TU	0353	0.9	0937	0.1	1611	0.9	2148	0.1
27	W	0420	0.9	1005	0.1	1640	0.9	2214	0.1
28	TH	0448	0.9	1033	0.1	1711	0.9	2240	0.1
29	F	0518	0.8	1102	0.1	1744	0.8	2308	0.2
30	SA	0552	0.8	1133	0.2	1824	0.8	2340	0.2
31	SU	0633	0.7	1212	0.2	1914	0.7		

APRIL

Date	Day	Time	m	Time	m	Time	m	Time	m
1	M	0022	0.3	0727	0.7	1312	0.3	2016	0.7
2	TU ☽	0133	0.3	0842	0.6	1518	0.3	2135	0.6
3	W	0356	0.3	1019	0.6	1705	0.3	2309	0.7
4	TH	0531	0.3	1151	0.7	1804	0.2		
5	F	0020	0.8	0624	0.2	1251	0.8	1848	0.1
6	SA	0112	0.9	0709	0.1	1339	0.9	1930	0.0
7	SU	0158	0.9	0752	0.0	1425	0.9	2010	0.0
8	M ●	0241	1.0	0834	0.0	1509	1.0	2050	0.0
9	TU	0324	1.0	0915	-0.1	1552	1.0	2129	0.0
10	W	0406	1.0	0955	0.0	1635	1.0	2207	0.0
11	TH	0448	1.0	1033	0.0	1719	0.9	2245	0.1
12	F	0531	0.9	1111	0.1	1805	0.9	2324	0.1
13	SA	0616	0.8	1151	0.2	1854	0.8		
14	SU	0007	0.2	0707	0.8	1239	0.2	1951	0.7
15	M ☾	0104	0.3	0808	0.7	1353	0.3	2057	0.7
16	TU	0238	0.4	0925	0.6	1555	0.3	2221	0.7
17	W	0441	0.3	1101	0.6	1720	0.3	2343	0.7
18	TH	0547	0.3	1212	0.7	1807	0.3		
19	F	0036	0.7	0626	0.2	1258	0.7	1842	0.2
20	SA	0115	0.8	0700	0.2	1334	0.8	1914	0.2
21	SU	0147	0.8	0732	0.1	1406	0.8	1945	0.2
22	M	0218	0.9	0804	0.1	1438	0.9	2015	0.1
23	TU	0248	0.9	0836	0.1	1509	0.9	2045	0.1
24	W ○	0318	0.9	0907	0.1	1541	0.9	2115	0.1
25	TH	0350	0.9	0938	0.1	1614	0.9	2145	0.2
26	F	0422	0.9	1009	0.1	1648	0.9	2216	0.2
27	SA	0456	0.9	1041	0.1	1726	0.8	2249	0.2
28	SU	0534	0.8	1116	0.2	1809	0.8	2328	0.3
29	M	0619	0.8	1201	0.2	1902	0.8		
30	TU	0018	0.3	0717	0.7	1309	0.3	2004	0.7

MAY

Date	Day	Time	m	Time	m	Time	m	Time	m
1	W ☽	0139	0.3	0830	0.7	1457	0.3	2118	0.7
2	TH	0329	0.3	0957	0.7	1624	0.3	2238	0.7
3	F	0455	0.3	1121	0.7	1725	0.2	2347	0.8
4	SA	0554	0.2	1222	0.8	1814	0.1		
5	SU	0040	0.9	0642	0.1	1312	0.9	1858	0.1
6	M	0127	0.9	0726	0.0	1358	0.9	1939	0.1
7	TU	0212	1.0	0809	0.0	1444	0.9	2021	0.0
8	W ●	0256	1.0	0852	0.0	1529	0.9	2102	0.0
9	TH	0341	1.0	0933	0.0	1614	0.9	2143	0.1
10	F	0425	0.9	1012	0.1	1659	0.9	2223	0.1
11	SA	0509	0.9	1051	0.1	1745	0.8	2305	0.2
12	SU	0556	0.8	1132	0.2	1836	0.8	2351	0.2
13	M	0647	0.8	1220	0.2	1931	0.7		
14	TU	0047	0.3	0745	0.7	1325	0.3	2029	0.7
15	W ☾	0202	0.3	0849	0.7	1448	0.3	2133	0.7
16	TH	0327	0.3	1000	0.7	1604	0.3	2238	0.7
17	F	0441	0.3	1111	0.7	1704	0.3	2336	0.7
18	SA	0535	0.3	1206	0.7	1750	0.3		
19	SU	0021	0.8	0617	0.2	1249	0.8	1828	0.2
20	M	0059	0.8	0654	0.2	1325	0.8	1903	0.2
21	TU	0134	0.8	0730	0.2	1401	0.8	1937	0.2
22	W	0209	0.9	0804	0.1	1436	0.9	2011	0.2
23	TH ○	0245	0.9	0839	0.1	1513	0.9	2045	0.2
24	F	0322	0.9	0914	0.1	1551	0.9	2121	0.2
25	SA	0401	0.9	0950	0.1	1631	0.9	2158	0.2
26	SU	0441	0.9	1028	0.2	1713	0.9	2239	0.2
27	M	0525	0.9	1110	0.2	1759	0.9	2325	0.2
28	TU	0613	0.8	1159	0.2	1851	0.8		
29	W	0021	0.3	0710	0.8	1304	0.2	1950	0.8
30	TH ☽	0133	0.3	0815	0.8	1421	0.3	2054	0.8
31	F	0253	0.3	0928	0.7	1534	0.2	2202	0.8

JUNE

Date	Day	Time	m	Time	m	Time	m	Time	m
1	SA	0410	0.2	1044	0.8	1640	0.2	2309	0.8
2	SU	0518	0.2	1150	0.8	1738	0.2		
3	M	0006	0.9	0615	0.1	1245	0.8	1828	0.1
4	TU	0058	0.9	0704	0.1	1335	0.9	1914	0.1
5	W	0146	0.9	0751	0.1	1423	0.9	1959	0.1
6	TH ●	0233	0.9	0835	0.1	1510	0.9	2043	0.1
7	F	0320	0.9	0917	0.1	1557	0.9	2126	0.1
8	SA	0407	0.9	0958	0.1	1643	0.9	2209	0.2
9	SU	0453	0.9	1038	0.1	1728	0.8	2251	0.2
10	M	0538	0.8	1118	0.2	1814	0.8	2335	0.2
11	TU	0625	0.8	1200	0.2	1902	0.8		
12	W	0024	0.3	0715	0.7	1249	0.3	1950	0.8
13	TH	0119	0.3	0807	0.7	1346	0.3	2040	0.7
14	F ☾	0220	0.3	0901	0.7	1446	0.3	2131	0.7
15	SA	0323	0.3	0959	0.7	1548	0.3	2225	0.7
16	SU	0427	0.3	1101	0.7	1649	0.3	2319	0.7
17	M	0527	0.3	1157	0.7	1742	0.3		
18	TU	0007	0.8	0616	0.2	1244	0.8	1825	0.3
19	W	0052	0.8	0658	0.2	1327	0.8	1905	0.3
20	TH	0134	0.8	0738	0.2	1408	0.8	1944	0.2
21	F	0217	0.9	0817	0.1	1451	0.9	2024	0.2
22	SA ○	0302	0.9	0857	0.1	1534	0.9	2105	0.2
23	SU	0347	0.9	0938	0.1	1617	0.9	2148	0.2
24	M	0431	0.9	1019	0.1	1700	0.9	2233	0.2
25	TU	0517	0.9	1102	0.1	1746	0.9	2321	0.2
26	W	0605	0.9	1149	0.2	1835	0.9		
27	TH	0013	0.2	0657	0.9	1243	0.2	1928	0.9
28	F ☽	0112	0.2	0755	0.8	1342	0.2	2025	0.9
29	SA	0217	0.2	0858	0.8	1447	0.2	2126	0.9
30	SU	0327	0.2	1008	0.8	1556	0.3	2232	0.8

SUNRISE AND SUNSET TIMES

GIBRALTAR
At 36°08′N 5°21′W
European Standard Time (UT+0100)

		Sunrise	Sunset
Jan	01	0832	1818
	15	0832	1830
Feb	01	0822	1848
	15	0809	1903
Mar	01	0752	1916
	15	0732	1929
European Summer Time (UT+0200)			
Apr	01	0808	2043
	15	0748	2055
May	01	0729	2109
	15	0715	2121
Jun	01	0706	2133
	15	0704	2140
Jul	01	0708	2142
	15	0716	2139
Aug	01	0729	2126
	15	0740	2111
Sep	01	0753	2049
	15	0804	2029
Oct	01	0816	2005
	15	0828	1945
European Standard Time (UT+0100)			
Nov	01	0744	1825
	15	0758	1814
Dec	01	0814	1807

GIBRALTAR
LAT 36°08'N
LONG 5°21'W

TIMES AND HEIGHTS OF HIGH AND LOW WATER (Heights in Metres)

TIME ZONE
European Standard Time (UT+0100)
For Summer Time (area enclosed in shaded box) add 1 hour

2024

JULY

Date	Day	Time	m	Date	Day	Time	m
1		0444	0.2	16		0426	0.3
		1120	0.8			1059	0.7
	M	1707	0.2		TU	1650	0.4
		2337	0.8			2314	0.7
2		0557	0.2	17		0541	0.3
		1224	0.8			1205	0.7
	TU	1809	0.2		W	1754	0.3
3		0036	0.9	18		0015	0.8
		0654	0.2			0634	0.2
	W	1321	0.8		TH	1259	0.8
		1901	0.2			1843	0.3
4		0130	0.9	19		0109	0.8
		0743	0.1			0719	0.2
	TH	1413	0.8		F	1348	0.8
		1949	0.2			1927	0.2
5		0221	0.9	20		0159	0.9
		0827	0.1			0801	0.1
	F	1502	0.9		SA	1433	0.9
	●	2033	0.2			2010	0.2
6		0309	0.9	21		0247	0.9
		0908	0.1			0842	0.1
	SA	1547	0.9		SU	1518	1.0
		2116	0.1		O	2054	0.1
7		0355	0.9	22		0334	1.0
		0946	0.1			0924	0.1
	SU	1629	0.9		M	1602	1.0
		2157	0.1			2139	0.1
8		0437	0.9	23		0419	1.0
		1022	0.1			1006	0.1
	M	1708	0.9		TU	1644	1.0
		2236	0.2			2223	0.1
9		0517	0.8	24		0504	1.0
		1057	0.1			1047	0.1
	TU	1746	0.9		W	1728	1.0
		2314	0.2			2308	0.1
10		0556	0.8	25		0550	1.0
		1131	0.2			1129	0.1
	W	1823	0.8		TH	1813	1.0
		2352	0.2			2355	0.1
11		0636	0.8	26		0639	0.9
		1206	0.2			1214	0.1
	TH	1900	0.8		F	1902	1.0
12		0032	0.2	27		0044	0.2
		0717	0.7			0731	0.9
	F	1245	0.3		SA	1305	0.2
		1939	0.8			1954	0.9
13		0117	0.3	28		0141	0.2
		0801	0.7			0830	0.8
	SA	1330	0.3		SU	1404	0.3
	☾	2022	0.7		☽	2051	0.9
14		0208	0.3	29		0248	0.3
		0851	0.7			0937	0.8
	SU	1424	0.3		M	1518	0.3
		2111	0.7			2158	0.8
15		0309	0.3	30		0419	0.3
		0949	0.7			1058	0.7
	M	1532	0.4		TU	1648	0.3
		2209	0.7			2316	0.8
				31		0554	0.3
						1216	0.8
					W	1805	0.3

AUGUST

Date	Day	Time	m	Date	Day	Time	m
1		0028	0.8	16		0618	0.3
		0654	0.2			1238	0.8
	TH	1319	0.8		F	1829	0.3
		1859	0.3				
2		0127	0.8	17		0052	0.8
		0739	0.2			0703	0.2
	F	1410	0.9		SA	1330	0.9
		1944	0.2			1913	0.2
3		0217	0.9	18		0145	0.9
		0818	0.2			0744	0.1
	SA	1454	0.9		SU	1415	1.0
		2024	0.2			1956	0.2
4		0301	0.9	19		0233	1.0
		0854	0.1			0824	0.1
	SU	1533	0.9		M	1459	1.0
	●	2102	0.1		O	2040	0.1
5		0340	0.9	20		0318	1.0
		0927	0.1			0905	0.0
	M	1607	0.9		TU	1542	1.1
		2138	0.1			2123	0.0
6		0416	0.9	21		0402	1.1
		0958	0.1			0945	0.0
	TU	1639	0.9		W	1623	1.1
		2212	0.1			2206	0.0
7		0449	0.9	22		0446	1.1
		1027	0.1			1024	0.0
	W	1709	0.9		TH	1705	1.1
		2244	0.1			2248	0.0
8		0521	0.9	23		0529	1.0
		1056	0.1			1104	0.1
	TH	1738	0.9		F	1748	1.1
		2316	0.2			2330	0.1
9		0552	0.9	24		0615	1.0
		1124	0.2			1145	0.1
	F	1807	0.9		SA	1833	1.0
		2348	0.2				
10		0625	0.8	25		0014	0.2
		1154	0.2			0705	0.9
	SA	1839	0.8		SU	1230	0.2
						1923	0.9
11		0022	0.2	26		0105	0.2
		0703	0.8			0803	0.8
	SU	1227	0.3		M	1325	0.3
		1917	0.8		☽	2020	0.9
12		0103	0.3	27		0212	0.3
		0751	0.7			0912	0.8
	M	1308	0.3		TU	1446	0.4
	☾	2005	0.8			2130	0.8
13		0157	0.3	28		0408	0.4
		0850	0.7			1043	0.7
	TU	1412	0.4		W	1644	0.4
		2105	0.7			2306	0.8
14		0324	0.4	29		0555	0.3
		1005	0.7			1215	0.8
	W	1600	0.4		TH	1805	0.4
		2223	0.7				
15		0514	0.3	30		0030	0.8
		1131	0.7			0648	0.3
	TH	1733	0.4		F	1315	0.8
		2348	0.8			1853	0.3
				31		0126	0.8
						0725	0.2
					SA	1359	0.9
						1931	0.2

SEPTEMBER

Date	Day	Time	m	Date	Day	Time	m
1		0208	0.9	16		0128	0.9
		0758	0.2			0721	0.1
	SU	1435	0.9		M	1352	1.0
		2005	0.2			1937	0.1
2		0244	0.9	17		0213	1.0
		0828	0.2			0800	0.1
	M	1507	1.0		TU	1435	1.1
		2038	0.2			2019	0.1
3		0316	0.9	18		0257	1.1
		0857	0.1			0839	0.0
	TU	1537	1.0		W	1517	1.2
	●	2110	0.1		O	2101	0.0
4		0347	1.0	19		0340	1.1
		0925	0.1			0918	0.0
	W	1604	1.0		TH	1558	1.2
		2141	0.1			2142	0.0
5		0415	1.0	20		0423	1.1
		0953	0.1			0957	0.1
	TH	1630	1.0		F	1640	1.2
		2211	0.1			2223	0.0
6		0443	0.9	21		0505	1.1
		1020	0.2			1036	0.1
	F	1656	1.0		SA	1722	1.1
		2240	0.2			2303	0.1
7		0511	0.9	22		0550	1.0
		1046	0.2			1115	0.2
	SA	1722	0.9		SU	1806	1.0
		2308	0.2			2344	0.2
8		0542	0.9	23		0639	0.9
		1113	0.2			1158	0.3
	SU	1752	0.9		M	1854	0.9
		2338	0.2				
9		0618	0.8	24		0030	0.3
		1143	0.3			0737	0.8
	M	1828	0.8		TU	1253	0.4
					☽	1952	0.8
10		0013	0.3	25		0137	0.4
		0705	0.8			0849	0.8
	TU	1219	0.4		W	1423	0.5
		1916	0.8			2108	0.8
11		0102	0.4	26		0355	0.4
		0808	0.7			1026	0.8
	W	1318	0.4		TH	1635	0.5
	☾	2021	0.7			2257	0.7
12		0241	0.4	27		0538	0.4
		0926	0.7			1159	0.8
	TH	1530	0.5		F	1749	0.4
		2147	0.7				
13		0456	0.4	28		0021	0.8
		1102	0.7			0623	0.3
	F	1716	0.4		SA	1253	0.9
		2328	0.8			1830	0.3
14		0559	0.3	29		0109	0.8
		1216	0.8			0656	0.3
	SA	1812	0.3		SU	1331	0.9
						1904	0.3
15		0036	0.9	30		0144	0.9
		0642	0.2			0725	0.2
	SU	1308	0.9		M	1403	1.0
		1855	0.2			1936	0.2

OCTOBER

Date	Day	Time	m	Date	Day	Time	m
1		0215	0.9	16		0149	1.0
		0753	0.2			0732	0.1
	TU	1432	1.0		W	1406	1.1
		2007	0.2			1954	0.1
2		0244	1.0	17		0232	1.1
		0822	0.2			0811	0.1
	W	1459	1.0		TH	1449	1.2
	●	2038	0.1		O	2036	0.0
3		0313	1.0	18		0315	1.1
		0850	0.2			0850	0.1
	TH	1526	1.0		F	1531	1.2
		2108	0.1			2117	0.0
4		0340	1.0	19		0358	1.1
		0918	0.2			0930	0.1
	F	1553	1.0		SA	1614	1.1
		2138	0.1			2157	0.1
5		0409	1.0	20		0442	1.1
		0946	0.2			1010	0.1
	SA	1620	1.0		SU	1657	1.1
		2207	0.2			2237	0.1
6		0438	1.0	21		0527	1.0
		1013	0.2			1051	0.2
	SU	1649	1.0		M	1742	1.0
		2236	0.2			2317	0.2
7		0510	0.9	22		0616	0.9
		1042	0.3			1135	0.3
	M	1721	0.9		TU	1832	0.9
		2305	0.3				
8		0548	0.9	23		0003	0.3
		1113	0.3			0714	0.8
	TU	1758	0.9		W	1232	0.4
		2340	0.3			1931	0.8
9		0637	0.8	24		0109	0.4
		1152	0.4			0825	0.8
	W	1849	0.8		TH	1403	0.5
					☽	2046	0.7
10		0029	0.4	25		0309	0.4
		0740	0.8			0951	0.8
	TH	1256	0.4		F	1556	0.4
	☾	1957	0.8			2221	0.7
11		0220	0.4	26		0447	0.4
		0859	0.7			1115	0.8
	F	1513	0.5		SA	1708	0.4
		2124	0.7			2345	0.8
12		0428	0.4	27		0540	0.4
		1030	0.8			1211	0.9
	SA	1650	0.4		SU	1753	0.3
		2305	0.8				
13		0530	0.3	28		0033	0.8
		1146	0.9			0616	0.3
	SU	1746	0.3		M	1250	0.9
						1829	0.3
14		0014	0.9	29		0110	0.9
		0614	0.2			0648	0.3
	M	1239	1.0		TU	1323	0.9
		1831	0.2			1902	0.2
15		0104	1.0	30		0141	0.9
		0654	0.1			0718	0.2
	TU	1324	1.0		W	1353	1.0
		1913	0.1			1934	0.2
				31		0211	1.0
						0748	0.2
					TH	1422	1.0
						2006	0.2

NOVEMBER

Date	Day	Time	m	Date	Day	Time	m
1		0240	1.0	16		0253	1.0
		0818	0.2			0828	0.1
	F	1451	1.0		SA	1508	1.1
	●	2038	0.2			2057	0.1
2		0310	1.0	17		0338	1.0
		0848	0.2			0910	0.1
	SA	1522	1.0		SU	1553	1.0
		2110	0.2			2139	0.1
3		0341	1.0	18		0423	1.0
		0918	0.2			0952	0.2
	SU	1554	1.0		M	1639	1.0
		2141	0.2			2220	0.1
4		0414	1.0	19		0510	0.9
		0948	0.3			1036	0.2
	M	1627	1.0		TU	1726	0.9
		2212	0.2			2302	0.2
5		0450	0.9	20		0559	0.9
		1021	0.3			1123	0.3
	TU	1703	0.9		W	1816	0.9
		2246	0.3			2348	0.3
6		0531	0.9	21		0654	0.8
		1057	0.3			1219	0.3
	W	1745	0.9		TH	1913	0.8
		2324	0.3				
7		0620	0.8	22		0047	0.4
		1143	0.4			0756	0.8
	TH	1836	0.8		F	1333	0.4
						2016	0.7
8		0017	0.4	23		0209	0.4
		0721	0.8			0903	0.8
	F	1255	0.4		SA	1456	0.4
		1942	0.8		☽	2125	0.7
9		0157	0.4	24		0332	0.4
		0833	0.8			1012	0.8
	SA	1444	0.4		SU	1608	0.4
	☾	2101	0.8			2240	0.7
10		0342	0.4	25		0439	0.4
		0953	0.8			1114	0.8
	SU	1610	0.3		M	1705	0.3
		2230	0.8			2343	0.8
11		0449	0.3	26		0530	0.3
		1108	0.9			1201	0.8
	M	1712	0.3		TU	1751	0.3
		2343	0.8				
12		0541	0.2	27		0028	0.8
		1205	0.9			0610	0.3
	TU	1803	0.2		W	1241	0.9
						1830	0.2
13		0037	0.9	28		0106	0.9
		0624	0.2			0646	0.3
	W	1254	1.0		TH	1316	0.9
		1848	0.1			1906	0.2
14		0124	1.0	29		0140	0.9
		0706	0.1			0720	0.2
	TH	1338	1.1		F	1349	0.9
		1931	0.1			1941	0.2
15		0209	1.0	30		0214	0.9
		0746	0.1			0753	0.2
	F	1423	1.1		SA	1424	0.9
	O	2014	0.1			2016	0.2

DECEMBER

Date	Day	Time	m	Date	Day	Time	m
1		0248	0.9	16		0329	0.9
		0825	0.2			0902	0.1
	SU	1500	0.9		M	1542	1.0
	●	2051	0.2			2133	0.1
2		0324	0.9	17		0415	0.9
		0859	0.2			0946	0.1
	M	1538	0.9		TU	1629	0.9
		2126	0.2			2214	0.1
3		0401	0.9	18		0459	0.9
		0934	0.2			1030	0.2
	TU	1616	0.9		W	1715	0.9
		2201	0.2			2254	0.1
4		0440	0.9	19		0544	0.9
		1012	0.3			1114	0.2
	W	1657	0.9		TH	1801	0.8
		2239	0.2			2335	0.2
5		0522	0.9	20		0631	0.8
		1054	0.3			1202	0.2
	TH	1740	0.9		F	1849	0.8
		2322	0.2				
6		0610	0.9	21		0020	0.2
		1144	0.3			0720	0.8
	F	1830	0.8		SA	1255	0.3
						1938	0.7
7		0014	0.3	22		0113	0.3
		0704	0.9			0811	0.8
	SA	1249	0.3		SU	1355	0.3
		1928	0.8		☽	2030	0.7
8		0125	0.3	23		0214	0.3
		0807	0.8			0905	0.7
	SU	1408	0.3		M	1458	0.3
	☾	2035	0.8			2126	0.7
9		0245	0.3	24		0321	0.3
		0915	0.8			1003	0.7
	M	1525	0.3		TU	1604	0.3
		2149	0.8			2231	0.7
10		0359	0.3	25		0431	0.3
		1026	0.9			1102	0.7
	TU	1635	0.2		W	1708	0.3
		2306	0.8			2337	0.7
11		0504	0.2	26		0532	0.3
		1131	0.9			1156	0.8
	W	1737	0.2		TH	1801	0.3
12		0010	0.8	27		0031	0.7
		0559	0.2			0619	0.3
	TH	1227	0.9		F	1243	0.8
		1830	0.1			1846	0.2
13		0104	0.9	28		0115	0.8
		0647	0.2			0659	0.3
	F	1317	1.0		SA	1325	0.8
		1918	0.1			1925	0.2
14		0153	0.9	29		0155	0.8
		0732	0.1			0736	0.2
	SA	1405	1.0		SU	1406	0.9
		2005	0.1			2004	0.2
15		0241	0.9	30		0235	0.9
		0817	0.1			0812	0.2
	SU	1454	1.0		M	1448	0.9
	O	2049	0.1		●	2041	0.1
				31		0314	0.9
						0849	0.2
					TU	1530	0.9
						2119	0.1

BREST – TIDAL COEFFICIENTS 2023

The tidal co-efficients for Brest are used in many marinas in N and NW France to denote the time of opening of lock gates.
Mean spring tides have co-efficient of 95, average tides 70, mean neaps 45.
Tidal streams and heights vary in proportion to the co-efficient.

	January		February		March		April		May		June		July		August		September		October		November		December	
am	1	61	1	59	1	67	1	47	1	42	1	57	1	58	1	51	1	68	1	77	1	81	1	75
pm		58		55		62		41		40				58		55		73		81		82		76
am	2	54	2	50	2	57	2	36	2	42	2	61	2	59	2	59	2	77	2	83	2	82	2	77
pm		51		46		51		33				65		60		63		80		85		82		77
am	3	47	3	42	3	45	3	33	3	46	3	69	3	63	3	67	3	83	3	86	3	81	3	76
pm		44		38		40				52		73		65		71		85		87		80		75
am	4	41	4	35	4	35	4	38	4	59	4	77	4	68	4	75	4	86	4	86	4	78	4	74
pm		39				31		45		67		80		70		77		86		86		75		72
am	5	38	5	34	5	31	5	54	5	74	5	82	5	72	5	79	5	86	5	84	5	72	5	69
pm		38		36				64		81		84		74		81		85		82		68		67
am	6	39	6	39	6	35	6	73	6	87	6	85	6	76	6	81	6	83	6	80	6	64	6	64
pm				45		42		83		93		86		77		82		81		76		59		61
am	7	41	7	52	7	50	7	91	7	97	7	85	7	78	7	81	7	78	7	72	7	54	7	58
pm		45		59		60		99		99		84		78		80		75		68		49		55
am	8	49	8	67	8	70	8	105	8	101	8	82	8	77	8	78	8	71	8	63	8	45	8	54
pm		54		76		80		109		101		80		76		76		66		57		42		53
am	9	59	9	83	9	89	9	112	9	100	9	77	9	75	9	73	9	61	9	52	9	40	9	53
pm		65		91		97		113		97		74		72		69		56		45		40		54
am	10	70	10	97	10	104	10	112	10	93	10	70	10	70	10	65	10	50	10	40	10	43	10	56
pm		76		103		110		109		89		66		67		61		44		34				
am	11	80	11	107	11	114	11	105	11	84	11	62	11	64	11	57	11	39	11	31	11	48	11	60
pm		85		109		116		99		77		58		60		52		33		31		54		64
am	12	89	12	110	12	116	12	93	12	71	12	54	12	56	12	47	12	29	12	34	12	61	12	68
pm		92		110		115		85		64		50		53		42		28				69		72
am	13	95	13	107	13	111	13	76	13	58	13	46	13	49	13	38	13	31	13	41	13	76	13	77
pm		96		103		106		67		51		43		45		34				49		83		80
am	14	97	14	97	14	99	14	58	14	45	14	41	14	42	14	32	14	37	14	59	14	89	14	84
pm		96		90		90		49		40		39		39				45		68		94		86
am	15	94	15	83	15	82	15	42	15	37	15	38	15	37	15	32	15	54	15	78	15	98	15	88
pm		91		74		72		35		35		39		36		34		64		86		101		89
am	16	87	16	65	16	62	16	31	16	34	16	40	16	37	16	38	16	74	16	95	16	102	16	89
pm		82		56		52		30								45		83		101		102		89
am	17	76	17	48	17	44	17	32	17	36	17	42	17	38	17	52	17	91	17	107	17	101	17	87
pm		70		42		36				38		45		41		60		99		110		98		85
am	18	64	18	37	18	31	18	36	18	42	18	48	18	45	18	68	18	105	18	112	18	94	18	82
pm		59						41		46		51		50		75		110		112		89		79
am	19	54	19	35	19	30	19	47	19	50	19	55	19	55	19	83	19	113	19	111	19	83	19	75
pm		50		37		32		52		54		59		60		90		115		108		77		71
am	20	48	20	41	20	37	20	58	20	58	20	62	20	65	20	96	20	114	20	103	20	71	20	66
pm				46		43		62		62		66		71		101		112		97		64		62
am	21	47	21	52	21	50	21	67	21	66	21	69	21	76	21	105	21	108	21	89	21	57	21	57
pm		48		58		56		71		69		72		81		107		102		81		51		52
am	22	51	22	63	22	62	22	75	22	72	22	74	22	85	22	108	22	94	22	72	22	46	22	48
pm		54		68		67		78		74		76		89		107		86		63		42		44
am	23	58	23	73	23	72	23	80	23	76	23	78	23	92	23	104	23	77	23	54	23	39	23	41
pm		62		77		76		82		77		80		94		100		67		47		38		39
am	24	66	24	80	24	80	24	83	24	78	24	80	24	95	24	94	24	57	24	40	24	38	24	37
pm		70		82		83		84		79		81		94		88		48		35				
am	25	73	25	84	25	85	25	84	25	78	25	80	25	93	25	80	25	40	25	34	25	39	25	37
pm		75		86		87		84		78		79		91		71		35				42		38
am	26	78	26	86	26	88	26	82	26	76	26	78	26	87	26	62	26	33	26	35	26	45	26	40
pm		79		86		88		80		74		76		82		54				38		49		43
am	27	80	27	86	27	87	27	77	27	71	27	73	27	77	27	46	27	34	27	43	27	53	27	46
pm		81		84		86		74		69		70		71		41		39		48		57		50
am	28	80	28	82	28	85	28	70	28	65	28	67	28	65	28	37	28	45	28	54	28	60	28	54
pm		80		79		82		65		62		65		59				51		59		64		58
am	29	78	29	76	29	79	29	60	29	59	29	62	29	54	29	37	29	57	29	64	29	67	29	62
pm		76		72		75		55		56		60		50		41		64		68		70		66
am	30	74			30	70	30	49	30	54	30	58	30	47	30	45	30	69	30	72	30	72	30	69
pm		71				65		45		53						51		73		75		74		72
am	31	67			31	59			31	53			31	47	31	57			31	78			31	75
pm		64				53				55				48		63				80				78